11/67

QA
2.73
H2.3

Introduction to
PROBABILITY
AND
STATISTICAL DECISION THEORY

HOLDEN-DAY SERIES IN INDUSTRIAL ENGINEERING
AND MANAGEMENT SCIENCE

GERALD J. LIEBERMAN AND ANDREW SCHULTZ, JR., *Editors*

Introduction to Probability and Statistical Decision Theory
G. Hadley

Introduction to Operations Research
Frederick S. Hillier and Gerald J. Lieberman

Introduction to Scientific Inference
Robert Hooks

Introduction to
PROBABILITY
AND
STATISTICAL DECISION THEORY

G. HADLEY

1967

HOLDEN-DAY, INC.
San Francisco, Cambridge, London, Amsterdam

ii

Preface

During the past thirty years, probability theory and statistics have been applied in a remarkable variety of ways throughout the physical and social sciences as well as in engineering. Indeed, probability concepts have become so important that today it is believed that the most basic laws of physics can only be described probabilistically. One of the newer areas in the application of probability and statistics is the study of decision making under uncertainty. Statistical decision theory, as it is called, has received widespread attention only in the last ten years. Because of its great practical importance, however, interest in the subject is growing rapidly.

This work is intended as a modern introduction to probability and statistical decision theory for those with no previous training in these areas. An effort has been made to provide a lucid and detailed development. The material is introduced at a sufficiently elementary level so that it can be used by students unfamiliar with calculus. This is accomplished by initially presenting only the theory for event sets containing a finite number of simple events, and delaying until Chapter 7 a discussion of those topics which require the use of analysis. Material employing calculus is presented, of course, but such material is delayed until relatively late in the theoretical development. Such an approach has much to recommend it, even for mathematically sophisticated readers.

The Bayesian approach to decision theory, based on the use of prior probabilities and utilities, is emphasized in this text, although consideration is also given to methods which do not make use of prior probabilities. It is the author's feeling that a sound understanding of the elements of probability theory is needed in decision theory, and for this reason probability theory is treated in considerable detail. One of the characteristics of the Bayesian approach is that one must frequently make use of the subjective interpretation of probability in addition to the more familiar frequency interpretation, and in this work subjective probabilities are assumed to be legitimate.

The modern theory of utility also plays an important role in decision theory, and thus an entire chapter is devoted to the study of this subject. Before analyzing problems where experimental results are combined with prior probabilities through the use of Bayes' law to obtain posterior probabilities, the conceptually simpler case where no experiment is performed is examined. This avoids the simultaneous introduction of too many new ideas.

An attempt has been made to write this text so that it can be used in a variety of single semester courses which differ both in content and in level. Enough material has been provided to make such a variety possible. Typical one semester courses in which it might usefully be employed are

1. An introduction to probability and decision theory, for students who have had no calculus background.
2. A course similar to 1, but at a slightly higher level, for students familiar with calculus or who are currently taking a mathematics course which covers topics in calculus.
3. An introduction to decision theory, for students familiar with probability and calculus.
4. An introduction to probability (without decision theory), for students who are familiar with or who are concurrently studying calculus.

The text could also be used for a full year course introducing probability and decision theory to students who are familiar with or concurrently studying calculus.

A possible sequence of topics for a one semester course in probability and decision theory without calculus is all of Chapter 1; Chapter 2, possibly omitting Section 2-8; Sections 3-1, 3-2, and 3-5; Sections 4-1 through 4-4, 4-6, and 4-7, and perhaps two of the other sections; Chapter 5 and Chapter 6, omitting Section 6-9; Sections 7-1 through 7-4, 7-15, and possibly 7-16 and 7-17; Sections 8-1 through 8-4. For the one semester course in probability and decision theory in which calculus is used, the above topics would be covered a little more rapidly and some additional sections in Chapter 7 and one or two more sections in Chapter 8 would be added. For a one semester course in decision theory for those familiar with probability and calculus, Chapters 2, 3, 4, 8, 9, and 11 would be covered. Some time should be allowed, however, for a review of certain topics in probability. For a one semester course in probability alone (without decision theory), Chapters 1, 5, 6, 7, and 10 would be covered, perhaps with the addition of some material in Chapter 9. In a full year course, the entire book would be covered.

The author is indebted to the University of Hawaii for assistance in reproducing the manuscript, and especially to Mrs. Jessie Nakata for typing much of the more mathematical sections. He also appreciates the helpful comments made by the reviewers.

Contents

Chapter 9.   Connection with Classical Statistics

Chapter 10.   The Poisson Process

Chapter 11.   Sequential Decision Problems

Introduction to

PROBABILITY

AND

STATISTICAL DECISION THEORY

CHAPTER 1

FOUNDATIONS OF PROBABILITY THEORY

All nature is but art, unknown to thee;
All chance, direction which thou canst not see; . . .

Alexander Pope, *An Essay on Man*

1-1 STATISTICAL DECISION THEORY

During the past fifteen years, considerable effort has been devoted to the development of quantitative techniques that can be used to solve many of the various types of problems faced by decision makers in industry, commerce, the military, and government. Virtually every type of problem encountered by decision makers has received at least some attention. The result of this effort was the growth of a new field, referred to as operations research or management science. To cope with the specialized problems of certain classes of decision makers, a number of individual areas (such as linear and nonlinear programming, dynamic programming, stochastic programming, inventory theory, game theory, and queuing theory) have appeared within the field of operations research. There is, of course, often a considerable amount of overlap between individual areas; for example, linear and dynamic programming and queuing theory are all useful in the study of inventory problems. Frequently, the specialized areas initially evolved around some particular mathematical model or computational procedure, such as the linear programming model and the simplex technique for solving linear programming problems, the lot size model of inventory theory, or the computational method of dynamic programming.

Essentially, every decision which a decision maker must undertake involves some element of uncertainty. The notion of chance or uncertainty is so fundamental that it is difficult to explain what it means in terms of more fundamental ideas. When we say a decision involves an element of uncertainty, we mean that at the time of the decision, the decision maker cannot be absolutely sure as to precisely what every ramification of any action he takes will be.   The final outcome will depend on which of a number of different combinations of subsequent events will occur, and it is not known when making the decision which combination will actually occur, that is, it is uncertain which set of events will be encountered after the decision is made.   For some problems the effects of uncertainty are sufficiently small that they can be ignored in making a decision.   In such cases the decision problem can be very conveniently imagined to be deterministic, that is, one in which there is no uncertainty at all.   It is useful to subdivide all decision problems into two classes, one consisting of all those problems that can be considered to be deterministic, and the other consisting of those that cannot be treated as deterministic because the effects of uncertainty play an important role which cannot be ignored.

Conceptually, deterministic decision problems are much easier to handle than nondeterministic ones.   The general procedures which one employs are reasonably clear cut and with a sufficient amount of computation one should always be able to make the best decision.   A number of special mathematical models have been developed to aid decision makers solve deterministic problems.   Linear programming is one of the best known of these.   The conceptual (and computational) problems that arise in making decisions when uncertainty is important are significantly more difficult than in the deterministic case, and this is what statistical decision theory is all about.   *Statistical decision theory is concerned with the development of techniques for making decisions in situations where uncertainty plays a crucial role.*   Since in a general way statistical decision theory is concerned with all decision problems where uncertainty must be taken into account, the subject matter is much broader than that for many of the areas of operations research listed above.   Indeed, a number of these areas, such as stochastic programming, inventory theory, queuing theory, and game theory can be considered to be part of statistical decision theory.   In addition, considerable portions of statistics as well as other areas such as quality control can with equal validity be treated as parts of statistical decision theory.

In this text we shall be concerned with developing techniques that can be applied to wide classes of decision problems.   We shall not be interested in studying in great detail special areas such as inventory theory or stochastic programming.   To illustrate the procedures developed, however, an introductory analysis of several of these subjects will be undertaken. The techniques developed in statistical decision theory offer new approaches for treating problems in some areas which had been rather extensively developed previous to the introduction of these new methods.   This is true of large segments of statistics.   It is interesting and informative to compare the new and older methods of treating the same problem, and this will be done in later portions of this text.

Statistical decision theory makes use of mathematics and mathematical models as the basic tools for solving decision problems involving uncertainty. It relies very heavily on probability theory and, in addition, makes considerable use of what is referred to as the modern theory of utility. Before studying decision theory, we must first develop some of the fundamentals of probability theory and discuss the theory of utility. This is done in this chapter and the following one. Then in Chapter 3 we begin our study of decision making under uncertainty. We shall find need for more and more developments in the theory of probability as we proceed through this text. Such developments are introduced as they are needed.

1-2 MATHEMATICAL MODELS

In the previous section the term mathematical model was used several times. Since the notion of a mathematical model is very important in statistical decision theory as well as in many other areas, it seems appropriate at the outset to describe in a little more detail what we mean when using this term. Generally speaking, one can usually consider the process by which one applies mathematics to solve real world problems as a two step process. First, we construct what is referred to as a mathematical model of those relevant portions of the real world, and then we analyze the mathematical model and obtain a "solution" to the model. The solution to the mathematical model then provides the solution to the real world problem.

What do we mean by referring to the "construction of a mathematical model"? Mathematics does not directly involve the sorts of things met in the real world, namely, physical objects, materials, people, dollars, atoms, etc. It deals only with numbers and symbols and with the relations between such elements. One must then in one way or another describe the relevant portions of the real world in mathematical terms. This process of describing the real world mathematically corresponds to what we shall refer to as the construction of a mathematical model.

A mathematical model consists of nothing but a collection of symbols, a set of statements describing any relevant characteristics of the symbols, and a set of mathematical expressions which relate the symbols. In order to obtain a model, one must keep several things in mind. First of all, the model need not and, indeed, cannot provide a complete description of the system under consideration. One need only represent those features of the system which are relevant for the problem of interest. For example, in a particular problem, the only characteristic of a given item which may be of interest to us is its cost.   Its shape, color, materials of construction, etc. may be entirely irrelevant and hence need not be represented in the mathematical model.   One task then, and one that may be difficult, is to determine precisely what characteristics of the real world should be represented in the model.

Another important thing to realize is that it is essentially never true that one can describe the nature of the relevant parts of the real world with complete accuracy in a model.   Certain approximations must always be made.   The nature of these approximations can vary widely depending on circumstances.   Whether or not a given approximation can be considered valid depends on the accuracy needed in the results.   An approximation which is suitable for one degree of accuracy may be totally unsuitable for another.   Thus it is possible to construct entirely different mathematical models of the same real world situation, one model being appropriate for one level of accuracy, while an entirely different model must be used for another level of accuracy.   One of the most difficult tasks in constructing models is that of deciding what are realistic and allowable approximations to make.

It is remarkable that many different real world problems in such diverse areas as physics, engineering, and economics can all lead to basically the same mathematical model.   Thus, for example, linear programming is useful in deciding how to operate a refinery, how to route ships, how to develop an oil field, how to mix feed for cattle, and how to distribute a product from a number of warehouses to many retail outlets.   Similarly, it is true that the mathematical models we shall develop in studying statistical decision theory are applicable in a wide variety of circumstances.

It is often convenient to imagine that a model of some real world system can be subdivided into several (perhaps interacting) parts, each of which in itself can be imagined to be a mathematical model of some facet of the real world.   Indeed, one procedure frequently used is the employment, as building blocks in the construction of models, certain models already in existence.   Thus a linear programming model might simply be one part (a building block) in some more extensive model.   We shall find this building block notion very useful; indeed, probability theory and utility theory may be conveniently viewed as mathematical models which form building blocks in a statistical decision theory model.

To conclude this section we might note that although the term mathematical model has been in general usage for only a relatively short time, the process of constructing such models has been carried out for hundreds of years in the physical sciences and engineering.   In fact, most of engineering and theoretical physics, for example, are mainly concerned with developing and analyzing mathematical models of the real world.

1-3 PROBABILITY AND RELATIVE FREQUENCIES

The word probability is often used in everyday life, as are the words chance and uncertainty. In ordinary usage there is a rather close connection between the notion of probability and that of chance and uncertainty. We would now like to make more precise the relationships between these ideas, while simultaneously clarifying what we mean when we use the term probability. This is done in the next two sections. The notion of probability, like that of chance and uncertainty, is very basic, and it is not easy to provide a simple definition of it. Interestingly enough, as we shall point out in more detail in the historical resume at the end of this chapter, even at the present time, no general agreement exists as to precisely how the definition should be made.

Let us begin with an example. It is common experience that if we toss a coin and catch it in the palm of our hand, we are unable to predict before tossing the coin whether it will land heads or tails up. Sometimes a head will turn up and sometimes a tail. It is common terminology to say that at the time we toss the coin there is uncertainty as to whether it will land heads or tails up, and that chance determines the outcome. This sort of behavior occurs regardless of how careful we may be in always attempting to toss the coin in precisely the same way each time. Indeed, it will be observed even if we build a machine to toss the coin.

Why are we unable to predict ahead of time whether the coin will fall heads or tails up? Presumably, the motion of the coin is described by Newton's laws of mechanics which are deterministic laws. It is indeed true that the motion of the coin does, to a very good approximation, behave in accordance with such laws. The difficulty, however, stems from the fact that the final state of the coin, head or tail, is very critically dependent on small changes in the initial velocity given to the coin, the initial toss angle, the precise density of the air, the nature of any air currents, etc. It is not possible for us to have a precise knowledge of all these things at the time the coin is tossed, and it is for this reason that we are unable to predict the outcome of any given toss. If a determination of all these things were possible before the coin was tossed, then we could compute at the time of tossing whether it would land as a head or tail. To do this would require not only that we could predict the launch conditions exactly, but that in addition we could predict all influences such as the behavior of the air at each instant after the coin was tossed. It would not be possible to do all this regardless of how much effort was expended. Thus the outcome of tossing a coin cannot be predicted in advance, and we say that chance determines the final state.

In the above example chance refers to the large number of small effects which can critically influence the motion of the coin. In general, in real world situations where the outcome of something is critically dependent on a variety of small effects which cannot be determined in advance, we expect to find situations in which chance or uncertainty plays a crucial role in determining the outcome, and hence the outcome will not be predictable in advance.

Although the result of a single toss of a coin is not deterministic, it is a well-known fact obtained from experience that a certain regularity does appear if we examine what happens on tossing the same coin a large number of times. For example, the author selected two coins, a penny and a quarter, from the change in his pocket and tossed each 100 times. The coins were always tossed heads up, and an effort was made to toss the coins in precisely the same way each time. The tossed coin was caught in the palm of the author's hand and on each toss it was noted whether the coin landed heads or tails up (tosses where the author failed to catch the coin were discarded). In accordance with the discussion given above, it was true that the coin landed heads up sometimes and other times tails up. It was not possible to predict ahead of time which was going to occur. Suppose, however, that using the results tabulated above we determine the total number of heads n_h obtained in the first n tosses. Instead of looking at what happened in a single toss, we look at what happened after n tosses. In our experiment, n can have the values 1, 2, 3, up to 100. In Figures 1-1 and 1-2 we have illustrated graphically the results obtained

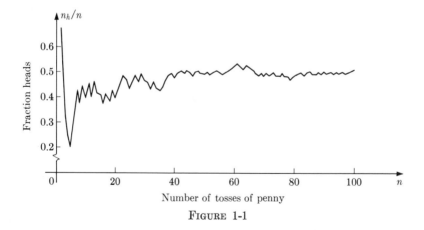

Number of tosses of penny

FIGURE 1-1

for the penny and for the quarter, respectively, by plotting the *fraction* n_h/n of heads obtained in n tosses versus n. Observe that in both cases the fraction of the total number of tosses on which a head was obtained fluctuates violently at first, and then as n, the number of tosses, increases

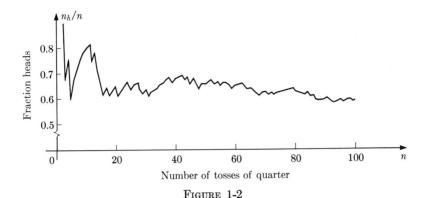

FIGURE 1-2

it becomes more and more stable, that is, the fluctuations die out and the fraction of the time we obtain a head appears to be approaching a unique number. Interestingly enough, however, this number seems to be different for the penny than for the quarter.

Here we have encountered a general and important characteristic of certain types of phenomena, or experiments as we shall call them, whose outcome is determined by chance, but which can be repeated over and over again as in tossing a coin. Even though we cannot predict the outcome on any given performance of the experiment, it is a characteristic of the real world that if the experiment is repeated a large number of times, the fraction of the total number of times we observe any particular outcome will become more and more nearly a constant as the number of repetitions of the experiment is increased.

It is now helpful to idealize the situation outlined above to a case where we imagine that the experiment is repeated unendingly. In the real world, of course, there is a limit to how often we can repeat an experiment such as tossing a coin, since if nothing else terminates the experimenting, the coin ultimately wears out. Let us assume that in the conceptual situation just suggested, the outcome on one performance of the experiment has no influence on what happens on later repetitions. Also assume that conditions do not change from one repetition to the next. This implies, for example, with the coin tossing experiment that there is never any wear of the coin. Consider one specific outcome, which we shall denote symbolically by A. Then experience in the real world indicates that if the experiment could be repeated unendingly in the manner just described, the fraction of the time in which we observe the outcome A would ultimately settle down, showing less and less fluctuation, and approach a unique number p. *The number p is called the probability that on any performance of the experiment we shall observe the outcome A,* and p tells us what fraction of the time A would be observed in the limit as the number of repetitions of the experiment was made arbitrarily large. Also, and more importantly, p tells us approximately what fraction of the time A will be observed if we perform the experiment a fairly large number of times.

We shall often refer to the fraction of the time we observe outcome A in performing the experiment n times as the *relative frequency of A* in n trials (one trial referring to one performance of the experiment). Then the probability of A can be looked upon as the *long run relative frequency of A*, long run implying that the experiment is repeated an indefinitely large number of times. For each possible outcome A of the experiment, we can imagine that there exists a number interpretable as the long run relative frequency A, which we call the probability of A. This set of probabilities then permits a numerical characterization of the manner in which uncertainty plays a role in the experiment. Thus we can make use of probabilities to yield a precise numerical description of chance effects. We might note in passing that since the long run relative frequency of A is the fraction of the total number of experiments which had outcome A, it follows that the long run frequency cannot be negative or greater than one. It must lie between 0 and 1. Furthermore, since the probability of A will be numerically equal to this long run frequency, it follows that this probability must be between 0 and 1, that is, $0 \le p \le 1$.

It now seems appropriate to ask the following question. Given that we are unable to predict the outcome on any given trial of the experiment, of what value is it to be able to make certain predictions concerning what will happen if the experiment is performed a large number of times? The answer, of course, is that it is extremely useful to be able to do this. The reason is that many real world situations can be imagined to consist of a repetition of the same "experiment" over and over again, the experiment having the characteristic that the outcome on any given trial is determined by chance and is independent of what happened on previous trials. In such situations the decision maker frequently wishes to formulate his policies so that things will work out as well as possible in the long run. To obtain such policies, a knowledge of the probabilities for each possible outcome of the experiment can be extremely useful.

It is quite easy to give practical illustrations of situations of the type just described. Perhaps the best known are the colorful examples provided by the Las Vegas gambling casinos. Their very existence depends on the long run stability of the relative frequencies in the various games of chance. Another example is that of insurance companies, whose entire existence, like that of the gambling houses, depends on the ability to predict what will happen in the way of deaths, accidents, etc. in very large groups of people, although these predictions cannot be made for any particular individual. The two examples just given are especially striking examples of the relevance of what we have been discussing. However, there are many important situations that arise in business and industry which exhibit similar characteristics.

To take a simple, everyday example, the demand for a particular type of bread in a supermarket on a given day cannot be predicted in advance. However, except for special holidays, a specified day of the week, say Tuesday, is like every other Tuesday. If one records the demand for this type of bread on Tuesdays, the relative frequencies for various numbers of loaves being demanded will be stable, and this information is very pertinent in deciding how much bread to stock each Tuesday morning. Note that we did not claim that every day was like every other day. The situation on Fridays, for example, might be quite different from Tuesdays.

A somewhat different sort of example concerns the behavior of a well-controlled production process involving one or more machines and men. Experience indicates that for no apparent reason a defective item is occasionally produced. The explanation for the defective unit lies in the chance occurrence of one or more small effects such as a slight imperfection in the raw material, a fluctuation in the line voltage on a machine, a change in the way the operator handled this unit, etc. Because defective units are caused by small unpredictable effects, it is impossible to determine ahead of time whether any given unit will be defective when it is finished. However, the long run fraction defective in such a situation is stable and is an important number for the production manager to know.

As a final example, consider the manufacture of color television sets. The manufacturer cannot predict how long any given set will operate before it suffers its first failure. However, the fractions of the sets produced in any month which fail in the first week of operation, the first month, and in the first six months are stable from one month to the next because of the huge numbers of sets produced per month. These fractions are clearly very important to the manufacturer, and manufacturers go to considerable trouble to obtain them.

In this section we have studied phenomena or, as we called them, experiments that are capable of, in one way or another, being repeated over and over again, and whose outcome on any given trial is determined by chance. In certain cases, the experiment may always be performed with the same "equipment," that is, we always toss the same penny. In other cases, each trial of the experiment uses a different piece of equipment as when one considers failures of television sets or occurrences of automobile accidents. What we were illustrating then was the fact that individual events, whose outcome is chance determined, in the aggregate show a behavior which comes close to being deterministic, and which if we imagine the aggregate to be arbitrarily large is deterministic. In the hypothetical situation where we imagine that the experiment under consideration is repeated unendingly, we identify the limiting relative frequency, that is, the long run relative frequency, of some particular outcome A with a number lying between 0 and 1 which we call the probability of A. The set of probabilities for each of the possible outcomes then allows us to describe in quantitative terms the way in which uncertainty influences our experiment. In the above discussion we did not really make clear whether we were defining probability as a long run relative frequency or whether long run relative frequencies were merely a convenient conceptual interpretation of probability. Let us now discuss this point.

Some years ago a determined effort was made to define rigorously probability as a long run relative frequency. Thus the probability p of obtaining some event A in an experiment whose outcome is determined by chance would be defined as

$$p = \lim_{n \to \infty} \frac{n_A}{n}, \tag{1-1}$$

where n_A is the number of times the outcome was A in n trials of the experiment. Equation (1-1) is read the probability p of A is the limit as n becomes arbitrarily large of the relative frequency of A. One still finds probabilities defined by (1-1) in many textbooks without any analysis of what it means. Such an attempt to "define" probability runs into several difficulties. First of all, (1-1) has only a conceptual interpretation and no operational one, since in the real world one can only perform an experiment a finite number of times. Also, and more importantly, even the conceptual interpretation leaves something to be desired, because difficulties which have never been resolved have been encountered in attempting to give (1-1) a precise mathematical meaning. It has not been found possible to give a precise mathematical interpretation to (1-1) without using the notion of probability in doing so. However, the fact that (1-1) cannot be used to provide a rigorous definition of probability does not imply that one cannot think of probabilities intuitively as being numerically equal to long run relative frequencies when the experiment under consideration is capable of repetition. It is extremely helpful to do so. All the above discussion implies is that this useful intuitive idea does not provide a basis for a sound mathematical development. How do we proceed then?

We shall find it convenient to think of probability itself as the basic concept, and we shall not try to define it in terms of more fundamental ideas. This has a number of advantages over that of trying to provide a precise definition. For example, it eliminates the mathematical difficulties referred to above. This is not all it does, however. Even if there were no difficulties involved in defining probability using (1-1), it turns out that, as we shall see in the next section, we shall not always want to think of probabilities as long run relative frequencies. Thus the definition (1-1) could not serve to cover all the situations of interest, and different definitions of probability would have to be introduced for the various interpretations. This could possibly be done, but it is much more convenient simply to take probability as the fundamental idea. We shall, however, in following this approach, try to make as clear as possible the physical interpretation of probability in various situations. We would now like to turn to a study of phenomena where probabilities cannot be given a relative frequency interpretation.

1-4   PROBABILITY AND THE DEGREE OF RATIONAL BELIEF

In the last section we studied experiments which could be repeated over and over again, and which had the characteristic that the outcome of the experiment on any given trial was determined by chance and did not depend in any way on the outcomes of previous trials. Decision makers are sometimes faced, however, with problems that have never occurred before and will never occur in the future in precisely the same form. In such situations it is again true that the decision maker is unable at the time the decision is made to determine all possible implications of any action he takes, and it is convenient to imagine that chance will play a role in determining how the particular action selected will turn out. In situations of this sort we shall once again assume that by using the probability concept it will be possible to express quantitatively the way in which uncertainty enters the situation. Indeed, the use of the word probability in everyday language generally refers to such situations.

What do statements we read in the newspapers such as: "The probability that there will be a nuclear war in the next ten years is 0.5," or "The probability is 0.8 that Hamilton wrote the Federalist Papers," or "The probability is 0.7 that the stock market will be 100 points above its current level one year from today," really mean? The situations referred to have the characteristic that they are not of a sort which have any frequency interpretation. They cannot or will not be repeated. Thus we cannot interpret the word probability here, as we did in the previous section, to mean a long run relative frequency. We shall, nonetheless, assume that the above statements illustrate a legitimate use of the concept of probability. When using probability in this way, we say that probability is being used to express one's *degree of rational belief*. Such probabilities are often referred to as *personal or subjective probabilities*.

Although there may not exist any historical relative frequencies from which one could determine roughly the probabilities of the various possible outcomes, it is nonetheless true that decision makers frequently have definite feelings, often strong feelings, about the likelihood of the various possible outcomes in some decision situation where the outcome is determined by chance. Probability provides a quantitative way for the decision maker to express his feeling about each outcome. He does this by selecting a number on a scale which goes from 0 to 1. If he assigns a number 0 to an outcome, this means that he believes that it is impossible for it to occur, and if he assigns it a value 1, this means that he believes that it is certain to occur. A number between 0 and 1 indicates his feelings as to its likelihood of occurrence. A set of such numbers, one for each possible outcome, then represent the decision maker's personal probability assessment of the way in which uncertainty enters into the situation under consideration.

In statistical decision theory, personal probabilities play a role, just as important, if not more important, than that played by probabilities which have a frequency interpretation. *We shall be making the fundamental assumption then in the rest of our work that decision makers can indeed express in quantitative terms, i.e., through the specification of personal probabilities their feelings about situations involving uncertainty for which no historical frequency data are available.* There is clearly a limit to how closely a decision maker can specify a personal probability, that is, there will generally be some vagueness about precisely what its numerical value is. We shall examine this problem in more detail later. For the present we shall suppose that the probabilities can be specified.

Personal probabilities are subjective in the sense that it is by no means true that different individuals will necessarily agree as to the probability that should be assigned to a given outcome. People will assign probabilities on the basis of their own experience and background and their knowledge of the situation under study. People with different backgrounds and knowledge of the situation may quite possibly assign different probabilities to a given outcome. However, we would expect that two individuals with the same background and understanding of the situation should assign approximately the same personal probabilities to each of the possible outcomes.

The interpretations of probability presented in this section and in the previous one are quite different. The interpretation in this section is applicable to experiments which can be performed only once and not repeated, while that of the previous section dealt with phenomena where we could repeat the experiment a very large number of times. These two alternatives really turn out to be more or less limiting cases. As we shall see later, most real world problems of the type which will be of interest to us lie somewhere in between. There will exist some relevant historical data on roughly similar situations, but it will not be enough to determine precisely the probabilities of interest, and some personal judgment will have to enter in in specifying these probabilities. Thus the probabilities will not have a strict frequency interpretation, or a strict personal probability interpretation which is independent of any frequency data. The mathematical theory of probability that we shall develop will not differentiate between probabilities which are to be interpreted as long run relative frequencies and those which are subjective probabilities. Probabilities will simply be probabilities, and how they can be interpreted will be irrelevant. A personal probability can be used interchangeably with a frequency probability. That this is really a desirable feature follows from the observation just made that most real world situations require that we use a mixture of both concepts in obtaining probabilities.

1-5 SET THEORY

We are now about ready to set up the basic mathematical model of probability theory. In developing the subject it will be very convenient to make use of some elementary notions from a part of mathematics known as set theory. We shall develop the material needed in this section. The notion of a set of elements or a collection of objects is familiar to everyone. The mathematical concept of a set of elements is precisely the same as that used in everyday life. The objects or elements which form a particular set of interest can in general be anything at all. For example, they may be people, automobiles, apples, or numbers. The thing which distinguishes the elements of a set from everything else in the universe is some special property or properties which the elements of the set possess. For example, a particular set of interest might be the set of all human males in the United States of age 45 or older. The characteristics distinguishing the elements of this set from everything else are (1) they must be human and male; (2) they must be in the United States; and (3) they must be 45 years of age or older. Equally well, one could consider sets consisting of all the integers, the set of all positive integers less than 50, the set of all numbers x satisfying $0 \leq x \leq 1$, etc. It should be clear that the notion of a set of elements is, indeed, a very general concept. Only rather recently have the advantages of using set concepts been recognized by mathematicians.

The reader will recall that it is very convenient to use symbols to represent numbers when we do not wish to indicate any specific numerical value. It is also convenient to introduce symbols to represent sets. Generally, we shall employ the convention that sets will be denoted by upper case light face letters such as A, B, or X. The symbols used to represent the elements of the sets will vary, but will often be lower case letters such as a, b, e_j, or f_i. To indicate that a particular element, say e, belongs to the set A, we use the notation $e \in A$. To indicate that some element, say b, is not an element of the set A, we write $b \notin A$. A set may contain either a finite or infinite number of elements. If a set has a finite number of elements and we wish to exhibit these explicitly, we enclose them in braces. For example, if A is the set containing the first five natural numbers, we can write

$$A = \{1, 2, 3, 4, 5\}.$$

If A is the set of n elements $a_1, \ldots, a_n$, we can write

$$A = \{a_1, \ldots, a_n\}$$

or

$$A = \{a_j, \quad j = 1, \ldots, n\}.$$

(1-2)

In the second form of (1-2) we simply illustrate the typical element a_j and indicate what values the subscript j takes on.

We shall now introduce several useful definitions.

EQUALITY. *Two sets A, B are said to be equal, written $A = B$, if they contain precisely the same elements, that is, every element of A is also an element of B, and every element of B is also an element of A.*

Thus if $A = \{1, 2, 3, 4\}$ and $B = \{1, 2, 3, 4, 5\}$, A and B are not equal, written $A \neq B$, since 5 appears in B but not in A. The sets $A = \{1, 2, 4\}$ and $B = \{2, 4, 1\}$ are equal since they contain the same elements (we do not require that they have to appear in the same order when we write down the sets).

SUBSET. *A subset of a set A is a set all of whose elements are in A. However, not all elements of A need to be in the subset B.*

A given set may have many subsets. Note that according to the above definition A is a subset of itself. The set B is said to be a *proper subset* of A if A contains at least one element which is not in B. Note that A cannot be a proper subset of itself. To indicate that B is a subset of A, the notation $B \subseteq A$ is used. If we wish to indicate specifically that B is a proper subset of A we use the symbolism $B \subset A$. If A is the set of all human males in the United States, then the set B of all boys in the United States in the sixth grade is a proper subset of A. If $A = \{1, 2, 3, 4\}$, then $B = \{1, 2\}$, $C = \{2, 3, 4\}$, $D = \{2\}$, and $F = \{1, 3, 4\}$ are examples of proper subsets of A.

INTERSECTION. *The intersection of two sets A and B, written $A \cap B$, is the set of elements common to A and B, i.e., $a \in A \cap B$ if and only if $a \in A$ and $a \in B$.*

Thus if $A = \{1, 3, 5, 7\}$ and $B = \{3, 4, 6, 7, 9\}$, then the set of elements in both A and B consists of 3 and 7, so $A \cap B = \{3, 7\}$. The notion of intersection can easily be generalized to situations involving more than two sets. Thus the intersection of the sets $A_1, \ldots, A_n$, written $A_1 \cap A_2 \cap \cdots \cap A_n$, is the set of elements common to $A_1, \ldots, A_n$.

It may turn out that there are no elements common to A and B. For example, A may be a set containing certain positive numbers, and B a set containing certain negative numbers. There are no numbers which are both positive and negative, so that $A \cap B$ has no elements in this case. The reader may now wonder what we call $A \cap B$ if it contains no elements. For convenience, we also refer to this as a set and call it the *empty* or *null* *set*. The null set is the set with no elements and is denoted by the symbol $\emptyset$. It may seem strange to define "something" which does not contain any elements as a set. However, it is very convenient to make this definition. We shall also agree, by definition, to consider $\emptyset$ to be a subset of every set.

UNION. *The union of two sets A and B, written $A \cup B$, is the set of elements which are in either A or B or both.*

The union of two sets then contains all elements that are in at least one of the two sets. Thus every element in A is in $A \cup B$, and every element in B is in $A \cup B$. For example, if $A = \{1, 2, 5, 7\}$ and $B = \{2, 4, 6, 7, 9\}$, then $A \cup B = \{1, 2, 4, 5, 6, 7, 9\}$. If A is the set of all boys in the United States who are in the sixth grade, and B is the set of all girls in the United States who are in the sixth grade, then $A \cup B$ is the set of all boys and girls in the United States who are in the sixth grade. The notion of union can easily be extended to case involving more than two sets. The union of n sets $A_1, \ldots, A_n$, written $A_1 \cup A_2 \cup \cdots \cup A_n$, is the set of elements which are in at least one of the sets $A_1, \ldots, A_n$.

In situations with which we shall be concerned, every set of interest will be a subset of one particular master set or universe. Let us denote this master set by E. Given the notion of a master set E, we can now define a new operation called complementation as follows.

COMPLEMENT *of A. Given any set A which is a subset of E, the complement of A with respect to E, written A^c, is the set of all elements in E which are not in A.*

For example, if E is the set of all positive integers, and A is the set of all positive integers whose value is less than or equal to 100, then A^c is the set of all positive integers which are greater in value than 100. As another example, suppose that E is the set of all male children in a given school, and A is the set of all male children in the eleventh grade. Then A^c is the set of all male children in the school which are not in the eleventh grade.

The various operations involving sets can be given a simple geometric interpretation if we imagine that the elements of the sets are points in a plane. In Figure 1-3, if A is the set of points inside the figure with the solid line as a boundary, and B is the set of points inside the figure with the dashed boundary line, then $A \cap B$ is the set of points represented by the shaded region. In Figure 1-4, if A is the set of points inside the figure

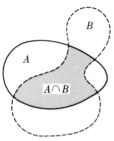

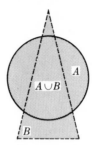
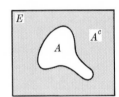

FIGURE 1-3   FIGURE 1-4   FIGURE 1-5

with the solid boundary line, and B is the set of points inside the figure with the dashed boundary line, then $A \cup B$ is the set of points represented by the shaded region. In Figure 1-5, suppose that the universe E is the set of all points inside the rectangle shown, and that A is the set of points inside the figure with the solid boundary; then A^c is the set of points represented by the shaded region.

1-6 THE EVENT SET

Consider some real world situation whose outcome is determined by chance. We would like to develop a model of the situation which will allow us to make quantitative statements about the way in which uncertainty enters into the situation. As we have done previously, we shall find it convenient to refer to the situation just described as an experiment, even though it may not in any way be considered an experiment in the sense usually thought of in the physical sciences. Experiment here simply refers to some situation we are studying whose outcome is determined by chance. It is conventional to refer to an experiment in the sense we are using the term here as a *random experiment*. We shall use the word random frequently in a number of different contexts. Like probability and uncertainty, it is not easy to provide a simple definition of random in terms of more fundamental ideas. Here, random simply emphasizes the fact that the outcome of the experiment is determined by chance and is not deterministic.

Let us now examine the possible outcomes of the random experiment which we are considering. Imagine that we make a list of all possible outcomes. Let us list these outcomes in such a way that one and only one of them will actually be observed after the experiment is completed. In other words, we set down the outcomes in such a way that they are mutually exclusive and collectively exhaustive. By mutually exclusive we mean that after the experiment is performed only one of the outcomes will have occurred; it is not possible to have two or more actually be observed. By collectively exhaustive we mean that one of the outcomes must occur; there are no outcomes that have been omitted from our list. We shall call each outcome defined in the manner just discussed a *simple event*. It will be assumed that there are a finite number of simple events. This is no restriction because everything in the real world is discrete, and thus automatically there will be only a finite number of outcomes. The number may be exceedingly large, but it will always be finite. We shall use symbols to represent the simple events in the mathematical model. Let us arrange them in any order we desire. We shall use the symbol e_1 to denote the first one, e_2 the second, or in general, e_j to denote the jth one. Suppose that there are m simple events in total. Consider now the set

$$E = \{e_1, e_2, \ldots, e_m\}, \tag{1-3}$$

whose elements are the simple events. The set E will be referred to as the *event set*. It has m elements.

It is by no means true that there is only one way to define a set of simple events for an experiment. Generally, there will be many possible ways. We have no basis for making a choice among the possible alternative definitions without knowing what the model is to be used for. This knowledge generally eliminates all but a few alternative definitions. It will not necessarily lead to a unique method of definition, however. Any of the remaining alternatives can be used, and the choice among these is usually made on the basis of which is easiest to work with. In complicated problems it can be difficult to find any definition of outcomes which yields a convenient mutually exclusive and collectively exhaustive set. In most problems with which we shall be concerned, this will be a fairly simple task; indeed, there will frequently be some "natural" method of definition which suggests itself without too deep a study of the situation. Let us now illustrate the above discussion with several examples. In these examples we shall use subscripts to distinguish between different event sets for the same experiment, i.e., E_1, E_2, etc. Different symbols will also be used for simple events belonging to different event sets.

EXAMPLES. *1.* Consider the random experiment which consists of tossing a coin once and noting whether it lands heads or tails up. How do we describe the outcomes of this experiment? It seems perfectly natural to say that there are two possible outcomes: (1) the coin lands heads up; or (2) the coin lands tails up. These two events are mutually exclusive since the coin cannot land both heads and tails up. They are also collectively exhaustive, because the coin will land either heads or tails up. The two outcomes described above can then serve as simple events, and if we denote the first by e_1 and the second by e_2, the event set is $E_1 = \{e_1, e_2\}$.

This is the event set that one would normally use in working with this experiment, although it is not the only possible event set. Suppose we consider as a description of the outcomes just the single event e, that of the coin landing either heads or tails up. This single event is mutually exclusive and collectively exhaustive, since the coin will land either heads or tails up and can land no other way. Thus e can serve as a simple event, and the corresponding event set is $E_2 = \{e\}$. This characterization of the outcomes, while allowable, would not turn out to be suitable for most purposes for which the model might be intended.

Our description of the outcome of tossing a coin could have been made much more detailed than that given above. We could have observed how many times the coin turned over when tossed, how high in the air it went, etc. In describing the outcomes of an experiment, it is only necessary to characterize the things which are relevant. We were implicitly assuming in the above description that the only relevant thing to observe was whether the coin landed heads or tails up. We assumed that how many times it turned over or how high it went was totally irrelevant. To understand what is relevant and irrelevant, we must understand thoroughly the nature of the real world situation.

2.   Consider next an experiment which consists of tossing once an ordinary six-sided die. Suppose that the only thing that is relevant, so far as the outcome of this experiment is concerned, is the number of dots on the face that turns up. A natural way to characterize the outcomes in this case is to consider six possibilities corresponding to the number of dots on the face that turns up. These can be used as simple events because the outcomes as defined are mutually exclusive and collectively exhaustive. If we denote by e_j the simple event that a face with j dots turns up, then the event set in this case would be $E_1 = \{e_1, e_2, e_3, e_4, e_5, e_6\}$.

This is by no means the only way of subdividing the outcomes into simple events. We could characterize the experiment as having only two outcomes, which are (1) a face with an even number of dots turns up, or (2) a face with an odd number of dots turns up. These can indeed be used as simple events since a face must turn up with either an even or odd number of dots on it, and it cannot simultaneously be even and odd. If we denote the event of the appearance of an even numbered face by the symbol e^* and that of an odd numbered face by e^+, then the event set for this subdivision of outcomes would be $E_2 = \{e^*, e^+\}$. We could also characterize the experiment as having only two outcomes by taking the outcomes to be (1) the face that turns up has three or less dots on it, and (2) the face that turns up has more than three dots on it. These are indeed simple events, which taken together, yield a mutually exclusive and collectively exhaustive set. There are many more ways in which the outcomes of this experiment could be subdivided to yield a set of simple events. We might note that if the experiment was described by only two outcomes as follows: (1) the face which turns up has three or less dots on it, and (2) the face which turns up has three or more dots on it; these would not yield a set of mutually exclusive events. The reason is that if the face with three dots on it turns up, it satisfies the description of both outcomes, and we cannot uniquely characterize it as belonging to only one of the two outcomes. For most purposes the event set involving six simple events, which we first described, would be the most appropriate one to use in a mathematical model.

3. As a final simple example, consider the experiment in which we toss two pennies (rather than just a single coin as in the first example). Once again we shall only be interested in whether the coins land heads or tails up. One way to describe the experiment is to consider that there are the following three outcomes: (1) both coins land heads up; (2) one coin lands heads up and the other tails up; and (3) both coins land tails up. These are mutually exclusive and collectively exhaustive outcomes and can be used as a set of simple events. Let us denote these simple events by the symbols $\bar{e}_1$, $\bar{e}_2$, $\bar{e}_3$, so that the event set, which consists of three elements, is $E_1 = \{\bar{e}_1, \bar{e}_2, \bar{e}_3\}$.

If we think a little more, there comes to mind another eminently reasonable way to subdivide the outcomes. Let us imagine that we make the coins distinguishable, perhaps by painting a number on them, or more simply by noting which was tossed first. It then seems appropriate to consider the following four outcomes: (1) both coins land heads up; (2) coin 1 lands heads up and coin 2 tails up; (3) coin 1 lands tails up and coin 2 lands heads up; and (4) both coins land tails up. These form a mutually exclusive and collectively exhaustive set and can be used as a set of simple events. Let us denote these by the symbols e_1, e_2, e_3, and e_4 so that the event set, which now consists of four elements, is $E_2 = \{e_1, e_2, e_3, e_4\}$.

There are of course a number of other ways to subdivide the outcomes to yield a mutually exclusive collectively exhaustive set. Unlike the previous examples, both event sets E_1 and E_2, which we developed above could, for most applications, be used in constructing the mathematical model. It turns out for reasons that will appear later that one would normally use E_2 because it is somewhat easier to handle. The difference between the sets E_1 and E_2 is one which arises frequently in probability theory. It is essentially that of whether we wish to distinguish between different orders of occurrence or not.

If the reader pauses and thinks in some depth about the examples just given, it will become apparent that we have not considered every possible outcome of the experiments discussed, and therefore what we have called event sets really are not event sets according to our previous definition. Consider the first example concerned with the single toss of a coin. It is not necessarily true that the coin will land heads or tails up at all. Conceivably it might land standing on its edge, or it might not land at all because a stray shot destroys it in midair, or it may be blown away by a sudden hurricane gust of wind, so that we cannot find it to determine whether it landed heads or tails up. There are a whole host of alternative possibilities of this sort. Why did we not include these possibilities in setting up the event set? The first thing to note is that we could have included any or all of them had we wished. It would be perfectly valid to include them.

The type of events that we are now considering, such as the coin landing on its edge, are what we might call extremely rare events. Probably no one has ever seen a coin land this way on a flat surface. However, there is no physical principle which says that it cannot do so. It cannot be ruled out as being impossible. Ruling out such events can sometimes be justified by stipulating that if they occur, the experiment is considered invalid and must be repeated. Thus we might agree that if the coin lands on its edge, we ignore the experiment (as the author did in tossing a coin when he did not catch it) and toss the coin again. In other words, we limit the possible outcomes by defining what will be considered a valid experiment.

There are situations, however, where the occurrence of these odd and very rare events would not invalidate the experiment. The justification for omitting them in this case is usually based on the fact that the results which are obtained from the mathematical model will be the same regardless of whether they are included or not, that is, their inclusion will not have any influence whatever on the action which the decision maker should take. We shall see later that this is indeed normally the case. It is important to note, however, that it is *not* always a valid procedure to exclude these very rare events. For example, suppose that an individual is offered the opportunity to play a game that involves tossing a coin once. If it lands heads up he wins $1000, if it lands tails up he loses $200, and if it lands standing up on its edge, he faces the firing squad. In such a situation, even though it is extremely unlikely that the coin will land on its edge, the individual would probably not wish to ignore this possible outcome in making his computations. If the consequences of one of these odd and very rare events are extremely serious, then one is not in general justified in excluding such outcomes without a rather detailed study. It may quite possibly be the case that they should be included as events. Of course, among the very rare events only those that have extremely serious consequences need to be included.

1-7 THE BASIC PROBABILITY MODEL

Once the event set has been decided upon, the next step in constructing the mathematical model is to assign to each simple event e_j the probability of that event, which we shall denote by p_j. It is important to note that the purpose of the model is *not* to assist us in determining the probabilities of the simple events. These probabilities are part of the model, and the model gives us no assistance whatever in evaluating them. They must be determined from our knowledge of the real world. In the next section we shall study in somewhat more detail what is involved in their estimation. The reader may very well feel at this point that if we can determine the p_j, then the problem is essentially solved and there is no need for any model. Interestingly enough, the theory of probability starts out by assuming that we know the p_j and then goes on from there. It is certainly true that a great deal of empirical study may be necessary to determine the p_j in any given situation. It is also true that in certain cases we are close to being finished once the p_j have been obtained. Indeed, all the problems studied in Chapter 1 through Chapter 4 are of this type. However, for a great number of important and interesting situations, much more analysis needs to be done, and this is where the theory of probability is really useful.

We now have the event set E and a real number p_j associated with each element $e_j \in E$. This association of the number p_j with the event e_j defines what we call a *function* on the set E, or more specifically, a real valued function. A function is simply another name for a rule that associates with each element in a given set A one and only one element in another set B. For our situation, the set A is E, and we can take B to be the set of all real numbers. The set E is referred to as the *domain* of the function, and the set of p_j is called the *range* of the function. The number p_j is called the *image* of the element e_j in the domain. It is convenient to introduce a symbolic representation for functions just as we do for numbers. The function is completely described by specifying the image of each element in the domain. The fact that p_j is the image of e_j could be indicated using several notations, such as (e_j, p_j), or $e_j \to p_j$. We shall find it convenient to use the notation $p_j = p(e_j)$; $p(e_j)$ is the symbol for the image of e_j, and this is p_j. We read $p_j = p(e_j)$ as, p_j is the probability of e_j.

The event set E and the function $p_j = p(e_j)$ essentially describe, that is, are the mathematical model of the real world random experiment. To complete the description of the model, we must specify the restrictions on how we may assign probabilities to the events e_j and provide the fundamental rule which tells us how to use the model. We cannot assign arbitrary numbers as probabilities. In discussing the frequency interpretation of probabilities, we noted that it should be true that the probability has a value between 0 and 1. We agreed in the discussion of personal probabilities that the decision maker would select a number between 0 and 1 for his probability. Thus, in all cases it would appear that we must require that $0 \leq p_j \leq 1$ for each j. We shall then require in our mathematical model that the p_j satisfy this requirement, i.e.,

$$0 \leq p_j \leq 1, \quad \text{all } j. \tag{1-4}$$

Note that (1-4) is not a result that we have proved from our mathematical model. It is a requirement which experience suggests that we should impose on the p_j. Therefore, we shall require that the probabilities assigned to the e_j in our mathematical model satisfy (1-4). In geometry (1-4) would be called an axiom which the probabilities must satisfy. We can refer to it as one of the axioms for our probability model.

Equation (1-4) is not the only restriction that must be placed on the values assigned to the p_j. Suppose that the random experiment under consideration can be repeated, so that the probabilities can be interpreted as long run frequencies. Let us now perform the experiment n times, and let n_j be the number of times which the simple event e_j occurs. Since only one simple event can occur each time the experiment is performed, and since one simple event must occur, it follows that

$$n_1 + n_2 + \cdots + n_m = n, \tag{1-5}$$

if there are m simple events. On dividing (1-5) by n, we obtain

$$\frac{n_1}{n} + \frac{n_2}{n} + \cdots + \frac{n_m}{n} = 1. \tag{1-6}$$

Equation (1-6) holds for every value of n. Now as n becomes larger and larger, n_j/n must come closer and closer to p_j. In the limit as n becomes arbitrarily large, we imagine that p_j becomes numerically equal to n_j/n. Thus it would appear that we should also require that the probabilities p_j of our model must sum to 1, i.e.,

$$p_1 + p_2 + p_3 + \cdots + p_m = 1. \tag{1-7}$$

When we think of probabilities as personal probabilities, it is by no means clear that (1-7) should hold. For an event set involving three events, for example, there would appear to be no reason, based on what we have discussed thus far, why a decision maker might not assign a probability of 0.7 to one of the simple events, a probability of 0.5 to another one, and a probability of 0.4 to the third. We have indicated previously, however, that we wish to develop a theory that treats all probabilities in the same way, and in which we can use interchangeably probabilities that have a frequency and subjective interpretation. If this is to be so, then we must require that (1-7) holds in all cases. This is what we shall do. We shall require that the probabilities p_j, which we introduce as the probabilities of the simple events, must sum to 1, that is, must satisfy (1-7). Just as with (1-4), we have not proved (1-7); it is a condition which we impose on the p_j based on how we wish the p_j to behave. This is in turn based on what happens in the real world when we can give a frequency interpretation to probabilities. Thus, (1-7) can also be considered to be an axiom for our system.

The probability model that we have developed will mainly be useful for computing the probabilities of events other than simple events. What do we mean by events other than simple events? Before presenting a general discussion of what we have in mind here, let us study a simple example. Consider the experiment in which we toss an ordinary six-sided die once and observe which face turns up. Let us use as the event set E_1, described on p. 18, consisting of six simple events, the jth of which, e_j, corresponds to having a face with j dots on it turn up. Suppose now that we wish to compute the probability that the face which turns up will either have one dot or two dots. We can refer to this outcome, call it A, as an event, of course. The interesting thing to observe is that it is related to the simple events e_j of E_1. Note that e_1 is the event that a face with one dot turns up, and e_2 is the event that a face with two dots turns up. Thus A will occur if either e_1 or e_2 occurs. We shall refer to the event A as being the *union* of the two simple events e_1 and e_2, and we shall write

$$A = e_1 \cup e_2, \qquad (1-8)$$

using the set symbol $\cup$ to represent *or*. The use of the union symbol is very appropriate here and suggests some additional valuable terminology. Let $\{e_1\}$ and $\{e_2\}$ be subsets of E_1, each of which contains only a single element. If we now rewrite (1-8) as $A = \{e_1\} \cup \{e_2\}$ and interpret this as being a statement about sets, it says that the set A is the union of the sets $\{e_1\}$ and $\{e_2\}$, i.e., A is the set $A = \{e_1, e_2\}$. What does this mean? It means that the event A occurs when any one of the simple events in the set A occurs. Thus A occurs if e_1 occurs, and A occurs if e_2 occurs. A cannot occur unless one or the other of these simple events occur. Thus we can think of the description of A in terms of simple events by (1-8) and by $A = \{e_1, e_2\}$ as meaning precisely the same thing.

Suppose that instead of desiring to compute the probability that a face turns up with one dot on it or two dots, we were interested in the event, call it B, that the face which turns up has an even number of dots on it. Let us note that B is expressible in terms of simple events, just as A was. An even number of dots will appear on the face which turns up if e_2 or e_4 or e_6 occurs, that is, if there are 2, 4, or 6 dots on the face. The event B will not occur otherwise. Thus we say that B is the union of the simple events e_2, e_4, and e_6, and we can write

$$B = e_2 \cup e_4 \cup e_6 \quad \text{or} \quad B = \{e_2, e_4, e_6\}, \qquad (1\text{-}9)$$

so that we can conveniently think of B as a subset of E_1 consisting of the simple events e_2, e_4, and e_6.

Let us now turn to the general case. Consider an arbitrary random experiment with the event set $E = \{e_1, e_2, \ldots, e_m\}$. We can form new events by considering the union of any two or more simple events. For example, we might be interested in the probability that either e_2 or e_9 occurs. We can refer to this as an event, and if we denote it by the symbol A, then we can characterize A by writing $A = e_2 \cup e_9$ or $A = \{e_2, e_9\}$. *An event which is the union of two or more simple events is called a composite event.* The basic purpose of our probability model will be to compute the probabilities of composite events. Note that if we select any subset of E containing two or more simple events, this subset defines a composite event, which is the event that one of the simple events in the subset occurs. *More generally, any subset of E containing one or more elements will be called an event.* If the subset contains two or more elements of E, it is a composite event; if it contains just a single element, it is a simple event. *The set of all events which our mathematical model is capable of dealing with can then be conveniently characterized as the set of all subsets of E containing one or more simple events.* In the future we shall frequently use the set symbolism, i.e., upper case letters to denote events. In general we shall allow these events to be either simple or composite events. It is convenient to use the same symbol to represent the event and the subset of E representing the event, as we have done above. Note that with this convention e_j and $\{e_j\}$ will mean the same thing to us, although from a mathematical point of view e_j, being an element of E, and $\{e_j\}$, being a subset of E containing the single element e_j, are not the same thing.

Our above development now makes it possible for us to explain the logical basis for defining the simple events e_j, which make up the event set E. *We must define the simple events in such a way that every other event A whose probability we wish to determine is a subset of E.* To illustrate, consider once again the experiment of tossing a die. Suppose that among other things we wish to compute both the probability of the event A that the face which turns up has either one dot on it or seven dots on it and the probability of the event B that the face which turns up has either two dots or three dots on it. Suppose we decided to use as the event set $E_2 = \{e^*, e^+\}$, where e^* is the simple event that a face turns up with an even number and e^+ is the simple event that the face which turns up has an odd number of dots. The only subset of E_2 representing a composite event is E_2 itself. The other subsets corresponding to simple events are e^* and e^+. None of these subsets represents either the event A or the event B, and a model having E_2 for the event set could not be used to compute the probability of A or B.

To use our mathematical model, we must know how to compute the probability of any composite event A from the probabilities for the simple events. How do we do this? The procedure that we should use for doing this is once again suggested by looking at the case where the random experiment can be repeated over and over again. Consider an event A which is the union of the events e_1, e_2, e_3, and e_4, i.e., $A = \{e_1, e_2, e_3, e_4\}$. Let us perform the random experiment n times. Let n_1, n_2, n_3, and n_4 be the number of times that the simple events e_1, e_2, e_3, and e_4 respectively occur. Now A occurs if e_1 or e_2 or e_3 or e_4 occurs, and A does not occur otherwise. Thus n_A the number of times that A occurs is

$$n_A = n_1 + n_2 + n_3 + n_4,$$

or by dividing by n,

$$\frac{n_A}{n} = \frac{n_1}{n} + \frac{n_2}{n} + \frac{n_3}{n} + \frac{n_4}{n}. \tag{1-10}$$

As n gets larger and larger, n_1/n, n_2/n, n_3/n, and n_4/n approach p_1, p_2, p_3, and p_4, the probabilities of the simple events e_1, e_2, e_3, and e_4; and n_A/n approaches the probability of A, which we shall denote by $p(A)$. From (1-10) we then conclude that it should be true that

$$p(A) = p_1 + p_2 + p_3 + p_4. \tag{1-11}$$

The same sort of reasoning suggests that whenever the probabilities can be given a frequency interpretation, then the probability of any event A should be the sum of the probabilities of the simple events whose union is A. Since we wish to employ the same rules for all probabilities, this suggests that the basic rule that we should use in our mathematical model to compute the probability of any composite event A is simply to sum the probabilities of the simple events whose union is A. This is the rule which we shall use. Let

$$A = \{e_\alpha, e_\beta, \ldots, e_\delta\},$$

and let the probabilities of the simple events e_α, e_β, $\ldots$, e_δ be p_α, p_β, $\ldots$, p_δ, respectively. Then $p(A)$, the probability of A, will be assumed to be

$$p(A) = p_\alpha + p_\beta + \cdots + p_\delta. \tag{1-12}$$

The fundamental rule for using our mathematical model is equation (1-12), since it tells how we can compute the probability of any composite event from the probabilities of the simple events making up E. Note that we have not derived (1-12) from our mathematical model. It will be taken as an axiom for our model. We noted that if probabilities are to be interpreted as long run relative frequencies, then (1-12) should hold. However, since long run relative frequencies do not have a rigorous mathematical interpretation, this was not a proof. Even if we could have proved (1-12) in the frequency case, this still would not have proved it for subjective probabilities. Thus we simply take (1-12) as an axiom—something that is not proved but which is instead a characteristic of our mathematical system.

We have now completed our development of the basic mathematical model which will be used throughout the remainder of the text when developing topics in probability theory. The model consists of the event set E; the function $p_j = p(e_j)$, which assigns to each simple event e_j the probability of that event; the two axioms (1-4) and (1-7), which place restrictions on the way in which we can select the p_j; and the axiom described by (1-12), which tells us how to compute the probability of any composite event A in terms of the p_j. Every result in probability theory that applies to random experiments with a finite number of outcomes can be derived from this model when additional definitions are made as needed.

1-8 EVALUATION OF THE PROBABILITIES OF THE SIMPLE EVENTS

It was pointed out in the previous section that the model builder must supply the probabilities of the simple events. The mathematical model does not tell us how to compute them; they are inputs which describe the nature of the real world. In fact, it is by specifying the event set E and the probabilities p_j that we really describe in mathematical terms the particular random experiment under consideration and differentiate it from all other random experiments. How then do we determine the p_j?

To estimate the p_j, we must make use of the physical interpretations of probability which were discussed in Sections 1-3 and 1-4 and our knowledge of the real world. Let us begin by considering a random experiment which can, at least in principle, be repeated over and over again, so that the probabilities can be given a frequency interpretation. In practice, of course, we can repeat the experiment only a finite number of times. Suppose that we perform the experiment n times, and the simple event e_j occurs n_j times. What value shall we take for p_j, the probability of e_j? Intuitively, p_j is the limit of n_j/n as n becomes indefinitely large. But for the fixed n, should we set $p_j = n_j/n$? The important thing to observe at this point is that in using the data from the experiments to estimate p_j, we must make a subjective evaluation of what p_j is. We may decide that from all the information we have available, the best estimate we can obtain for p_j is n_j/n. However, other considerations, perhaps of a type that will be discussed below, may enter in and suggest that we should not take $p_j = n_j/n$, but should use a somewhat different value of p_j. In any event, even when we can obtain some frequency information to help estimate the probabilities, in the end we cannot avoid making a subjective evaluation; and hence, at least in part, the probabilities even for this case will be personal probabilities.

Now there are situations in the physical sciences, in the insurance business, and in the operation of gambling casinos where one has the opportunity to perform a very large number of experiments, in fact, even millions of experiments in the insurance business. In such cases, the relative frequencies will have been quite stable over a considerable range of n values, and in such cases very little of the subjective element enters into the estimation of the probabilities. Such situations, however, are not the type one normally encounters in business and industry. Generally, when frequency data are available, they are available only for a relatively small number of repetitions of the experiment, frequently less than 100 and often even less than 25. To illustrate how difficult it is to determine probabilities accurately, even when one has 100 trials, consider Figures 1-1 and 1-2. On the basis of Figure 1-1, what is the probability that the penny will land heads up? Even though the relative frequency has stabilized quite a bit after 100 trials, it is by no means true that it is close to being constant over a considerable interval of n. From $n = 50$ to $n = 100$, the relative frequency of heads fluctuated from 0.467 to 0.525. We would no doubt feel quite safe in saying that the probability of a head was between 0.40 and 0.60. Given that the relative frequency actually turned out to be 0.50 for $n = 100$, would we feel justified in saying that the probability of a head was between 0.49 and 0.51? We would, no doubt, be much more hesitant to make such a claim. What value would we then assign to the probability of a head? If we had no other outside information, we would very likely state that our best estimate of the probability is the relative frequency of heads in the 100 trials performed. This number happened to be 0.50. We would not necessarily feel confident that this was the actual probability, but without additional trials we could not make a better estimate. Similarly, for the quarter we would be apt to take the probability of a head to be the relative frequency in the 100 trials, if no other information was available. This number turned out to be 0.590.

When one has considerably less than 100 trials, it is fairly clear that the subjective element in ascertaining probabilities will become greater and greater as the number of trials which are available for making estimates decreases. It is also often the case that in practice whatever frequency information is available does not really represent repeated trials of the random experiment being investigated, but instead represents trials of somewhat similar but not equivalent random experiments. This, of course, makes subjective judgment even more important in making use of frequency data of this type.

By now it should be apparent to the reader that the distinction between the frequency interpretation of probability and the subjective interpretation, which seemed very sharp in Sections 1-3 and 1-4, is not nearly so sharp when we turn to the problem of actually estimating probabilities. We reach the same conclusion if we start with a random experiment which is not capable of repetition.   Even here, there will often be historical data available on somewhat similar situations which the decision maker will use almost as if they represented frequency data for the random experiment under consideration.   The less closely these historical data approximate the current random experiment the more important the subjective element will be.

An assignment of probabilities will automatically satisfy (1-4).   However, it does not automatically follow that (1-7) will be satisfied.   Hence one must check that (1-7) holds, modifying as necessary the original probability estimates.   It is not easy for the decision maker to be consistent in assigning probabilities when the subjective element is important.   Thus in addition to making sure that (1-7) is satisfied, it is often desirable to have some additional consistency checks.   These can be made by having the decision maker estimate the probability of some composite event and then checking to see if this is the sum of his estimates of the probabilities of the simple events which make up the composite event.

The above discussion has shown that in practice we can encounter situations spanning the whole range of possibilities, from those where tremendous quantities of frequency data are available and almost no subjective element is needed in the estimation of the required probabilities to those where no frequency data of any sort are available and the probability estimate is entirely subjective.   Most situations, however, tend to be somewhere between these two extremes, that is, some sort of frequency information is available, but not enough to determine the probabilities without the need for subjective judgment.   We can also conclude from the above discussion that if we so desire, we can look at all probabilities as being subjective probabilities.   In cases where the experiment can be repeated and frequency data are available, these data simply aid the decision maker in making his personal evaluation of the probabilities.   This interpretation of all probabilities as being personal probabilities is certainly a valid way to look at things.   It is very important, however, to keep the frequency interpretation in mind, and it is for this reason that we have introduced it.

By now the reader may be wondering why it is that if we are considering a random experiment capable of repetition, we do not repeat it sufficiently often to estimate the probabilities very accurately from the frequency data obtained.   There are a variety of reasons why we may not be able to obtain very much data even when in principle it could be collected. One might be that it is too expensive to repeat the experiment sufficiently often.   Another may be that it would take too much time to generate the necessary data.   Still another reason may be that we are not free to perform the experiment whenever we wish because nature determines when the experiment is performed, and we must simply use whatever historical data are available. A final and very important reason is that the nature of most situations is continually changing with time, and any data that are very much out of date have little relevance for the current situation, that is, the probabilities of the simple events are changing with time.

At this point it might be worthwhile to show that there is an interesting intuitive way of looking at probabilities in which the distinction between the subjective interpretation and the frequency interpretation disappears. This makes use of a notion first introduced in physics—that of an ensemble of systems. Consider some random experiment, and let us refer to the part of the real world which concerns this experiment as the system. Let us now imagine that we have a large number n of identical systems. It may be the case that such a collection can exist only in our imaginations, since in the real world it may be impossible to replicate the system. This does not place a limitation on the usefulness of the concept to be introduced. We shall refer to these n identical systems as an *ensemble of systems*. Let us now imagine that we start all the systems "operating." In the process of operation each system will carry out the random experiment under consideration. In each case the outcome will be determined by chance and will vary from system to system. Let n_j be the number of systems in which the simple event e_j is observed. Then p_j can be thought of as the limit of n_j/n as the number of systems in the ensemble becomes arbitrarily large. Now p_j becomes the ensemble relative frequency of e_j. Note that with this interpretation it is irrelevant whether the random experiment can be repeated in time. In physics one often can approximate an ensemble simply, for example, by having a large number of containers of a given type of gas under identical conditions. For situations of interest to us, however, the notion of an ensemble will normally be a conceptual one. It can be usefully employed, however, in attempting to determine personal probabilities. One tries to answer the question: If we imagined that there were in the universe a large number of worlds in precisely the same state as ours, in what fraction of them would we expect the event A to occur as they develop through time?

In this section we have discussed in a general way the problems involved in estimating the probabilities of the simple events. We have seen that it is often a difficult task to determine these probabilities and that in all cases a certain subjective element cannot be avoided. A very important thing to note is that normally we shall not be able to determine the p_j with great accuracy. There will be a certain amount of vagueness in our minds as to what their values really are. Nothing can be done about this in many cases. It is simply a characteristic of the real world. This does not imply a failure on the part of the theory. Probability theory is not the only case, by any means, where one has difficulty in determining with great accuracy certain parameters or physical constants which enter into the model. The basic question is whether the theory is useful in spite of its limitations. The answer to this is that it definitely has been found to be very useful.

1-9 THE CASE OF EQUALLY LIKELY SIMPLE EVENTS

In this section we would like to discuss a special technique for obtaining subjective probabilities which can be very useful in certain situations. This technique makes use of what we shall refer to as symmetry considerations. Let us begin our study of this method with an example. Suppose that we have ten balls, numbered 1 to 10, in a bowl. The random experiment we shall consider consists of picking one ball from the bowl and noting the number which appears on the ball. Let us take a simple event to be the number on the ball drawn, so that e_j corresponds to the ball with the number j on it being drawn. The event set E then consists of ten simple events. What should be the probability assigned to each simple event? Offhand, we do not know what to say. It depends on how the balls are arranged in the bowl and the manner in which a ball is selected from these. Suppose next that someone tells us that before the drawing is made the balls are thoroughly mixed, and the person drawing the ball has no opportunity to see the ball being selected. The balls are all of the same size, so it is not possible for him to have any method of differentiating between them. Does this help us to answer the question? Almost everyone would now agree that any one ball is as likely as any other to be chosen, i.e., the simple events are equally likely. What equally likely means is that each simple event has the same probability, or in other words, each ball has the same probability of being drawn. What is this probability? Since the probabilities must sum to 1, it follows that if $p_j = p$ (p is the same for each j), then

$$p_1 + p_2 + \cdots + p_{10} = 10p = 1,$$

or $p = 0.1$. Consequently, it appears that we should assign a probability of 0.1 to each simple event.

The above illustrates the use of a very interesting logical process for obtaining the probabilities of the simple events, which we shall refer to as reasoning by symmetry. Note that no frequency information was used in obtaining the probabilities. They are strictly personal probabilities. If we actually repeated the experiment a large number of times, would the relative frequency of each ball be essentially 0.1? This depends on how closely the actual situation conforms to the symmetry conditions hypothesized. If the balls are thoroughly mixed, etc., then the long run relative frequency of each simple event should be 0.1.   Experiments that have been performed confirm this.

It is convenient to introduce a special terminology to describe a random experiment having the characteristics just described.   If it is indeed true that the probability of selecting any given ball is 0.1, then we say that the random experiment is one in which a ball is *selected at random.*   We introduce the word random again, and by selected at random, we mean that one ball is just as likely to be selected as any other.   The word random will be used in this sense frequently in the future.   Thus we can speak of selecting a resistor at random from the resistors in a box, or selecting a card at random from a deck of playing cards, etc.

To gain a better understanding of how the symmetry principle can be employed, let us now study a couple of other examples.   Suppose that we are shown a coin and asked what is the probability that, if it is tossed, it will land heads up and what is the probability that it will land tails up.   Imagine that no frequency data are available for this coin.   If we examine the coin and it looks new, showing no signs of wear, we are then tempted to say that heads and tails should be equally likely; and since these represent the two events in our event set we feel that the probability of a head is 0.5, and thus the probability of a tail is 0.5 also.   A coin for which the probability of a head is actually 0.5 is called a fair coin.   Does it follow that the coin under consideration will show a long run relative frequency of heads equal to 0.5 if it is tried out?   Not at all.   It depends on whether the coin is fair or not.   Experience in the real world shows that coins frequently behave as if they were fair or very close to being fair.   The results illustrated in Figure 1-1 obtained by tossing a penny indicate that it is not unreasonable to think of the penny as being a fair coin.   However, the results for the quarter shown in Figure 1-2 are somewhat different.   Most people would have considerable doubts that the quarter is fair.   Nonetheless, shown the data of Figure 1-2, an individual might decide using symmetry arguments that the probability of a head for the quarter is indeed 0.5, saying that the deviation from 0.5 of the relative frequency of heads in the first 100 tosses was not sufficient to make him abandon the notion that the coin is fair.

Let us next return to the random experiment in which we toss a six-sided die and note which face turns up.   Suppose we take as the simple events the number of dots on the face which turns up.   There are six of these which compose the event set.   What probability should be assigned to each simple event?   In the absence of any other information we can reason that by symmetry one face is just as likely to turn up as any other face.   Thus all simple events should have the same probability, and since these probabilities must sum to 1, each will have the value $\frac{1}{6}$.   A die having the characteristic that each face has a probability of $\frac{1}{6}$ of turning up is called a fair die. Whether or not the relative frequency of each face will be about $\frac{1}{6}$ for the die actually under consideration depends on how close it is to being fair. If we enter a game of chance thinking that a die is fair and it is not (a die which is not fair is often referred to as being loaded), we may lose our shirts.

Let us now study an example which shows that we must be extremely careful in applying the symmetry principle if serious errors are to be avoided. Consider the experiment described on p. 19 in which we toss two pennies and note how many heads there are. Assume that experiments indicating that each penny is a fair coin have been carried out. Consider first the event set E_1 consisting of the three simple events $\bar{e}_1$, $\bar{e}_2$, and $\bar{e}_3$, $\bar{e}_1$ being the event that both coins land heads up, $\bar{e}_2$ that one coin lands heads and the other tails up, and $\bar{e}_3$ that both coins land tails up. Now one might be convinced that these three events are equally likely and hence each should have a probability of $\frac{1}{3}$. But then someone points out that the event set E_2 can be used also, and it appears that the four simple events in E_2 are equally likely. Recall that $E_2 = \{e_1, e_2, e_3, e_4\}$, where e_1 is the event that both coins land heads up, e_2 that coin 1 lands heads up and coin 2 lands tails up, e_3 that coin 1 lands tails up and coin 2 lands heads up, and e_4 that both coins land tails up. If the simple events in E_2 are equally likely, then each must have a probability of $\frac{1}{4}$.

We can now note that it is impossible for both the simple events in E_1 and the simple events in E_2 to be equally likely, since according to the assignment of probabilities in E_1 the probability that both coins land heads up is $\frac{1}{3}$, while using the assignment in E_2 gives $\frac{1}{4}$ for this probability. The same discrepancy arises for the event that both coins land tails up. The event that one coin lands heads up and one tails up is a simple event, if we use E_1, and has a probability of $\frac{1}{3}$. However, if we use E_2, it is not a simple event, but is the event $\{e_2, e_3\}$ and hence when the simple events in E_2 are taken as equally likely, it has the probability $\frac{1}{4} + \frac{1}{4} = \frac{1}{2}$. Since both probability assessments cannot be correct, which one is? Most people would agree, after having it pointed out that one head and one tail can be obtained in two different ways, that the correct assignment would be one which takes each of the four simple events in E_2 to be equally likely. It might not be true that everyone would agree to this, however. The only way the issue can be resolved is by actually repeating the experiment a large number of times and noting the values of the relative frequencies. These results would show that two heads occur about $\frac{1}{4}$ of the time, two tails about $\frac{1}{4}$ of the time, and one head and one tail about $\frac{1}{2}$ the time. This is in agreement with the assumption that the simple events in E_2 are equally likely and refutes the idea that the simple events in E_1 are equally likely.

In the future we shall make frequent use of symmetry in ascertaining the probabilities of the simple events.   From what we have seen above, the key to the use of this procedure is to find an event set such that if certain symmetry conditions are satisfied (i.e., we have a fair die, we select a ball at random, etc.) the simple events are equally likely.   Then if there are m simple events, each is assigned the probability $1/m$.   It should be observed that this type of probability assessment is usually done in the absence of frequency information and thus represents a subjective assignment of the probabilities.   The important thing, however, is that the assumption of equally likely events is often very closely approximated by real world situations.   Frequently, though, one must be very careful about the manner in which the experiment is performed if the symmetry assessments are to accurately portray what will happen.   The need for this is illustrated by the experiment considered above in which we draw a ball from a bowl.   In order that each ball has an equal chance of being drawn, it is necessary to take precautions that a ball is drawn at random.   This means that balls must be well mixed, etc., before the drawing.

1-10   SOME SIMPLE RESULTS

In this section we shall make use of our mathematical model to obtain some elementary but frequently useful results.   Let us assume that we have an event set E containing m simple events, and let p_j be the probability that has been assigned to the simple event e_j.   Recall that any event A which might be of interest is then some subset of E, i.e., is the union of one or more simple events in E.   Consider now any two events A and B, which can be simple or composite events.   The sets A and B may or may not have one or more simple events in common.   If they have no elements in common, they are said to be mutually exclusive, or simply exclusive.   For exclusive events, $A \cap B = \varnothing$.   We can then give the following definition.

MUTUALLY EXCLUSIVE EVENTS.   *Two events A and B are said to be mutually exclusive if $A \cap B = \varnothing$, that is, if A and B have no simple events in common.*

When A and B are exclusive events, it is impossible to observe both A and B in one trail of the random experiment, since one and only one simple event will actually occur, and A and B have no simple events in common. Thus if a simple event in A occurs, this event is not in B and hence B does not occur.   Similarly, if B occurs, A cannot occur.

Let us next note that if A and B are events, then so is $A \cup B$, which is the event that A or B or both occur.   Mathematically, the reason $A \cup B$ is an event is that $A \cup B$ is a subset of E which consists of the simple events in A and in B.

Denote the probability of A by $p(A)$ and that of B by $p(B)$. We shall now prove that if A and B are exclusive events, then $p(A \cup B)$, the probability that A or B occurs, is the sum of $p(A)$ and $p(B)$, that is,

$$p(A \cup B) = p(A) + p(B) \quad \text{when } A \cap B = \varnothing. \qquad (1\text{-}13)$$

To prove this, we note that if

$$A = \{e_\alpha, \ldots, e_\delta\}, \quad B = \{e_a, \ldots, e_h\}, \qquad (1\text{-}14)$$

then by (1-12), the axiom which tells us how to compute the probability of any composite event,

$$p(A) = p_\alpha + \cdots + p_\delta, \quad p(B) = p_a + \cdots + p_h. \qquad (1\text{-}15)$$

Of course (1-15) holds also if A or B are simple events since only the probability of that simple event will then appear on the right-hand side. Now inasmuch as A and B have no elements in common,

$$A \cup B = \{e_\alpha, \ldots, e_\delta, e_a, \ldots, e_h\}, \qquad (1\text{-}16)$$

and by (1-12)

$$p(A \cup B) = p_\alpha + \cdots + p_\delta + p_a + \cdots + p_h, \qquad (1\text{-}17)$$

so that on substituting the values of $p(A)$ and $p(B)$ from (1-15), we obtain (1-13) which is what we wished to prove.

When A and B are not exclusive, then $A \cap B$ is a subset of E containing at least one simple event, and hence $A \cap B$ is an event as well as $A \cup B$. Let us now obtain an equation similar to (1-13) which holds when A and B are not exclusive. Assume that

$$A = \{e_\alpha, \ldots, e_\gamma, e_r, \ldots, e_y\}, \quad B = \{e_a, \ldots, e_g, e_r, \ldots, e_y\}. \quad (1\text{-}18)$$

We shall suppose that $e_r, \ldots, e_y$ are the simple events common to A and B. Then the events $A \cap B$ and $A \cup B$ are respectively

$$A \cap B = \{e_r, \ldots, e_y\};$$
$$A \cup B = \{e_\alpha, \ldots, e_\gamma, e_a, \ldots, e_g, e_r, \ldots, e_y\}. \qquad (1\text{-}19)$$

Applying (1-12) to determine $p(A)$, $p(B)$, $p(A \cap B)$, and $p(A \cup B)$, we have

$$p(A) = p_\alpha + \cdots + p_\gamma + p_r + \cdots + p_y; \qquad (1\text{-}20)$$

$$p(B) = p_a + \cdots + p_g + p_r + \cdots + p_y; \qquad (1\text{-}21)$$

$$p(A \cap B) = p_r + \cdots + p_y; \qquad (1\text{-}22)$$

$$p(A \cup B) = p_\alpha + \cdots + p_\gamma + p_a + \cdots + p_g + p_r + \cdots + p_y. \quad (1\text{-}23)$$

On adding (1-20) and (1-21), we obtain

$$p(A) + p(B) = p_\alpha + \cdots + p_\gamma$$
$$+ p_a + \cdots + p_g + 2(p_r + \cdots + p_y). \quad (1\text{-}24)$$

But from (1-22) and (1-23), we see that (1-24) is (1-22) plus (1-23), i.e.,

$$p(A) + p(B) = p(A \cup B) + p(A \cap B). \tag{1-25}$$

If we solve (1-25) for $p(A \cup B)$, we obtain

$$p(A \cup B) = p(A) + p(B) - p(A \cap B). \tag{1-26}$$

In words, (1-26) says that the probability of the event $A \cup B$ is equal to the probability of the event A plus the probability of the event B minus the probability of the event $A \cap B$. Equation (1-26) holds when events A and B have one or more simple events in common, while (1-13) holds for exclusive events. Equations (1-13) and (1-26) are useful because they allow us to compute the probability of $A \cup B$ from the probabilities of A and B, and $A \cap B$ (if it is needed) without referring back to the simple events (or without even knowing how the simple events are defined).

EXAMPLES. *1.* If someone tells us that the probability of A is 0.32 and that of B is 0.14 and that of A and B is 0.06, then from (1-26) we can easily determine the probability of $A \cup B$. It is

$$p(A \cup B) = 0.32 + 0.14 - 0.06 = 0.40.$$

2. Consider the random experiment which involves the tossing of a fair die. The probability of the event e_j that a face with j dots on it turns up is $\frac{1}{6}$. Let A be the event that a face with two or less dots on it turns up. Then $A = \{e_1, e_2\}$, and $p(A) = \frac{1}{3}$. Let B be the event that a face with two or three dots on it turns up. Then $B = \{e_2, e_3\}$, and $p(B) = \frac{1}{3}$. Note that $A \cap B = \{e_2\}$ which is the event that the face with two dots on it turns up, whence $p(A \cap B) = \frac{1}{6}$. From (1-26)

$$p(A \cup B) = \frac{1}{3} + \frac{1}{3} - \frac{1}{6} = \frac{1}{2}.$$

Now $A \cup B = \{e_1, e_2, e_3\}$, which is the event that a face with three or less dots turns up, and its probability according to (1-26) is equal to $\frac{1}{2}$, in agreement with what one obtains by summing the probabilities of the simple events whose union is $A \cup B$.

These examples are very simple ones. Later we shall give examples which illustrate better the usefulness of the above formulas.

Recall that in Section 1-5 we introduced the complement of a set A with respect to the universal set E, the complement A^c being the set of all elements of E which are not in A. It is convenient to use this notion to define an event which we call the complement of A.

COMPLEMENT OF A. *Let A be an event which is a proper subset of E. The event A^c, called the complement of the event A, is defined as the set of all simple events which are not in A.*

Clearly A^c is a subset of E containing one or more elements, and is an event. Furthermore, $A \cap A^c = \varnothing$, and $A \cup A^c = E$. Thus by (1-13),

$$p(A) + p(A^c) = p(A \cup A^c) = p(E) = 1,$$

since from (1-7), $p(E) = 1$. Hence

$$p(A) = 1 - p(A^c). \tag{1-27}$$

Sometimes, to compute $p(A)$ it is much easier to first compute $p(A^c)$ and then use (1-27), rather than attempting to compute $p(A)$ directly. We shall see some good examples of this later. For the present, let us illustrate (1-27) with a very simple example.

EXAMPLE. Consider once again the random experiment that involves tossing a fair die and noting which face turns up. Let the event A be that a face with five or less dots on it turns up. Then A^c is the event that the face with six dots on it turns up. Now $p(A^c) = \frac{1}{6}$ for a fair die. Thus, by (1-27), $p(A) = 1 - \frac{1}{6} = \frac{5}{6}$, which is what we obtain by direct computation of $p(A)$, summing the probabilities of the five simple events contained in A.

In the above we have always presumed that an event A consisted of one or more simple events. We have noted, however, that the intersection of two events may be the null set. The question now arises in our minds: Shall we call the null set an event also? It is very convenient to do this. What sort of an event is $\varnothing$? It contains no simple events. But one and only one simple event will occur. Thus we can think of $\varnothing$ as an impossible event or the union of all events that cannot occur and are not included in our model. We then make the following definition.

IMPOSSIBLE EVENT. *The null set will be called the impossible event.*

Let us now return to the discussion of Section 1-6 so that we may obtain a better understanding of the impossible event. We noted there that there are a whole host of rare and odd events which we frequently do not include in our model and are impossible so far as the model is concerned. They may actually occur in the real world, however. They are not physically impossible. Thus our model is only an approximation to the real world in that it says such events are impossible, whereas in actuality they are not physically impossible.

What probability should be assigned to the event $\varnothing$? We cannot compute it from our previous rules since it does not consist of one or more simple events. Intuitively, anything that is impossible should have a probability of 0. We shall then in our model *define* the probability of $\varnothing$ to be 0, i.e.,

$$p(\varnothing) = 0. \tag{1-28}$$

With this definition, we then see that (1-13) holds even if one or both of the events A and B happen to be $\varnothing$, since, for example, if $B = \varnothing$, while $A \neq \varnothing$, $A \cup \varnothing = A$. Therefore, $A \cup \varnothing$ and A are the same event and have the same probability, i.e.,

$$p(A \cup \varnothing) = p(A). \tag{1-29}$$

But this is what (1-13) reduces to when $B = \varnothing$, since $p(\varnothing) = 0$. Similarly, if $A = B = \varnothing$, then $A \cup B = \varnothing$ and $p(A \cup B) = 0$, which is what (1-13) reduces to in this case since $p(A) = p(B) = 0$. Therefore, (1-13) holds for *any* two events A and B, provided that $A \cap B = \varnothing$.

We can note next that given (1-28), (1-13) is simply a special case of (1-26), since if $A \cap B = \varnothing$, then $p(A \cap B) = 0$ and (1-26) reduces to (1-13). The fact that (1-26) holds when either A or B or both are $\varnothing$ follows from what we proved about (1-13), since in this case $A \cap B = \varnothing$. *Consequently, we conclude that (1-26) is a general equation which holds for any two events A and B; it reduces it to (1-13) in the case where $A \cap B = \varnothing$.* Similarly, (1-27) holds even if $A = \varnothing$ or $A^c = \varnothing$.

Once we agree to call $\varnothing$ an event, it follows that *any* subset of E is an event. Furthermore, if A and B are events, so are A^c, $A \cap B$, and $A \cup B$. We no longer need to require that A and B contain at least one simple event or that $A \cap B \neq \varnothing$, in order to be called events, or that A be a proper subset of E in order that A^c be an event. By including $\varnothing$ as an event, we can simplify considerably our presentation by not always having to introduce restrictions to insure that the events we are discussing contain at least one simple event.

We might next note that E itself is an allowable subset of E. We call E the sure event. Since in our model we assume that one of the simple events must occur, then E is certain to occur. Thus we have the following definition.

Sure event. *The event set E forms an event which we call the sure or certain event.*

As we have noted previously, it follows from (1-7) that

$$p(E) = 1. \tag{1-30}$$

We have arranged our mathematical model so that the sure event has probability 1 and the impossible event probability 0. Nothing in the restrictions we have developed prevents us from assigning a probability of 0 or 1 to one of the simple events. Does assigning a probability of 0 to a simple event imply that it cannot occur, or a probability of 1 that it is certain to occur? The model does not answer the question of how to interpret such assignments; we must return to our intuitive understanding of what probability means. Consider first the case where the probabilities can be interpreted as long run relative frequencies. Does $p_j = 0$ imply that e_j can never occur? Not necessarily, because $p_j = 0$ implies only that as n becomes arbitrarily large, n_j/n tends to 0 as a limit. The event e_j can occur, but its long run relative frequency must be 0. Thus, intuitively, we can say that if $p_j = 0$, then we are implying either that e_j is impossible or that e_j can occur but it will do so only very rarely. The model does not distinguish between these two interpretations. Similar reasoning shows that $p_j = 1$ does not necessarily mean that e_j will always occur. Intuitively, if $p_j = 1$, we mean either that e_j is certain to occur or that e_j may not occur now and then, but it will almost always occur.

In our discussion of personal probability, we indicated that a decision maker would assign a probability of 0 to an event he considered impossible. Hence he would normally exclude such an event from the set of simple events. In contrast, to an event he feels is certain to occur, he assigns a probability of 1. Such an event would normally be the only event in the event set and would be the sure event.

Having discussed the possible intuitive interpretations of events with probability 0 or 1, we would now like to point out their implications for our model of a random experiment. We have already mentioned that the mathematical model does not distinguish between the various intuitive interpretations of such events. Thus if we assign a probability 0 to some simple event, the results obtained from the model will be the same regardless of whether we assume that the event is impossible or whether it may occur but only very rarely. A similar comment applies to an event with probability 1.

Let us next note that if we have assigned a probability 0 to a simple event e_r in E, we can drop this event and form a new event set E_1 with one less simple event, and the resulting model will yield precisely the same results as the original one. To see this, it is only necessary to note that the probabilities of events which do not involve e_r will not be changed on dropping e_r. Furthermore, even events which contain e_r, but are different from e_r itself, will not suffer any change in probability because e_r contributed nothing to the sum (1-12). The only possible effect could then come from e_r itself. However, as can be easily checked as we go along, there is no effect here either, since $p_r = 0$; hence it is irrelevant whether we include or omit e_r. We are saying then that if we have a set of mutually exclusive events, some of which have probability 0 for a given random experiment, we may include or omit all or any such events in the event set, and it will in no way influence our model. It is intuitively evident that things should work out this way. We shall on occasions in the future find it convenient to include impossible events in the set of simple events by assigning them a probability 0.

Consider now a deterministic situation in which the event e_v occurs with certainty. Sometimes, we shall find it convenient to think of such a deterministic situation as a special case of a random experiment in which $p_v = 1$. We shall in such cases usually think of the event set as containing more than a single simple event; the other simple events will have probability 0. Conversely, if we have a probability model in which the simple event e_v has a probability 1, we can then, if we desire, imagine this to be a model of a deterministic situation in which e_v will occur. The results obtained from the probability model will be just the same as if we treated the situation as deterministic.

1-11 RANDOM VARIABLES

In applying probability theory to decision problems we shall always go through a procedure whereby we associate a number with each simple event. This number will be some sort of figure of merit and will be of great interest. Consider any rule which associates with each simple event e_j a number ξ_j. This rule then defines a function whose domain is event set E and whose range is the set of real numbers ξ_j. We can represent this function symbolically as

$$\xi_j = x(e_j), \quad j = 1, \ldots, m, \tag{1-31}$$

where $x(e_j)$ is the symbol for the image of e_j under the function. The reason why we use x in $x(e_j)$ will appear below. Any function defined on the event set whose range is a set of real numbers is called a random variable. We can then give the following formal definition.

RANDOM VARIABLE. *A function* $\xi_j = x(e_j)$ *whose domain is the event set and whose range is a set of real numbers is called a random variable.*

This definition is rather abstract. Yet, the notion of a random variable has a very clear and simple intuitive meaning. To see this, let us begin with some examples.

EXAMPLES. *1.* Consider a game of chance which involves the tossing of a die as the chance mechanism that determines how much the player wins. Let us use as the event set the usual one with the six simple events e_j, e_j being the event that a face with j dots on it turns up. Suppose that the amount won for each simple event is that shown in Table 1-1. Negative numbers mean that the player loses the amount. Now the sum won on a given play can be thought of as a random variable. Table 1-1 gives the function $\xi_j = x(e_j)$; we see that the winnings are $x(e_1) = -5$, $x(e_2) = -3$, $x(e_3) = -1$, $x(e_4) = 2$, $x(e_5) = 4$, and $x(e_6) = 3$. Let us now

TABLE 1-1

Simple event	e_1	e_2	e_3	e_4	e_5	e_6
Amount won	-5	-3	-1	2	4	3

note why it is convenient to call the amount won a random variable. Before the game is played, the player does not know how much he will win. We can think of the amount that he will win as a variable, and we can use x, the usual symbol used in algebra, to represent this variable. The variable x can take on the six different values given in Table 1-1. We are not free to select the value which it takes on; this value will be determined by the outcome of the random experiment. For this reason we call x a random variable, to emphasize that its value will be determined by the outcome of a random experiment.

2. Imagine that we have 100 cards and on each we write the name of a United States senator. Consider the experiment in which we place the cards in a bowl and select one at random. The event set will contain 100 simple events, each one a name on a card. Suppose that in addition on each card we also write the senator's age to the nearest year. Thus when a card is drawn we observe a number which is the age of the senator whose name appears on the card. We then have associated with each simple event a number which is the age of the individual whose name is the simple event. This association defines a random variable x for the experiment, and x is simply the age of the senator whose name is drawn.

3. Suppose we toss a coin and note whether it lands heads or tails up. As the event set, let us use $E = \{e_1, e_2\}$, where e_1 is the event that the coin lands heads up and e_2 is the event that it lands tails up. If we introduce a random variable x through the function $x(e_1) = 1$, $x(e_2) = 0$, then x is the number of heads obtained on performing the experiment, which is 1 if the coin lands heads up, and 0 if it lands tails.

In each example above the random variable had a simple intuitive interpretation, the winnings in the first case, the age of the senator in the second, and the number of heads in the third. Generally, random variables will have such a concrete meaning; for example, they may be profits, demands, ages, etc. *Intuitively, a random variable is any numerical quantity whose value will be determined by the outcome of a random experiment.* Rather than using the functional notation $\xi_j = x(e_j)$ to represent a random variable, it will be more convenient to use a single symbol such as x. Thus we may say simply, "Consider the random variable x." The possible values the random variable x can take on is the range of the function $\xi_j = x(e_j)$. The range is the set of numbers

$$R = \{\xi_1, \xi_2, \ldots, \xi_m\}. \tag{1-32}$$

Thus after the experiment is performed, x will be found to take on one and only one of the possible values in the set R. The particular symbol, such as x, which we use to denote a random variable is irrelevant. We shall frequently use x, but we shall also employ a variety of other symbols such as t, y, or z. The only thing that is of consequence about a random variable is the set of values it can take on and the rule that tells us what value it will assume for each simple event. Random variables will play a crucial role in everything that we shall be doing later. The notion of a random variable is a rather simple one, and the reader should try to understand it thoroughly.

1-12 EXPECTED VALUE OF A RANDOM VARIABLE

Generally speaking, we shall be especially interested in what will be called the *expected value* of a random variable. Let us begin by explaining the intuitive meaning of expected values. Consider a random experiment that can be repeated over and over again. Imagine that x is some random variable of interest, and suppose that if the simple event of e_j is observed, the value taken on by the random variable is ξ_j, i.e., $\xi_j = x(e_j)$. Let us now perform the experiment n times, and suppose that n_j ($n_j \geq 0$) is the number of times that we observe the simple event e_j. Each time the experiment is performed, some value of the random variable is determined. Assume now that we add up the values of the random variable so obtained and divide by n, the number of experiments. What does this give us? It gives what we call the arithmetic average of the values taken on by the random variable in n trials of the experiment. The reader will be well aware that arithmetic averages are often used in the real world. As an illustration, suppose that we play a game of chance five times and that our winnings are 2, -5, -1, -5, and 3. Our average winnings per play are then

$$\tfrac{1}{5}(2 - 5 - 1 - 5 + 3) = -\tfrac{6}{5} = -1.2,$$

that is, we lost an average of 1.2 per game. Now what is the average of the values of x for the general situation we have been discussing? Since e_j occurs n_j times, $x = \xi_j$ precisely n_j times. Thus the average of the values of x in n trials, which we shall denote by $\bar{\xi}$, is

$$\bar{\xi} = \frac{1}{n}\left[\xi_1 n_1 + \xi_2 n_2 + \cdots + \xi_m n_m\right] \tag{1-33}$$

or

$$\bar{\xi} = \xi_1 \frac{n_1}{n} + \xi_2 \frac{n_2}{n} + \cdots + \xi_m \frac{n_m}{n}. \tag{1-34}$$

To determine $\bar{\xi}$ we multiply ξ_j by the relative frequency of e_j and add the results.

Next imagine that instead of performing the above experiment a finite number of times, we repeat it unendingly. As n becomes larger and larger, the relative frequency n_j/n must approach p_j the probability of e_j. Since

(1-34) holds for any n, we see that $\bar{\xi}$ must then approach a unique number we shall denote by μ_x, which is

$$\mu_x = \xi_1 p_1 + \xi_2 p_2 + \cdots + \xi_m p_m. \qquad (1\text{-}35)$$

The number μ_x is called the expected value of the random variable x, and for the case under consideration, it can be interpreted as the long run average value of x. *To compute the expected value of x, we multiply together the value x takes on if e_j occurs and the probability of e_j and add up the numbers so obtained for all possible j values.* The computation of μ_x then involves nothing but the function $\xi_j = x(e_j)$, which characterizes the random variable x, and the function $p_j = p(e_j)$, which gives the probabilities of the simple events.

Observe that we can compute an expected value of a random variable even if the probabilities involved are personal probabilities. Does the expected value have a simple intuitive meaning in this case? At the moment we are unable to provide one. However, as we shall see in the next chapter, expected values are of fundamental importance, regardless of what interpretations we give to the probabilities. From the point of view of our mathematical model, we shall simply define what we shall call the expected value μ_x of a random variable x by (1-35). The intuitive meaning of expected values, discussed above for the case where the probabilities can be interpreted as long run relative frequencies, lies outside the model and relies on our knowledge of the real world. Let us then introduce the following definition.

EXPECTED VALUE OF A RANDOM VARIABLE. *Let E be the event set for some random experiment and suppose that p_j is the probability of e_j. The expected value of a random variable x defined by the real valued function $\xi_j = x(e_j)$ having E as its domain is the unique number μ_x computed from (1-35).*

EXAMPLE. The use of expected values was first employed in studying games of chance. Consider the game described in the example on p. 39. Suppose that the die used is fair, so that the probability of each simple event is $\frac{1}{6}$. Let us compute the player's expected winnings μ_x per play of the game. According to (1-35),

$$\mu_x = \tfrac{1}{6}(-5) + \tfrac{1}{6}(-3) + \tfrac{1}{6}(-1) + \tfrac{1}{6}(2) + \tfrac{1}{6}(4) + \tfrac{1}{6}(3)$$
$$= \tfrac{1}{6}(-5 - 3 - 1 + 2 + 4 + 3) = 0.$$

The expected winnings per play are 0. A game having 0 as the expected winnings per play is called a fair game. A gambling house could not operate a game for which the expected winnings were positive because gamblers would quickly discover this and in time bankrupt the casino. Normally, the casino operates games in which the expected winnings of the players are slightly negative, that is, they lose money in the long run. In this way the casino gains enough to cover expenses and make a profit.

1-13 DISTRIBUTION OF A RANDOM VARIABLE

In Section 1-11 we explained what was meant by a random variable. A random variable x is completely specified by giving for each j the number ξ_j to be associated with the simple event e_j. We have not required that the numbers associated with different simple events must be different. Very frequently they will be, but they do not have to be. We might, for example, associate the number 34.2 with the event e_1 and this same number with the event e_{17}, i.e., $\xi_1 = \xi_{17} = 34.2$. Assume that the different values that x can take on are $x_1, x_2, \ldots, x_k$. Let us now subdivide E into k subsets S_i which have the property that each simple event $e_j \in S_i$ has associated with it the value x_i of the random variable x. Hence if $e_j \in S_i$, then $x(e_j) = \xi_j = x_i$. Now suppose that we have numbered the x_i so that $x_1 < x_2 < x_3 < \cdots < x_k$. Then the set

$$X = \{x_1, \ldots, x_k\} \tag{1-36}$$

is one whose elements are the different values the random variable x may take on.

The sets S_i, which we introduced above, are events. The probability of S_i is the sum of the probabilities of the simple events in S_i and is the probability that the random variable x will take on the value x_i. We shall denote this probability by $p(x_i)$. In associating with each $x_i \in X$ a number $p(x_i)$, we have defined a function whose domain is X. This function is called the probability function for the random variable x. More precisely, we can make the following definition.

PROBABILITY FUNCTION FOR A RANDOM VARIABLE. *Consider some random variable x, and let $X = \{x_1, \ldots, x_k\}$ be the set of different values that x may take on. Now consider the function which associates with each element $x_i \in X$ the probability $p(x_i)$ that $x = x_i$. This function is called the probability function for the random variable.*

The probability function for a random variable is sometimes referred to as the density function for the random variable. We shall use the term density function later in a somewhat different context and, hence, will not apply it here.

EXAMPLE. Consider once again a game of chance which involves tossing a fair die; the amount that the player wins depends on what face turns up. Let us use the usual event set consisting of six simple events to describe this random experiment. The amount won by the player can be considered a random variable x. Assume that Table 1-2 shows the amount won as a function of the simple event which occurs. The random

TABLE 1-2

Simple event	e_1	e_2	e_3	e_4	e_5	e_6
Amount won	2	-6	1	2	1	0

variable x can then take on four different values which are $x_1 = -6$, $x_2 = 0$, $x_3 = 1$, and $x_4 = 2$. The events S_i introduced above are in this case $S_1 = \{e_2\}$, $S_2 = \{e_6\}$, $S_3 = \{e_3, e_5\}$, and $S_4 = \{e_1, e_4\}$, since, for example, the event $x = x_1$ occurs only if e_2 occurs, and the event $x = x_4$ occurs if e_1 or e_4 occurs. Since the probability that $x = x_i$ is the sum of the probabilities of the simple events in S_i, we see that $p(x_1) = p(-6) = \frac{1}{6}$, $p(x_2) = p(0) = \frac{1}{6}$, $p(x_3) = p(1) = \frac{1}{3}$, and $p(x_4) = p(2) = \frac{1}{3}$. Thus the probability function for the random variable x is that given in Table 1-3.

TABLE 1-3

Value of x	-6	0	1	2
Probability	$\frac{1}{6}$	$\frac{1}{6}$	$\frac{1}{3}$	$\frac{1}{3}$

We have in the past used notations such as $p_j = p(e_j)$ and $\xi_j = x(e_j)$ to denote functions. These notations have the disadvantage that $\xi_j = x(e_j)$ is used not only to represent the entire function, but also to indicate that ξ_j is the image of a particular element in the domain e_j. Although for many purposes this dual interpretation causes no problems, it can create difficulties in dealing with the probability functions for random variables. For this reason, we shall find it convenient to differentiate between the symbol for the entire probability function and the symbol for the image of a particular element in the domain of the function. This differentiation can easily be made as follows: We shall use a symbolism such as $p(x)$ to denote the entire probability function for the random variable x, and $p(x_i)$ to denote the probability of the event $x = x_i$. Thus $p(x)$ represents a function, while $p(x_i)$ represents a number. We shall always use different symbols for a random variable and the particular values it can take on. It is necessary, unfortunately, to use symbols both for the random variable and its possible values. However, this makes it possible to distinguish between a function and its value for some particular element of the domain. In using $p(x)$ to represent the probability function, we are employing the usual mathematical notation for a function in which x is the independent variable.

We might note that the events corresponding to the different values $x_1, \ldots, x_k$ which the random variable x can take on are mutually exclusive and collectively exhaustive. Thus it would be possible to use as an event set for the random experiment one in which the simple events correspond to the values taken on by the random variable x. Very frequently, we shall be dealing with event sets in which the simple events are characterized by numbers. These numbers can be thought of as the possible different values of a random variable. The probability function for this random variable is then merely the function that assigns the probabilities to the simple events. For example, we have often in the past considered a random experiment that involves tossing a die and noting which face turns up. We normally use the event set in which the simple event e_j corresponds to a face with j dots on it turning up. Thus each simple event corresponds to a number, i.e., the number of dots on a face of the die. These numbers can be thought of as the possible values that a random variable can take on. The random variable here is the number of dots on the face of the die which turns up. When the simple events for a random experiment are characterized by numbers, we shall, in general, think of these numbers as being the possible values of some random variable. In such cases it is convenient to introduce some simplifications in terminology. Instead of using symbols e_j for the simple events and x_i for the values of the random variable, we shall use the values x_i of the random variable to denote the simple events also. Then the event set can be looked upon as the set $X = \{x_1, \ldots, x_k\}$. The probability of the simple event x_i, that is, the event that $x = x_i$, is $p(x_i)$, the probability that the random variable will assume the value x_i.

Frequently, it is convenient to represent graphically the probability function $p(x)$ for the random variable x. A convenient way to do this is to use what is called a bar diagram, an example of which is given in Figure 1-6. We select a point 0 on a horizontal axis as the point from which we make measurements. Then a unit of length is selected. The points corresponding to the numbers x_i are next located on this line, positive numbers lying to the right of 0 and negative numbers to the left. Now at each number x_i, we erect a vertical bar whose length is $p(x_i)$. In order to have a scale for measuring the lengths of the bars, we pass a vertical line through 0 and place a scale on the line. At the right hand end of the horizontal axis, we give the symbol for the random variable or sometimes its name. At the top of the vertical axis, we place the symbol for the function being represented graphically. In Figure 1-6, we have represented a possible probability function for a random variable x which can take on the values -6, -4, -2, 0, 1, 3, 6, and 8. Note that the lengths of the vertical bars must sum to one. The reason for this lies in the fact that for any probability function

$$p(x_1) + p(x_2) + \cdots + p(x_k) = 1. \qquad (1\text{-}37)$$

This follows from (1-7). The bar diagram for the probability function of the random variable representing the winnings in the game of chance

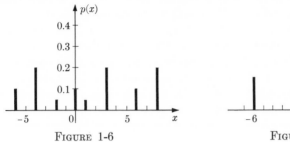

FIGURE 1-6

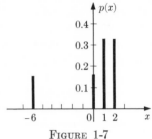

FIGURE 1-7

described on p. 43 is shown in Figure 1-7. It was constructed using Table 1-3.

The probability function completely describes the manner in which chance influences the value the random variable will take on, and thus it is a very important function to know. There is another function obtained from the probability function which we shall use frequently. It is called the *cumulative function or cumulative distribution* for the random variable x. The probability function when evaluated for a particular value of x, say x_i, gives the probability that x will take on the value x_i. Let us now compute the probability that x will take on the value x_i or a smaller value, that is, will take on one of the values x_1 or x_2 or . . . or x_i. To do this, let us begin by computing the probability that x takes on a value less than or equal to x_2, i.e., takes on the value x_1 or x_2. We shall represent this event symbolically by $x \leq x_2$. Now $x = x_1$ and $x = x_2$ are mutually exclusive events, and $x \leq x_2$ is the event $(x = x_1) \cup (x = x_2)$. Thus by (1-13), the probability of $x \leq x_2$, which we shall write $p(x \leq x_2)$, is the sum of the probabilities $p(x_1)$ and $p(x_2)$,

$$p(x \leq x_2) = p(x_1) + p(x_2). \tag{1-38}$$

Next, consider the probability that x takes on a value less than or equal to x_3, which we shall denote symbolically by $x \leq x_3$. Now $x \leq x_3$, if $x = x_1$ or $x = x_2$ or $x = x_3$, that is, if $x \leq x_2$ or $x = x_3$. However, $x \leq x_2$ and $x = x_3$ are exclusive events. Therefore, $p(x \leq x_3)$, the probability of $x \leq x_3$, is given by

$$p(x \leq x_3) = p(x \leq x_2) + p(x_3),$$

or by (1-38),

$$p(x \leq x_3) = p(x_1) + p(x_2) + p(x_3). \tag{1-39}$$

By repeating these arguments it becomes clear that the probability that $x \leq x_i$ is

$$p(x \leq x_i) = p(x_1) + p(x_2) + \cdots + p(x_i) \tag{1-40}$$

for each i, $i = 2, \ldots, k$. Now $p(x \leq x_1) = p(x_1)$, since if $x \leq x_1$, x must be equal to x_1 because there exist no allowable values of x less than x_1. Thus we can interpret (1-40) as holding for all i, $i = 1, \ldots, k$.

We can then associate with each element x_i of the set X containing the values that the random variable x can assume a number $p(x \leq x_i)$, which is the probability that x will be observed to take on a value less than or equal to x_i. This rule defines a function over the set X, which we shall call the cumulative function or cumulative distribution of the random variable x. Instead of using $p(x \leq x_i)$ to denote the probability of the event $x \leq x_i$, we shall use the simpler notation $P(x_i)$. Thus we define $P(x_i)$ by

$$P(x_i) = p(x \leq x_i) = p(x_1) + \cdots + p(x_i), \quad i = 1, \ldots, k. \quad (1\text{-}41)$$

We shall use the notation $P(x)$ to describe the entire cumulative function, just as $p(x)$ denotes the probability function for x.

Equation (1-41) shows how we can determine the function $P(x)$ when we know the function $p(x)$. Equally well, we can determine the function $p(x)$ from $P(x)$, since from (1-41),

$$p(x_i) = P(x_i) - P(x_{i-1}), \quad i = 2, \ldots, k, \quad (1\text{-}42)$$

and

$$p(x_1) = P(x_1). \quad (1\text{-}43)$$

EXAMPLE. The cumulative function for the random variable whose probability function is shown in Figure 1-7 is the following:

$$P(-6) = p(-6) = \tfrac{1}{6}; \quad P(0) = p(-6) + p(0) = \tfrac{1}{3};$$
$$P(1) = p(-6) + p(0) + p(1) = \tfrac{2}{3};$$
$$P(2) = p(-6) + p(0) + p(1) + p(2) = 1.$$

Note that if x_k is the largest value that the random variable x can take on, then from (1-37) and (1-41), $P(x_k) = 1$. Also note that

$$P(x_{i+1}) = p(x_{i+1}) + P(x_i), \quad i = 1, \ldots, k - 1. \quad (1\text{-}44)$$

It is often useful to represent $P(x)$ graphically, as we did $p(x)$. We can use precisely the same sort of bar diagram representation. The graphical representation of the $P(x)$ function determined above from Figure 1-7 is shown in Figure 1-8. Note that as one moves from left to right, the length of the bars can never decrease, since inasmuch as $p(x_{i+1}) \geq 0$, it follows from (1-44) that $P(x_{i+1}) \geq P(x_i)$.

Either one of the functions, $p(x)$ or $P(x)$, completely describes the manner in which chance influences the value that the random variable x will take on when the random experiment under consideration is performed. The manner in which x behaves can be thought of as being controlled by a certain type of chance mechanism. We shall refer to the particular chance mechanism that controls x as *the distribution of the random*

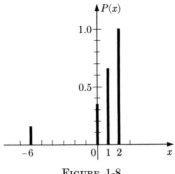

FIGURE 1-8

variable x.   Either function $p(x)$ or $P(x)$ provides a quantitative representation of the distribution of x.   Thus we can use the terminology, x is a random variable with the distribution $p(x)$, or x is a random variable with the distribution $P(x)$.   What we mean is that x is a random variable whose behavior is determined by a chance mechanism characterized by the function $p(x)$ or the function $P(x)$.

To conclude this section, we shall show that if we know the probability function $p(x)$ for a random variable x, we can compute μ_x, the expected value of x, using this probability function.   Recall that μ_x is given by

$$\mu_x = \xi_1 p_1 + \xi_2 p_2 + \cdots + \xi_m p_m, \tag{1-45}$$

where $\xi_j = x(e_j)$.   Let us now consider all j for which $\xi_j = x_i$.   Then $e_j \in S_i$, where the S_i are the sets defined previously.   In the summation (1-45) we have x_i multiplying a sum of p_j, the sum being taken over all $e_j \in S_i$.   But this sum is precisely what we called $p(x_i)$.   Thus,*

$$\mu_x = x_1 p(x_1) + x_2 p(x_2) + \cdots + x_k p(x_k). \tag{1-46}$$

Equation (1-46) tells us how to compute the expected value of x from the probability function for x.   When using this expression, there is no need to make use of the simple events, nor is there even a need to know how they are defined.   To compute μ_x, we list each different value x_i that x can take on, multiply this value by the probability that $x = x_i$, and add the results.   Equation (1-46) is a useful one, which we shall employ frequently in the future.   Thus using (1-46), the expected value of the random variable whose probability function is illustrated graphically in Figure 1-7 is

$$\mu_x = (-6)(\tfrac{1}{6}) + 0(\tfrac{1}{6}) + 1(\tfrac{1}{3}) + 2(\tfrac{1}{3}) = 0,$$

which is the same result that we obtained on p. 42.

The expected value μ_x of the random variable x is also often referred to

---

*A number of authors use $E\{x\}$ to denote the expected value of x in place of or in addition to μ_x.   We shall not use the $E\{x\}$ notation in this text.

as the expected value of the distribution of the random variable or the *mean* of the distribution of the random variable. In the future we shall frequently refer to the mean of a probability function $p(x)$. The mean of $p(x)$ is the number μ_x computed from (1-46) and is the expected value of the random variable whose probability function is $p(x)$. The reason that it is convenient to associate the number μ_x with the function $p(x)$, as well as with the random variable x, is that many random variables may have the same probability function, and we shall be interested in studying the characteristics of certain probability functions without being concerned about how the associated random variable is to be interpreted.

1-14 THE SUMMATION NOTATION

In the last several sections we frequently found it necessary to add together a number of probabilities. To avoid continually writing out these long sums, it is convenient to introduce a special notation for summations, called the summation notation. To characterize completely the sum of n elements a_j, which we have been writing as $a_1 + a_2 + \cdots + a_n$, all we need to do is specify the general form of the elements to be added, here a_j, indicate what values j takes on, and introduce a symbol to represent the operation of summation. A special symbol $\sum$ (the capital Greek letter sigma) is used in mathematics to represent the operation of summation. It is called the *summation sign*. We shall then represent the sum under consideration as

$$\sum_{j=1}^{n} a_j.$$

Immediately after the summation sign we place the symbol a_j for the general form of the elements being summed. We call j the *summation index*, and when j takes on all integral values between two integers, we give the smallest value of j (1 in our example) below the summation sign and the largest value (n in our example) on top of the summation sign. These largest and smallest values of j are referred to as the *limits of the summation*. Thus, by definition,

$$\sum_{j=1}^{n} a_j = a_1 + a_2 + \cdots + a_n. \tag{1-47}$$

We read the left hand side of (1-47) as "the sum from j equal one to j equal n of a_j." More generally, if m and n are any two integers such that $n > m$, then

$$\sum_{j=m}^{n} a_j = a_m + a_{m+1} + \cdots + a_n. \tag{1-48}$$

The symbol used for the summation index is irrelevant; it need not be j. Thus,

$$\sum_{j=1}^{n} a_j, \quad \sum_{i=1}^{n} a_i, \quad \sum_{k=1}^{n} a_k,$$

all mean the same thing, i.e., $a_1 + \cdots + a_n$.

EXAMPLES.   1.   If $a_j = j$, then

$$\sum_{j=1}^{n} j = 1 + 2 + \cdots + n.$$

2.   Suppose that $a_j = j^2$; then

$$\sum_{j=1}^{m} j^2 = 1^2 + 2^2 + \cdots + m^2.$$

3.   If $a_j = 1 + j$, then

$$\sum_{j=1}^{n} (1 + j) = (1 + 1) + (1 + 2) + \cdots + (1 + n).$$

4.

$$\sum_{j=-3}^{2} a_j = a_{-3} + a_{-2} + a_{-1} + a_0 + a_1 + a_2.$$

5.   If $a_j = \lambda$ (a constant), then

$$\sum_{j=1}^{n} \lambda = \underbrace{\lambda + \lambda + \cdots + \lambda}_{n \text{ times}} = n\lambda.$$

Note carefully that the summation here is $n\lambda$ and not λ.

6.

$$\sum_{i=1}^{k} p(y_i) = p(y_1) + p(y_2) + \cdots + p(y_k).$$

We shall next obtain several useful properties of the summation operation. First, let us introduce a convenient definition which is

$$\sum_{j=m}^{m} a_j = a_m. \tag{1-49}$$

Now note that since

$$a_m + a_{m+1} + \cdots + a_q + a_{q+1} + \cdots + a_n$$
$$= (a_m + \cdots + a_q) + (a_{q+1} + \cdots + a_n),$$

it follows that

$$\sum_{j=m}^{n} a_j = \sum_{j=m}^{q} a_j + \sum_{j=q+1}^{n} a_j, \quad m < q < n. \tag{1-50}$$

In particular, because of (1-49), this holds even if $q + 1 = n$, i.e.,

$$\sum_{j=m}^{n} a_j = \sum_{j=m}^{n-1} a_j + a_n, \quad n \geq m + 1. \tag{1-51}$$

It is often convenient to break up summations into two or more "partial sums," and (1-50) tells us how to do this.

Next observe that

$$\sum_{j=m}^{n} (a_j + b_j) = (a_m + b_m) + \cdots + (a_n + b_n)$$

$$= (a_m + \cdots + a_n) + (b_m + \cdots + b_n)$$

$$= \sum_{j=m}^{n} a_j + \sum_{j=m}^{n} b_j,$$

that is,

$$\sum_{j=m}^{n} (a_j + b_j) = \sum_{j=m}^{n} a_j + \sum_{j=m}^{n} b_j. \tag{1-52}$$

Thus when each of the terms in the summation can be written as the sum of two terms, the resulting sum can be split into two summations as indicated in (1-52). The same reasoning shows, of course, that if each term in the summation can be written as the sum of r terms, then the summation can be split up into r summations.

Finally, observe that

$$\sum_{j=m}^{n} \lambda a_j = \lambda a_m + \cdots + \lambda a_n = \lambda(a_m + \cdots + a_n) = \lambda \sum_{j=m}^{n} a_j,$$

or

$$\sum_{j=m}^{n} \lambda a_j = \lambda \sum_{j=m}^{n} a_j. \tag{1-53}$$

In words, all that (1-53) says is that a common factor may be taken outside the summation sign.

1-15　EXPECTED VALUES AGAIN

In working with a random experiment, we shall frequently be dealing not with a single random variable, but with several random variables simultaneously. Consider a random experiment with the event set $E = \{e_1, \ldots, e_m\}$, and imagine that we are interested in two random variables x and y, where x is defined by the function $\xi_j = x(e_j)$ and y is defined by the function $\zeta_j = y(e_j)$. Now for each j, suppose that we compute the number

$$\theta_j = a\xi_j + b\zeta_j + c, \quad j = 1, \ldots, m, \tag{1-54}$$

where a, b, and c are some specified numbers.   In this way we associate with each e_j a new number θ_j.   But then this rule of association automatically defines a new random variable, call it z, characterized by the function $\theta_j = z(e_j)$.   Because of (1-54), we can write

$$z(e_j) = ax(e_j) + by(e_j) + c,$$

or symbolically we can write $z = ax + by + c$.   What do we mean by writing $z = ax + by + c$?   We mean that for whatever simple event occurs, the value of z will be a times the value of x plus b times the value of y plus the number c.

We shall now show that there is a very simple relation between the expected value for the new random variable z and the expected values of the random variables x and y.   Denote the expected values of x, y, and z by μ_x, μ_y, and μ_z, respectively.   Then by the definition given in Section 1-12, we have on using the summation notation introduced in the previous section

$$\mu_x = \sum_{j=1}^{m} \xi_j p_j, \quad \mu_y = \sum_{j=1}^{m} \zeta_j p_j, \quad \mu_z = \sum_{j=1}^{m} \theta_j p_j. \tag{1-55}$$

If we now use in the expression for μ_z, the value of θ_j given by (1-54), we have

$$\mu_z = \sum_{j=1}^{m} (a\xi_j + b\zeta_j + c)p_j = \sum_{j=1}^{m} (a\xi_j p_j + b\zeta_j p_j + cp_j). \tag{1-56}$$

In (1-56) each term on the right can be looked upon as the sum of three terms.   Thus, from the generalization of (1-52),

$$\mu_z = \sum_{j=1}^{m} a\xi_j p_j + \sum_{j=1}^{m} b\zeta_j p_j + \sum_{j=1}^{m} cp_j, \tag{1-57}$$

which on using (1-53) becomes

$$\mu_z = a \sum_{j=1}^{m} \xi_j p_j + b \sum_{j=1}^{m} \zeta_j p_j + c \sum_{j=1}^{m} p_j. \tag{1-58}$$

On using the definitions of μ_x and μ_y, we obtain

$$\mu_z = a\mu_x + b\mu_y + c \sum_{j=1}^{m} p_j. \tag{1-59}$$

However, recall that the probabilities of the simple events must sum to 1. Thus, $\sum_{j=1}^{m} p_j = 1$, and

$$\mu_z = a\mu_x + b\mu_y + c. \tag{1-60}$$

Equation (1-60) is important and will be used repeatedly in our future work.   It states that given the random variables x and y and their expected values μ_x and μ_y, then if the new random variable $z = ax + by + c$ is formed, the expected value of z can be obtained immediately.

We can easily generalize (1-60) to the case where there are more than two random variables. Suppose that we have several random variables $x, y, \ldots, t$ with expected values $\mu_x, \mu_y, \ldots, \mu_t$. Then if we form a new random variable

$$z = ax + by + \cdots + gt + h, \tag{1-61}$$

the expected value of z, μ_z, is given by

$$\mu_z = a\mu_x + b\mu_y + \cdots + g\mu_t + h. \tag{1-62}$$

The proof is precisely the same as the proof given above.

At this point the reader may wonder why we would ever be interested in forming a new random variable z from x and y by writing $z = ax + by + c$. Interestingly enough, it is something that we shall be doing very frequently. To illustrate how such operations can arise naturally, consider a random experiment representing some sort of business venture. The profit to be received from this venture will be a random variable. Let us suppose that as usual the profit can be obtained by subtracting from the revenues received the costs incurred. Suppose that both the revenues and costs are also random variables. Then if we denote the revenues by the random variable x, the costs by the random variable y, and the profit by the random variable z, we have $z = x - y$; and this is of the form $z = ax + by + c$ if we take $a = 1$, $b = -1$, and $c = 0$. Thus according to (1-60), the expected profit is equal to the expected revenues received minus the expected costs incurred.

1-16 FUNCTIONS OF A RANDOM VARIABLE

We noted in the previous section that frequently we must be concerned not with just a single random variable but with several different random variables. Often it turns out that all of the random variables of interest are functions of one particular random variable. We wish to study such situations in this section.

What do we mean by saying that a random variable y is a function of another random variable x? Suppose that we associate with each possible value x_i which the random variable x can take on a unique number y_i. This association defines a function whose domain is the set $X = \{x_1, \ldots, x_k\}$, and whose range will be denoted by Y. We can denote the image of x_i by $g(x_i)$, so that $y_i = g(x_i)$, and $y_i \in Y$. Let us now show that the set Y can be considered as the set of values which some random variable y can take on. To do this, we need only show that associated with each simple event e_j there is a unique number in Y. Since

x is a random variable, a unique number $\xi_j = x(e_j)$ is associated with each e_j, and ξ_j will be one of the possible values x_i which x can take on. But then the function $g(x)$ determines a unique element of Y, say y_t, given by $y_t = g(\xi_j)$. Thus there is a unique number in Y associated with each e_j. We can represent the relationship by combining $y_t = g(\xi_j)$ and $\xi_j = x(e_j)$ to yield $y_t = g[x(e_j)]$. Thus the function $y_i = g(x_i)$ defines a new random variable y which can take on the values in Y. We can conveniently show the relation between y and x by the symbolism $y = g(x)$. This simply means that y is a random variable whose value is determined by the value of another random variable x through the function $g(x)$, and we say that y is a function of x.

EXAMPLES. *1.* If x is a random variable, then some examples of functions which serve to define a new random variable y are

$$y = 2x; \quad y = x^2; \quad y = 3x^2 - 2x + 1; \quad y = \frac{4 - x}{x^2 + 2}.$$

2. Suppose x is a random variable defined over the event set

$$E = \{e_1, e_2, e_3, e_4, e_5\},$$

and $x(e_1) = -2$, $x(e_2) = 0$, $x(e_3) = 4$, $x(e_4) = -2$, $x(e_5) = 1$. Suppose that we now introduce a new random variable $y = x^2$. Let us determine the function $y(e_j)$ which associates a value of y with each e_j. Now $y(e_j) = g[x(e_j)]$, and since $x(e_1) = -2$, the value of y associated with e_1 is $(-2)^2 = 4$, giving $y(e_1) = 4$. Similarly, $y(e_2) = 0^2 = 0$, $y(e_3) = 4^2 = 16$, $y(e_4) = (-2)^2 = 4$, and $y(e_5) = 1^2 = 1$.

3. Suppose that x and y are random variables defined over E, and y is a function of x, $y = g(x)$. When the random experiment is performed, values of both x and y will be determined. If we know the observed value of x is x_i, then we know also the value of y. It is $g(x_i)$. However, if we knew just the value of y, this might not tell us the value observed for x if more than one value of x could yield the same value of y. This happens when $y = x^2$, for example. If $y = 4$, this could imply that $x = 2$ or $x = -2$ if x can take on both these values.

We have noted that if a random variable x can take on values in the set $X = \{x_1, \ldots, x_k\}$, then these values can be used as simple events, in which case X becomes the event set for the random experiment. It may not always be possible to use X as the event set, because it is not necessarily true that every event whose probability we may wish to compute is the union of simple events in X. However, it is important to note that for any probabilistic computations that we may wish to make which involve only the random variable x, then in such cases the set X can be used as the event set. This is equivalent to saying that all we need in making such computations is a knowledge of the probability function $p(x)$ for x. The reason for this is clear; X contains as elements the different values that x can assume. There are no more "simple" events which involve only the random variable x. Every event involving x must be one of these simple events, or the union of two or more of them, or the impossible event. All such events can be considered as subsets of X.

We can now go on to note that if we are making computations that involve only x and random variables which are functions of x, it is again true that we may use the set X for the event set. All that is needed to demonstrate this is to show that any event involving y, $y = g(x)$, can be thought of as a subset of X. To show this, we note that there are no more simple events involving y than the different values which y can take on. There is no value of y which is not the image of at least one x_i, i.e., at least one element of X. Thus the event that y assumes a particular value, say ζ, is represented by the event that one of those x_i for which $\zeta = g(x_i)$ occurs. Hence, the event $y = \zeta$ is a subset of X, and all other events involving y must be subsets of X. Since all events involving x only and y only are subsets of X, all events involving the union or intersection of events involving x and/or involving y will be subsets of X. Thus all probabilistic computations that we wish to make involving x and y can be made using X as the event set, or in other words, can be made using only $p(x)$, the probability function for x. This is a very important observation. Even though we may wish to use a more complicated event set when making other computations involving our random experiment, we can always convert to the use of X in any computations involving only x and random variables that are functions of x. This is often a convenient thing to do, and from what we have shown above, we will obtain precisely the same results as we would if we did not convert to using X, but always used the more complicated original event set. For a considerable number of problems which we shall study there will never be any need to use any event set other than X. All computations can be carried out using only the probability function $p(x)$.

We might now note that if we use X as the event set, then the function $y = g(x)$ which defines the random variable y in terms of the random variable x is nothing but the function that defines the random variable y, i.e., which shows how to associate with each simple event a unique real number. In these terms, then, $y_i = g(x_i)$ has precisely the same interpretation as the function $\xi_j = x(e_j)$.

Let us now consider a random variable $y = g(x)$ and see how to determine the expected value μ_y of y. We can imagine X to be the event set, and the function $y_i = g(x_i)$ simply serves to define the random variable y.

In this case, $p(x_i)$ is the probability of the simple event x_i. Then, according to the definition of the expected value of y,

$$\mu_y = \sum_{i=1}^{k} y_i p(x_i),$$

or since $y_i = g(x_i)$,

$$\mu_y = \sum_{i=1}^{k} g(x_i)p(x_i) = g(x_1)p(x_1) + \cdots + g(x_k)p(x_k). \qquad (1\text{-}63)$$

We shall frequently use (1-63) to compute the expected value of a random variable that is function of x.

An important special case of (1-63) will now be considered. Suppose that $y = ax + b$. Then, by (1-52) and (1-53),

$$\mu_y = \sum_{i=1}^{k} (ax_i + b)p(x_i) = a \sum_{i=1}^{k} x_i p(x_i) + b \sum_{i=1}^{k} p(x_i).$$

However,

$$\sum_{i=1}^{k} x_i p(x_i) = \mu_x; \quad \sum_{i=1}^{k} p(x_i) = 1.$$

Therefore,

$$\mu_y = a\mu_x + b, \quad \text{when } y = ax + b. \qquad (1\text{-}64)$$

The expected value of y is a times the expected value of x plus b. When we form a new random variable y from x by writing $y = ax + b$, we say that y is obtained by an *affine transformation* on x. Suppose that in (1-64) we take $a = 1$ and $b = -\mu_x$. Then, $y = x + (-\mu_x) = x - \mu_x$, and we have $\mu_y = \mu_x - \mu_x = 0$, that is,

$$\mu_y = 0, \quad \text{when } y = x - \mu_x. \qquad (1\text{-}65)$$

Let us explain the intuitive meaning of (1-65). When $y = x - \mu_x$, y measures the deviation of the random variable x from its expected value. All (1-65) states is that if we repeat the experiment unendingly, the deviations of x from its expected value will average out to 0. This is, of course, what we expect intuitively.

Situations where we deal with random variables that are all functions of one particular random variable arise very frequently. For example, consider a game of chance in which the winnings depend on the face turned up when we toss a die. Let x be the random variable representing the number of dots observed. If y is the random variable representing the amount won, then y will be a function of x. As another example, consider the problem involving the demand for bread on a particular day of the week in a supermarket. If we let x be the random variable representing the number of loaves demanded, and y the profit earned on bread sales for the day, then once we decide how much to stock, the profit earned will be a function of the demand, that is, y will be a function of x.

1-17   THE VARIANCE OF A RANDOM VARIABLE

Consider a random variable x whose probability function is $p(x)$ and whose expected value is μ_x.   In the previous section we introduced a random variable $y = x - \mu_x$, which measured the deviation of x from its expected value.   We have proved that $\mu_y = 0$.   It is frequently of great interest to know something about the deviations of the observed values of x from μ_x that will be encountered if we repeat the experiment under consideration many times.   In this section we would like to introduce a numerical measure of these fluctuations.   Before doing this, however, let us study in a little more detail the nature of the problem.

Consider two random variables x and y which have the probability functions shown in Figures 1-9 and 1-10, respectively.   Both random

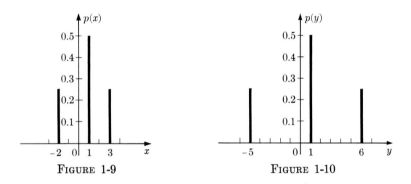

FIGURE 1-9   FIGURE 1-10

variables have precisely the same expected value of 0.75, since from the figures we see that*

$$\mu_x = 0.25(-2) + 0.5(1) + 0.25(3) = 0.75$$
$$\mu_y = 0.25(-5) + 0.5(1) + 0.25(6) = 0.75.$$

Now consider the results of twenty-five performances of an experiment involving the random variable x and twenty-five performances of a random experiment involving the random variable y.   In Figures 1-11 and 1-12 we have shown the values of the random variables x and y observed on each trial of the experiments.   The way to perform an experiment whose outcome yields a value of the random variable x with the probabilities indicated in Figure 1-9 is to mark the number -2 on one ball, the number 1 on two balls, and the number 3 on one ball.   Then draw a ball from a bowl in which the balls were well mixed and observe the number on the

---

*The reader might observe that these examples illustrate the fact that μ_x may be different from any of the values $x_1, \ldots, x_k$ which the random variable x may take on.

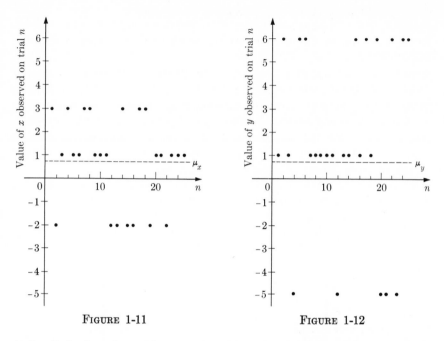

FIGURE 1-11   FIGURE 1-12

ball. It is clear from Figures 1-11 and 1-12 that although x and y have
the same expected value, the sequences of values observed in each case are
not similar.   Intuitively, we would say that y fluctuates much more than
x does. It is very useful to have some numerical measure that describes
what sort of fluctuations about the expected value will occur if we repeat
the experiment a number of times.

Now at first glance it would seem reasonable that the simplest and best
method of measuring fluctuations is to use $x_k - x_1$, the difference between
the largest and smallest values which the random variable can take on.
This number is referred to as *the range of the random variable*.   Then
$x_k - \mu_x$ is the maximum amount of fluctuation above μ_x, and $\mu_x - x_1$ is
the maximum fluctuation below μ_x. For our simple example, this would
be a good way to characterize the fluctuations.   In general, however, and
especially in situations where x can take on quite a few different values,
the range may be of relatively little interest for measuring what we are
really interested in.   Suppose that x_1 and x_k have very small probabilities,
so that on the average they do not occur very frequently.   Then $x_k - x_1$
might be a very poor measure of the spread of the observed values about
the mean.   It is true that the spread can be this great and no greater,
but most of the observed values may be much more closely grouped around
the mean.   What we really want to know in most cases is not the greatest
possible deviation from the mean, but a measure of the average deviation

from the mean. Sometimes the maximum deviation is important, but for many purposes an average-type measure is much more relevant. What we need then is something that weights each fluctuation by its probability of occurrence.

In weighting the values $x_i - \mu_x$ by the probability of observing x_i, i.e., $p(x_i)$, we cannot simply compute $\sum_{i=1}^{k} (x_i - \mu_x)p(x_i)$ because, as we have noted previously, this has the value 0 and does not measure the fluctuations about μ_x at all. The trouble is that for some x_i, $x_i - \mu_x > 0$ and for others $x_i - \mu_x < 0$. We want all $x_i - \mu_x$ to contribute to the sum, and we do not want those with $x_i - \mu_x < 0$ to subtract from it, i.e., we do not care whether $x_i > \mu_x$ or $x_i < \mu_x$ in studying the fluctuations. All we care about is how far from μ_x each observed value of x is. What we are saying is that we are interested in the magnitude of $x_i - \mu_x$ and not in its sign, so that we should use $x_i - \mu_x$ if this is positive or $\mu_x - x_i$ if this is positive. The magnitude of a number a, which is its value independent of sign, i.e., a if $a > 0$ and $-a$ if $a < 0$, is called the absolute value of a and is denoted by $|a|$. Now,

$$|x_i - \mu_x| = \begin{cases} x_i - \mu_x, & \text{if } x_i - \mu_x \geq 0 \\ \mu_x - x_i, & \text{if } x_i - \mu_x < 0 \end{cases}. \tag{1-66}$$

It would then appear that the sort of measure that we are looking for is the expected value of the random variable $v = |x - \mu_x|$, that is,

$$\sum_{i=1}^{k} |x_i - \mu_x|p(x_i). \tag{1-67}$$

This would indeed be a useful measure. However, it turns out to be very clumsy to work with mathematically, and for this reason, a slightly different one is commonly used.

Notice that the number $(x_i - \mu_x)^2$ is positive whether $x_i - \mu_x$ is positive or negative. Furthermore, $(x_i - \mu_x)^2$ is a measure of the magnitude of the deviation of x_i from μ_x, just as $|x_i - \mu_x|$ is. Consider then the number, denoted by σ_x^2, which is defined to be the expected value of the random variable $z = (x - \mu_x)^2$, so that

$$\sigma_x^2 = \sum_{i=1}^{k} (x_i - \mu_x)^2 p(x_i). \tag{1-68}$$

This number is called the *variance* of the random variable x. Note that the variance of x is completely determined by the probability function for x. We were led to introduce the variance of a random variable in our search for a way of measuring the fluctuations about μ_x which could be expected if we repeat the experiment a number of times. The variance turns out to be a useful measure to introduce even when experiments cannot be repeated, and hence we shall introduce the notion of the variance into our mathematical model with the following formal definition.

VARIANCE OF A RANDOM VARIABLE. *The variance of a random variable x with distribution $p(x)$ is the unique non-negative number $\sigma_x{}^2$ computed according to (1-68).*

The variance of x is also frequently referred to as the variance of the distribution of x, the same terminology being used as that for the expected value. It should be kept in mind that the variance is the expected value of the random variable $z = (x - \mu_x)^2$; z is the square of the random variable $y = x - \mu_x$, which measures the deviation of x from its expected value.

We could use $\sigma_x{}^2$ itself as the measure of fluctuations about the mean. However, $\sigma_x{}^2$ has a defect, which we should note. Normally, the random variables with which we shall be dealing will have physical dimensions. For example, x could be the profit obtained from some project and would then have the dimensions of dollars. We think of probabilities as not having dimensions and thus the expected value of x must have the same physical dimensions as x (as we know it should intuitively). However, x and $\sigma_x{}^2$ will not have the same dimensions, since $(x_i - \mu_x)^2$ has physical dimensions that are the square of those of x, that is, if x has the dimensions of dollars, $\sigma_x{}^2$ has the dimensions of dollars squared   A quantity having the same physical dimensions as x is desirable in measuring the spread of x-values about μ_x. For this reason, it is convenient to use instead of $\sigma_x{}^2$ the positive square root of $\sigma_x{}^2$, which we shall denote by σ_x (this explains why $\sigma_x{}^2$ was used to denote the variance). The number σ_x is called the *standard deviation* of the random variable x and the standard deviation of the distribution of x. More formally, we can introduce the definition of σ_x as follows.

STANDARD DEVIATION OF A RANDOM VARIABLE. *The standard deviation of the random variable x with distribution $p(x)$ is the non-negative number $\sigma_x = \sqrt{\sigma_x{}^2}$, where $\sigma_x{}^2$ is the variance of x.*

To compute the standard deviation, we must first compute the variance and then take the positive square root.

We can give an intuitive interpretation of σ_x in the case where the random experiment can be repeated. Let us perform the experiment n times, and let n_i be the number of times that x_i is observed. Suppose that we compute

$$s_x = \left[\frac{1}{n} \sum_{i=1}^{n} (x_i - \mu_x)^2 n_i \right]^{1/2} \tag{1-69}$$

Then s_x is the square root of the average of the squares of the deviations of x from μ_x. This is referred to as the root mean square deviation. As n is increased more and more, s_x approaches σ_x, so that σ_x can be interpreted as the long run root mean square deviation. The value of σ_x also gives us some (but not a great deal of) information about what the bar diagram of $p(x)$ will be like. If we consider two different probability functions with the same mean, the one with the higher standard deviation will tend to look more spread out than the one with the lower standard deviation. This, of course, does not give us much precise information on the differences between the two bar diagrams. Let us now study some examples illustrating the material developed above.

EXAMPLES. *1.* First, we shall compute the variance of the distribution illustrated in Figure 1-7. We have shown previously that the mean of this distribution is 0. Thus,

$$(x - \mu_x)^2 = x^2,$$

and

$$\sigma_x^2 = \tfrac{1}{6}(-6)^2 + \tfrac{1}{6}(0)^2 + \tfrac{1}{3}(1)^2 + \tfrac{1}{3}(2)^2 = 6 + \tfrac{1}{3} + \tfrac{4}{3} = 7.67.$$

The standard deviation is $\sigma_x = \sqrt{7.67} = 2.76$.

2. Let us compute the variance and standard deviations of the random variables whose distributions are shown in Figures 1-9 and 1-10. The expected value of each random variable is 0.75. For x,

$$\sigma_x^2 = 0.25(-2 - 0.75)^2 + 0.50(1 - 0.75)^2 + 0.25(3 - 0.75)^2$$
$$= 1.89 + 0.03125 + 1.27 = 3.19,$$

and $\sigma_x = 1.78$. For y,

$$\sigma_y^2 = 0.25(-5 - 0.75)^2 + 0.50(1 - 0.75)^2 + 0.25(6 - 0.75)^2$$
$$= 8.29 + 0.03125 + 6.88 = 15.20,$$

and $\sigma_y = 3.88$. Thus, as we expected, $\sigma_y > \sigma_x$.

3. For an experiment that can be repeated over and over again, we have noted previously that $\bar{\xi}$, the arithmetic average of the observed values of x, should approach μ_x as the number of times that the experiment is repeated gets larger. This suggests that if we wished to estimate μ_x for some random variable x in a case where $p(x)$ was not known, we could repeat the experiment a number of times, determine $\bar{\xi}$, and use this as an approximate estimate of μ_x. If we add up the x values in Figure 1-11 and divide by 25, we obtain $\bar{\xi} = 0.72$. This is quite close to $\mu_x = 0.75$. However, if we add up the y values in Figure 1-12 and divide by 25, we obtain $\bar{\zeta} = 1.6$, and this is a rather poor approximation to $\mu_y = 0.75$. What this example illustrates is that we must, in general, expect to need more repetitions of an experiment to obtain a good estimate of the mean of a random variable in those cases where the standard deviation is large than is necessary in those cases where the standard deviation is small. This is something that we shall wish to investigate in more detail later.

Let us conclude this section by deriving an alternative equation for $\sigma_x{}^2$, which will be more convenient for computing the variance in particular cases.   Recall that

$$(x - \mu_x)^2 = x^2 - 2\mu_x x + \mu_x{}^2.$$

If we use this in the definition of $\sigma_x{}^2$, given by (1-68), we obtain

$$\sigma_x{}^2 = \sum_{i=1}^{k} (x_i{}^2 - 2\mu_x x_i + \mu_x{}^2) p(x_i),$$

or on applying (1-52) and (1-53),

$$\sigma_x{}^2 = \sum_{i=1}^{k} x_i{}^2 p(x_i) - 2\mu_x \sum_{i=1}^{k} x_i p(x_i) + \mu_x{}^2 \sum_{i=1}^{k} p(x_i). \qquad (1\text{-}70)$$

However,

$$\sum_{i=1}^{k} x_i p(x_i) = \mu_x; \quad \sum_{i=1}^{k} p(x_i) = 1.$$

Thus,

$$\sigma_x{}^2 = \sum_{i=1}^{k} x_i{}^2 p(x_i) - 2\mu_x{}^2 + \mu_x{}^2,$$

or

$$\sigma_x{}^2 = \sum_{i=1}^{k} x_i{}^2 p(x_i) - \mu_x{}^2. \qquad (1\text{-}71)$$

In words, the variance of x is equal to the expected value of x^2 minus the square of the expected value of x.   Equation (1-71) is especially useful in computing numerically $\sigma_x{}^2$, since it is unnecessary when using (1-71) to compute the numbers $x_i - \mu_x$ for each i value.

1-18   BRIEF HISTORICAL SUMMARY

Interest in probability concepts originally arose in connection with games of chance.   The first mathematical analysis of the subject was developed by the French mathematicians Fermat and Pascal in the seventeenth century and by Laplace in the eighteenth century.   Laplace introduced a definition of probability which, although rather reasonable for the types of problems he was studying, was a rather unfortunate choice.   Laplace defined the probability of an event A as follows: Divide up the possible outcomes of the experiment into equally likely ones.   Suppose that there are n of these.   If m of these equally likely outcomes are favorable to A, then the probability of A is m/n.   Laplace did not make use of the notion of an event set, but in our terminology he was assuming that it is always possible to select an event set such that the simple events are equally likely.   The problem is, of course, that in general such an event set does not exist. For example, if we consider the random experiment that involves the tossing of a loaded die and observing which face turns up, there is no way to obtain a set of equally likely simple events.

The most astonishing thing about the Laplace definition was that it was used essentially unmodified until the 1920's. The Laplace definition, even today, continues to be used in many high school and college algebra texts treating probability. Unfortunately, it is totally unsuitable for many practical applications. It was in the 1920's that R. von Mises, an Austrian mathematician, introduced the interpretation of probabilities as long run relative frequencies. Von Mises is, in a real sense, the father of modern probability theory. In von Mises' opinion, probability could be rigorously defined as a long run relative frequency. His work stimulated the interest of mathematicians in the subject, and they felt that von Mises' approach did not provide a suitable basis for a rigorous development of the subject. Mathematicians then moved in the direction of developing probability theory axiomatically, making use of the theory of sets. One of the characteristics of an axiomatic development is that one does not need to define what the elements are which satisfy the axioms. This made it unnecessary for mathematicians to get involved with the problem of defining what probability is. A considerable number of mathematicians were involved in this work. Two prominent names are those of the Russian Kolmogorov, and the American Doob. To von Mises, the work of the mathematicians seemed to be a complete perversion of the subject, and he had a number of rather heated quarrels with them. This is a classic case of complete misunderstanding on all sides since the spirit of the mathematicians' work was very close to that of von Mises. They were not trying to define probability but instead to construct a rigorous mathematical theory.

The notion of subjective probabilities has occurred to a number of people at various times, and it is not clear who first thought of the idea. A man whose work influenced others greatly was di Finetti. The book by the physicist Jeffries, published in 1939, takes a personal view of probability. Von Mises considered personal probabilities and said that they had no meaning. To him, probabilities could only be interpreted as long run relative frequencies. The most important work on personal probability from the point of view of decision theory is that given by L. J. Savage in his book *The Foundations of Statistics*, published in 1954. Savage succeeded in showing that if instead of taking probability as the fundamental concept, we move back several steps and assume that an individual behaves so as to satisfy certain axioms, then it can be proved that a personal probability function exists for the individual. To Savage, all probabilities are personal probabilities.

The brief history above brings us up to the present time. Interestingly enough, there is currently no general agreement as to what probability is.

There are many statisticians who refuse to use personal probabilities and accept only probabilities that have a relative frequency interpretation. Others claim that only personal probabilities have meaning. We have taken the position in this text that it is convenient to take probability as the fundamental concept, and that both the personal and long run frequency interpretations are useful. In our development of the theory no differentiation is made among the various ways of interpreting probability.

REFERENCES

1. Feller, W., *An Introduction to Probability Theory and Its Applications*, Vol. 1, 2nd. ed. Wiley, New York, 1957.
An excellent and widely used text. Although calculus is not needed, the level of this text can be considered as advanced.

2. Gnedenko, B. V., and A. Ya. Khinchin, *An Elementary Introduction to the Theory of Probability*. Freeman, San Francisco, 1961. (paperback)

3. Hodges, J. L., Jr., and E. L. Lehmann, *Elements of Finite Probability*. Holden-Day, San Francisco, 1965.
A very good introductory text, which requires little mathematical background.

4. Jeffreys, H., *Theory of Probability* (2nd. ed. 1948). Oxford University Press, Oxford, 1939.

5. Mosteller, F., R. E. K. Rourke, and G. B. Thomas, Jr., *Probability with Statistical Applications*. Addison-Wesley, Reading, Mass., 1961.
A good introductory work, which like reference [3] does not require much mathematical background.

6. Parzen, E., *Modern Probability Theory and Its Applications*. Wiley, New York, 1960.
A well-known text, which assumes a knowledge of calculus as background.

7. Savage, L. J., *The Foundations of Statistics*. Wiley, New York, 1954.

8. von Mises, R., *Probability, Statistics, and Truth*, 2nd. English ed. Macmillan, New York, 1957.
This very interesting little book presents von Mises' approach to probability. It is well worth reading.

PROBLEMS

Section 1-3

1. Toss a penny one hundred times. On each toss, record whether it lands heads or tails up. Determine the total number of tails n_t obtained after n tosses, for each n, $n = 1, 2, \ldots, 100$, and also determine the fraction of the tosses which yielded a tail. Plot the fraction of tails in n tosses against n as in Figure 1-1.

2. Take two pennies and consider the following experiment. We toss one of the pennies and then toss the second one. Note whether both land heads up, both land tails up, or one lands heads up and one lands tails up. Repeat this experiment 100 times, recording on each trial which of the three above outcomes is observed. After n trials, let n_{hh}, n_{tt}, and n_{ht} be the number of times that both landed heads up, both landed tails up, and one landed heads up and the other tails up, respectively. Compute for each n the ratios n_{hh}/n, n_{tt}/n, and n_{ht}/n. Construct a diagram such as that shown in Figure 1-1 for each of these ratios. What are the values of the ratios when $n = 100$?

3. Open the telephone book to any page. Starting with the first name on that page, record the last digit of the individual's telephone number. Do this for the next name. Continue this for two hundred names, so that two hundred digits are obtained corresponding to the last digit of the individual's telephone number. If an individual has more than one number, use the first one listed and skip the others. Determine the relative frequency of each digit 0, 1, ..., 9. Does the appearance of various digits here have the characteristics of chance phenomena?

4. Take five pennies and mark on them the numbers 1 through 5, one number per penny. Place the pennies in a container and shake it so that they are thoroughly mixed. Now select one penny from the container without looking. Record the number on the penny selected. Repeat this experiment 100 times. Determine the relative frequency of each penny in the 100 trials.

Section 1-4

1. Under what conditions would it be meaningful to discuss whether an individual made the "correct" assignment of a personal probability for some event? In general, can we say that an individual made an incorrect determination of a personal probability? When probabilities can be interpreted as relative frequencies, we can in principle decide whether a number someone claims is the probability of an event is correct, but can this be done for personal probabilities?

2. In some parts of the country weather reports include statements such as "There is a 3 in 10 chance that it will rain this afternoon." What does this statement mean?

3. Do personal probabilities always refer to what we normally think of as chance phenomena? If your answer is no, provide some examples.

4. When a politician says that "90 percent of the people believe that the government should act more aggressively in civil rights," what does this mean?

5. Are there any probabilities that have an objective existence? Discuss and indicate what is meant when we say that we wish to "determine" a probability experimentally. How can you (or can you?) justify the use of probabilities which do not have an objective significance?

Section 1-5

In Problems 1 through 5 list all subsets of the given set.

1. $A = \{1, 3, 5, 8\}$.   **2.** $A = \{a_1, a_2, a_3\}$.

3. $X = \{4, 5, 8, 12\}$.   **4.** $E = \{e_1, e_2, e_3, e_4\}$.

5. $B = \{2, 4, 6, 8, 10\}$.

In Problems 6 through 12 what is the intersection of the given sets?

6. $A = \{1, 3, 5, 7\}$;
$B = \{2, 4, 5, 8, 9\}$.

7. $A = \{1, 5, 7, 8, 11\}$;
$B = \{1, 4, 7, 9, 11\}$.

8. $A = \{3, 4, 6\}$;
$B = \{-3, -4, -6\}$.

9. $A = \{1, 3, 5, 7, 9\}$;
$B = \{1, 5, 9\}$.

10. A is the set of all numbers which are greater than or equal to 2, and B is the set of all numbers which are less than or equal to 10.

11. A is the set of students at a given university which have taken the introductory physics course, and B is the set of students at the same university which have taken the introductory calculus.

12. A is the set of all persons who filed a California state income tax form in 1965, and B is the set of all persons who filed either a New York state or Massachusetts state income tax form in 1965.

13. Find the intersection of the following three sets.

$$A_1 = \{-3, 2, 1, 5, 7\}; \quad A_2 = \{-2, 2, 1, 6, 7\}; \quad A_3 = \{2, 6, 7\}.$$

In Problems 14 through 19 determine the union of the given sets.

14. $A = \{1, 2\}$;
$B = \{1, 4, 5\}$.

15. $A = \{a_1, a_2\}$;
$B = \{b_1, b_2, b_3\}$.

16. $A = \{-5, -4, 0, 2, 1, 3\}$;
$B = \{-4, 0, 1, 3, 5, 8, 11\}$.

17. $A = \{1, 4, 7, 11\}$;
$B = \varnothing$.

18. Let A be the set of Presidents of the United States, and B the set of Chief Justices of the United States.

19. Let A be the set of individuals in the United States who own an Oldsmobile, and B the set of individuals who have \$10,000 or more invested in stocks.

20. Show that it is always true that $(A \cap B) \subseteq (A \cup B)$.

21. Show that if $B \subset A$, then $A \cap B = B$; illustrate this geometrically.

22. Show that if $B \subset A$, then $A \cup B = A$; illustrate this geometrically.

23. We define the set of all elements in A which are not in B to be the difference between A and B, written $A - B$. If

$$A = \{1, 3, 4, 5, 7\} \quad \text{and} \quad B = \{3, 5, 7, 11, 13\},$$

what is $A - B$ in this case?

24. Let $E = \{e_1, e_2, \ldots, e_{10}\}$ be the universal set, and $A = \{e_1, e_3, e_5\}$. What is A^c?

25. For the sets A and B of Problem 23, determine

$$A \cap B, \quad A \cup B, \quad (A \cap B)^c, \quad (A \cup B)^c, \quad A^c \cap B^c, \quad A^c \cup B^c,$$
$$(A - B) \cap A^c, \quad (A - B) \cup B, \quad (A - B) \cap B.$$

26. Show that for any sets A and B

$$(A \cap B)^c = A^c \cup B^c; \quad (A \cup B)^c = A^c \cap B^c.$$

Give an example to illustrate these equations. Also, provide a geometric interpretation for a specific case. Hint for first one: Show that $(A \cap B)^c \subseteq A^c \cup B^c$, and $A^c \cup B^c \subseteq (A \cap B)^c$.

27. Prove that for any sets A, B, and C

$$A \cap (B \cup C) = (A \cap B) \cup (A \cap C);$$
$$A \cup (B \cap C) = (A \cup B) \cap (A \cup C).$$

Give an example to illustrate these equations. Also, provide a geometric interpretation for a specific case.

Section 1-6

In Problems 1 through 5 determine whether or not the situation described represents a function.

1. $A = $ a set of books, and $B = $ a set including the authors of all the books in A. Consider the association with each book in A its author or authors in B.

2. Consider the correspondence between the rainfall in Sydney, Australia in a given year and the rainfall in the following year over the period 1870 to 1960.

3. $A = $ set of all numbers, and $B = $ set of all integers. The correspondence is that which for a given real number a drops in the decimal representation of a everything coming after the decimal point.

4. $A = \{x, \text{ all numbers } x\}$, and $B = \{y\}$, where for each $x \in A$ we compute the number y, which is the larger of x^2 and $3x - 2$.

5. $A = \{x, \text{ all numbers } x\}$, and $B = \{y\}$, where

$$y = \begin{cases} 2x, & x \geq 0 \\ x^2, & x \leq 2 \end{cases}.$$

6. Construct an example of a function where each element in the range is the image of precisely three elements of the domain, and the domain consists of more than three elements.

7. Let $A = \{a_1, a_2, a_3, a_4, a_5\}$, and $B = \{b_1, b_2, b_3, b_4\}$. Suppose that we define a function on A as follows: Associate with a_1 the element b_2, with a_2 the element b_1, with a_3 the element b_4, with a_4 the element b_2, and with a_5 the element b_4. Represent the elements of A by a set of points in the plane, and similarly represent the set B. Show that if we draw a line from each point representing an element of A to its image, these lines completely describe the function. Actually, illustrate this geometrically.

8. Consider a random experiment in which we place three balls in an urn, mix the balls thoroughly, and then select one without looking to see which one is selected. The balls are identical, except that each ball has a different number painted on it (either 1, 2, or 3). List all the ways you can think of for subdividing the outcomes of this experiment into mutually exclusive and collectively exhaustive events. Each such subdivision can be used to construct an event set. What are these event sets? Give a characterization of the simple events in each such set. Is there one set that seems most natural and most generally useful?

9. Consider a random experiment in which we place three balls, numbered 1, 2, and 3 in an urn, mix them well, and then select two of them without looking to see which ones are selected. List all the ways that you can think of for subdividing the outcomes of this experiment into mutually exclusive and collectively exhaustive events. Each such subdivision can be used to construct an event set. What are these event sets? Give a characterization of the simple events in each such set. Are there one or two sets which seem especially natural to use?

10. Consider a random experiment in which we toss three pennies and note how many heads and tails are obtained. List all the ways you can think of for dividing the outcomes of this experiment into mutually exclusive and collectively exhaustive events. Each such subdivision can be used to construct an event set. What are these event sets? Give a characterization of the simple events in each such set. Are there one or two sets which seem especially natural?

11. Consider an experiment in which we toss two six-sided dice and note the number of dots on each of the faces which turn up. Let us use as a characterization of the simple events the number of dots on each of the faces which turn up, i.e., one die turns up two dots and the other turns up five dots. How many simple events are there in this case? What is the event set? Suppose now that instead of using the simple events to which we just referred, we distinguish between the dice, perhaps by using one green one and one red die. Now let the simple events be characterized by the number of dots turned up on the green die and the number of dots turned up on the red die. How many simple events are there in this case? What is the event set? What is the difference between the two event sets just constructed?

12. Consider a random experiment in which we place in an urn four balls, numbered 1 to 4, mix them thoroughly, and then without looking draw out two of them. Suppose we characterize the simple events by noting the numbers on the balls, so that a simple event might be that one ball had the number 1 and the other the number 3. How many simple events are there? What is the event set? Next imagine that the simple events are characterized instead as follows. We note the number on the first ball drawn out; then we observe what number appears on the second ball drawn out. How many simple events are there in this case? What is the event set? What is the difference between the two event sets constructed here?

13. Suppose that we have an urn containing one green and two red balls and another urn containing three pennies and two quarters. Consider the random experiment in which we draw without looking a ball from one urn and a coin from the other. We can then consider as a simple event the specification of the color of the ball and the denomination of the coin. List each of the possible simple events. Describe the event set for this case. Now suppose that we paint a number on each ball and on each coin and repeat the experiment. Let us take as a simple event the specification of the number on the ball and the number on the coin. List the possible simple events. Describe the event set for this case.

Section 1-7

1. Consider the random experiment that involves the tossing of a die and noting which face turns up. Let a simple event be characterized by the number of dots on the face that turns up. Express each of the following events as subsets of E, and explain what the subset means in each case.
  (a) A face with four or less dots on it turns up.
  (b) A face with an odd number of dots on it turns up.
  (c) A face with six or less dots on it turns up.
  (d) The face which turns up has two or less dots on it or five or more dots on it.

2. Consider an experiment in which we toss three pennies, and note how many heads and tails there are. Let us use an event set E in which the simple event is characterized by the number of heads and the number of tails observed. Express each of the following events as subsets of E, and explain what the subset means in each case.
  (a) At least two heads appear.   (c) No tail appears.
  (b) Precisely one tail appears.   (d) One or more tails appear.

3. Suppose that for the situation described in Problem 2, we now paint a number on each coin, so that they are numbered 1, 2, and 3. Let us use as a simple event the specification of whether coin 1 lands heads or tails up, and similarly for the other two coins. Answer Problem 2 using this event set.

4. Consider Problem 11 of Section 1-6. If we use the first event set referred to there, express each of the following events as subsets of that event set, and explain the meaning of each.
  (a) The total number of points (dots) on the two faces which turn up is 4.
  (b) The total number of points on the two faces is less than or equal to 4.
  (c) The total number of points is either 4 or 10.

5. Answer Problem 4 using the second event set referred to in Problem 11 of Section 1-6.

6. Answer Problem 4 for the following events:
  (a) At least one of the faces has four dots on it.
  (b) One face has four dots on it, and the other has either one dot or five dots.

7. Answer Problem 5 for the events listed in Problem 6.

8. Consider Problem 12 of Section 1-6. If we use the first event set referred to there, express each of the following events as subsets of that event set, and explain the meaning of each subset.
  (a) The sum of the numbers on the two balls is 4.
  (b) The sum of the numbers on the two balls is at least 4.
  (c) One of the balls has the number 1 on it.

9. Answer Problem 8, using the second event set referred to in Problem 12 of Section 1-6.

10. Consider Problem 13 of Section 1-6. If we use the first event set referred to in this problem, express each of the following events as subsets of that event set, and explain the meaning of each subset.

(a) The ball drawn is red.
(b) The coin drawn is a penny.
(c) The ball is red, or the coin drawn is a penny, or both.
(d) The ball is red, but the coin drawn is not a penny.

11. Answer Problem 10 when the second event set referred to in Problem 13 of Section 1-6 is used.

12. Consider an urn that contains two red balls, one yellow ball, and one green ball. Consider the random experiment in which we pick out of the urn, without looking at the balls selected, three of the balls. Let a simple event be one characterized by noting the color of each ball. List the simple events. Express each of the following events as subsets of the event set.

(a) One ball is yellow, and one ball is green.   (c) At least one ball is red.
(b) No green ball appears.   (d) No red ball appears.

13. Indicate which of the following are allowable probability functions defined on the set $E = \{e_1, e_2, e_3\}$. For those which are not allowable, explain why.

(a) $p(e_1) = 0.5;$ $p(e_2) = 0.3;$ $p(e_3) = 0.2.$
(b) $p(e_1) = 0.4;$ $p(e_2) = 0.6;$ $p(e_3) = 0.$
(c) $p(e_1) = -0.4;$ $p(e_2) = 0.8;$ $p(e_3) = 0.6.$
(d) $p(e_1) = 0.6;$ $p(e_2) = 0.3;$ $p(e_3) = 0.2.$
(e) $p(e_1) = 0;$ $p(e_2) = 1;$ $p(e_3) = 0.$

14. Consider a random experiment having the event set $E = \{e_1, e_2, e_3, e_4, e_5\}$ with the probabilities of the simple events being $p_1 = 0.1$, $p_2 = 0.2$, $p_3 = 0.1$, $p_4 = 0.3$, $p_5 = 0.3$. Compute the probabilities of the events:

(a) $A = \{e_1, e_2\}.$ (b) $B = \{e_1, e_3, e_4\}.$ (c) $C = \{e_1, e_4, e_5\}.$
(d) $B \cap C.$ (e) $A \cup B.$ (f) $A \cup B^c.$ (g) $(A \cap B)^c.$

15. Consider a random experiment having the event set $E = \{e_1, e_2, e_3, e_4, e_5, e_6\}$ with the probabilities of the simple events being $p_1 = 0.05$, $p_2 = 0.25$, $p_3 = 0.10$, $p_4 = 0.20$, $p_5 = 0.30$, $p_6 = 0.10$. Compute the probabilities of the events:

(a) $A = \{e_1, e_2, e_5\}.$ (b) $B = \{e_2, e_3, e_4, e_5\}.$ (c) $C = \{e_1, e_6\}.$ (d) $A \cap B.$
(e) $B \cup C.$ (f) $(A \cap C) \cup B.$ (g) $(A \cap C) \cup (A \cap B).$ (h) $(A^c \cup B) \cap C.$

Section 1-8

1. Suppose you were the supply officer at an air base and were faced with the problem of deciding how many units of a certain type of spare part to have in stock for the coming month. How would you estimate the probability that r units will be demanded for each r from 0 up to the maximum number which could possibly be demanded?

2. Suppose you are a defense contractor who is about to accept a contract for developing a weapon system. This contract has a specified completion date. How would you estimate the probability of completing the schedule on time?

3. How would you proceed to estimate the probability that a given space vehicle intended to orbit around the moon would do so successfully?

4. If you were commander of the Strategic Air Command, how would you estimate the probability that an accident involving a nuclear weapon would occur due to the crash of one of the SAC bombers during the next five years?

Section 1-9

1. In a random experiment we toss three pennies, and a simple event is characterized by the number of heads and tails observed. List the simple events and denote this event set by E_1. Now imagine a number is painted on each of the coins, and let a simple event be characterized by whether coin 1 lands heads or tails, and similarly for the other two coins. List the simple events and denote this set by E_2. Show that E_1 and E_2 cannot both consist of equally likely events. In which of the sets should the simple events be equally likely? Why? What symmetry conditions must be satisfied? What is the probability of each simple event?

2. Use the results of Problem 1 to compute the probabilities for the following:

(a) Two coins land heads up and the other one tails.
(b) Two or more coins land heads up.
(c) No more than two coins land heads up.
(d) Precisely one coin lands tails up, or precisely one coin lands heads up.

3. Consider Problem 9 of Section 1-6. Suggest an event set in which the simple events might be considered equally likely. List the simple events and determine the probability of each. What symmetry conditions must be satisfied if the simple events are to be equally likely? Can you think of two different event sets in which the events are equally likely if the above mentioned symmetry conditions are satisfied?

4. Use the results of Problem 3 to compute the probability that

(a) One of the balls drawn is numbered 1.
(b) The ball with number 3 on it is not drawn.
(c) Either the ball numbered 1 or the ball numbered 2 is drawn or both are drawn.

5. Consider Problem 11 of Section 1-6. Show that it is impossible for the simple events in both the event sets developed there to be equally likely. If certain symmetry conditions are satisfied, it seems reasonable to assume that the simple events in one of these event sets are equally likely. Which one is it, and what are the symmetry conditions which should be satisfied? Determine the probability of each simple event for this set in which the simple events are equally likely.

6. Use the results of Problem 5 to compute the probability that

(a) At least one of the dice turns up a face with only one dot.
(b) Neither die turns up a face with six dots.
(c) One die turns up a face with two dots, and the other turns up a face with three dots.

7. Use the results of Problem 5 to compute the probability that
   (a) The sum of the number of points (dots) on the two faces is 8.
   (b) The sum of the number of points on the two faces is 11.
   (c) The sum of the number of points on the two faces is less than or equal to 6.

8. Use the results of Problem 5 to compute the probability that
   (a) The sum of the number of points (dots) on the two faces is 12 or is less than or equal to 3.
   (b) The sum of the number of points on the two faces is less than or equal to 8, and one of the faces has 4 dots on it.

9. Consider the random experiment in which we select without looking two balls from an urn containing two red balls, a white ball, and a green ball. First make a list of the simple events when a simple event is characterized by the color of each of the balls selected. Call this event set E_1. Next imagine that we paint numbers on the balls, 1 and 2 on the red balls, 3 white, and 4 green, and we characterize a simple event by the numbers on the balls drawn. List the simple events for this case, and call the event set so obtained E_2. Finally, consider the case of a simple event characterized by the number on the first ball and then the number on the second ball drawn. List the simple events in this case, and call the event set E_3. Show that if the simple events in E_3 are equally likely, then the simple events in E_2 are equally likely. Show that it is inconsistent to assume both that the events in E_2 or E_3 are equally likely and that the events in E_1 are equally likely. One normally feels that the events in E_2 and E_3 are both equally likely if certain symmetry conditions are satisfied. Why is this? What are the symmetry conditions? Determine the probability of each simple event in E_2 and in E_3 when the symmetry conditions are satisfied.

10. Use the results of Problem 9 to determine the probability that
    (a) One of the balls drawn is red.
    (b) One of the balls drawn is red, and the other is green.
    (c) No red ball is drawn.

11. Use the results of Problem 9 to compute the probability that
    (a) At least one red ball is drawn.
    (b) The red ball numbered 2 is drawn.
    (c) One of the balls is red or one is white or both.

Section 1-10

For Problems 1 through 5 take the event set to be $E = \{e_1, e_2, e_3, e_4, e_5\}$ with the probabilities of the simple events $p_1 = 0.15$, $p_2 = 0.10$, $p_3 = 0.20$, $p_4 = 0.05$, $p_5 = 0.50$.

1. Are the following events exclusive? Prove whatever statement you make.
   (a) $A = \{e_1, e_3\}$; $B = \{e_2, e_4\}$.   (b) $A = \{e_1, e_3\}$; $B = \{e_2, e_3, e_4\}$.
   (c) $C = A \cup B$ and $D = \{e_2, e_4\}$, where $A = \{e_1, e_3\}$, $B = \{e_1, e_2, e_3\}$.

2. Let $A = \{e_1, e_3\}$, and $B = \{e_2, e_5\}$. Compute $p(A \cup B)$ using (1-13) as well as directly by determining the simple events in $A \cup B$.

3. Let $A = \{e_1, e_3\}$, and $B = \{e_2, e_3, e_5\}$. Compute $p(A \cup B)$ using (1-26) as well as directly by determining the simple events in $A \cup B$.

4. Let $A = \{e_1, e_2, e_3\}$, and $B = \{e_2, e_3, e_4\}$. Compute $p(A \cup B)$ using (1-26) as well as directly by determining the simple events in $A \cup B$.

5. Let $A = \{e_1, e_2, e_3, e_4\}$, and $B = \{e_1, e_2\}$. Compute $p(A \cup B)$ using (1-26) as well as directly by determining the simple events in $A \cup B$.

6. Prove that if $B \subseteq A$, then $p(A) \geq p(B)$.

7. Prove that if $B \subseteq A$, then $p(A \cup B) = p(A)$.

8. Consider three events A, B, and C. Suppose that $A \cap B = \varnothing$, $A \cap C = \varnothing$, and $B \cap C = \varnothing$. The three events are then called mutually exclusive. Show that it is not possible for two or more of these events to occur simultaneously. Also, show that

$$p(A \cup B \cup C) = p(A) + p(B) + p(C).$$

9. Consider Problem 9 of Section 1-9. Compute the probability of the event A that one of the balls drawn is red and the probability of the event B that one of the balls drawn is green; and then compute the probability of $A \cup B$ using the methods of this section, and also directly by summing the probabilities of the simple events in $A \cup B$.

10. Consider the event set $E = \{e_1, e_2, e_3, e_4\}$ with the probabilities of the simple events $p_1 = 0.20$, $p_2 = 0.30$, $p_3 = 0.40$, $p_4 = 0.10$. Compute $p(A^c)$ using (1-27) when

    (a) $A = \{e_1, e_2\}$.   (b) $A = \{e_1, e_3, e_4\}$.   (c) $A = E$.

Verify the results by determining the set A^c and by summing the probabilities of the simple events in A^c.

11. Show that for any three events A, B, and C

$$p(A \cup B \cup C) = p(A) + p(B) + p(C) - p(A \cap B) - p(A \cap C)$$
$$- p(B \cap C) + p(A \cap B \cap C).$$

Make up a numerical example to illustrate this result. (Hint: First let $D = B \cup C$, and apply (1-26) to $A \cup D$. Then use the results of Problem 27 for Section 1-5.)

Sections 1-11 through 1-13

1. Consider the event set $E = \{e_1, e_2, e_3, e_4, e_5\}$. Which of the following defines a random variable on this event set?

    (a) $x(e_1) = 2; x(e_2) = 2; x(e_3) = 3; x(e_4) = 4; x(e_5) = 0$.
    (b) $x(e_1) = 0; x(e_2) = 0; x(e_3) = 0; x(e_4) = 2; x(e_5) = 2$.
    (c) $x(e_1) = 1; x(e_2) = 1; x(e_3) = 1; x(e_4) = 1; x(e_5) = 1$.
    (d) $x(e_1) = 1; x(e_2) = 2; x(e_3) = 0$.
    (e) $x(e_1) = 2; x(e_2) = 3; x(e_3) = 4; x(e_4) = 5; x(e_5) = 6; x(e_1) = 4$.
    (f) $x(e_1) = \sqrt{2}; x(e_2) = \sqrt{3}; x(e_3) = 17; x(e_4) = 28; x(e_5) = -6$.

2. Consider the event set $E = \{e_1, e_2, e_3\}$ with the probabilities of the simple events $p_1 = 0.25$, $p_2 = 0.60$, $p_3 = 0.15$. Consider the random variable x defined by the function $x(e_1) = -17$, $x(e_2) = 2$, $x(e_3) = -1$. Determine the probability function for this random variable, and construct a bar diagram to illustrate it graphically. Compute the expected value of x, first using (1-35) and then using (1-46). Determine the cumulative distribution of x, and illustrate it graphically.

3.   Consider the event set $E = \{e_1, e_2, e_3\}$ with the probabilities of the simple events $p_1 = 0.20$, $p_2 = 0.50$, $p_3 = 0.30$. Consider the random variable x defined by the function $x(e_1) = 2$, $x(e_2) = -4$, $x(e_3) = 2$. Determine the probability function for this random variable, and construct a bar diagram to illustrate it graphically. Compute the expected value of x, first using (1-35) and then using (1-46). Determine the cumulative distribution of x, and illustrate it graphically.

4.   Consider the event set $E = \{e_1, e_2, e_3, e_4, e_5\}$ with the probabilities of the simple events $p_1 = 0.05$, $p_2 = 0.15$, $p_3 = 0.10$, $p_4 = 0.50$, $p_5 = 0.20$. Let the random variable x be defined as $x(e_1) = 9$, $x(e_2) = 1$, $x(e_3) = 3$, $x(e_4) = 5$, $x(e_5) = 9$. Determine the probability function for this random variable, and construct a bar diagram to illustrate it graphically. Compute the expected value of x, first using (1-35) and then using (1-46). Determine the cumulative distribution of x, and illustrate it graphically.

5.   Consider the event set

$$E = \{e_1, e_2, e_3, e_4, e_5, e_6, e_7, e_8, e_9, e_{10}\}$$

with the probabilities of the simple events $p_1 = 0.10$, $p_2 = 0.15$, $p_3 = 0.05$, $p_4 = 0.07$, $p_5 = 0.13$, $p_6 = 0.20$, $p_7 = 0.03$, $p_8 = 0.06$, $p_9 = 0.10$, $p_{10} = 0.11$. Let the random variable x be defined as $x(e_1) = 0$, $x(e_2) = -3$, $x(e_3) = 3$, $x(e_4) = 5$, $x(e_5) = 3$, $x(e_6) = 3$, $x(e_7) = 3$, $x(e_8) = 5$, $x(e_9) = 7$, $x(e_{10}) = 0$. Determine the probability function for this random variable, and construct a bar diagram to illustrate it graphically. Compute the expected value of x, first using (1-35) and then using (1-46). Determine the cumulative distribution of x, and illustrate it graphically.

6.   Use the results of Problem 5 of Section 1-9 to determine the probability function for the random variable x which is the sum of the number of points on the two faces which turn up on the tossing of two fair dice. Determine the expected value of this random variable. Also, determine the cumulative function. Illustrate graphically both the probability function and the cumulative function.

7.   A jewelry store is considering stocking seven of an expensive pin for the Christmas season. The demand may turn out to be for $0, 1, 2, \ldots, 8$ pins. The owner estimates the probabilities of each of these events to be 0.05, 0.10, 0.10, 0.10, 0.10, 0.20, 0.20, 0.05, 0.10, and the corresponding profits are $-\$200$, $-\$150$, $-\$100$, $\$0$, $\$10$, $\$200$, $\$250$, $\$300$, $\$250$. Compute the expected profit if the seven units are stocked.

8.   An urn contains four balls numbered 1, 2, 3, 4. The balls are well mixed and two are drawn. Set up an event set in which the events should be equally likely. Let x be the random variable representing the sum of the two numbers on the balls drawn. Determine the probability function for x, and illustrate it graphically. Determine also the expected value of x. Finally determine the cumulative function for x, and illustrate it graphically.

9. Let the cumulative function for the random variable x which can take on the values in $X = \{-6, -4, 0, 2, 6, 9\}$ be $P(-6) = 0.2$, $P(-4) = 0.3$, $P(0) = 0.5$, $P(2) = 0.7$, $P(6) = 0.95$, $P(9) = 1.0$. Determine the probability function for x and the expected value of x.

10. There is another function called the complementary cumulative function, which completely characterizes the distribution of a random variable x, and which is sometimes convenient to use. Let us represent the complementary cumulative function symbolically by $Q(x)$. Then $Q(x_i)$ is the probability that the random variable takes on a value $x \geq x_i$. Prove that

$$Q(x_i) = p(x_i) + p(x_{i+1}) + \cdots + p(x_k),$$

where x_k is the largest value x can take on. Also show that

$$P(x_{i-1}) + Q(x_i) = 1, \quad i = 2, \ldots, k.$$

Determine the complementary cumulative function for the random variable described in Problem 5.

11. Let x be a random variable which can take on the values $X = \{1, 2, \ldots, n\}$, and let $Q(x)$ be the complementary cumulative function for x. Prove that μ_x, the expected value of x, is given by

$$\mu_x = \sum_{i=1}^{n} Q(i).$$

Is this result true for an arbitrary random variable?

12. Let x be a random variable defined over the event set E. Show that if $p_r = 1$ (so that all other $p_j = 0$), then the expected value of x is ξ_r.

13. Let x be a random variable defined over the event set E. Suppose that $p_r = 0$. Show that the expected value of x does not depend on ξ_r, and hence e_r could be omitted from the event set without changing the expected value of x.

14. Consider a random variable x with expected value μ_x. Show that $x_1 < \mu_x < x_k$, where x_1 is the smallest value x can take on and x_k is the largest value, provided that $p_1 > 0$ and $p_k > 0$.

15. What is the intuitive meaning of the expected value of the random variable introduced in the second example for Section 1-11?

16. Compute the expected value of the random variable introduced in the third example for Section 1-11. How is this to be interpreted intuitively?

17. In Problem 7, what is the expected number of pins demanded? How is this expected value to be interpreted intuitively?

Section 1-14

In Problems 1 through 8 express the sums using summation notation.

1. $b_1 + b_2 + b_3 + b_4 + b_5$.

2. $1 + 2 + \cdots + 10$.

3. $a_1 b_1^2 + a_2 b_2^2 + \cdots + a_n b_n^2$.

4. $a_1 b_2^2 + a_2 b_3^2 + \cdots + a_n b_2^{n+1}$.

5. $(a_1^2 + b_1) + (a_2^2 + b_2) + \cdots + (a_m^2 + b_m)$.

6. $(a_6 b_9 - c_7) + (a_7 b_{10} - c_8) + \cdots + (a_{25} b_{28} - c_{26})$.

7. $a_1b_2 + a_2b_4 + a_3b_6 + \cdots + a_{100}b_{200}$.

8. $a_1b^3 + a_2b^5 + a_3b^7 + \cdots + a_{30}b^{61}$.

In Problems 9 through 13 write out explicitly the indicated summations.

9. $\displaystyle\sum_{i=1}^{5} i a_i$.

10. $\displaystyle\sum_{j=3}^{7} (j+1)^2 a^j$.

11. $\displaystyle\sum_{j=0}^{8} (6a_j - j^2 b)$.

12. $\displaystyle\sum_{j=0}^{5} a_j b^{3j}$.

13. $\displaystyle\sum_{j=1}^{7} (-1)^j a_{2j}$.

14. Show that

$$\sum_{j=1}^{n} a_{j+3} = \sum_{k=4}^{n+3} a_k.$$

15. Show that

$$\sum_{j=3}^{n} a^j = a^3 \sum_{j=0}^{n-3} a^j.$$

Section 1-15

1. Consider the event set $E = \{e_1, e_2, e_3, e_4\}$ with the probabilities of the simple events $p_1 = 0.15$, $p_2 = 0.30$, $p_3 = 0.25$, $p_4 = 0.30$. Let two random variables x and y be defined by the functions $x(e_1) = -3$, $x(e_2) = 1$, $x(e_3) = 0$, $x(e_4) = -2$ and $y(e_1) = 2$, $y(e_2) = 0$, $y(e_3) = 4$, $y(e_4) = -1$. Suppose that we now define a new random variable z by writing $z = 4x + y - 2$. Determine the function which specifies the value of z to be associated with each simple event. Compute the expected value of z using (1-60). Also, determine the probability function for z and the expected value of z using this function.

2. Consider the event set $E = \{e_1, e_2, e_3, e_4, e_5, e_6, e_7\}$ with the probabilities of the simple events $p_1 = 0.08$, $p_2 = 0.12$, $p_3 = 0.14$, $p_4 = 0.06$, $p_5 = 0.20$, $p_6 = 0.30$, $p_7 = 0.10$. Let two random variables x and y be defined by the functions $x(e_1) = 0$, $x(e_2) = 4$, $x(e_3) = 7$, $x(e_4) = 1$, $x(e_5) = 5$, $x(e_6) = 9$, $x(e_7) = 0$ and $y(e_1) = 5$, $y(e_2) = 0$, $y(e_3) = -2$, $y(e_4) = -5$, $y(e_5) = 1$, $y(e_6) = 3$, $y(e_7) = -5$. Suppose that we define a new random variable z by writing $z = 3x - 2y + 11$. Determine the function which specifies the value of z to be associated with each simple event. Compute the expected value of z using (1-60). Also, determine the probability function for z and the expected value of z using this function.

3. Consider the random experiment in which two fair dice are tossed. What is the expected value of the random variable representing the sum of the number of points on the two faces turned up? Solve the problem for the case where n fair dice are tossed and the random variable is the sum of the number of dots on the n faces turned up.

4. Consider the random experiment in which a fair coin is tossed n times, and let x be the random variable representing the number of heads obtained. What is the expected value of x?

5. Let x be a random variable, and let $y = (x - 6)^2$. Express the expected value of y in terms of the expected value of x and the expected value of x^2.

Section 1-16

1. When in the general definition of a function the domain A is a set of numbers and so is the range B, then the function is usually referred to as a function of one variable. The notation generally used is of the form $y = f(x)$; x is called the independent variable, and y is the dependent variable. Also $f(x_1)$, the image of a particular element x_1 in the domain, is called the value of the function at x_1. Thus the notation we are using to indicate that a random variable y is a function of the random variable x is the usual notation for functions of one variable. Now any function of one variable whose domain contains the set X of values which the random variable x can take on, can be used in defining a new random variable y, a function of x. Consider a random variable x which can take on values in the set $X = \{-2, 0, 1, 4, 8, 10\}$. For each of the following functions, determine the set of values which the random variable y can take on.

(a) $y = 2x^2 + 3x.$ (b) $y = \dfrac{3x - 2}{x + 1}.$ (c) $y = x + \dfrac{1}{x + 1}.$

2. If the random variable x can take on values in the set $X = \{-5, -2, 0, 5, 11\}$, determine whether each of the following functions defines a new random variable y? If any does not, explain why.

(a) $y = x.$ (b) $y = \dfrac{1}{x + 2}.$ (c) $y = x + \dfrac{1}{x}.$

(d) y is the larger of x and x^2.

3. Consider the event set $E = \{e_1, e_2, e_3, e_4, e_5\}$ with the probabilities of the simple events $p_1 = 0.25$, $p_2 = 0.10$, $p_3 = 0.30$, $p_4 = 0.05$, $p_5 = 0.30$. Let the random variable x be defined by the function $x(e_1) = 6$, $x(e_2) = -1$, $x(e_3) = 1$, $x(e_4) = 2$, $x(e_5) = 1$. Suppose we now define a new random variable through the function $y = 3x^2 - 2x$. Compute μ_y by first determining the probability function for x and using (1-63). Next determine explicitly the function $y_t = g[x(e_j)]$, which associates with each e_j a value of y, and then determine the probability function for y. Finally, determine μ_y using the probability function for y.

4. Consider the event set $E = \{e_1, e_2, e_3, e_4, e_5, e_6\}$ with the probabilities of the simple events $p_1 = 0.05$, $p_2 = 0.10$, $p_3 = 0.20$, $p_4 = 0.30$, $p_5 = 0.25$, $p_6 = 0.10$. Let the random variable x be defined by the function $x(e_1) = 0$, $x(e_2) = 2$, $x(e_3) = 3$, $x(e_4) = 4$, $x(e_5) = 5$, $x(e_6) = 7$. Suppose we now define a new random variable through the function $y = (x - 2)/(x + 3)$. Compute μ_y by first determining the probability function for x and using (1-63). Next determine explicitly the function $y_t = g[x(e_j)]$, which associates with each e_j a value of y, and then determine the probability function for y. Finally, determine μ_y using the procedure introduced in Section 1-15.

5. Consider the random variable x which can take on the values in the set $X = \{0, 1, 2, 3, 4, 5\}$ and whose probability function is $p(0) = 0.10$, $p(1) = 0.20$, $p(2) = 0.30$, $p(3) = 0.20$, $p(4) = 0.10$, $p(5) = 0.10$. Compute μ_x and consider the random variable $y = x - \mu_x$. Determine the probability function for y, and illustrate graphically both the probability function for y and the probability function for x. What is the relation between the two probability functions?

6. Consider the random variable x which can take on the values in the set $X = \{0, 1, 2, 3, 4, 5\}$ and whose probability function is $p(0) = 0.40$, $p(1) = 0.30$, $p(2) = 0.20$, $p(3) = 0.08$, $p(4) = 0.01$, $p(5) = 0.01$. Compute μ_x. Consider the random variable $y = 2x + 3$. Compute μ_y from (1-64). Also, determine the probability function for y, and compute μ_y directly using it. Illustrate graphically both the probability function for y and the probability function for x. What is the relation between the two probability functions?

7. Let x be a random variable defined over E with expected value μ_x. Also let $y = g(x)$. Show by an example that it is not true in general that $\mu_y = g(\mu_x)$. Give an intuitive explanation for this.

8. An individual plays a game of chance which involves the tossing of a fair die. Suppose that he wins a dollar if a face with an even number of dots turns up and loses a dollar if a face with an odd number of dots turns up. Let x be the random variable representing the number of dots showing and y the random variable representing the amount won or lost. Show that y is a function of x. Determine the expected value of y.

9. An individual plays a game of chance which involves the tossing of a fair die. He wins the square of the number of the dots turned up if this number is odd, and wins eight dollars less the square of the number of dots turned up if this number is even (when the sum is negative, he loses the corresponding amount). If x is the random variable representing the number of dots turned up and y the amount won, show that y is a function of x. What is the expected value of y?

Section 1-17

1. Consider a random variable x which can take on the values in $X = \{-3, 0, 1, 2, 6\}$ with the probability function $p(-3) = 0.10$, $p(0) = 0.20$, $p(1) = 0.40$, $p(2) = 0.20$, $p(6) = 0.10$. Compute μ_x and σ_x. Illustrate graphically the probability function for x. On the horizontal axis of this bar diagram, indicate the points μ_x, $\mu_x - \sigma_x$, $\mu_x + \sigma_x$, $\mu_x - 2\sigma_x$, $\mu_x + 2\sigma_x$, $\mu_x - 3\sigma_x$, $\mu_x + 3\sigma_x$.

2. Consider the random variable described in Problem 1. Using pennies, construct a random experiment which will generate values of the random variable x in accordance with its probability function $p(x)$. Repeat the experiment 35 times and construct a figure of the form of Figure 1-11, indicating the value of x obtained on each trial. Compute $\bar{\xi}$, the average of the values of the random variable obtained on the 35 trials, and compare it with μ_x obtained in Problem 1. On the figure draw horizontal lines through the points μ_x, $\mu_x - \sigma_x$, and $\mu_x + \sigma_x$ on the vertical axis.

3. Consider a random variable x which can take on the values in $X = \{0, 1, 2, 3, 4\}$ with the probability function $p(0) = 0.40$, $p(1) = 0.25$, $p(2) = 0.15$, $p(3) = 0.10$, $p(4) = 0.10$. Compute μ_x and σ_x. Illustrate graphically the probability function for x. On the horizontal axis of the bar diagram, indicate the points μ_x, $\mu_x - \sigma_x$, $\mu_x + \sigma_x$, $\mu_x - 2\sigma_x$, $\mu_x + 2\sigma_x$, $\mu_x - 3\sigma_x$, $\mu_x + 3\sigma_x$.

4. Consider the random variable described in Problem 3. Using pennies, construct a random experiment which will generate values of the random variable x in accordance with its probability function $p(x)$. Repeat the experiment 35 times and construct a figure of the form of Figure 1-11, indicating the value of x obtained on each trial. Compute $\bar{\xi}$, the average of the values of the random variable obtained on the 35 trials, and compare it with μ_x obtained in Problem 3. On the figure draw horizontal lines through the points μ_x, $\mu_x - \sigma_x$, and $\mu_x + \sigma_x$ on the vertical axis.

5. Consider the event set $E = \{e_1, e_2, e_3, e_4, e_5, e_6\}$ with the probabilities of the simple events $p_1 = 0.12$, $p_2 = 0.08$, $p_3 = 0.05$, $p_4 = 0.15$, $p_5 = 0.40$, $p_6 = 0.20$. Let the random variable x be defined by the function $x(e_1) = 4$, $x(e_2) = 0$, $x(e_3) = 4$, $x(e_4) = 2$, $x(e_5) = 0$, $x(e_6) = 5$. Compute the variance of x directly, without obtaining the probability function for x.

6. Consider any random experiment with the event set $E = \{e_1, \ldots, e_m\}$ and probabilities of the simple events given by the function $p_j = p(e_j)$. Let a random variable x be defined by the function $\xi_j = x(e_j)$. Then show that the variance of x is given by

$$\sigma_x^2 = \sum_{j=1}^{m} (\xi_j - \mu_x)^2 p_j.$$

7. Compute the variance of the random variable introduced in Problem 2 for Sections 1-11 through 1-13.

8. Compute the variance of the random variable introduced in Problem 3 for Sections 1-11 through 1-13.

9. Compute the variance of the random variable introduced in Problem 4 for Sections 1-11 through 1-13.

10. Compute the variance of the random variable introduced in Problem 5 for Sections 1-11 through 1-13.

11. Compute the variance and standard deviation for the random variable representing the sum of the number of points turned up on throwing two dice, the probability function for which was obtained in Problem 6 for Sections 1-11 through 1-13.

12. Consider the random variable x with the probability function $p(x)$. Denote the variance of x by σ_x^2. Consider now the random variable $y = ax + b$. Prove that the variance of y is given by $\sigma_y^2 = a^2 \sigma_x^2$. Verify this directly in a specific case by considering the random variable x defined in Problem 1 and writing $y = 2x + 3$. Make the verification by determining the probability function for y and computing σ_y^2 directly.

13. Consider a random variable x with probability function $p(x)$, expected value μ_x, and standard deviation σ_x. Consider the random variable defined by $y = (x - \mu_x)/\sigma_x$. Show that $\mu_y = 0$ and $\sigma_y = 1$. This proves that given any random variable x it is possible through an affine transformation to obtain a random variable y whose expected value is 0 and whose standard deviation is 1.

14. Apply the results of Problem 13 to the random variable x defined in Problem 1 to obtain a random variable y with $\mu_y = 0$ and $\sigma_y = 1$. Determine the probability function for y, and illustrate it graphically.

15.   Consider a random experiment having the event set $E = \{e_1, \ldots, e_m\}$ with probability p_j of the simple event e_j. Let two random variables x and y be defined by the functions $\xi_j = x(e_j)$ and $\zeta_j = y(e_j)$. Let us now define a new random variable z by $z = ax + by + c$. Use the result of Problem 6 to prove that if σ_x^2, σ_y^2, and σ_z^2 are the variances of x, y, and z, then

$$\sigma_z^2 = a^2\sigma_x^2 + b^2\sigma_y^2 + 2ab\sigma_{xy},$$

where σ_{xy} is a new quantity we have not studied before and is given by

$$\sigma_{xy} = \sum_{j=1}^{m} (\xi_j - \mu_x)(\zeta_j - \mu_y)p_j.$$

The number σ_{xy} is called the *covariance of x and y*. The covariance of x and y is the expected value of the random variable $(x - \mu_x)(y - \mu_y)$. Why is this a random variable?

16.   Verify the results of Problem 15 by using the situation described in Problem 1 of Section 1-15 and by computing σ_z^2 according to the equation of Problem 15 and directly using the probability function for z.

17.   Generalize the results of Problem 15 to the case where z is given by (1-61).

18.   Under what conditions can it be true that $\sigma_x = 0$? Show that if $p_j = 1$ for some simple event, then $\sigma_x = 0$.

19.   Let x be a random variable with expected value μ_x and variance σ_x^2. Also let $y = |x - \mu_x|$ so that y measures the magnitude of the deviation of x from its expected value. If $p(y \geq \epsilon)$ is the probability that $y \geq \epsilon$, prove that

$$p(y \geq \epsilon) \leq \sigma_x^2/\epsilon^2.$$

This is referred to as the *Chebyshev inequality*. Hint: Denote by $\lambda_1, \ldots, \lambda_u$ the values of x for which $y < \epsilon$ and by $\gamma_1, \ldots, \gamma_v$ the values of x for which $y \geq \epsilon$. Then

$$\sigma_x^2 = \sum_{i=1}^{u} (\lambda_i - \mu_x)^2 p(\lambda_i) + \sum_{j=1}^{v} (\gamma_j - \mu_x)^2 p(\gamma_j)$$

$$\geq \sum_{j=1}^{v} (\gamma_j - \mu_x)^2 p(\gamma_j) \geq \epsilon^2 \sum_{j=1}^{v} p(\gamma_j).$$

But

$$p(y \geq \epsilon) = \sum_{j=1}^{v} p(\gamma_j).$$

The Chebyshev inequality is often very conservative in the sense that $p(y \geq \epsilon)$ is frequently very much smaller than σ_x^2/ϵ^2.

20.   Compute $p(y \geq \epsilon)$ and σ_x^2/ϵ^2 for the random variables defined in Problem 5 for Sections 1-11 through 1-13 in the cases where $\epsilon = 0.1, 1, 10,$ and 100. What can you conclude from these computations?

CHAPTER 2

THE THEORY OF UTILITY

*We live in deeds, not years; in thoughts, not
breaths; in feelings, not in figures on a dial.*

P. J. Bailey

2-1 INTRODUCTION

The mathematical model developed in the previous chapter allows us to
describe chance phenomena in quantitative terms. This probability model
will be an important building block in the mathematical models we shall
develop to aid us in solving decision problems under uncertainty. However, before we can consider such decision models, we must first develop
still another building block. This will be a mathematical model which
describes the decision maker's behavior in situations involving uncertainty.
It will then be our mathematical representation of the decision maker.
This model and the theory associated with it often are referred to as the
theory of utility, although a more appropriate name might be the theory of
rational decision making.

Before turning to the problem of characterizing the decision maker's
behavior under uncertainty, it will first be very helpful to examine the
manner in which decisions can be made in deterministic situations. These
decision rules are very important in themselves, and generalizations of
them turn out to be useful when uncertainty is important.

2-2 PROJECTS

We would like to examine the rules which a decision maker typically
uses in practice to select precisely one of several competing projects to
undertake in situations which can be treated as deterministic. Prior to

obtaining the rules, however, it will be necessary to explain in some detail precisely what we mean by a project and then to develop a mathematical model of a project. It will be this mathematical model that will be used when we consider the decision rules themselves.

In its simplest form, what we shall call a project is what a businessman or engineer normally thinks of as a project. It may be the building of a new refinery in a given location, the undertaking of a government contract to develop and produce a new weapons system, the installation of a large scale data processing system, etc. A project will generally be undertaken by an existing organization. Often this project may influence directly or indirectly all phases of the organization. We shall be assuming that all such influences which are at all relevant can be determined as accurately as desired. In practice, it can be a hopelessly complicated undertaking, for example, to determine every effect which a new refinery can have on a large petroleum company. Of course, many of these effects are totally irrelevant to the decision of whether to build a new refinery. The important thing in practice is to determine the important effects. Let us suppose that we have traced through all the relevant implications of the project for the remainder of the organization. We then associate with the project the relevant characteristics of these effects. After having done this, we can then isolate the project from the rest of the organization, the interactions now being considered as part of the project itself. It is important to keep in mind that in the real world often this can be done only approximately. For our model, however, we shall assume that it can be done exactly. This means that our model will then only approximately describe the real world.

The next thing to note about projects is that usually they extend over a period of time. How far into the future do they extend? For certain situations such as those involving government contracts, it may be relatively clear that the project will terminate at a specified time in the future. In other situations, however, such as in the construction of a refinery there is no natural termination date for the project. It is not clear therefore that there is any natural end to the project. We shall imagine in our model of a project that it terminates after a specified known time, although in certain cases we shall study later it will be convenient to imagine that there is no end to the project. For the present, however, we shall imagine that the project terminates after a finite time. In practice, the precise time we select for terminating the project is not too crucial. The reason for this is, as we shall see in more detail later, that the distant future generally has little influence on current decisions.

Thus far our interpretation of a project is no different from that of the businessman. Now, however, we would like to generalize the notion of a project in two respects, which will lead to a concept of a project which can be quite different from that which the businessman uses. One reason we need to generalize the idea lies in the fact that our definition is going to be such that only one of several competing projects will be undertaken. We do not consider the possibility of undertaking more than one. We shall define a project in such a way that it can be interpreted as a collection of several of what a businessman thinks of as a project, and thus there will be no loss in generality in assuming that only one project will be undertaken, since this project may really correspond to several businessman's projects. For example, if we were considering building two new chemical plants, to be located in two of three cities, call them 1, 2, and 3, then instead of considering each plant as a project we could imagine that both plants form a single project and that there exist three different projects (1, 2), (1, 3), and (2, 3) corresponding to the three possible ways of selecting two of the three cities in which plants could be constructed. If the plants were to be of different sizes, there would be six projects because we would also need to specify in which city we would build the larger of the two plants. If a variety of plant sizes were being considered this would further increase the number of projects.

As we have formulated the problem, there is only one decision to make and this determines the project to be undertaken. In most real-world situations, the initial decision is only a first step, and at later times additional decisions must be made concerning the project. It would appear that we have not made any provision for the necessity of these later decisions. For example, the initial decision might involve the location of a new refinery, and a later decision might involve whether we should increase the capacity of this refinery or build still another new one. Once again by generalizing the notion of a project a little more, we can easily make provision for decisions which must be made later. To see this, suppose that at the current time we must select between two possible actions, call them a_1 and a_2. If we select a_1, then after two years we must select between three possible actions, say b_1, b_2, and b_3. If after selecting a_1, we also select action b_1, then in another two years, we must select between two actions c_1 and c_2. Similarly, if we select b_2 we must later select between actions d_1 and d_2, and if we select action b_3, we must select between actions e_1 and e_2. These are the last decisions. A somewhat similar sequence of decisions is required if we initially select action a_2. The whole array of possible sequences of decisions can be very conveniently represented by the branchlike figure shown in Figure 2-1 which is called a *decision tree.* The black dots, called *nodes of the decision tree,* represent points at which decisions must be made. The alternative actions being considered at a given node are represented by straight lines emanating from the node which are referred to as *branches of the tree.* The decision tree then completely describes the sequence of decisions to be made, since it indicates

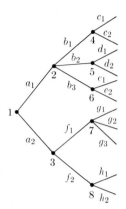

FIGURE 2-1

for each node what actions are open to the decision maker and also indicates the node (new decision situation) which will be reached as the result of taking any specified action. It is sometimes convenient to number the nodes and label them with other information such as the time at which the decision is to be made. We shall use decision trees quite frequently in our future work to clarify decision problems.

We can now note that for deterministic problems, we need not wait until the time that a decision is required before making it; all decisions can be made at the same point in time. In other words, at the time we decide whether to take action a_1 or a_2, we can also decide whether we should take actions b_1, b_2, or b_3, given that action a_1 is decided upon, etc. The reason for this is that since the problem is deterministic we know everything about it at the time the first decision is to be made, and hence all decisions can be made at this time. This characteristic of deterministic systems will definitely not be a characteristic of systems in which uncertainty is important. It is now fairly clear how by the proper definition of a project we can take account of decisions which are made after the initial decision, but which under the assumption that the system is deterministic can all be made at the time of the initial decision. Each possible sequence of decisions will be referred to as a different project. Thus in Figure 2-1 the situation characterized by the decisions a_1, b_1, and c_1 would be one project, while that characterized by a_1, b_3, and e_2 would be another, etc. For example, referring back to the situation considered earlier regarding the building of refineries, building a refinery in a given location L_1, and later increasing the capacity of this refinery would be one project. Another project would be initially building the refinery in location L_1 and later building another refinery in location L_2. Still another project would be initially building the refinery in location L_3 and then later enlarging the capacity as appropriate.

In the above we have discussed what we shall be thinking of when we refer to a project, and we have given some discussion of how one might proceed to uniquely characterize a project. Let us now turn to the problem of representing a project mathematically, i.e., to the problem of developing a mathematical model of a project. There are many models that could be developed. The model we wish to develop is one to which the various criteria for selecting a project can be applied. The decision criteria which we shall consider in the next section are economic criteria based in one way or another on profitability, and thus our model needs to represent only these economic characteristics of the project. In order to undertake a project certain costs must in general be incurred. It is convenient to subdivide these costs into capital costs and operating costs. Capital costs are frequently referred to as investments. The distinction between the two types of costs lies in the fact that investments are made for things like land, machinery, and buildings, which have a useful life extending over a considerable period of time, while operating costs refer to such things as workers' salaries, power costs, and raw material costs, which are incurred as a result of operating the project and which have not resulted in the procurement of a tangible asset. In certain cases, the distinction between the two concepts is not clear, but we shall not need to be concerned about such finer points. Frequently, in any event, we have no choice about how to classify such costs since this may be specified by income tax laws. The costs just considered are usually, but not always, incurred for the purpose of generating revenues. Thus we can suppose, in general, that there will be income generated by the project (which could be always zero if there is no income) over its lifetime. Finally, there may be taxes of various types. We could include these in the operating costs, but for clarity we shall treat them separately.

The time pattern of the costs incurred and revenues received provides an economic characterization of a project. Let us now make explicit how we shall find it convenient to describe the time pattern of the flows of funds. Let t^* be the length of the project. Suppose that we now select n times t_j, such that

$$0 < t_1 < t_2 < \cdots < t_n = t^*.$$

These times then divide the life of the project into n periods, the jth of which extends from time t_{j-1} to t_j. This is shown graphically in Figure 2-2. Normally, the times t_j are chosen so that periods are of equal length, but we do not have to do this. Now let R_j, C_j, I_j, and T_j be the revenue received, the operating costs incurred, the investment needed, and the taxes to be paid, respectively, in period j. Some or all of these quantities may be zero in any given period. Each is non-negative, however. It will be assumed that the periods are chosen to be sufficiently short, so that we need not be concerned about the precise times within a period at which

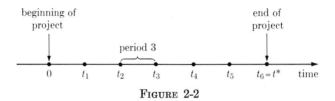

FIGURE 2-2

R_j, C_j, I_j, and T_j are received or incurred. We shall then find it convenient to imagine that each is received or incurred precisely at the end of the period, that is, at t_j. This is obviously an approximation, since R_j and C_j may well be incurred continuously throughout the period. However, as the periods get shorter and shorter, the approximation becomes better and better. Depending on the project, a suitable length for a period might be a year, a month, a week, or even a day. We shall assume there is one more cost to be considered. This is the initial investment needed to get the project started. We shall denote this by I_0 and imagine that it is incurred at the beginning of the first period. Additional investments may be needed later in the project, and these are represented by the I_j. The reader will recall that the new project will often become an integral part of an existing organization. Thus the numbers R_j, C_j, and T_j are really to be interpreted as the changes in these quantities for the organization as a whole as a result of the project.

We now have all we need to formulate what will serve as our mathematical model of a project. This model of the project will consist of nothing but the number I_0, the initial investment, and n sets of numbers $\{R_j,\ C_j,\ I_j,\ T_j,\ t_j\}$, the first four numbers in each set being the revenue, operating costs, investment, and taxes for period j, and the last being the time at which these are imagined to be received or incurred. Now having explained what we mean by a project and having developed a mathematical model of it, which will be suitable for our purposes, we can next turn to the problem of deciding which one of several projects should be undertaken.

2-3 DECISION RULES

Suppose that we have w projects which we shall denote symbolically by $A_1, \ldots, A_w$. For mathematical purposes, A_q is given by our mathematical model of a project, i.e., A_q is the set of numbers

$$A_q = \{I_{q0},\ (R_{qj},\ C_{qj},\ I_{qj},\ T_{qj},\ t_j),\ j = 1, \ldots, n_q\}. \qquad (2\text{-}1)$$

We now use two subscripts on the revenues and costs, the first, q, referring to the project and the second, j, referring to a given time period. Let us assume that the periods into which a project is broken up all have the same length. This length can vary from one project to another, however.

We wish to study a situation in which we shall undertake one and only one of these projects. How do we decide on which one to select? One procedure might be as follows. We simply compute the total profit to be obtained from each project (or equivalently the change in the organization's profit) and pick the project with the largest profit. Now the total profit for a project is the total revenues received minus the total costs incurred minus taxes, that is, if we denote the total profit from project A_q by $\mathcal{P}_q$, then

$$\mathcal{P}_q = -I_0 + \sum_{j=1}^{n_q} (R_j - C_j - I_j - T_j). \tag{2-2}$$

According to the criterion just suggested, we would then select the project v for which $\mathcal{P}_v$ was the largest of the values $\mathcal{P}_q$.

The criterion just suggested has a very serious deficiency. It completely ignores the time phasing of the income and cost streams. For example, this criterion would say that receiving $10,000 twenty years from now would be just as good as receiving $10,000 today. Are we really indifferent between receiving $10,000 today or twenty years from now? Almost everyone would prefer to have $10,000 today. Why is this true? There may be many reasons, such as wanting to spend the money now instead of waiting, since we are afraid we may not be around to get it twenty years from now. This is a valid reason, but not the one that is of interest to us. There is a very concrete economic reason for preferring $10,000 now, and this is that by investing the $10,000 we could earn interest on it, and in twenty years we would have considerably more than $10,000.

Let us investigate the process by which interest is earned in a little more detail. Suppose that we have a sum I which we can invest, perhaps by depositing it in a bank, and earn interest at a rate i. We shall imagine that i is expressed as a decimal, i.e., is the percentage interest rate divided by 100, so that if the interest rate is 4%, $i = 0.04$. It will be imagined that interest is computed once a year. Thus if we invest I now, at the end of a year we shall have I plus interest iI, or a total of $(1 + i)I$. Suppose now we invest the interest earned also. Then after two years we shall have

$$(1 + i) [(1 + i)I] = (1 + i)^2 I,$$

or at the end of r years we shall have $(1 + i)^r I$.

We now have an economic basis for deciding how much a sum I_1 available r years from now would be worth to us today. The way we decide this is to determine the sum I_0 that on investment would accumulate to I_1 after r years. Thus I_0 and I_1 are related by the equation

$$(1 + i)^r I_0 = I_1,$$

or

$$I_0 = \frac{I_1}{(1 + i)^r}. \tag{2-3}$$

We call I_0 the *present worth*, *present value*, or *discounted value* of I_1 (I_1 not being available until the end of r years). Thus if the only factors which we consider are the economic ones relating to how much we can obtain by investing our money, we should be indifferent between receiving the sum I_0 today and the sum I_1 after a period of r years has elapsed.

We have just developed a convenient economic basis for comparing sums of money which will be obtained at different points in time. We compute the present worth of each sum and then compare these present worths or discounted values. This procedure is often referred to as the process of discounting future flows of funds. The notion of discounting allows us to develop a much more realistic criterion for selecting the project to undertake than using (2-2) and selecting the one with the largest total profit. Instead of computing the profit $\mathcal{P}_q$ (which in the future we shall refer to as the undiscounted profit), we shall instead compute what is called the *discounted profit or present worth profit*, which we shall denote by P_q. Note that a script $\mathcal{P}$ denotes undiscounted profit, while an ordinary upper case P denotes discounted profit. To compute the discounted profit, we compute the profit in the usual way except that instead of the actual values of the revenues or costs we use their discounted values. Suppose that i_q is the interest rate for the periods of length used in describing project q. This will not be the annual interest rate unless the period is one year in length. For example, if $i = 0.10$ per year, then if the periods are six months in length for project q, we would use $i_q = 0.05$. If we imagine that interest is computed once per period, and if we then take the beginning of the project as the point in time to which we discount all revenues, the discounted profit for project q is

$$P_q = -I_0 + \sum_{j=1}^{n_q} \frac{1}{(1 + i_q)^j} (R_j - C_j - I_j - T_j), \qquad (2\text{-}4)$$

or written out in more detail

$$P_q = -I_0 + \frac{1}{(1 + i_q)} (R_1 - C_1 - I_1 - T_1)$$

$$+ \frac{1}{(1 + i_q)^2} (R_2 - C_2 - I_2 - T_2)$$

$$+ \cdots + \frac{1}{(1 + i_q)^{n_q}} (R_{n_q} - C_{n_q} - I_{n_q} - T_{n_q}).$$

Discounted profits provide the basis for an economically sound way of choosing which of the w projects (2-1) we wish to undertake. We compute the discounted profit for each project and select that project which yields the largest discounted profit. For deterministic decision problems, we shall take as our mathematical model of the decision maker, the rule which says to act so as to maximize the discounted profit. In other words, we assume that the decision maker selects among projects by looking for the one which yields the greatest discounted profit.

The discounted profit P_q will change as we vary the interest rate i_q. In practice, how do we decide what i_q is? It is important to note that normally i_q will not be the interest rate paid by banks, but instead will represent the return which could be obtained by investing the funds elsewhere in the organization. Now the return one can earn by investing funds elsewhere in the organization (or outside the organization, for that matter) depends on a variety of factors such as the amount of money that is available to invest, the length of time for which it can be invested, the general economic climate, etc. These observations serve to point out the fact that it may be difficult to determine i_q accurately in practice. The usual procedure is to use the average return obtained on investments in the recent past.

We might note that if the total lifetime of a project is very short, say six months or less, then each period used in describing the project will be short, and i_q will normally be so small that $1/(1 + i_q)^i$ will be essentially 1. Thus P_q will be essentially equal to $\mathcal{P}_q$. In other words, for projects whose life is very short, one can use undiscounted profits instead of discounted profits in selecting among competing projects. However, for projects whose lifetime is greater than one year, usually one will want to use discounting. If the interest rate is very high, discounting may be needed even for shorter periods.

Selecting the project for which the discounted profit is the largest is the logically sound criterion to use if one is considering only economic factors, and it is the one which all economists would advocate using. It is by no means true, however, that this is the criterion businessmen always use. A variety of other criteria, some of which have no sound economic basis whatever, are sometimes used. We shall now mention a few of these and indicate some of their deficiencies.

A yardstick frequently used in evaluating projects is the profit per dollar of investment. This can be given a variety of interpretations. Often the businessman will compute the undiscounted profit divided by the initial investment, i.e., $\mathcal{P}_q/I_0$. This criterion does not seem too sensible both because it ignores the time phasing of the flows of funds and because, in fact, it is not the profit per dollar of investment that one is interested in. A project with very little total profit could give a large profit per dollar of initial investment simply because little initial investment is needed. Other forms which this yardstick could take are

$$\frac{\mathcal{P}_q}{I_0 + \sum_{j=1}^{n_q} I_j}, \qquad \frac{P_q}{I_0}, \qquad \frac{P_q}{I_0 + \sum_{j=1}^{n_q} \dfrac{I_j}{(1 + i_q)^i}}, \qquad (2\text{-}5)$$

the first of these being the undiscounted profit per dollar of total investment, the second the discounted profit per dollar of initial investment, and
the third the discounted profit per dollar of discounted total investment.
Although none of these criteria provides a sound method for selecting
projects, P_q/I_0 can be of some value in situations of the following type.
In our above discussions we did not assume that there were any limitations
on how large the initial investment I_0 could be. Frequently, however,
funds available for investment are strictly limited. This does not cause
any problems in the formulation which we have adopted because if we
must have $I_0 \leq \beta$, we would merely select the project with the largest discounted profit having $I_0 \leq \beta$. Now we have defined a project in such a
way that only one of the projects will be selected, whereas businessmen,
as indicated earlier, usually think in simpler terms, as particular tasks to
be undertaken such as building a refinery, and with this interpretation,
several projects can be undertaken. In our formulation we would have a
project for every combination of one or more of what businessmen think
of as projects. Our formulation can lead to a very large number of projects, and this is one reason why businessmen do not look at things in this
way. Given that they will not do this, however, they are faced with the
problem of selecting several projects to undertake while not exceeding the
funds available for investment. The way this is done is to undertake the
project for which P_q/I_0 is greatest. If more investment funds are available the project with the next highest P_q/I_0 is also undertaken, and so forth,
until the investment funds are used up. Unlike our procedure, this does
not necessarily lead to undertaking the most desirable combination of projects, for the reason that it may not lead to using up exactly the funds
available for investment. In this case, some other combinations of the
businessman's projects which used up the funds, but did not contain the
projects with the highest P_q/I_0 values, might yield a higher total discounted profit. Thus the yardstick P_q/I_0 could be useful when a businessman did not wish to use our concept of a project, but it would not necessarily guarantee that he would take the best possible action.

The reader may now be wondering why I_0 is used above, and we do not
worry about limitations on investment funds which will be needed later in
the project. There are two reasons why frequently it is sound to consider
limitations only on the initial investment. One is that later investments
may be so small as to be of no concern. Another is that the project may
itself generate sufficient revenues to meet the later investments as they
are required. If these conditions are not satisfied then, of course, it may
be necessary to consider limitations on later investments.

Another criterion businessmen sometimes use in evaluating projects, is
called the payout period. Suppose we determine the smallest value of k
for which

$$-I_0 + \sum_{j=1}^{k} (R_j - C_j - I_j - T_j) \geq 0. \qquad (2\text{-}6)$$

Then we say that the payout period for the project is k periods. The payout period is usually thought of as the length of time needed to recover the initial investment I_0. The payout period is frequently used in situations of a very risky nature involving large sums in initial investments, such as building plants in a foreign country with an unstable government. Since here we are studying deterministic situations, the payout period really has little relevance as a criterion for evaluating projects. Moreover, as we shall see later, it frequently has little relevance even for the sort of risky situations to which it is normally applied.

A final yardstick which we shall consider is a favorite with businessmen, at least in certain industries. Consider equation (2-4). Note that as i_q is increased the present worth of any future receipt or cost becomes smaller and smaller, so that for very large i_q revenues and costs which are received very far in the future make almost no contribution to the discounted profit. Thus as i_q increases, the discounted profit will decrease and for very large i_q will be negative and essentially equal to $-I_0$. If we compute P_q for a number of different values of i_q and draw a smooth curve through the points, we might obtain something like the curve shown in Figure 2-3.

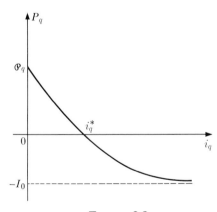

FIGURE 2-3

At $i_q = 0$, $P_q = \mathcal{P}_q$, and for very large i_q, $P_q = -I_0$. Consider that value of i_q, which we shall denote by i_q^*, which makes $P_q = 0$. The interest rate i_q^* when expressed as an annual rate is what businessmen call the *rate of return* on the project. Businessmen frequently like to select the project with the highest rate of return. Denote by i^* the rate of return on the project (i^* being i_q^* converted to an annual rate). What is the economic significance of i^*?   It is that value of the interest rate which makes $P_q = 0$.   Why should the businessman be interested in this interest rate?   It is not entirely clear.   The value i^* is relevant only if funds earned by the project can actually be invested at an interest rate of i^*.   If they cannot, then i^* is essentially irrelevant.   Generally, if for a given interest rate the discounted profits for two projects, say k and h, satisfy $P_k > P_h$, then the rate of return on k will be greater than on h, so that selecting the project with the greatest rate of return tends to yield the same project as selecting the one with the greatest discounted profit for a given interest rate.   However, as will be seen in the problems, it is not necessarily true that if $P_k > P_h$, then the rate of return on k will be greater than for h.   This depends on the precise time phasing of the flows of funds.   Therefore using the rate of return can be looked on only as an approximation to the correct procedure of maximizing the discounted profit.   Since it is more complicated to compute the rate of return than the discounted profit, we can ask again, why do businessmen use it?   Probably one reason is that they are not sure what interest rate to use in computing the discounted profit, and to avoid this question they use the rate of return.   It might be worthwhile to note that the term rate of return is used not only in the sense in which we have defined it, but also sometimes to refer to any interest rate which is used in (2-4).

Let us conclude this section by noting some properties of (2-4), and some special situations which can lead to alternative interpretations of the rule that we select the project whose discounted profit is the largest.   We shall now introduce two new quantities S_q and K_q defined by

$$S_q = \sum_{j=1}^{n_q} \frac{R_j}{(1+i_q)^j}, \quad K_q = I_0 + \sum_{j=1}^{n_q} \frac{(C_j + I_j + T_j)}{(1+i_q)^j}. \tag{2-7}$$

Then S_q is the discounted value of the total revenues received from project q, and K_q is the discounted value of the total cost of project q, the total cost including investment, operating costs, and taxes.   Then according to (2-4),

$$P_q = S_q - K_q, \tag{2-8}$$

that is, the discounted profit is equal to the discounted total revenue minus the discounted total cost.   Equation (2-8) is a useful one to remember.   Next note that if we write

$$\pi_{qj} = R_{qj} - C_{qj} - I_{qj} - T_{qj}, \tag{2-9}$$

then

$$P_q = -I_0 + \sum_{j=1}^{n_q} \frac{\pi_{qj}}{(1+i_q)^j}. \tag{2-10}$$

We can think of π_{qj} as the net return from the project q in period j.   It is really the profit received from the project in period j if in computing the profit we deduct all costs, including investments, incurred in the period. Of course, π_{qj} might not be what accountants would claim the profit from the project is in period j, because investments are often depreciated over a considerable period rather than being written off in the period incurred. Tax laws frequently require they be depreciated. None of this influences the fact that P_q is the discounted profit, however. Furthermore, P_q is given by (2-10) regardless of whether we interpret π_{qj} as having any special significance or not.

Let us now consider a special situation in which the discounted revenue received is the same for each project. Call this common value S^*, that is, $S_q = S^*$ for all $q = 1, \ldots, w$. Then to select the project to undertake, we determine the largest of the numbers $S^* - K_1, S^* - K_2, \ldots, S^* - K_w$. Now it is clear that the largest of these numbers will be the one with the smallest K_q. Hence the project to select is the one with the smallest discounted cost. What we have ,hen shown is that *if the discounted revenues are the same for all projects, then we can ignore the revenues completely and simply select the project having the smallest discounted total cost.* This is a useful fact to keep in mind, and one we shall use frequently in the future. A particular case where the discounted revenues are the same for each project occurs when there are no revenues at all, that is, the discounted revenues are 0. Then one can proceed by selecting the project which minimizes the discounted total cost.

In this section we have introduced the notion of discounting and have shown that when choices are made on economic grounds alone, one should proceed in deterministic situations to choose the project to undertake by finding the one which yields the largest discounted profit. We have considered the deterministic case in some detail because it is important in its own right, and because a slight generalization of the rule of maximizing discounted profits will often be useful in situations involving uncertainty. The generalization we shall use is one where we imagine some or all of the revenue and cost terms to be random variables, and we shall make selections by maximizing the expected value of the discounted profit.

2-4   EXAMPLES

We shall now give some simple examples of the material covered in the previous section.

1. Let us compute the present worth of \$10,000 to be received at the end of a period of ten years, for several different interest rates, $i = 0.05, 0.10, 0.25, 0.50$. Now by (2-3) the present worth is

$$I = \frac{10,000}{(1 + i)^{10}}.$$

For $i = 0.05$, $(1 + i)^{10} = 1.6285$ and $1/(1 + i)^{10} = 0.6139$, so that $I = \$6139$. When $i = 0.10$, $(1 + i)^{10} = 2.594$ and $1/(1 + i)^{10} = 0.3854$, so $I = \$3854$. When $i = 0.25$, $(1 + i)^{10} = 9.314$ and $1/(1 + i)^{10} = 0.1074$ so $I = \$1074$. Finally when $i = 0.50$, $(1 + i)^{10} = 57.67$ and $1/(1 + i)^{10} = 0.01733$, so $I = \$173.3$. Thus if $i = 0.50$, \$10,000 to be received 10 years hence is equivalent to receiving only \$173.3 today.

2. Let us illustrate the use of (2-4) in selecting projects, with an extremely simple case in which there are just two projects to be evaluated. The company under consideration is a petroleum company which is faced with the task of choosing between the development of one of two reservoirs of crude petroleum. Information about the size of the reservoirs and the nature of the crude is available and assumed reliable. The pattern of development of both of the fields is determined by tax considerations and state regulations. In making the computations it is convenient to use a period of a year and an interest rate of $i = 0.15$. Let us refer to the reservoirs or fields as they are called, as a and b. The initial investment is the cost of buying production rights on the fields. This comes to 5 million dollars for field a and 9 million dollars for field b. Additional investments are mainly for drilling wells. In general it takes several years for all wells to be drilled. The price received per barrel of crude depends on its quality. For crude from field a the price at the point of sale will be \$3.85 per barrel and for crude from field b will be \$4.15 per barrel. Operating costs include salaries, costs of transporting crude to point of sale, and power costs for operating the wells. In taxes we shall include both state and government income taxes, land taxes, and royalties (which are based on the number of barrels produced in a year). Production from field a will cease after seven years and that in field b after ten years. The relevant data for the fields are presented in Tables 2-1 and 2-2. These tables can easily be extended to provide a convenient format for determining the discounted profit as indicated. All monetary sums shown in the tables represent dollar values. In the computations we make the simplifying assumption used in the previous section: that all revenues and costs associated with a given year are received or incurred at the end of the year. From the tables we see that the discounted profit from field a is \$1,006,000 and from field b is \$2,270,000. Thus it would be better to undertake the development of field b, according to our criterion of choosing the project with the greatest discounted profit.

2-5 INTRODUCTION OF UNCERTAINTY

Let us move on now to study the problems involved in making decisions in which, because of uncertainty, we cannot determine at the time of

TABLE 2-1

DATA AND COMPUTATIONS FOR FIELD a

Year j	Barrels produced	Revenues received	Operating costs	Taxes	Investment	Net return for year j	$(1.15)^j$	$\dfrac{\pi_j}{(1.15)^j}$
1	300,000	1,155,000	50,000	20,000	2,000,000	−915,000	1.15	−795,000
2	500,000	1,925,000	60,000	30,000	1,500,000	335,000	1.32	253,000
3	700,000	2,695,000	65,000	50,000	700,000	1,880,000	1.52	1,235,000
4	1,000,000	3,850,000	70,000	100,000	0	3,680,000	1.75	2,110,000
5	1,000,000	3,850,000	70,000	100,000	0	3,680,000	2.01	1,830,000
6	700,000	2,695,000	50,000	80,000	0	2,565,000	2.31	1,110,000
7	200,000	770,000	30,000	40,000	0	700,000	2.66	263,000

$$\sum_{j=1}^{7} [\pi_j/(1.15)^j] = 6{,}006{,}000$$

$$I_0 = 5{,}000{,}000$$

Discounted total profit = $1,006,000

TABLE 2-2

DATA AND COMPUTATIONS FOR FIELD b

Year j	Barrels produced	Revenues received	Operating costs	Taxes	Investment	Net return for year j	$(1.15)^j$	$\dfrac{\pi_j}{(1.15)^j}$
1	450,000	1,865,000	70,000	40,000	2,500,000	−745,000	1.15	−649,000
2	900,000	3,735,000	90,000	50,000	2,500,000	1,095,000	1.32	825,000
3	1,000,000	4,150,000	90,000	80,000	1,000,000	2,980,000	1.52	1,970,000
4	1,200,000	4,980,000	80,000	120,000	500,000	4,280,000	1.75	2,450,000
5	1,200,000	4,980,000	80,000	140,000	0	4,760,000	2.01	2,370,000
6	1,000,000	4,150,000	85,000	120,000	0	3,940,000	2.31	1,710,000
7	800,000	3,320,000	85,000	75,000	0	3,160,000	2.66	1,190,000
8	600,000	2,490,000	70,000	60,000	0	2,360,000	3.06	772,000
9	400,000	1,660,000	60,000	40,000	0	1,560,000	3.52	442,000
10	200,000	830,000	40,000	20,000	0	770,000	4.05	190,000

$$\sum_{j=1}^{10} [\pi_j/(1.15)^j] = 11,270,000$$

$$I_0 = 9,000,000$$

$$\text{Discounted total profit} = \$2,270,000$$

making a decision all the implications of any action. To begin, let us return to the problem considered earlier of deciding how much bread to stock in the supermarket on a given day of the week. The number of loaves demanded will be a random variable x. Suppose that from historical data or by other means the store has determined that the probability function for x is $p(x)$. Now the profit the store will obtain as a result of stocking h loaves will be a random variable which is a function of the random variable x. Denote the profit obtained if h loaves are stocked and the demand turns out to be x_i, by $\rho_h(x_i)$. If the supermarket stocks h loaves every time, the long run average profit per day will be the expected value of $\rho_h(x)$, i.e.,

$$\sum_{i=1}^{k} \rho_h(x_i)p(x_i).$$

A very reasonable way to proceed would appear to be to select that number of loaves h to stock which yields the largest value of the long run average profit per day, that is, of the expected profit per day, since on the average this will yield the largest possible profit per day. This is indeed a very logical way to proceed in this case, and we shall proceed in this way when studying such problems in more detail later. From this example it might appear at first glance that all we need to do is generalize the criterion introduced for the deterministic case and select the action which yields the largest expected profit (using the discounted profit when discounting is required). It will indeed turn out that this criterion is the appropriate one to use in many cases.

The notion that it would be reasonable to make selections on the basis of maximizing expected profits was obtained by considering situations which were repeated over and over again so that the expected profit could be interpreted as the long run average profit. We may now ask whether in a situation which will occur only once and never be repeated, it makes any sense to select an action which maximizes the expected profit. Offhand, it is not at all clear that this does provide a sensible criterion in such situations. Currently we have no way to decide whether it is a reasonable criterion or not, nor have we any logical basis for deciding how to make selections in situations which will not be repeated, that is, where the probabilities have no frequency interpretation.

We can next note by considering a specific example that there definitely do exist cases where the maximization of expected profits is an inappropriate decision rule, and this may be true even for situations which have a frequency interpretation. Consider the following greatly simplified situation. A businessman is contemplating which of two contracts a or b he should undertake. The ultimate profit to be received from the contracts will be determined by a sequence of unpredictable events. To make the situation as simple as possible, let us suppose that for each contract the businessman decides that the discounted profit will have only two possible values, and in each case, one of these values will represent a loss. The decision maker has also estimated his personal probability of each outcome for each contract. The results are summarized in Table 2-3.

TABLE 2-3

SUMMARY OF TWO CONTRACTS BEING CONSIDERED

Contract a		Contract b	
Discounted profit	Probability	Discounted profit	Probability
$100,000	0.60	$50,000	0.30
−$100,000	0.40	−$10,000	0.70

Thus the businessman believes that if he takes contract a he will either get $100,000 with probability 0.60 or lose $100,000 with probability 0.40, and if he takes contract b, he will either get $50,000 with probability 0.30 or lose $10,000 with probability 0.70. The expected value of the discounted profit for contract a is

$$100,000(0.60) - 100,000(0.40) = \$20,000,$$

and the expected value for contract b is

$$50,000(0.30) - 10,000(0.70) = \$8,000.$$

Thus if the businessman selected the contract with the largest expected value of the discounted profit, he would select contract a. It is by no means true, however, that every businessman would prefer contract a to contract b. Why is this? The reason is that some businessmen would find a loss as large as $100,000 horrifying to contemplate. Such a loss might wipe out such businessmen completely, and they simply could not afford to undertake any contract which held out the possibility of so large a loss, regardless of the fact that the expected value of the discounted profit was as large as $20,000. Such businessmen would prefer contract b where the maximum loss of $10,000 is much smaller. They would prefer contract b in spite of the fact that the expected discounted profit from contract a is greater than from contract b. Other businessmen, for whom the loss of $100,000 would not be such a serious event, would probably prefer contract a. What this means is that expected monetary values do not always accurately reflect a decision maker's true feelings about situations. This is especially true when the sums of money involved are large compared to the decision maker's resources.

No doubt by this time it will have occurred to the reader that even for situations which can be considered deterministic, there are many cases where factors other than monetary factors have an influence on a decision maker's choice, and these may indeed be much more important than the monetary factors. Thus it would appear that our mathematical model of a decision maker in deterministic situations as one who makes selections by maximizing the discounted profit, is not always valid. Even here something more seems to be needed. What we are seeking then is a more general model of a decision maker which allows factors other than monetary ones to influence decisions, provides a way for making decisions when uncertainty is important, and a way for determining when such specialized rules as maximizing the expected profit are legitimate to use. The theory of utility provides such a model. It does so in the following way. First a model is given of what we shall call a *rational decision maker*. The model, like our probability model, is characterized by a set of axioms. A rational decision maker is one whose decision making processes satisfy these axioms. No claim is made that every decision maker is a rational decision maker in the sense we shall use the term. Our notion of a rational decision maker will be one who conforms to our mathematical model. Throughout the remainder of the text, however, we shall always be assuming that the decision makers involved are rational. Our model may only approximate the nature of some actual decision makers, and just like any other model its usefulness is determined by whether it represents with sufficient accuracy any particular real world situation. Given the model of a decision maker, we shall then prove that for any decision maker who conforms to this model, there exists a numerical function, called a utility function, defined over the events of interest, having the property that the decision maker will be making a choice in accordance with his true preferences if he chooses that action which maximizes his expected utility. This then provides the fundamental rule for choosing among alternatives in all situations which will be of interest to us.

In order to introduce the model of a decision maker and prove the existence of the function we call a utility function, it will be convenient first to provide a simple and concrete framework in which to discuss decision making under uncertainty. We shall use some special games of chance in order to do this, but as we shall see as we go along, the results obtained are independent of the use of this artifice. The games merely provide a convenient way to discuss things. We shall describe these games of chance in the next section.

2-6 SINGLE STAGE, TWO STAGE, AND n-STAGE LOTTERIES

We would like here to introduce some games of chance which we shall refer to as single stage, two stage, and n-stage lotteries. To become a player in a single stage lottery, an individual in one way or another obtains a ticket to the lottery, perhaps by purchasing it. The lottery operates as follows. The player with a ticket comes up to a table where there is a roulette wheel with m different numbers painted on its circumference. He hands the ticket to the operator who then spins the wheel. If the wheel stops at the number j, the player wins a prize which we shall symbolize by e_j. The use of the word prize should not be interpreted as meaning that all e_j are favorable. For example, if the wheel stops at the number 1, the player may have to pay the casino \$50. However, at whatever number the wheel stops there will be some sort of a prize for the player. Now, in general, the prizes or events e_j can be anything at all. They need not represent monetary payments to be made to or by the player. For example, e_1 might be the event that the player is fired from his job, while e_2 might mean that the player wins a ten million dollar contract for his firm. We shall not place any restrictions whatever on the nature of the prizes e_j. Furthermore, the process of receiving the prize may extend over a considerable period of time. We shall, however, assume that no two prizes are precisely the same. This is no restriction; it is only a restriction on the way we subdivide the roulette wheel. We shall also assume that the prizes reflect any sum which the player had to pay for a ticket, so that this sum never needs to be considered—it is accounted for in the prizes.

With the above restrictions we can think of the lottery just described as a random experiment with the event set $E = \{e_1, \ldots, e_m\}$. What is the probability of the simple event e_j? If the roulette wheel is well balanced, then by symmetry arguments it would appear that p_j is the fraction of the total circumference of the wheel which is devoted to the number j. Thus by alloting the appropriate space to each of the numbers, the p_j can be made anything we desire. We shall represent a single stage lottery symbolically by L. The lottery is completely characterized by the event set E, which describes the prizes, and by the function $p_j = p(e_j)$, which gives the probability of getting each prize. We shall find it convenient to represent the mathematical model of a single stage lottery as follows:

$$L = \{(p_1, e_1), (p_2, e_2), \ldots, (p_m, e_m)\}.$$

This gives a complete description of what we shall mean by a single stage lottery. There is also a useful geometric representation of the lottery L which uses a tree-like diagram like that in Figure 2-1. This representation is shown in Figure 2-4. We have m branches emanating from a single node. There is one branch for each prize, and at the end of each branch we indicate one of the e_j. On the branch we show the probability p_j of getting the prize e_j. Now interestingly enough, a single stage lottery can be thought of as a decision problem. It is not the player who makes the decision, however. Who makes the decision? We shall think of nature as the one who makes the decision. Nature will decide at what number the

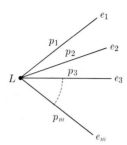

FIGURE 2-4

roulette wheel will stop. There are m actions nature can take, corresponding to the m different numbers at which the wheel may stop. Although
we cannot know in advance what action nature will take, we do have some
information in the form of probabilities. Thus the node in Figure 2-4 can
be looked upon as a point where nature makes a selection among m possible
actions. The reader should realize that the introduction of nature as a
decision maker has no mystical significance. It is simply a convenient
way to discuss things, which we shall often use in the future.

Let us next describe what we shall refer to as a two stage lottery. Once
again the player procures a ticket and goes to a table where there is a
roulette wheel. He gives the ticket to the operator who then spins the
wheel. Suppose that there are k numbers on the wheel, and that the
wheel stops on number i. Now, at this point the player does not win a
prize, but rather a ticket to one of k single stage lotteries of the type discussed above, so that if this first wheel stops on number i, he receives a
ticket to the ith single stage lottery. He then takes this ticket to the ith
single stage lottery and gives it to the operator, who spins the wheel. At
this point the player receives one of the prizes which we shall denote by
$e_1, \ldots, e_m$. We shall assume that the set of prizes is the same regardless
of which of the single stage lotteries he ends up in. However, the probabilities of obtaining these prizes will, in general, vary from one lottery
to another.

It will be clear to the reader that a two stage lottery can be looked on as
a random experiment with the event set $E = \{e_1, \ldots, e_m\}$. It is a more
complicated experiment than the single stage lottery, however, since it is
necessary to pass through two chance mechanisms before reaching the
prize. The question now is, what are the probabilities of the simple events
in this case? It takes a little thought and computation to decide what
they are.

First let us note that this random experiment can be thought of as
being decomposable into two random experiments. The first corresponds
to spinning the first roulette wheel to see which single stage lottery the

player goes to.   The simple events in this experiment can be thought of as the numbers $1, \ldots, k$, which are the numbers on the first roulette wheel.   Let the probability of the simple event i be q_i; q_i might be determined by experiment or by noting the fraction of the circumference of the wheel devoted to the number i.   Now if the wheel comes to rest on number i, the player goes to the single stage lottery i.   Let this lottery be denoted by L_i, where

$$L_i = \{(p_{i1}, e_1), (p_{i2}, e_2), \ldots, (p_{im}, e_m)\}. \tag{2-11}$$

The probability of the prize e_j will here depend on i.

Let us now see that the information just given is sufficient to determine the probabilities of the simple events in the two stage lottery.   Suppose that we play this two stage lottery a large number of times n, and let n_j be the number of times we win prize j, that is, e_j.   Now prize j may be won regardless of which single stage lottery L_i we end up in.   Thus, let n_{ij} be the number of times we end up in lottery i and win prize j.   Then

$$n_j = \sum_{i=1}^{k} n_{ij}, \quad \text{or} \quad \frac{n_j}{n} = \sum_{i=1}^{k} \frac{n_{ij}}{n}. \tag{2-12}$$

Observe that as n gets larger and larger, n_j/n will approach the probability of the simple event e_j, which we are seeking to determine.   We next need to investigate what the ratio n_{ij}/n approaches.   Note that one will end up in a single stage lottery L_i if and only if on the spin of the first roulette wheel, it stopped at the number i.   Let m_i be the number of times in n plays of the game that the first roulette wheel stopped on number i.   If we multiply and divide by m_i, we have

$$\frac{n_{ij}}{n} = \frac{m_i}{n} \frac{n_{ij}}{m_i}. \tag{2-13}$$

Consider the ratio m_i/n.   This is the fraction of the number of plays on which the first roulette wheel stopped on the number i.   As n gets larger and larger, this should approach q_i, the probability that the wheel stops on number i.   Consider next n_{ij}/m_i; m_i is the number of times we get in lottery L_i, and n_{ij} is the number of times prize e_j is obtained in our playing in lottery L_i.   Thus n_{ij}/m_i is just the fraction of the time we get prize e_j when we play lottery L_i.   Now as n gets larger and larger so will m_i, since m_i/n approaches q_i which we shall assume is positive.   Thus n_{ij}/m_i should approach p_{ij}, the probability of getting prize e_j when playing in lottery L_i. Therefore n_{ij}/n should approach $q_i p_{ij}$, which is the product of the probability that we end up in L_i and the probability of getting e_j in playing L_i. Finally, according to (2-12), n_j/n, the probability of the simple event e_j, should approach $\sum_{i=1}^{k} q_i p_{ij}$.   If we denote the probability of e_j by p_j, what we are then claiming is that

$$p_j = \sum_{i=1}^{k} q_i p_{ij} = q_1 p_{1j} + \cdots + q_k p_{kj}. \tag{2-14}$$

If one actually played this two stage lottery many times, he would find that the relative frequency n_j/n of getting prize e_j would ultimately get closer and closer to p_j given by (2-14). We note that even in a situation where the two stage lottery could not be repeated and the probabilities q_j and p_{ij} could not be given a frequency interpretation, the notion of an ensemble relative frequency would lead to precisely the same sort of analysis gone through above, and would suggest that the personal probabilities which an individual should assign to the events e_j are given by (2-14). We shall represent a two stage lottery symbolically using a script $\mathcal{L}$. Note that $\mathcal{L}$ is completely characterized by the single stage lotteries L_i which make up $\mathcal{L}$, and the probabilities q_i that we end up in L_i. We can provide this complete description by writing

$$\mathcal{L} = \{(q_1, L_1), \ldots, (q_k, L_k)\}. \tag{2-15}$$

We list the lotteries L_i which make up $\mathcal{L}$ and give the corresponding probabilities q_i. We can make the description even more explicit by indicating each L_i precisely, with the notation

$$\mathcal{L} = \{q_1[(p_{11}, e_1), \ldots, (p_{1m}, e_m)], \ldots, q_k[(p_{k1}, e_1), \ldots, (p_{km}, e_m)]\}. \tag{2-16}$$

This suggests that we can think of a two stage lottery as a single stage lottery in which the prizes are single stage lotteries. We can illustrate diagramatically the nature of a two stage lottery using a tree as shown in Figure 2-5. Just as with a single stage lottery, we can interpret this as a decision problem in which nature decides first what single stage lottery the player goes to and then what prize he obtains. We imagine that nature makes the decision by determining where the roulette wheels will

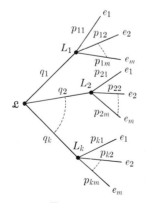

FIGURE 2-5

stop.   There is a single stage lottery which has the same probabilities of getting the various prizes as the two stage lottery $\mathcal{L}$.   We shall denote this single stage lottery by L^*, and in L^* the probability p_j of e_j is given by (2-14).   We can easily determine the p_j in L^* without remembering (2-14) if we use (2-16).   To obtain L^* from $\mathcal{L}$ in (2-16) we proceed as if each q_i multiplied the probabilities which appear in the brackets immediately following it.   This would yield

$$\{[(q_1p_{11}, e_1), \ldots , (q_1p_{1m}, e_m)], \ldots , [(q_kp_{k1}, e_1), \ldots , (q_kp_{km}, e_m)]\}.$$

We now collect together all the expressions involving e_j and add up the corresponding probabilities in these.   This then gives us a single stage lottery which is L^*, i.e.,

$$L^* = \left\{\left(\sum_{i=1}^{k} q_i p_{i1}, e_1\right), \ldots , \left(\sum_{i=1}^{k} q_i p_{im}, e_m\right)\right\}.$$

In the above we assumed that each lottery L_i which forms a part of $\mathcal{L}$ has the same set of prizes.   This is not really any restriction, because if a given prize e_u does not occur in lottery L_i, we can include e_u and assign to it a probability of 0, that is, $p_{iu} = 0$.   From our discussion of Section 1-10, adding e_u to L_i with a probability $p_{iu} = 0$ does not change L_i at all.   By this artifice we can always imagine that all the lotteries L_i include the same set of prizes.   However, it may be true then that some $p_{iu} = 0$.

EXAMPLE.   Let us consider a very simple two stage lottery $\mathcal{L}$.   We shall suppose that $\mathcal{L}$ consists of three single stage lotteries L_1, L_2, and L_3.   There are only two prizes which might be denoted by e_1 and e_2.   Imagine that the four roulette wheels involved are subdivided as shown in Figure 2-6.

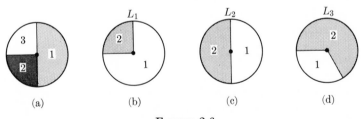

FIGURE 2-6

Thus by symmetry, assuming well-balanced wheels, we see from Figure 2-6a, which represents the first stage wheel, that the probability that the player will end up in single stage lottery 1 is 0.50, in single stage lottery 2 is 0.25, and in single stage lottery 3 is 0.25, that is, $q_1 = 0.50$, $q_2 = 0.25$, and $q_3 = 0.25$.   From Figure 2-6b we see that if the player goes to L_1 the probability of getting prize e_1 is 0.75 and prize e_2 is 0.25, that is, $p_{11} = 0.75$

and $p_{12} = 0.25$. From Figure 2-6c, it is seen that if the player goes to L_2, the probability of getting prize e_1 is 0.50 and of getting prize e_2 is 0.50, that is, $p_{21} = 0.50$ and $p_{22} = 0.50$. Finally, from Figure 2-6d, assuming that the part of the wheel devoted to 1 takes up 0.33 of the circumference, then the probability of getting prize e_1 if the player ends up in L_3 is 0.33 and that of e_2 is 0.67, i.e., $p_{31} = 0.33$ and $p_{32} = 0.67$. What then is the probability that a player who plays this two stage lottery game will get the prize e_1? According to (2-14), p_1 is the probability that he ends up in L_1 times the probability of getting e_1 in L_1 plus the product of the probability of ending up in L_2 and the probability of getting e_1 in L_2, plus the product of the probability of ending up in L_3 and the probability of getting e_1 in L_3. Thus

$$p_1 = 0.50(0.75) + 0.25(0.50) + 0.25(0.33) = 0.5825.$$

Similarly,

$$p_2 = 0.50(0.25) + 0.25(0.50) + 0.25(0.67) = 0.4175.$$

Note that $p_1 + p_2 = 1$ as must be true, since e_1 and e_2 are the simple events for the random experiment representing the two stage lottery.

We now note that we could easily define three stage lotteries as a generalization of two stage lotteries, four stage lotteries as a generalization of three stage lotteries, etc. For a three stage lottery, the player would first go to a table where the spin of the roulette wheel would send him to one of k other roulette wheels, the probability of going to the ith one being r_i. Then if he goes to the ith roulette wheel, a spin of this wheel puts him in one of s single stage lotteries, the probability of its being L_u given by q_{iu}. A three stage lottery is a single stage lottery whose prizes are two stage lotteries. In this way we can define an n-stage lottery inductively as a single stage lottery whose prizes are $(n\text{-}1)$-stage lotteries. It is very clumsy to write down the expressions for the probabilities of the prizes in a single stage lottery which has the same probabilities of getting the prizes as in a given n-stage lottery. We will never need these directly, although we shall make use of the notion of an n-stage lottery. For the most part, however, we shall never need anything more complicated than a two stage lottery. Frequently, when we do not care to indicate how many stages a lottery has, or when it is obvious from the discussion, we shall simply use the term lottery rather than one stage lottery, etc.

2-7 SUMMARY OF THE MODEL OF RATIONAL BEHAVIOR

We shall show in Chapter 3 that every decision problem reduces to a problem in which the decision maker must select from among a number of lotteries the one he prefers most. The lotteries may be single stage or multistage lotteries or a combination of both. Thus if a decision maker can express preferences between lotteries, he is capable, in principle at least, of solving any decision problem. The model of rational behavior to be developed in detail in the next section is concerned with precisely this problem of expressing preferences among lotteries. In this section we shall summarize the theory of utility or the model of rational behavior, which characterizes the behavior of what we call a rational decision maker. A rational decision maker is any decision maker whose behavior satisfies a set of six axioms to be described in the next section.

The most important result which follows from the model of a rational decision maker is that if we are given a function called the decision maker's utility function, we can decide for ourselves which of a number of different lotteries he prefers most. Once we have the decision maker's utility function, this is all we need to know about the decision maker to know what his preferences will be for any given set of lotteries. Let us explain then what the utility function is and how it can in principle be measured. Consider some set of events $E = \{e_1, \ldots, e_m\}$, and assume that E can serve as the event set for every one of the lotteries under consideration, so that the prize obtained on playing any particular lottery will be one and only one of the e_j's. A rational decision maker has the capability to arrange the events e_j in order of preference. Let us imagine that they have been numbered in order of preference, so that e_1 is the most preferred of all the prizes and e_m is the least preferred. For each event e_j, $j = 2, \ldots,$ $m - 1$, let us ask the decision maker to consider the following situation. There is a single stage lottery, which we shall write $\{(u, e_1) (1 - u, e_m)\}$, having only two prizes e_1 and e_m (the most and least preferred events). We then ask him, what value would u, the probability of receiving e_1, have to be in order for him to be indifferent between receiving e_j with certainty and playing the lottery? Let u_j be the value of u. A rational decision maker will be able to specify u_j. For each e_j, $j = 2, \ldots, m - 1$, we then determine a number u_j, $0 \leq u_j \leq 1$, that is, we can associate with e_j the number u_j. Let us in addition associate with e_1 the number $u_1 = 1$ and with e_m the number $u_m = 0$. By this procedure we have obtained a function $u_j = u(e_j)$ whose domain is E. This function is called a *utility function* for the decision maker. The number u_j we shall call the utility of e_j, and u_j serves as a numerical figure of merit for e_j in much the same way as a profit or a cost. The utility function is a very personal thing, however. It is by no means true that every rational decision maker will have the same utility function. Every rational decision maker will have a utility function, but the function may quite possibly differ from one decision maker to another. The way the function is determined for any particular decision maker is by the process outlined above where he specifies the numbers u_j. The procedure described determines a unique utility function for the decision maker.

Once the utility function $u_j = u(e_j)$ is known for the decision maker, we can without ever consulting him again determine his preferences with respect to any set of lotteries whose prizes are in E. We can then think of E as being the event set for each lottery. When E is the event set for a lottery, then the function $u_j = u(e_j)$ defines a random variable u, which we shall call the utility for the lottery (random experiment). Consider a particular lottery $\mathcal{L}$ and let p_j be the probability that the lottery will yield the prize e_j. The expected utility μ_u for this lottery is then

$$\mu_u = \sum_{j=1}^{m} u_j p_j.$$

Suppose that we compute the expected utility for every lottery in the set. The lottery which the rational decision maker prefers most is then the one for which his expected utility is the largest. We shall prove this interesting result in the following section. In other words, a rational decision maker, in ranking a set of lotteries in order of preference, proceeds as if he were ranking them in order of decreasing expected utility. Thus in making decisions a rational decision maker behaves as if he were a maximizer of his expected utility. We can now see that the notion of the expected value of a random variable will play a very important role in decision theory, since the way in which the action to be taken is determined is to find the one which maximizes the decision maker's expected utility. This is true even for decision problems which will not be repeated and where the expected values cannot be interpreted as long run averages.

The utility function introduced above is not the only one that could be used to determine which lottery the decision maker prefers most. If we define a new function $U_j = U(e_j)$ by writing $U_j = au_j + b$, $a > 0$, then $U_j = U(e_j)$ can also be used as a utility function, i.e., the lottery which yields the largest expected value of U will be the one that the decision maker prefers most. This is equivalent to saying that one has the same freedom in selecting a utility scale as in selecting a scale for a thermometer. The zero point for the utility can be selected arbitrarily and so can the unit of utility. Still another way of saying the same thing is that the utility of e_1 and e_m can be selected arbitrarily, with the restriction that $U(e_1) > U(e_m)$, and once this is done a unique utility function will be determined.

The above summarizes the model of a rational decision maker. In our future work, we shall always be assuming that the decision maker is rational, so that he possesses a utility function and makes decisions as if he were a maximizer of his expected utility. At this point, the reader may if he wishes move on to Section 2-9, omitting on first reading the following section which develops in detail the model of the rational decision maker. All that will be needed later has been outlined in this section.

2-8 THE MODEL OF RATIONAL BEHAVIOR

We are now ready to present the model of what we shall call a rational decision maker and to derive the important implications of this model. Recall that we indicated previously that the model consists of a set of axioms, and anyone whose behavior satisfies these axioms we shall call a rational decision maker. Several different sets of axioms have been developed which are roughly, but not quite precisely, equivalent. An especially convenient and easy to work with set is contained in Luce and Raiffa's book *Games and Decisions* [2]*, and it is essentially this set of axioms which will be used here. There are six of these axioms, whose meaning we shall discuss as we go along.

Consider a set of events $E = \{e_1, \ldots, e_m\}$. The events e_j may be anything whatever. The first axiom deals with the decision maker's ability to express preferences among these events. If the decision maker prefers event e_i to e_j, we shall use the symbolism $e_i > e_j$ to indicate this. If the decision maker is indifferent between e_i and e_j, we shall use the symbolism $e_i \sim e_j$. By $e_i \gtrsim e_j$ we mean that the decision maker prefers e_i to e_j or is indifferent between e_i and e_j. The first axiom is then the following:

AXIOM 1. *Given any two events e_i and e_j, one and only one of the following holds: either $e_i > e_j$, or $e_i \sim e_j$, or $e_j > e_i$, so that either e_i is preferred to e_j, or there is indifference between i and j, or e_j is preferred to e_i. Furthermore, if $e_i \gtrsim e_j$ and $e_j \gtrsim e_u$, then $e_i \gtrsim e_u$; in other words, if e_i is preferred or indifferent to e_j and e_j is preferred or indifferent to e_u, then e_i is preferred or indifferent to e_u. This is referred to as the transitivity of preferences.*

At first glance this seems like a perfectly reasonable axiom. Certainly a decision maker should be able to decide whether he prefers e_i to e_j or e_j to e_i or is indifferent between the two. In reality, however, it is by no means always easy to make such decisions, especially when the events are very complicated and extend over considerable periods of time. For example, if the events referred to two oil fields such as those considered in Tables 2-1 and 2-2, it might be very difficult to make a decision on which was preferred if there were also factors other than economic factors which had to be taken into account. There are also indications that certain types of events are basically not comparable and this makes it impossible for one to express preferences among them. This does not seem to be so much of a problem in the sort of decision problems one encounters in business and industry, however. The events are comparable, but they are so complex

*Numbers in brackets refer to the bibliographical references.

that the decision maker has great difficulties in expressing preferences.

When a decision maker satisfies axiom 1, then it is possible for him to arrange the events in sequence so that the first is preferred or indifferent to the next, which is in turn preferred or indifferent to the following one, etc. What we are saying is that the events can be arranged in order of preference. To prove this we proceed as follows. Let $e_1, \ldots, e_m$ be any m events, not necessarily numbered in order of preference. Consider e_1. Either $e_1 > e_2$, $e_1 \sim e_2$, or $e_2 > e_1$, that is, either $e_1 \succeq e_2$ or $e_2 \succeq e_1$. Denote by e_1^* the preferred of these two events, or either one if there is indifference. Then $e_1^* \succeq e_1$ and $e_1^* \succeq e_2$. Let us next take e_1^* and compare it with e_3. Let e_2^* be the preferred of these two events, or either one if there is indifference. Then $e_2^* \succeq e_1^*$ and $e_2^* \succeq e_3$. However, since $e_1^* \succeq e_1$ and $e_1^* \succeq e_2$, we conclude by the transitivity property that $e_2^* \succeq e_1$ and $e_2^* \succeq e_2$, so that $e_2^* \succeq e_1$, $e_2^* \succeq e_2$, and $e_2^* \succeq e_3$. Now compare e_2^* with e_4 and let e_3^* be the preferred one of these or either one if there is indifference. Then using the transitivity property again, we conclude that $e_3^* \succeq e_1$, $e_3^* \succeq e_{,2}$ $e_3^* \succeq e_3$, and $e_3^* \succeq e_4$. Continuing this procedure we find after $m - 1$ repetitions an event which is preferred or indifferent to all the other events. Considering next the set which does not include the most preferred event, the preferred event in this set is found. This will be the second most preferred event in E. In this way one can order the events. Since the numbering of the events in E is arbitrary, let us number them so that e_1 is the most preferred, e_2 is the next most preferred (or is indifferent to e_1), etc., until e_m is the least preferred. Then we have

$$e_1 \succeq e_2 \succeq \cdots \succeq e_m. \tag{2-17}$$

In the future, to avoid trivial situations in which there is indifference between all events, we shall always assume that e_1 is preferred to e_m.

To order the events as in (2-17) we had to use the transitivity property. Now it seems fairly reasonable that if e_i is preferred or indifferent to e_j and e_j is preferred or indifferent to e_u, then e_i is preferred or indifferent to e_u. Experiments with individuals suggest, however, that their preferences do not always satisfy the transitivity property. Sometimes when this is pointed out a person will re-evaluate the situation and agree that his original evaluation did not in fact express his preferences, and he will arrive at a new ordering which does satisfy the transitivity property. This is not always the case, however. For what we shall call a rational decision maker, it will be true that his preferences do satisfy the transitivity property.

Let us now turn to the second axiom which deals with situations in which uncertainty exists.

AXIOM 2. *A rational decision maker is indifferent between a two stage lottery $\mathcal{L}$ of the type discussed in the previous section and the single stage* *lottery L^* which has the same probability of getting each prize as the two stage lottery, that is, $\mathcal{L} \sim L^*$. Furthermore, a rational decision maker is indifferent between an n-stage lottery and a single stage lottery in which the probabilities of getting each prize are the same as in the n-stage lottery.*

Roughly speaking, what this axiom says is that the only thing that matters to the decision maker is the probabilities of the various events and not the precise nature of the random experiment. More specifically, it does not matter to him whether he passes through a two stage process (or an n-stage process) with uncertainty at each stage, or a single stage process, provided that the probabilities of the events e_j are the same in each case. Thus the axiom says that if

$$\mathcal{L} = \{(q_1, L_1), \ldots, (q_k, L_k)\} \quad \text{and} \quad L_i = \{(p_{i1}, e_1), \ldots, (p_{im}, e_m)\},$$

then the decision maker is indifferent between $\mathcal{L}$ and a single stage lottery with the probabilities of the prizes given by (2-14).

AXIOM 3. *For any event $e_j \in E$, different from e_1 and e_m, the rational decision maker is indifferent between having e_j occur with certainty and playing some lottery in which there are only two prizes, the best and worst events e_1 and e_m. In other words there exists a probability, call it u_j, such that the decision maker is indifferent between a lottery having a probability u_j of getting e_1 and a probability $1 - u_j$ of getting e_m, and simply getting e_j with certainty.*

Let us represent symbolically the lottery involving the best and worst events only, which has the property that the decision maker is indifferent between playing this lottery and getting e_j with certainty, by

$$L(e_j) = \{(u_j, e_1), (1 - u_j, e_m)\}. \tag{2-18}$$

We can think of $L(e_j)$ as a lottery involving all the events in E but in which only e_1 and e_m have positive probabilities of occurring. Then $e_j \sim L(e_j)$. What this axiom really says is that a rational decision maker can sit down and with sufficient thought and computation, determine a number u_j, $0 \le u_j \le 1$, such that he is indifferent between getting e_j with certainty and playing the lottery $L(e_j)$ given by (2-18) which involves only the best and worst events. Note that if he plays the lottery $L(e_j)$, he cannot receive e_j as a prize. Only e_1 or e_m will be received as prizes.

This is a very important and in some respects subtle axiom. It implies that the decision maker can evaluate situations involving uncertainty to the extent that given any lottery involving only the best and worst events he can decide whether he is indifferent between playing this lottery or getting e_j with certainty. Such decisions are often extremely difficult to make in practice. When $e_1 > e_j > e_m$, it seems rather reasonable that by making the probability of getting e_1 sufficiently high in a lottery involving only e_1 and e_m then he should actually prefer playing the lottery to getting e_j with certainty, and if the probability of e_1 is low enough, he should prefer e_j to the lottery. From this it then seems reasonable that there should exist a probability such that he is indifferent between e_j and the lottery. In any real situation, the difficulty lies in deciding what value this probability should have.

The fourth axiom generalizes somewhat what is stated in the third axiom. To introduce this axiom consider any single stage lottery $L = \{(p_1, e_1),$ $\ldots, (p_m, e_m)\}$. Consider now a two stage lottery $\mathcal{L}^* = (p_1, L_1), \ldots,$ (p_m, L_m). Assume that $\mathcal{L}^*$ has the peculiar characteristic that the probability of getting into lottery L_j is p_j, where p_j is the probability of getting prize e_j in L. There are as many single stage lotteries L_j in $\mathcal{L}^*$ as there are prizes in L. Let us now specify the lotteries L_j. These will be very peculiar types of lotteries. For one particular j, call it r, we shall take $L_r = L(e_r)$, where $L(e_r)$ is given by (2-18) and is the lottery such that the decision maker is indifferent between getting e_r with certainty or playing the lottery $L(e_r)$. For all other j, L_j will be a lottery in which there is only one prize e_j, and the probability of getting e_j is 1, that is, $L_j = \{(1, e_j)\}$, $j \neq r$. Note that L_j can be looked on as a lottery in which all prizes in E exist, but only e_j has a positive probability. We can now write out explicitly $\mathcal{L}^*$. It is

$$\mathcal{L}^* = \{p_1(1, e_1), p_2(1, e_2), \ldots, p_{r-1}(1, e_{r-1}), p_r[(u_r, e_1), (1 - u_r, e_m)],$$
$$p_{r+1}(1, e_{r+1}), \ldots, p_m(1, e_m)\}.$$

Note that in $\mathcal{L}^*$ the prize e_r does not appear. The decision trees for L and $\mathcal{L}^*$ are shown in Figures 2-7 and 2-8.

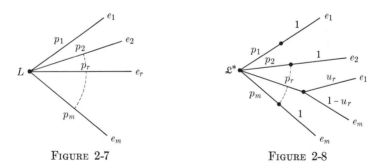

FIGURE 2-7   FIGURE 2-8

The next axiom says that a rational decision maker is indifferent between L and $\mathcal{L}^*$. Formally, we have:

Axiom 4. *A rational decision maker is indifferent between the single stage lottery L and the two stage lottery $\mathcal{L}^*$, $\mathcal{L}^*$ being constructed in the manner just described.*

What this axiom says is that if the decision maker is indifferent between e_r and $L(e_r)$, then in any lottery involving e_r, he should be able to replace

e_r by $L(e_r)$ and obtain a new (two stage) lottery such that he is indifferent between the original single stage lottery and the new two stage lottery. It is important to observe that if $p_r > 0$, then it is possible to obtain the prize e_r when playing L. However, in $\mathcal{L}^*$ the prize e_r does not appear, since e_r was replaced by $L(e_r)$ which does not have e_r as a prize. Thus the probabilities of the prizes are not the same in L and $\mathcal{L}^*$. In $\mathcal{L}^*$, e_r has a probability of 0, while the probabilities of e_1 or e_m or both will be increased over their values in L.

Let us now give the remaining two axioms. Then we shall be able to prove some very interesting results.

AXIOM 5. *Consider any two lotteries, either one or both of which may be a single stage, two stage, or n-stage lottery. Call them lotteries a and b. Then the rational decision maker either prefers a to b, is indifferent between a and b, or prefers b to a. Furthermore, preferences among lotteries satisfy the transitivity property.*

This axiom is the equivalent of axiom 1 for lotteries. Indeed, we can look at axiom 1 as being merely a special case of axiom 5. The reason for this is that the event e_j being obtained with certainty can be described by a single stage lottery in which e_j has the probability 1, while all other events have the probability 0. Therefore axiom 5 can be interpreted as applying also to situations in which the decision maker is comparing some event with a lottery. Just as axiom 1 implies that the decision maker can rank the events in order of preference, one can prove in precisely the same way that axiom 5 implies that the decision maker can arrange any given set of lotteries in order of preference.

Note that nothing in our axioms gives any indication of the process which the decision maker uses to determine his preferences with respect to a pair of events. However, axiom 6 will tell us something about how a decision maker expresses preferences between a given pair of lotteries of a certain type. From this and the other axioms we shall then prove that there is a very simple characterization of the way a rational decision maker ranks a set of lotteries in order of preference.

AXIOM 6. *Consider two single stage lotteries which involve only e_1 and e_m as prizes. Denote these lotteries by L_a and L_b and let p_a be the probability of winning e_1 in L_a and p_b be the probability of winning e_1 in L_b. Then $L_a > L_b$ if $p_a > p_b$, $L_a \sim L_b$ if $p_a = p_b$, and $L_b > L_a$ if $p_b > p_a$.*

Since one and only one of the following can hold

$$p_a > p_b, \quad p_a = p_b, \quad p_b > p_a,$$

axiom 6 makes it possible for the rational decision maker to determine easily the preference relationship referred to in axiom 5 for any two single stage lotteries which involve only e_1 and e_m.

We shall now prove that the above axioms provide a criterion by which a rational decision maker can rank any set of lotteries in order of preference. As a first step in doing this consider any single stage lottery L.   Now let us return to axiom 4.   Recall that this axiom states that $\mathcal{L}^* \sim L$.   However, by axiom 2 we can reduce $\mathcal{L}^*$ to a single stage lottery, call it L^*, such that $\mathcal{L}^* \sim L^*$.   What is L^*?   It can immediately be determined using the process referred to on page 104.   To be specific, let us determine L^* in the case where $r = 2$.   Then if we write out $\mathcal{L}^*$ explicitly we have

$$\mathcal{L}^* = \{p_1(1, e_1), p_2[(u_2, e_1), ((1 - u_2), e_m)], p_3(1, e_3), \ldots, p_m(1, e_m)\},$$

and therefore

$$L^* = \{(p_1 + p_2 u_2, e_1), (0, e_2), (p_3, e_3), \ldots, (p_m + p_2(1 - u_2), e_m)\}. \quad (2\text{-}19)$$

In L^* the prize e_2 is not obtained.   According to axiom 4, $L \sim \mathcal{L}^*$, and according to axiom 2, $\mathcal{L}^* \sim L^*$.   Thus by the transitivity property assumed in axiom 5, $L \sim L^*$.   By the process just described we have converted an arbitrary single stage lottery L to a single stage lottery L^* which does not have e_2 as a prize, and $L \sim L^*$.   We can now continue the process and form from L^* a lottery L^{**} which does not have e_3 for a prize, such that $L^* \sim L^{**}$ and hence $L \sim L^{**}$; L^{**} is the lottery

$$L^{**} = \{(p_1 + p_2 u_2 + p_3 u_3, e_1), (0, e_2), (0, e_3), (p_4, e_4), \ldots,$$
$$(p_m + p_2(1 - u_2) + p_3(1 - u_3), e_m)\}.$$

After $m - 2$ repetitions of this process we obtain a lottery $\overline{L}$ having as prizes only e_1 and e_m, such that the decision maker is indifferent between lotteries L and $\overline{L}$.   The lottery $\overline{L}$ is the lottery

$$\overline{L} = \left\{ \left(p_1 + \sum_{j=2}^{m-1} p_j u_j, e_1 \right), \left(p_m + \sum_{j=2}^{m-1} p_j(1 - u_j), e_m \right) \right\}. \quad (2\text{-}20)$$

We have now proved that if we are given any single stage lottery, we can reduce this lottery to one involving only the best and worst events as prizes, in such a way that the decision maker is indifferent between the original lottery and the new lottery of the form (2-20).

Given what we have just proved, it is now a straightforward matter for the decision maker to rank any set of lotteries which may be offered to him in order of preference.   To see how this is done, let us assume that he is considering k single stage lotteries, the ith of which is

$$L_i = \{(p_{i1}, e_1), (p_{i2}, e_2), \ldots, (p_{im}, e_m)\}. \quad (2\text{-}21)$$

Without any loss in generality we can assume that each lottery involves the same set of prizes E.   The procedure we are about to describe applies equally well to ranking two stage or n-stage lotteries.   If any of the lotteries in the given set are multistage lotteries, we apply axiom 2 to obtain a new set of single stage lotteries and the problem is reduced to the case we are considering now.   From what we have proved above, we know that there exists a lottery $\overline{L}_i$ involving only the best and worst prizes, such that $L_i \sim \overline{L}_i$.   In fact, $\overline{L}_i$ is the lottery

$$\overline{L}_i = \left\{ \left(p_{i1} + \sum_{j=2}^{m-1} p_{ij}u_j,\ e_1 \right), \left(p_{im} + \sum_{j=2}^{m-1} p_{ij}(1 - u_j),\ e_m \right) \right\}. \quad (2\text{-}22)$$

Now axiom 6 tells us how a rational decision maker will rank any two lotteries $\overline{L}_i$.   He prefers most the one with the greatest probability of getting e_1.   The most preferred of all the lotteries $\overline{L}_i$ is then the one for which $p_{i1} + \sum_{j=2}^{m-1} p_{ij}u_j$ is the greatest, and the least desirable is the one with this number the smallest.   Recall that the u_j are the probabilities of the event e_1 in $L(e_j)$, where $L(e_j)$ is the lottery involving only e_1 and e_m as prizes and having the property that $e_j \sim L(e_j)$.   Since the numbering of the original lotteries is arbitrary, suppose we number them so that

$$p_{11} + \sum_{j=2}^{m-1} p_{1j}u_j \geq p_{21} + \sum_{j=2}^{m-1} p_{2j}u_j \geq \cdots \geq p_{k1} + \sum_{j=2}^{m-1} p_{kj}u_j. \quad (2\text{-}23)$$

Then if we use axiom 6 and the method introduced after axiom 1 for ordering events, we immediately conclude that

$$\overline{L}_1 \gtrsim \overline{L}_2 \gtrsim \cdots \gtrsim \overline{L}_k. \quad (2\text{-}24)$$

However, $L_i \sim \overline{L}_i$.   Thus $L_1 \sim \overline{L}_1$, $\overline{L}_1 \gtrsim \overline{L}_2$, and $L_2 \sim \overline{L}_2$.   Thus by transitivity $L_1 \gtrsim L_2$, etc., or in general

$$L_1 \gtrsim L_2 \gtrsim \cdots \gtrsim L_k. \quad (2\text{-}25)$$

Conversely, if (2-25) represents the decision maker's preferences, then (2-24) must hold, and by axiom 6, (2-23) must hold.

We have just obtained a very important result.   It says that if a decision maker is confronted with a set of lotteries of the form (2-21), the one which he will most prefer to play is the one for which $p_{i1} + \sum_{j=2}^{m-1} p_{ij}u_j$ is the largest.   Thus if we know the numbers u_j for a rational decision maker, we do not need to ask him which lottery in the set (2-21) he prefers. We can easily determine this for ourselves simply by finding the lottery which has the largest value of $p_{i1} + \sum_{j=2}^{m-1} p_{ij}u_j$.   Note that this computation can be made directly from the data given in (2-21) when the u_j are known.   No process of reducing lotteries to a different form needs to be carried out.   The numbers u_j then completely determine how the rational decision maker will behave when choosing among lotteries whose prizes are elements of E.   We have proved that *the decision maker will be reflecting his true preferences if he says that the lottery he prefers most is the one for which* $p_{i1} + \sum_{j=2}^{m-1} p_{ij}u_j$ *is the greatest.*

Let us review the steps which led to this simple rule which the decision maker can use to select among alternative lotteries.   Axiom 5 specifies that the decision maker can express a preference or indifference between any two given lotteries, and that such preferences are transitive. Thus by the procedure used to show that events can be ordered, we can prove as a result of this axiom that the decision maker can order lotteries in order of preference. Axiom 6 tells us something which seems very reasonable. If the decision maker is confronted with two single stage lotteries having only e_1 and e_m as prizes, he will prefer the one with the larger probability of getting e_1, and if the probability of e_1 is the same in both lotteries, then he is indifferent between them. From this and the other axioms, we then proved that if the decision maker arranges the lotteries in order of preference and if we number them so that (2-25) holds, then (2-23) will hold, and if (2-23) holds, then (2-25) must hold.

We have proved that once the decision maker has determined the numbers u_j, he will be reflecting his actual preferences if when confronted with any set of lotteries, he computes for each lottery $p_{i1} + \sum_{j=2}^{m-1} p_{ij} u_j$ and says that he prefers that lottery for which this number is the largest. It is unnecessary for him to make further introspective evaluations once the u_j have been determined.

There is a very convenient way to interpret this rule for selecting among lotteries. We have associated with each e_j, $j = 2, \ldots, m - 1$, a number u_j. Let us also associate with e_1 the number 1 and with e_m the number 0. Then we have associated with each element of E a unique number u_j, where $u_1 = 1$ and $u_m = 0$. This defines a function $u_j = u(e_j)$ over E. Now each lottery L_i can be thought of as a random experiment for which we can use E as the event set. Then the function $u_j = u(e_j)$ serves to define a random variable, call it u. We have now made an interesting reinterpretation of the numbers u_j. Originally they were probabilities in the $L(e_j)$. Now we imagine that associated with any prize there is a number u_j which takes the form of a numerical valuation of the prize, similar to the profit or discounted profit in deterministic situations. To show this more explicitly, let us prove that if $e_j > e_i$ then $u_j > u_i$, if $e_i > e_j$ then $u_i > u_j$, and if $e_j \sim e_i$ then $u_j = u_i$, and conversely if $u_j > u_i$ then $e_j > e_i$, etc. To do this recall that $e_j \sim L(e_j)$ and $e_i \sim L(e_i)$. By transitivity if $e_j > e_i$ then $L(e_j) > L(e_i)$. But by axiom 6 this implies that $u_j > u_i$. Conversely, if $u_j > u_i$ then by axiom 6, $L(e_j) > L(e_i)$ and by transitivity $e_j > e_i$. Similarly, if $e_j \sim e_i$ then $L(e_j) \sim L(e_i)$ and by axiom 6, $u_i = u_j$. We originally agreed to number the e_j so that $e_1 \gtrsim e_2 \gtrsim \cdots \gtrsim e_m$. Therefore we must have

$$u_1 = 1 \geq u_2 \geq \cdots \geq u_{m-1} \geq u_m = 0. \tag{2-26}$$

We have now constructed a real valued function $u_j = u(e_j)$ defined over E having the property that $e_j > e_i$ if and only if $u_j > u_i$ and $e_j \sim e_i$ if and only if $u_j = u_i$. This function is generally called a *utility function* for the rational decision maker, and the random variable u is referred to as *the utility*. We can next give a very interesting interpretation to the rule obtained above, which the decision maker can use to determine the lottery he prefers most. Since $u_1 = 1$, and $u_m = 0$ by our definition, $p_{i1} + \sum_{j=2}^{m-1} p_{ij}u_j$ is the expected value of the utility for the ith lottery, that is,

$$\sum_{j=1}^{m} u_j p_{ij},$$

and hence the lottery which the decision maker prefers most happens to be the one which yields the largest value of his expected utility. The utility function $u_j = u(e_j)$ is, of course, a very personal thing, and it does not necessarily follow that two different rational decision makers when presented with the same set of lotteries will agree as to the most preferred lottery. The utility function reflects all of the decision maker's feelings about the various events e_j, and may well include factors other than monetary factors. We have then obtained the following very important result that will be fundamental in all of our future treatment of decision problems.

BASIC DECISION RULE. *A rational decision maker behaves in selecting among lotteries as if he were choosing the lottery which maximizes his expected utility. In other words, if we know his utility function we can determine which lottery he prefers most by finding the one which maximizes his expected utility.*

Recall that what we call a rational decision maker is a decision maker which satisfies the six axioms presented above. It is not claimed that everyone in the real world is a rational decision maker, or even that anyone is. However, it would seem that many decision makers' behavior is sufficiently close to rational behavior that if in developing the theory we always assume that decision makers are rational, we will not deviate too far from reality. Therefore, in discussing decision theory, we shall take as our model of a decision maker a rational decision maker. In fact, the only thing we need to know about a rational decision maker is his utility function. Consequently, our mathematical model of a decision maker will simply be the utility function $u_j = u(e_j)$, and our mathematical rule for determining which of a number of lotteries the decision maker prefers most will be the maximization of the expected value of the decision maker's utility.

We might note before going on that the basic decision rule is not merely restricted to making choices between lotteries, but applies equally well to making choices among lotteries and events that will occur with certainty. If one of the alternatives involves obtaining e_j with certainty, we use u_j, the utility of e_j, for the index in ranking the alternatives. To see that this is correct we note that getting e_j with certainty can be looked on as a lottery in which e_j is the only prize, so that the probability of e_j is 1. The expected utility of this lottery is merely u_j.

The axioms describing a rational decision maker contain implicitly a procedure by which one could in principle measure experimentally a decision maker's utility function. Axiom 3 provides the basis for this. To determine u_j, we ask the decision maker what the probability of e_1 should be in a lottery in which the only prizes are e_1 and e_m, such that he is indifferent between playing this lottery and getting e_j with certainty. The number he gives us is then u_j, as we see from the above theory. In practice, of course, it is very hard for an individual to specify these desired probabilities. Furthermore, the transitivity relations are often not satisfied initially and reappraisals are necessary. Some of the reasons why it is so difficult for an individual to express his feelings will be considered in more detail later. Fortunately, for a great many situations of practical interest, it is unnecessary to measure the decision maker's utility. We shall see soon why this is so.

Is the utility function unique, that is, is there only one function such that if we maximize the expected value of this random variable we shall determine the most desired lottery? We have seen how to determine one such function above. This function is not unique, however. There are in fact an infinite number of different functions which will serve as well. The situation is similar to choosing a scale for making any sort of measurements, where we are free to choose the origin and the unit of measure. In our case we can select arbitrarily the utility of e_m and e_1. Having done this, the other utilities will be uniquely determined. What we are saying is that instead of using the random variable u introduced above we can equally well take as the utility any random variable $U = au + b$ where $a > 0$. From what we proved in the previous chapter, if μ_u and μ_U are the expected values of u and U respectively, then

$$\mu_U = a\mu_u + b. \tag{2-27}$$

If we now consider several different lotteries L_i, then for each one we will have a μ_u and μ_U, call them $\mu_u{}^i$ and $\mu_U{}^i$. Then from (2-27), if $\mu_u{}^r$ is the largest $\mu_u{}^i$, then $\mu_U{}^r$ will be the largest $\mu_U{}^i$ and if $\mu_U{}^r$ is the largest of the $\mu_U{}^i$, then $\mu_u{}^r$ will be the largest of the $\mu_u{}^i$. Therefore, we will select precisely the same lottery if we maximize the expected value of U as we will if we maximize the expected value of u, and hence U will serve just as well for a utility function as u. Note that we must require in the above that $a > 0$. If $a < 0$, then the reader should convince himself that maximizing the expected value of u would correspond to minimizing the expected value of U. Suppose we specify a and b in $U = au + b$. What then are the utilities of e_1 and e_m? Now $u_m = 0$. Thus $U_m = b$. Next $u_1 = 1$. Thus $U_1 = a + b$. Hence if we desire to have $U_m = \beta$ and $U_1 = \alpha$, we can achieve this by setting $b = \beta$ and $a = \alpha - \beta$. The utilities of the other events are then given by $U_j = (\alpha - \beta)u_j + \beta$.

We now know that if $u_j = u(e_j)$ is the utility function determined in the manner described above, and having $u_1 = 1$ and $u_m = 0$, then $U_j = U(e_j)$ can also be used as a utility function if $U_j = au_j + b$, $a > 0$, all j. Let us next ask: Do there exist any functions $U_j = U(e_j)$ which will serve as utility functions and which do not have the property that $U_j = au_j + b$, $a > 0$? The answer is no, as we can now easily see. Recall that

$$e_j \sim \{(u_j, e_1), (1 - u_j, e_m)\} = L(e_j).$$

Now if $U_j = U(e_j)$ serves as a utility function, then since $e_j \sim L(e_j)$, U_j must be equal to the expected utility for the lottery $L(e_j)$. However, the expected utility of this lottery is $u_j U_1 + (1 - u_j)U_m$. Hence it must be true that

$$U_j = (U_1 - U_m)u_j + U_m, \quad \text{all } j.$$

However, since by assumption $e_1 > e_m$, it must be true that $U_1 > U_m$ and $U_1 - U_m > 0$. Thus if we write $a = U_1 - U_m$ and $b = U_m$, we conclude that $U_j = au_j + b$, $a > 0$, all j, and the random variable U is related to u by an equation of the form $U = au + b$, $a > 0$. Therefore every possible utility variable U is related to u by an equation of the form $U = au + b$, $a > 0$.

We might note that in general the actual numerical value of the utility will not have any meaning. In particular, if $u(e_i) = 2u(e_j)$, this does not imply that e_i is preferred twice as much as e_j, or if the expected utility for one lottery is twice that for another, this does not mean that one lottery is twice as desirable as the other. By changing the utility scale we can change these factors in an arbitrary way. We shall not really be concerned with questions such as how much more a decision maker prefers one event or one lottery to another. All we shall be concerned about is that he prefers one to the other.

In this rather long section we have characterized by a set of axioms what we call a rational decision maker, and we have obtained from these the very important conclusion that a rational decision maker behaves as if he is a maximizer of his expected utility. The utility concept has been in existence for a long time and goes all the way back to the Swiss mathematician D. Bernoulli who lived in the eighteenth century. Economists have long talked about utility and have even attempted to give meaning to numerical values of utility. Until very recently, one could only characterize most treatments of utility ideas as quite unsatisfactory. The modern theory of utility, which has very little in common with the previous "theories," was introduced by von Neumann and Morgenstern in their book *Theory of Games and Economic Behavior*, first published in

1944 [4]. It has so little in common with previous concepts that it would probably have been better not to use the name utility to avoid misunderstandings which can arise if one mistakenly assumes it to be similar to these earlier ideas. It is the von Neumann and Morgenstern theory which has been developed here. While it is certainly not without shortcomings, it does provide a very useful model to use in building up models in decision theory.

2-9 AN EXAMPLE

Let us now illustrate how the theory developed in the previous section can be used by decision makers. Suppose that the owner of a small business is trying to decide whether to undertake one of two contracts which have been offered to him. He definitely cannot undertake both. There is uncertainty about the final outcome of either contract. To simplify matters, he assumes that only three outcomes are possible for each contract. The discounted profits associated with each outcome and the probabilities which he assigns to the outcomes are summarized in Table 2-4.

TABLE 2-4

SUMMARY OF TWO CONTRACTS BEING CONSIDERED

Contract a		Contract b	
Discounted profit (dollars)	Probability	Discounted profit (dollars)	Probability
50,000	0.7	40,000	0.6
10,000	0.1	30,000	0.2
−20,000	0.2	−10,000	0.2

We can note at this point that each contract can be looked on as a single stage lottery, for there are certain prizes (the discounted profits) and certain probabilities of getting these prizes. This model of a contract and the model of a single stage lottery are precisely the same, and thus we can look at the problem as one in which the businessman is trying to decide whether to play one of two lotteries or not to play at all. If we assume that the businessman is a rational decision maker, then the theory of the previous section can be applied, and he should select the alternative which maximizes his expected utility.

In order to proceed we must then determine the decision maker's utility function for this situation. Considering both contracts together plus the alternative of not undertaking either one, there are seven events corresponding to the seven possible values of the discounted profit. These are 50,000, 40,000, 30,000, 10,000, 0, $-10,000$, and $-20,000$. If he does not accept either contract, then he will venture nothing and get a return of 0. This is the reason we included a discounted profit of 0 in the list. Let us imagine that these discounted profits reflect all of his feelings about each outcome so that no other factors need be considered in determining his utility function for this set of events. Denote the event 50,000 by e_1 and $-20,000$ by e_7. These are the best and worst events respectively. We shall determine that particular utility function for which $u(e_1) = 1$ and $u(e_7) = 0$. To determine the decision maker's utilities for the other events on this scale, consider the lottery

$$L = \{(u, e_1), (1 - u, e_m)\},$$

which has as prizes only the best and worst events. For each other event we then ask him for what value of u in L would he be indifferent between getting the event under consideration with certainty and playing the lottery L. The number he gives us is then the utility of the event, as we showed in the last section. Suppose he succeeds in answering these questions and in doing so tells us that his utility function is the following: $u(40,000) = 0.95$, $u(30,000) = 0.80$, $u(10,000) = 0.50$, $u(0) = 0.30$, $u(-10,000) = 0.20$. Given this information we can easily compute the expected utility for each contract. We find that the values are

Contract a: $0.7(1) + 0.1(0.50) + 0.2(0) = 0.75,$
Contract b: $0.6(0.95) + 0.2(0.80) + 0.2(0.20) = 0.77,$

so that the expected utility of contract a is 0.75 and that of contract b is 0.77. The utility of not undertaking either one is $u(0) = 0.30$. The largest of these three numbers is 0.77, and thus the businessman prefers undertaking contract b to undertaking a or not undertaking either one. Thus he should accept contract b.

Suppose we compute the expected value of the discounted profit for each contract. We obtain

Contract a: $50,000(0.7) + 10,000(0.1) - 20,000(0.2) = \$32,000,$
Contract b: $40,000(0.6) + 30,000(0.2) - 10,000(0.2) = \$28,000.$

Interestingly enough, if the businessman had selected the action which maximized his expected discounted profit, he would have undertaken contract a, whereas his true preference is for contract b. The reason he prefers contract b no doubt stems from the fact that the largest possible loss is smaller for contract b than for a, and he is willing to accept a smaller expected profit to avoid the risk of a large loss.

2-10 USE OF EXPECTED MONETARY VALUES

We noted in Section 2-5 that it seemed reasonable in certain cases for a decision maker to select that action which maximizes his expected profit (discounted if necessary).   We now want to investigate the circumstances under which maximizing expected profits will be equivalent to maximizing expected utility.   To study the situation let us examine the feelings a rational decision maker might have towards changes in his stock of money. To do this, let us select two sums, say $50,000 and −$50,000, the positive quantity indicating a gain and the negative quantity a loss.   Consider then the lottery

$$L = \{(u, 50{,}000), (1 - u, -50{,}000)\}.$$

Suppose we now select any other sum s lying between −50,000 and 50,000 and ask him for what value of u in L he is indifferent between getting s with certainty and playing the lottery L.   The number u which he specifies will then be his utility of a change s in his stock of money if we take the utility of −50,000 to be 0 and of 50,000 to be 1.   Let us ask him this question for a sizable number of different s values.   For each such s we determine a number u, and we can plot the pairs of numbers (s, u) on a graph.   Suppose that we do this and then draw a smooth curve through the points.   Generally speaking, there are three types of curves which we might obtain.   These are shown in Figure 2-9 and labeled a, b, and c.

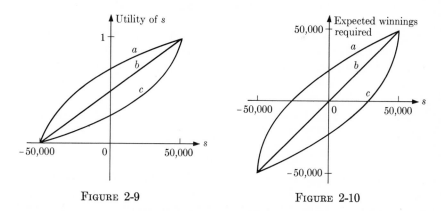

FIGURE 2-9   FIGURE 2-10

Recall that u is the probability of obtaining the prize of $50,000 when the lottery L is played.   The expected monetary winnings from L are $100{,}000u - 50{,}000$.   In Figure 2-10 we have plotted a curve corresponding to each one in Figure 2-9, giving the points $(s, 100{,}000u - 50{,}000)$.   Thus by looking at Figure 2-10 we can determine for any sum s to be obtained with certainty the expected return from L that is required so that the decision maker is indifferent between s and L. To begin, let us observe that for individual a, the expected monetary return from lottery L such that $L \sim s$ is always greater than s. This man tends to be on the cautious side, and the prospects of losing \$50,000 seem serious enough that he would not be indifferent between s and an L in which the expected monetary winnings are s. He would want higher expected monetary winnings before he would be indifferent between L and s. Individual b has the characteristic that he is always indifferent between s and an L whose expected winnings are s. The potential loss of \$50,000 in L does not bother him to the extent that he demands an expected winnings in L greater than s in order to be indifferent between L and s. Individual c might be considered to be a somewhat daring individual. For each s, the expected winnings in the L such that $L \sim s$ is less than s. Either because of the thrill of gambling or because the prize of \$50,000 would be especially valuable to this individual, he is willing to take an expected winnings of less than s and still have $s \sim L$.

Let us focus our attention now on decision makers whose behavior is like that of b in Figure 2-9. The curve b in Figure 2-9 is what we call a straight line. It is the graph of an equation of the form $u = \gamma s + \delta$ where $\gamma > 0$. In fact, since $u = 0$ when $s = -50,000$, we have $\delta = 50,000\, \gamma$, and since $u = 1$ when $s = 50,000$, $\gamma = 1/100,000$. The equation of the line b in Figure 2-9 is then

$$u = \frac{s + 50,000}{100,000}. \tag{2-28}$$

The reader might select several values of s, compute the corresponding u values using (2-28), and check that the points (s, u) do lie on curve b in Figure 2-9. When u and s are related by an equation of the form $u = \gamma s + \delta$, we say they are related by a linear equation. If $\gamma > 0$ as in the above case, then we can solve for s and write

$$s = \frac{1}{\gamma} u - \frac{\delta}{\gamma}, \quad \frac{1}{\gamma} > 0. \tag{2-29}$$

Now recall that if $U = au + b$, $a > 0$, then U can be used as a utility variable just as well as u. But if in (2-29) we write $a = 1/\gamma$, $b = -\delta/\gamma$, we see that (2-29) then has this form. In other words, we can use actual monetary values for the utility in this case, so that if in situations where the prizes can be completely characterized by monetary values, a decision maker of type b selects his action by maximizing his expected profit, he will indeed be choosing his most preferred action.

The above discussion has said nothing about how the decision maker expresses preferences with respect to monetary sums to be received at different points in time. It is not necessarily true that a rational decision maker will be indifferent between sums with the same present worth. However, if he is indifferent between various prospects whose discounted monetary values are the same, then provided his utility curve looks like curve *b* of Figure 2-9 for changes in his stock of money, this curve can be used to represent his preferences for changes occurring at different points in time, by use of discounted values. We have then obtained the criterion which tells us when it is appropriate to proceed by maximizing expected profits. It is

CRITERION FOR USING EXPECTED MONETARY VALUES. *Given a set of lotteries in which the prizes are completely characterized by monetary values, then if the rational decision maker's utility is related to discounted monetary values by a linear equation, monetary values can be used as utilities, and if the decision maker selects the lottery which maximizes the expected discounted profit he will select the lottery which is highest on his preference list.*

The restriction that the prizes be completely characterized by monetary values is an important one, because even if the decision maker's utility is related to monetary values by a linear equation when money is the only thing under consideration, this may be irrelevant if in selecting among the lotteries, factors other than monetary factors are important. Generally speaking, when monetary factors are of prime concern and when the sums are not too large it seems quite adequate in practice to select the action which maximizes the expected monetary value. Even if one wanted to be more precise, it would not be possible to obtain a more accurate estimation of the decision maker's utility function than is possible by using the profit function. It is when the monetary values are very large or when other factors are important that one cannot use expected profits, but instead must attempt to measure as best one can the decision maker's utility and make selections by maximizing expected utility. In the future we shall frequently use monetary values as utilities, because for the types of problems where this is done it seems quite appropriate.

We can now make one final important point. In Section 2-5 we noted that while it seemed reasonable to make selections in certain cases where the experiment could be repeated again and again, by maximizing expected profits, it was not clear that this criterion made any sense for situations where the experiment could not be repeated. Now we have proved that a rational decision maker always acts as if he is maximizing his expected utility, regardless of whether the situation is capable of repetition or not. Furthermore, if the criterion for using expected monetary values is satisfied, then monetary values can be used as utilities and it is appropriate to select the action which maximizes expected monetary values even if the experiment cannot be repeated. The result that maximizing expected monetary values is often appropriate even when the experiments are not capable of repetition is an interesting deduction from our model of a rational decision maker which was not intuitively obvious at the outset.

We have now covered sufficient background material that we are ready to begin the study of decision theory models. In the next chapter, we shall begin the study of such models.

REFERENCES

1. Davidson, D., P. Suppes, and S. Siegel, *Decision Making: An Experimental Approach.* Stanford University Press, Stanford, Calif., 1957.
  This book is concerned with the problem of the experimental measurement of utility.

2. Luce, R. D., and H. Raiffa, *Games and Decisions.* Wiley, New York, 1957.

3. Savage, L. J., *The Foundations of Statistics.* Wiley, New York, 1954.
  Gives an interesting historical summary of the development of utility theory.

4. Von Neumann, J., and O. Morgenstern, *Theory of Games and Economic Behavior.* Princeton University Press, Princeton, N. J., 1st ed., 1944, 2nd ed., 1947.

PROBLEMS

Section 2-2

1. A firm is considering building two new plants in two of six possible European countries. How many alternative projects are there if a project is defined so that only one project will be undertaken? Describe each project.

2. A firm is considering whether to expand capacity at some one of its five plants or to build a new plant in one of three possible cities, or to do both. How many alternative projects are there if a project is defined so that only one project will be undertaken? Describe each project.

3. Suppose a decision maker is faced with a situation for which the decision tree is as in Figure 2-11. If this can be imagined to be a deterministic situation, how many projects are there for the decision maker to consider? Describe each of the projects in terms of the decisions involved.

4. A chemical company is trying to decide whether to start manufacturing a new synthetic fiber, or whether it should increase its production of heavy chemicals. If it decides to produce the fiber, it can build a small plant now and in two years either increase the size of the plant or build a new one in a given city, or it can build a large plant now. If it expands production of heavy chemicals, it can do so by expanding production of either sulfuric acid, ammonia, or toluene or any combination of these. If any two or more of these is expanded, then in three years the company will either have to increase the size of its domestic-marketing organization or start up a foreign-marketing organization. If production of only one product is increased, after two years the company will either have to reduce the

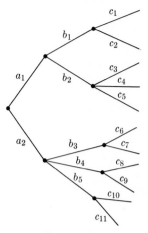

FIGURE 2-11

price of this product or begin manufacture of a line of products which use it for a raw material. Assume that everything is deterministic. How many projects are there? Describe each one.

5. An initial investment of one million dollars is needed for a given project with later investments of $500,000 at the end of the third and fifth years. Revenues received in the first year will amount to $300,000 and these will increase 20 percent per year (20 percent of the previous year's value) for six years and then decrease 10 percent per year for four years. The project terminates after ten years. Operating costs in the first year will be $50,000 and will decrease 10 percent per year for five years, after which they will remain constant until the end of the project. If a year is used for the length of a period, determine the mathematical representation of this project under the assumption that there are no taxes.

Sections 2-3 and 2-4

1. Determine the value ten years from now of $10,000 which is invested at an interest rate of 5 percent. Repeat the computation for an interest rate of 10 percent.

2. Determine the value twenty years from now of $10,000 which is invested at an interest rate of 5 percent. Repeat the computation for an interest rate of 10 percent.

3. Determine the present value of a sum of $25,000 to be received at the end of five years, if the interest rate is 10 percent. Repeat the computation for an interest rate of 15 percent.

4. Determine the present value of a sum of $25,000 to be received at the end of twenty years, if the interest rate is 10 percent. Repeat the computation if the interest rate is 15 percent.

5. Compute the present worth of $5000 to be received twenty years from now for $i = 0, 0.10, 0.20, 0.30, 0.50, 1$. Plot the present worth for each of these i values on a graph and draw a smooth curve through the points.

6. In our discussion of investing funds we assumed that interest was computed once per period, say once a year. Banks and other institutions sometimes compute interest more frequently. If interest is computed twice a year, we often say that interest is compounded semiannually, or if it is computed four times per year, we say that it is compounded quarterly. Suppose that interest is computed every six months and that the annual interest rate is i. If we invest I at the beginning of the year, then after six months an amount $iI/2$ will be added to our account, so that we will have $I[1 + (i/2)]$. At the end of the year we will then have $I[1 + (i/2)]^2$ instead of $I(1 + i)$ which would be the sum that we would have if interest is computed only once per year. Show that on computing interest twice per year we have an additional amount $Ii^2/4$ at the end of the year. Show that this is usually small compared to the interest earned for the year. If interest is compounded n times per year, then a sum I invested at the beginning of the year will yield $I[1 + (i/n)]^n$ at the end of the year. Compare this with $I(1 + i)$ for the case where $n = 5$ and $i = 0.10$. Conclude that, normally, even though interest may be compounded more than once a year, we are not making a large error if in our mathematical model we assume it is computed only once a year.

7. Consider a sum I to be received n years in the future. Let I_0 be the present worth of I. Let I_1 be the value of I discounted to the beginning of year n_1, $n_1 < n$. Prove that the present worth of I_1 is I_0. This proves that we can discount in two stages or a single stage, and the same answer will be obtained either way.

8. How much must we invest today if it is to accumulate to $50,000 after 35 years at an interest rate of 5 percent?

9. Consider one project which requires an investment of $500,000 now and will return $600,000 after ten years with no other revenues received or costs incurred in the intervening period. Consider a second project which requires an initial investment of $500,000 which returns $550,000 at the end of the second year with no other revenues received or costs incurred in the intervening period. Show that using the criterion (2-2) we would select the first project, while on using (2-4) with $i = 0.10$ we would select the second one. Why does it seem appropriate to select the second one?

10. Consider a project with an initial investment of one million dollars for which additional investments, revenues received, costs incurred, and taxes (all imagined to occur at the end of the year) are given in Table 2-5.
Determine the discounted profit for this project if $i = 0.15$.

11. For the project referred to in Problem 10 compute the discounted profit per dollar of initial investment, the discounted profit per dollar of discounted total investment, the undiscounted profit per dollar of initial investment, the undiscounted profit per dollar of total investment, and the payout period.

12. For the project referred to in Problem 10, compute approximately the rate of return.

TABLE 2-5

DATA FOR PROJECT

Year	Revenue received (dollars)	Costs incurred (dollars)	Taxes (dollars)	Investment needed (dollars)
1	200,000	100,000	0	0
2	400,000	200,000	5,000	100,000
3	800,000	200,000	10,000	0
4	1,200,000	300,000	30,000	200,000
5	1,000,000	300,000	30,000	200,000
6	800,000	100,000	20,000	0

13. For the project referred to in Problem 10, compute the discounted profit if it is imagined that the revenues and costs are received or incurred at the middle of the year rather than at the end of the year.

14. Consider a project which requires an initial investment of $50,000 and yields revenues of $30,000, $40,000, and $30,000 at the end of the first, second, and third years respectively. No other costs are involved. Determine the discounted profit for $i = 0$, 0.10, 0.20, 0.30, 0.50, 1, and 2, and plot the values of the discounted profits for each of these i values on a graph. Draw a smooth curve through the points and verify that it looks like that shown in Figure 2-3.

15. Consider two projects a and b both of which require an initial investment of $50,000. For project a we receive $100,000 at the end of five years with no other costs or revenues involved, while for project b we receive $60,000 at the end of one year with no other costs or revenues involved. Determine the rate of return for projects a and b and show that the rate of return is higher for b than for a. Show that, however, if $i = 0.11$ the discounted profit from a is greater than the discounted profit from b. Determine the discounted profit for projects a and b for several values of i and plot these results on a graph. Draw smooth curves through the points and determine that interval of i for which selecting the project with the largest rate of return yields the same project as selecting the one with the largest discounted profit.

16. Although by suitable definition of a project we can always arrange things so that a decision maker will be selecting precisely one from a number of projects, it is not always convenient to do this because the number of alternative projects can become enormous. Suppose then that we use a simpler definition of a project and that there are n such which a businessman is considering. Let the discounted profit from the jth one be P_q and the initial investment be I_q. Assume that for each project there is no investment required beyond the initial investment. The businessman can undertake one or more of these projects. However, he has only I dollars available for investment, that is, the sum of the investments in the projects cannot exceed this. He would like to select one or more projects in such a way that the total discounted profit is maximized, while the investments required do not exceed the available capital I. Give a mathematical formulation of this problem. (Hint: Introduce variables δ_q, where $\delta_q = 1$ if he undertakes project q and $\delta_q = 0$ if he does not. The resulting problem is referred to as an integer linear programming problem.

17. Show that when discounting is used, this automatically accounts for differences in initial investments, if they exist, among the various projects. One might feel that it is not reasonable to compare projects with different initial investments for the following reason. Suppose that we have a sum I to invest, and that we are considering two projects a and b. Imagine that a requires an initial investment of I, while b requires an initial investment of $I_0 < I$. It might then seem more reasonable to compare a with the combination of b and investing the remaining sum $I - I_0$. Show that this is precisely equivalent to simply comparing a and b, because the present worth of profits resulting from investing $I - I_0$ at the rate of interest i is 0 regardless of how long the period is for which we invest $I - I_0$. In other words, show that the discounted profit from investing any sum at the rate of interest used in the discounting is 0. Prove this only for the case where interest earned is reinvested. The result is true, however, regardless of whether this assumption is made.

18. From the result proved in Problem 17, conclude that if the i used in discounting really represents what the firm normally earns on investments, then on the average one would expect the discounted profits on projects undertaken not to differ greatly from 0. Therefore i can in reality be interpreted as an average rate of return on projects.

19. Illustrate the generality of the result referred to in Problem 17 by working out the following numerical example. Suppose that we invest \$10,000 at an interest rate of $i = 0.10$. At the end of each year for five years we take out the interest earned as profit, and then after five years we also get back what we invested. Show that the discounted profit from this project is 0 when $i = 0.10$ is used in the discounting. Show that the same result is obtained if the interest is allowed to accumulate and everything is removed after five years.

20. Are there any situations under which it might be desirable for a business to undertake a project having a negative discounted profit? Does a negative discounted profit imply that the undiscounted profit is negative?

21. A manufacturer has received a government contract that will last for precisely three years and will not be renewed. The contract is for the production of a certain type of helical gear, requiring a special type of machine which the contractor does not have. He has two choices, however. He can buy a new machine or he can modify a machine which he has but is no longer using. The new machine and the modified one will not be operationally equivalent. The relevant characteristics of the new machine and the modified machine are as follows. The installed cost of the new machine is \$100,000, while the cost of modifying the existing machine is \$90,000. Two men are needed to operate the new machine, while the modified machine needs only one. These operators earn \$3.50/hour including benefits. Upkeep and maintenance costs on the new machine are estimated to be \$1000, \$2000, and \$5000 in the first, second, and third years respectively, while the corresponding costs on the modified machine should be $5000, $5000, and $10,000. The new machine will have a salvage value of $8000 at the end of three years, while the modified machine will have zero salvage value. Neither machine will be used after the end of the contract. The number of units required by the contract is 1000 per month in the first year, 1500 per month in the second year and 2000 per month in the third year. It requires 0.09 hour to produce one unit on the new machine and 0.10 hour on the modified machine. Assume that 160 hours per month is available per shift on either machine, and if more than one shift is worked, men must be paid for a full shift even if they work only part of a shift. On the first shift, however, time is charged only for hours worked. The new machine is expected to turn out a fraction defective of 0.02, while the old machine should turn out a fraction defective of 0.05. Each defective unit must be scrapped and costs $2.00 in lost raw materials. The new machine can be rented out for as much as eight hours per week in the first year, ten hours per week in the second year, and thirteen hours per week in the third year. The same operators are used when the machine is rented. The rental rate is $10.00 per hour and any amount of time desired can be rented up to the amounts indicated. The modified machine cannot be rented. If the firm uses an interest rate of $i = 0.10$, should the new machine be purchased or should the existing machine be modified?

Section 2-5

1. Are there circumstances under which a decision maker might prefer a contract with one possible outcome being a rather large profit, even though the expected profit from the contract is less than that for another contract whose best outcome does not yield such a large profit? Describe any such circumstances.

2. What sort of rule seems reasonable to you to use to select among possible random experiments when the situation will never be repeated?

3. What factors other than monetary factors might influence a firm's decision as to where to build a plant?

4. What factors other than profit maximization might enter into the price a firm charges for a given product?

5. How can a firm justify producing a product on which it loses money?

Section 2-6

1. Consider a two stage lottery $\mathcal{L}$ in which there are only two single stage lotteries involved and three prizes e_1, e_2, and e_3. $\mathcal{L}$ is

$$\mathcal{L} = \{\tfrac{1}{4}[(\tfrac{1}{3}, e_1), (\tfrac{1}{3}, e_2), (\tfrac{1}{3}, e_3)], \tfrac{3}{4}[(\tfrac{1}{2}, e_1), (\tfrac{1}{4}, e_2), (\tfrac{1}{4}, e_3)]\}.$$

Construct a physical model of this lottery using pennies in a container rather than roulette wheels. Play this lottery 100 times and record on each play the prize obtained. Compute the relative frequency of each prize in 100 trials. Are these relative frequencies in fair agreement with the probabilities of the simple events determined using (2-14)?

2. Consider a two stage lottery $\mathcal{L}$ in which there are three single stage lotteries involved and only two prizes e_1 and e_2. $\mathcal{L}$ is

$$\mathcal{L} = \{\tfrac{1}{2}[(\tfrac{1}{3}, e_1), (\tfrac{2}{3}, e_2)], \tfrac{1}{4}[(\tfrac{1}{2}, e_1), (\tfrac{1}{2}, e_2)], \tfrac{1}{4}[(\tfrac{2}{3}, e_1), (\tfrac{1}{3}, e_2)]\}.$$

Construct a physical model of this lottery using pennies in a container rather than roulette wheels. Play this lottery 100 times and record on each play the prize obtained. Compute the relative frequency of each prize in 100 trials. Are these relative frequencies in fair agreement with the probabilities of the simple events determined using (2-14)?

3. Prove that the p_j in (2-14) sum to 1, as must be the case if they are to be the probabilities of the simple events.

4. Consider the two stage lottery $\mathcal{L} = \{0.2L_1,\ 0.5L_2,\ 0.3L_3\}$, where

$$L_1 = \{(0.1,\ e_1),\ (0.5,\ e_2),\ (0.2,\ e_3),\ (0.2,\ e_4)\}\,;$$
$$L_2 = \{(0.3,\ e_1),\ (0.2,\ e_2),\ (0.4,\ e_3),\ (0.1,\ e_4)\}\,;$$
$$L_3 = \{(0.2,\ e_1),\ (0.6,\ e_2),\ (0.1,\ e_3),\ (0.1,\ e_4)\}\,.$$

Determine the probability of each of the prizes.

5. Consider a three stage lottery which can be looked upon as a single stage lottery with two stage lotteries as prizes. Suppose that there are two stage lotteries $\mathcal{L}_1$ and $\mathcal{L}_2$ as prizes and let the probability of getting into $\mathcal{L}_1$ be r_1. Furthermore, let $\mathcal{L}_1$ and $\mathcal{L}_2$ be

$$\mathcal{L}_1 = \{q_{11}[(p_{11}^1,\ e_1),\ (p_{12}^1,\ e_2),\ (p_{13}^1,\ e_3)],\ q_{12}[(p_{21}^1,\ e_1),\ (p_{22}^1,\ e_2),\ (p_{23}^1,\ e_3)]\}\,;$$
$$\mathcal{L}_2 = \{q_{21}[(p_{11}^2,\ e_1),\ (p_{12}^2,\ e_2),\ (p_{13}^2,\ e_3)],\ q_{22}[(p_{21}^2,\ e_1),\ (p_{22}^2,\ e_2)(p_{23}^2,\ e_3)]\}\,.$$

Go through the same sort of procedure as used in the text to determine the probabilities of e_1, e_2, and e_3.

Sections 2-7 through 2-9

1. An individual tells us that he has the following preferences concerning the events e_1, e_2, e_3, e_4, and e_5;

$$e_5 > e_3,\quad e_2 > e_1,\quad e_2 > e_4,\quad e_4 > e_3,\quad e_1 > e_3.$$

Are these preferences consistent with axiom 1?

2. An individual tells us that he has the following preferences concerning the events e_1, e_2, e_3, e_4, and e_5;

$$e_2 \gtrsim e_4,\quad e_3 > e_1,\quad e_5 > e_4,\quad e_5 \gtrsim e_1,\quad e_3 \sim e_2,\quad e_5 \sim e_2.$$

Are these preferences consistent with axiom 1?

3. Can you suggest some events that it would be difficult to compare?

4. Given a set $E = \{e_1, \ldots, e_m\}$, how many pairwise comparisons of events must an individual make in order to arrange the events in order of preference? Actually determine this number for $m = 4$.

5. A decision maker tells us that he would prefer a single stage lottery to a two stage one even though the probabilities of the prizes are the same in each, since inasmuch as two chance mechanisms are involved in the two stage lottery, there is more uncertainty involved. Comment on this statement.

6. A decision maker tells us that he would prefer a single stage lottery to a two stage one even though the probabilities of the prizes are the same, because the single stage lottery is easier on his nerves, involving only one chance mechanism rather than two. Does this seem like a reasonable attitude, especially when thought of in terms of business problems rather than lotteries? Is this man what we call a rational decision maker?

7. Can you determine for what probability u you are indifferent between playing a lottery in which you receive \$100,000 with probability u and lose \$10,000 with probability $1 - u$, and a situation where you receive \$10,000 with certainty? What are the difficulties involved? How vague are you about the probability u?

8. Consider the lottery

$$L = \{(0.2, e_1), (0.4, e_2), (0.1, e_3), (0.17, e_4), (0.13, e_5)\}.$$

Suppose that

$$e_2 \sim \{(0.6, e_1), (0.4, e_5)\}; \quad e_3 \sim \{(0.4, e_1), (0.6, e_5)\}; \quad e_4 \sim \{(0.2, e_1), (0.8, e_5)\}.$$

Apply axioms 4 and 2 repeatedly to reduce L one step at a time to a lottery involving only e_1 and e_5, and having the property that the decision maker is indifferent between this lottery and L. At each step describe by means of a decision tree the two stage lottery obtained.

9. Consider the three single stage lotteries

$$L_1 = \{(0.1, e_1), (0.3, e_2), (0.2, e_3), (0.15, e_4), (0.25, e_5)\};$$
$$L_2 = \{(0.2, e_1), (0.2, e_2), (0.3, e_3), (0.2, e_4), (0.1, e_5)\};$$
$$L_3 = \{(0.3, e_1), (0.05, e_2), (0.35, e_3), (0.15, e_4), (0.15, e_5)\}.$$

Suppose that the decision maker gives us the following information about his preferences:

$$e_2 \sim \{(0.8, e_1), (0.2, e_5)\}; \quad e_3 \sim \{(0.7, e_1), (0.3, e_5)\}; \quad e_4 \sim \{(0.3, e_1), (0.7, e_5)\}.$$

Which of the three given lotteries does the decision maker prefer most?

10. We noted in the text that the utility of an event acts in a manner similar to a profit as a numerical evaluation of the event. State why the u_j in $L(e_j)$ really expresses this sort of measure even when interpreted as a probability.

11. Consider an event set $E = \{e_1, e_2, e_3, e_4, e_5\}$. Suppose that an individual expresses his feelings about the events as follows:

$$e_2 \sim \{(0.8, e_1), (0.2, e_5)\}; \quad e_3 \sim \{(0.6, e_1), (0.4, e_5)\}; \quad e_4 \sim \{(0.2, e_1), (0.8, e_5)\}.$$

Find that particular utility function for the individual, defined over E, which has $U_1 = 4$, $U_5 = -16$.

12. Re-solve Problem 9 using a utility function with $U_1 = 70$, $U_5 = -10$, and show that the same lottery is selected.

13. A businessman is trying to decide whether to undertake one of two contracts or neither one. He has simplified the situation somewhat and feels that it is sufficient to imagine that the contracts provide the alternatives shown in Table 2-6.

TABLE 2-6

SUMMARY OF CONTRACTS

Contract a		Contract b	
Discounted profit	Probability	Discounted profit	Probability
$100,000	0.2	$40,000	0.3
50,000	0.4	10,000	0.4
0	0.3	−10,000	0.3
−30,000	0.1		

His assessments of the probabilities are those given in the table.
He expresses his preferences with respect to the various events as follows:

$$50,000 \sim \{(0.8, 100,000), (0.2, -30,000)\};$$
$$40,000 \sim \{(0.7, 100,000), (0.3, -30,000)\};$$
$$10,000 \sim \{(0.5, 100,000), (0.5, -30,000)\};$$
$$0 \sim \{(0.3, 100,000), (0.7, -30,000)\};$$
$$-10,000 \sim \{(0.2, 100,000), (0.8, -30,000)\}.$$

Should the businessman undertake either one of the contracts? If so, which one? What would he do if he made decisions by maximizing his expected discounted profit?

14. A businessman is trying to decide which one, if any, of three contracts to undertake. Suppose that the contracts provide the alternatives shown in Table 2-7 with the probabilities indicated.

TABLE 2-7

SUMMARY OF CONTRACTS

Contract a		Contract b		Contract c	
Discounted profit	Probability	Discounted profit	Probability	Discounted profit	Probability
$100,000	0.2	$50,000	0.3	$40,000	0.4
0	0.5	10,000	0.2	10,000	0.1
−30,000	0.3	−10,000	0.5	0	0.2
				−10,000	0.3

Assume that the decision maker's preferences are those given in Problem 13. Which, if any one, of the contracts should he undertake? What one would he select if he chose the one with the greatest expected value of the discounted profit?

15. Suppose that $e_1 > e_2 > e_3 > e_4$ and $u_1 + u_4 = u_2 + u_3$. Consider the lotteries $L_1 = \{(0.5, e_1), (0.5, e_4)\}$ and $L_2 = \{(0.5, e_2), (0.5, e_3)\}$. Note that the expected utility is the same for both. Someone points out, however, that there is more "spread" in lottery 1 than in lottery 2, and therefore 2 should be preferred to 1. What is wrong with the argument?

16. Explain in some detail why we cannot conclude that if $(u_1 - u_2) > (u_3 - u_4)$, then the change in going from e_2 to e_1 is more preferred than the change in going from e_4 to e_3.

17. In evaluating a given set of alternatives we have assumed that the decision maker first evaluates the various events (the events not involving any elements of uncertainty), that is, he determines his utility function. Then he makes a subjective evaluation of what the probabilities are. Then we claim that his preferences are properly represented by his expected utility. Does it seem sound that one can always separate out the evaluation of a situation into an evaluation of the events and then the probabilities, or might these be so intertwined that they cannot be considered separately?

18. Our development of the utility concept has not provided a way to compute the utility of a composite event such as $e_2 \cap e_3$, given a knowledge of the utilities of e_2 and e_3. Under what conditions might the following hold?

$$u(e_2 \cap e_3) = u(e_2) + u(e_3)$$

19. The utility function for a decision maker is defined with respect to a given set of events E. Consider the set $E = \{e_1, \ldots, e_m\}$, where the events are numbered so that e_1 is the most preferred event and e_m is the least preferred one. Consider now an event $e \notin E$ such that $e_1 \succ e \succ e_m$. Let $E_1 = \{e_1, \ldots, e_m, e\}$. Can the utility of every event in E_1, except e, be determined if the decision maker's utility function with respect to E is known?

20. Consider two event sets $E_1 = \{e_1, \ldots, e_m\}$ and $E_2 = \{f_1, \ldots, f_k\}$. Suppose that the events are numbered in order of preference and that $e_1 \succ f_1 \succ f_k \succ e_m$. Assume that the decision maker's utility functions with respect to E_1 and E_2 are both known. Assume also that

$$f_1 \sim \{(u^*, e_1), (1 - u^*, e_m)\}; \quad f_k \sim \{(\bar{u}, e_1), (1 - \bar{u}, e_m)\}.$$

Show that the decision maker's utility function defined with respect to $E = E_1 \cup E_2$ can be determined from the above information. Determine the utility of each event in E in terms of the known utilities.

21. Given two event sets E_1 and E_2 and a decision maker's utility functions defined with respect to these two sets. What must be known in addition to determine the decision maker's utility function with respect to $E_1 \cup E_2$?

22. A businessman is considering which of two contracts he should undertake. Both contracts yield precisely the same expected profit. He decides to select the contract which minimizes the variance of the profit. Is this procedure consistent with maximization of expected utility? If your answer is yes, what do you think the businessman's utility function is? Is there something very peculiar about it?

Section 2-10

1. Consider a large international petroleum company. For what sorts of decisions would it seem reasonable to maximize expected profits? How large might the sums of money involved need to become before this would not be a suitable criterion? How might one determine this? In what sort of decisions might it not be safe to proceed by maximizing expected profits?

2. Suppose an individual gives us the following information about his feelings concerning changes in his stock of money.

$$\$13,000 \sim \{(0.95, 15,000), (0.05, -15,000)\};$$
$$10,000 \sim \{(0.90, 15,000), (0.10, -15,000)\};$$
$$5000 \sim \{(0.75, 15,000), (0.25, -15,000)\};$$
$$0 \sim \{(0.55, 15,000), (0.45, -15,000)\};$$
$$-5000 \sim \{(0.22, 15,000), (0.78, -15,000)\};$$
$$-10,000 \sim \{(0.08, 15,000), (0.92, -15,000)\}.$$

Assuming that the curve giving his utility of changes in money is smooth, draw this curve on a sheet of graph paper. Suppose this individual is offered the opportunity to play a game in which he wins \$2000 with probability $\frac{1}{3}$ and loses \$1000 with probability $\frac{2}{3}$. Should he play this game? Suppose he is offered the opportunity to play a game in which he wins \$10,000 with probability 0.6 and loses \$15,000 with probability 0.4. Should he play this game?

3. Prove that if an individual's utility is related to changes in money by a linear equation, then such an individual is always indifferent between having his stock of money changed by s with certainty and a lottery which has an expected monetary winnings of s. Also prove that such an individual will always be indifferent to whether he plays a fair game.

4. What conclusions could you draw if a decision maker, when asked to rank in order of preference a certain set of events, proceeded to do this by computing each associated discounted profit and then ranked the events in the same order as the discounted profits?

5. In Section 1-6 we indicated that there are many types of very rare events which are not physically impossible, but which we frequently exclude from the event set. Can you now provide a reason why it is legitimate to do this, and also give the conditions under which it is not legitimate to exclude some such event?

6. Is it inconsistent for a rational decision maker to use any of the rules introduced in Section 2-3 for selecting a project? What would have to be done to demonstrate that any particular one of these rules was not suitable for use by a given rational decision maker?

CHAPTER 3

SINGLE STAGE AND SEQUENTIAL DECISION PROBLEMS AND THEIR SOLUTION

So many gods, so many creeds,
So many paths that wind and wind, . . .

Ella Wheeler Wilcox, *The World's Need*

3-1 SINGLE STAGE DECISION PROBLEMS

Having developed a mathematical model for treating uncertainty and a mathematical model of a decision maker, we are now ready to turn to a study of decision making under uncertainty and to the task of developing mathematical models which will be of assistance in actually making decisions in the real world. The developments of the last chapter have brought us quite a way in this direction, and we have already seen how to solve certain simple types of decision problems. Before turning to an extension of what we developed in the last chapter, we would like to give a general discussion of decision problems and make the important distinction between what we shall call single stage decision problems and what we shall call multistage and sequential decision problems.

In formulating decision problems we shall find it convenient to proceed in much the same way as we did in Sections 2-2 and 2-3 in discussing deterministic problems, and imagine that each time that a decision maker makes a decision he wishes to select precisely one of a finite number of alternatives. Things will be defined in such a way that *only one* of the alternatives will be selected. It is typical to refer to these alternatives as possible *actions*; the decision maker will then be selecting one action to take. The notion of an action will be used here in a somewhat more general way than it normally is in everyday speech. By the term action we may be referring to something very complicated involving a number of what we usually think of as actions, or it might be something as simple as deciding to carry one's umbrella on a given day. A relatively complicated action would be the building of five new plants of given sizes, in given locations, at given times, the introduction of two new products in a foreign market, and the introduction of a profit sharing plan for employees. Note that carrying out an action may require an extended period of time. It is sometimes necessary to use relatively complicated actions in order that the decision maker will be selecting precisely one and not several actions simultaneously. The situation here is similar to that encountered in defining a project in the previous chapter. Our discussion of decision problems under uncertainty will be somewhat more general than the discussion given for the deterministic case. The actions which the decision maker is considering need not be interpreted as projects. They can be anything at all. An important special case, of course, is that where the different actions refer to different projects which may be undertaken.

What we wish to do is develop a mathematical model or models which will assist a decision maker in selecting the action he should take at any point in time when a decision is necessary. The task of selecting the appropriate action can be an extremely complicated one in general. Let us begin then by restricting our attention to a special class of decision problems which we shall refer to as *single stage* decision problems. As a class, these are the simplest of all decision problems to analyze. We shall now try to explain precisely what is meant by a single stage decision problem. Generally speaking, a single stage decision problem is one that can be looked at as a problem in which the decision maker makes precisely one decision. There then follows a random experiment, the outcome of which determines the "prize" to be received by the decision maker. Alternatively, we can say that a single stage decision problem is one in which precisely two decisions are made. First the decision maker selects an action, and then nature selects or reveals one of a number of its possible *states of nature*. The choice of the state of nature made by nature determines the outcome of the action selected by the decision maker. In other words, we can think of it as determining the prize that the decision maker gets. The prize will depend both on what action the decision maker selects and on the decision made by nature. At the time that the decision maker selects the action to take, he does not know what nature will do. However, we shall in general assume that he can estimate the probability that nature will select any particular one of the possible states of nature.

What are these states of nature referred to above? They are simply the various real world events which determine the outcome of any action selected. The different states of nature correspond to the different possible sets of real world events which can occur, and which have the property that at the time the decision maker makes the selection of an action, he does not know which set of real world events will actually transpire. Let us illustrate with an example. Suppose that before leaving home in the morning an individual is trying to decide whether to carry his umbrella. The states of nature will here describe the possible types of weather that can occur, if weather is the only thing that influences his decision as to whether or not to carry the umbrella. If other factors enter in, then they too should be considered in specifying the states of nature. However, even when we restrict the states of nature to describing the behavior of the weather, we note immediately that we can think of an arbitrarily large number of different weather patterns which might take place during the day, since we could describe the precise temperature at each minute; precisely when it rains if it does, and how much; precisely when the sun is shining; whether the sky is cloudy when the sun is shining, etc. It becomes clear at once that it is hopeless to try to describe the possible states of nature in great detail. It is also important to note that, fortunately, it is unnecessary to do this. All the individual is trying to do is decide whether or not to carry his umbrella. Therefore, all that we need to do is represent enough about the various weather possibilities to let him make a sound decision. For example, it would probably be adequate to consider that there are four possible states of nature. These are (1) the sun shines all day long; (2) the sun shines when the individual is out, but it rains at some other times; (3) it rains when he is out, but the sun shines part of the time; and (4) it rains all day. If the gentleman carries his umbrella and the state of nature turns out to be (1) he will feel silly, but if it turns out to be (4) he will be glad that he carried it. On the other hand, if he does not carry it, he will be very pleased if the state of nature turns out to be (1) and will feel wretched if it turns out to be (4). Thus we see that the prize obtained, i.e., the man's feelings in this case, depends not only on the state of nature, but also on the action selected.

Let us assume that there are m possible states of nature. We shall represent these by $e_1, \ldots, e_m$ so that the jth state of nature will be denoted by e_j. Then if the decision maker selects the action a_i and nature selects e_j, this pair of decisions determines the prize the decision maker will receive, which we shall denote by Q_{ij}. For a given i, there are m possible prizes, one for each e_j. We shall think of the states of nature having been defined so that they are mutually exclusive and collectively exhaustive. Then the e_j can be imagined to be the simple events for a random experiment. We can suppose that after the decision maker selects an action, say a_i, then a random experiment is performed to determine what the state of nature will be. Let p_{ij} be the probability of e_j when the decision maker chooses a_i. In general, the probabilities of the state of nature may depend on the action the decision maker selects. This random experiment is the best characterization the decision maker can obtain of what nature will do.   We have noted that the specification of an a_i and e_j determines a prize Q_{ij}.   Consider now the set of all prizes.   Let us suppose that the decision maker arranges these in order of preference and then proceeds to determine his utility function defined over them, using the procedure discussed in the previous chapter.   We shall always be assuming the decision maker is a rational decision maker, and hence this utility function does exist.   Denote by u_{ij} the utility of the prize Q_{ij} when the utility of the best event is 1 and of the worst event is 0.   We can now completely characterize the general single stage decision problem by a decision tree such as that shown in Figure 3-1.   The decision maker has the choice of selecting one

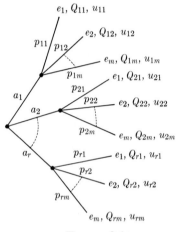

FIGURE 3-1

of r actions.   Once an action is selected, nature selects one of m states of nature, the set of these states being the same regardless of what action is selected.   This then leads to a unique prize and a unique utility associated with that prize.   It should be observed that there is no restriction in assuming that the states of nature are the same regardless of what action is taken.   If a particular action a_i rules out one state of nature, say e_u, then we simply set $p_{iu} = 0$, and this is equivalent in the mathematical model to omitting e_u as one of the simple events.   That it may sometimes be necessary to do this, can easily be seen by considering the example worked out in Section 2-9.   From the description of the problem, the simplest characterization of the states of nature is the prizes themselves.   However, both contracts do not involve the same prizes.   There is no reason to believe that there is any more fundamental set of events, which will be common to both contracts, that could be used as the states of nature.   Thus in this case the states of nature which can be encountered depend on the particular action that is selected.

We can now observe that a single stage decision problem is one in which a decision maker is faced with the problem of selecting one of r different single stage lotteries to play. If he selects action a_i, he will play lottery L_i, where

$$L_i = \{(p_{i1}, Q_{i1}), \ldots, (p_{im}, Q_{im})\}. \tag{3-1}$$

Given this observation, we now know how to solve a single stage decision problem. The theory of the previous chapter tells us that the action to select is the one which maximizes the decision maker's expected utility, that is, which yields the largest value of

$$\sum_{j=1}^{m} u_{ij} p_{ij}.$$

The utility function used need not be the one having the utility of the best event 1 and of the worst event 0; we can use any one of the other utility functions described in Chapter 2 of the form $U = au + b$, $a > 0$. Thus if U_{ij} is the utility of Q_{ij} in terms of any of these functions, the decision maker should select the action which maximizes

$$\sum_{j=1}^{m} U_{ij} p_{ij}.$$

From the description thus far given of a single stage decision problem, it may be difficult for the reader to really grasp what distinguishes single stage decision problems from those which are not single stage problems. To be able to make the distinction, it is necessary to understand the essential differences between single stage problems and what we shall call multistage problems. However, before turning to a discussion of multistage decision problems, it is desirable to clarify a few more points about single stage problems. In the previous chapter we found it convenient to take as the simple events the prizes in the lotteries and to assume that the same set of prizes was associated with each lottery. We could have proceeded in this way here. However, it is generally more convenient in dealing with decision problems not to use the prizes as the simple events in the relevant random experiments, but instead to use another set of events which we have referred to as the states of nature. We have assumed that the same set of states of nature are the simple events in the random experiment, regardless of what action the decision maker takes. As we have already noted, there is no real restriction implied in doing this. With this selection of the simple events, the set of prizes need not be the same for each possible action which the decision maker selects. Of course, if it is convenient, we can, as has already been indicated, take the prizes themselves as describing the states of nature, and in this case the set of prizes will be the same for each of the random experiments. It is important to note that the state of nature ultimately observed is not necessarily something that takes place at a single point in time.   The state of nature may be progressively revealed over a period of many years.   Similarly, the prizes may be revealed over a period of years.   This is quite allowable within the concept of a single stage decision problem, for regardless of how long it takes to get all of any given prize, the utilities serve to indicate the decision maker's feelings about these prizes.

3-2   MULTISTAGE AND SEQUENTIAL DECISION PROBLEMS

We noted when discussing deterministic projects that often more than a single decision must be made before a project is terminated, and that these decisions are made at different points in time.   We noted, however, that for deterministic situations, we can always make all decisions at the time when the initial decision is made.   It is here that we encounter a crucial distinction between deterministic problems and problems where uncertainty plays an important role.   For the latter types of problems, it is in general definitely not true that all decisions can be made at the same time as the initial decision.   Decisions which in time are to be made after an initial decision must in general be delayed as long as possible, when uncertainty is important, if the best possible decision is to be made.   Let us attempt to make clear what we are driving at through the use of a simple but realistic example.

A small metal working plant which specializes in finishing castings made of unusual alloys has received a government contract for 1000 special finished castings made from a particular alloy that the company has worked with before.   The specifications on the parts are very rigid in that the castings both before and after finishing must be x-rayed and subjected to other tests to verify that there are no imperfections or undesirable stress patterns in the metal.   Furthermore the tolerances on the finishing work are very high.   The manufacturing process can be viewed as a two stage process.   First the castings are made in the foundry, and then they are finished in the machine shop.   The company can do its own casting work, or, if desired, it can have the castings done by another firm which will guarantee that each casting purchased meets the government specifications.   In general, however, the cost of buying the castings on the outside is much higher than if they are produced in the contractor's own foundry.

Castings must be made in a batch.   The procedure is that one makes up a batch of the alloy and a suitable number of sand molds and then pours the molten metal into the molds and allows it to solidify under controlled conditions.   Unfortunately, one can never be sure how many of the castings will turn out to be good enough to meet the government specifications.   The casting operation is a very delicate one, and if the molten metal is not at precisely the right temperature, or if it is not poured into the mold at just the proper rate, or if the cooling rate is not exactly what it should be, a defective casting will be produced. Thus the casting operation can be viewed as a random experiment, and the number of good castings produced will be a random variable. With this type of alloy, the fraction of the castings which are defective can be as high as 50 percent.

The finishing operation is also rather tricky, and again there is no guarantee that a good casting going to the machine shop will end up as a finished product that meets specifications. Quite a few good castings may end up as defectives because the finishing process was not completed successfully. If u good castings are sent to the machine shop, the finishing process can also be looked upon as a random experiment and the number of finished castings which meet specifications can be looked upon as a random variable.

Now with this background on the production process, let us study the decisions which the general manager of the firm must make. Because of the high cost of buying castings on the outside, the firm has a policy that it will always try initially to make its own castings. If this initial effort does not yield a sufficient number of good castings, then the general manager has the option to buy additional castings on the outside if he desires to do so. He cannot, however, decide at the outset to buy all castings on the outside. We shall not attempt to decide whether this company policy is sound; we shall simply take it as a given constraint on the decision maker's actions. What decisions must the manager make? First he must decide on the number of castings to be made in the initial batch. We can imagine then that he must select one of a number of possible actions, each action corresponding to a possible number of castings to make in the first batch. Presumably, he would never schedule less than 1000 castings, since it is desired to produce this many finished units, but he might schedule any number greater than this, up to some upper limit. Once it is decided how many units to cast, a random experiment is performed for which the simple events are the number of good castings produced. What we have described thus far has the characteristics of a single stage decision problem, if we think of the states of nature as being the number of good units produced. However, in the present situation, the manager's problems are not over once the casting operation is carried out.

Suppose that r units turn out to be good castings. The manager must now decide whether the number r is sufficiently large that he does not need any more. If he does need more there arises the question of how many more, and whether these should be procured on the outside or whether he should try to procure them by having another batch cast in the foundry. To be specific, let us place the following restrictions on the nature of the situation. Let us suppose that the due date of the contract is such that the decision about getting more castings cannot be delayed beyond the time when the first batch is cast. In particular, this means that the manager does not have the option to put the r good pieces through the finishing operations and see how many meet specifications, and then decide how many more castings if any are needed. When the first batch of castings is finished, the manager must decide whether to buy some castings on the outside or make another batch (or both), and what the quantities of each should be. Once this decision is made, the outcome of the contract is determined. He will have no later opportunity to make additional corrections. If he makes the right decisions, the company will make a good profit. If he makes poor decisions, the company may make a poor profit, or even lose money, and it may even end up with an insufficient number of finished pieces to fulfill the contract, and thus incur a penalty and the wrath of the government agency.

How shall we characterize the alternative actions available to the manager in making this second decision? He can simply use the number of good castings that he has and not attempt to get any more; he can order some on the outside; he can schedule another batch to be made inside; or he can both get some on the outside and schedule another batch to be made in the foundry. The latter alternative may not seem reasonable, but there is no need to exclude it at the outset. We might now note that all of the above can be conveniently represented simultaneously if we think of the decision as being one in which a pair of numbers v and w are selected, v being the number of units scheduled to be cast in the foundry and w the number of castings purchased on the outside. If $v = w = 0$, then no attempt is made to get additional castings; if $v = 0$, then w units will be purchased on the outside and nothing will be produced in the foundry; if $w = 0$, then nothing is purchased on the outside and v units will be cast in the foundry. Thus each pair of numbers (v, w) describes a different action. Note that when the decision maker specifies a $w > 0$, then by what we assumed above, the outside supplier will supply him with w good castings. We shall not concern ourselves with the outside supplier's problems in order to do this. We shall assume, however, that if w units are ordered, w good units will be supplied. On the other hand, if v units are cast in the foundry, it will normally be true that less than v of the castings will turn out to be good. In any event, after selecting a pair (v, w), we can then imagine that another random experiment is performed which determines the number of good finished pieces finally obtained. At this point the profitability of the contract to the firm is finally determined. The profitability will depend on the two decisions made and on the outcome of each of the random experiments.

The problem we have just described in some detail is an example of what we shall refer to as a two stage decision problem. Let us try to see very clearly the difference between this and a single stage problem. A two stage decision problem has the characteristic that two decisions must be made by the decision maker, and in addition, a random experiment is performed after the first decision is made and before the second decision whose outcome has an important influence on what the second decision should be. The crucial thing here is that the second decision must be delayed until after the first random experiment is performed, if one wants to make the best possible decision. The outcome of the random experiment provides some information to the decision maker which he will use in making the second decision. Thus, in the example just given, it would be ridiculous for the manager to attempt to decide what to do after the first casting operation at the same time that he decided how many castings to make initially. The number of good castings that he gets in this first batch is the thing which determines what he will do when making the second decision. Note how different the situation is here from the deterministic case where all decisions could be made at the beginning of a project. The introduction of uncertainty generally has the effect of forcing a decision maker to delay each decision as long as possible, so that as much information as possible is gained about any random events which may be observed and which may influence his decision.

We can conveniently represent a two stage decision problem graphically through the use of a decision tree, just as we did a single stage problem. The representation is more cumbersome in this case, however. In Figure 3-2 we have illustrated how this can be done in a special case where there are three possible initial actions. There are either two or three possible outcomes for the first random experiment, depending on what initial action is taken. Then the decision maker selects a second action. As we have drawn the tree, the second decision always involves the selection of one of two alternatives. Of course the alternatives do not have to be the same at every node. After the second decision is made, another random experiment is performed, and then the problem is imagined to be terminated. On the tree we have labeled the nodes with a D or N, D meaning that the decision maker makes the decision at that node and N indicating that nature makes the decision. The possible actions at the first decision are labeled a_1, a_2, and a_3. The actions for the second decision are labeled b_i in the order they appear on the tree. This notation does not imply that each b_i is necessarily a different action. However, it is assumed that each of the two b_i branches emanating from a given node represents a different action. No details about the experiments are indicated; we have simply numbered the possible outcomes. After the second random experiment

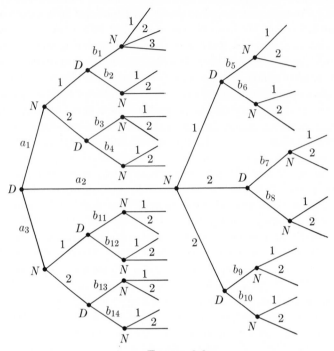

FIGURE 3-2

is performed, the problem is imagined to be terminated. This is indicated on the decision tree by having the branches associated with the second random experiment terminate without leading to more nodes. These branches are called *terminal branches*.

We can now generalize the notion of a two stage decision problem to what we shall call an *n*-stage or multistage decision problem. An *n*-stage decision problem is one in which the decision maker must make *n* decisions, and between each decision a random experiment is performed. Whatever information is available to the decision maker about the outcomes of some or all of the experiments performed prior to making a given decision, will be important in making the decision. Again, a decision tree can be used to represent an *n*-stage decision problem; however, even the simplest case gets very complicated and requires a very large sheet of paper to illustrate it with clarity.

In some decision problems the total number of decisions required will depend on the actions taken and the outcomes of the random experiments; that is, more decisions may be required for certain combinations of actions selected and outcomes of the experiments than for others. We shall refer to such problems as sequential decision problems. An n-stage problem implies that there are always n decisions to be made, while in a sequential decision problem, the number of decisions may not be fixed in advance but may depend on what happens. We shall use the term sequential decision problem in a general way to refer to any decision problem involving two or more decisions, and hence n-stage problems can be referred to also as sequential decision problems.

3-3* THE CONCEPT OF DECISION RULES AND STRATEGIES

In the previous section we did not develop any procedure for solving sequential decision problems. In this section and the next, we shall show how *in principle* any sequential decision problem involving a finite number of decisions can be solved in much the same way as a single stage problem. The "in principle" used in the above sentence is a very important one. The reason for this is that while the procedure to be described can be used to solve in principle any sequential decision problem, it may be of little value in actually trying to solve numerically some given problem. The computational problems, as we shall see, can become overwhelming very quickly. In general, sequential decision problems are very difficult to solve, and it is by no means true that numerical procedures exist currently for solving many of the problems of this type that we would like to solve. Even single stage problems can present tremendous computational problems in some cases. This will become clear later also. The difficulties in solving sequential decision problems are significantly greater than for single stage problems. The reader should not become too disheartened at this point, however. There are a considerable number of important sequential decision problems which can be solved. The above statements were intended merely to set the matter in perspective and to avoid giving the impression at the outset that it is relatively easy to solve sequential decision problems.

Let us begin by considering an n-stage decision problem. We would like to introduce the notion of a *decision rule*. Suppose that the decision maker is ready to make the kth decision, $k \geq 2$. What information does he have available to aid him in making this decision? First of all, he knows what decisions he made at stages $1, \ldots, k - 1$. Furthermore, $k - 1$ random experiments have been performed, and he has obtained some information from the outcomes of these experiments. This is all the information

---

* The reader can without complication defer the reading of Sections 3-3 and 3-4, dealing with the solution of sequential decision problems, until the material is made use of in Chapter 8.

he has, and this is what he must use in making his decision.   Denote by $d_1, \ldots, d_{k-1}$ the actions taken on the first $k-1$ decisions, respectively, and by $\alpha_1, \ldots, \alpha_{k-1}$ the information that he has obtained about each random experiment which has been performed.   It is important to note that the decision maker may not know in detail what the outcome of each experiment was; the symbols α_i denote only the information he has available. We can represent all his available information by the set of symbols $(d_1, \alpha_1, d_2, \alpha_2, \ldots, d_{k-1}, \alpha_{k-1})$.   We shall call this an *information vector* for the kth stage.   Now at the previous stages, the decision maker could have selected various actions, and the random experiments could have yielded a variety of outcomes.   Consider then the set D_k of all possible information vectors which are generated by considering all possible allowable combinations of actions and outcomes of the experiments at the first $k-1$ stages. For every possible action which the decision maker could have taken at the first $k-1$ stages and for every possible outcome of the $k-1$ random experiments, there will be generated an information vector for the kth stage.   In other words, there is associated with each node of the decision tree where the kth decision may be made, a unique information vector. D_k is the set of all such vectors.   Let us illustrate the set D_k for the second stage of the two stage problem illustrated in Figure 3-2.   The information vector in this case will be of the form (d_1, α_1) summarizing the decision made at the first stage and the information obtained from the first random experiment.   Let us now indicate the information yielded by the experiment simply by writing the number of the outcome.   If action a_1 is selected the random experiment can yield either of outcomes 1 or 2.   Thus $(a_1, 1)$, $(a_1, 2)$ are the two possible information vectors which correspond to selecting a_1 at the first stage.   If action a_2 is selected at the first stage, the random experiment can yield three different outcomes, and there are three information vectors $(a_2, 1)$, $(a_2, 2)$, $(a_2, 3)$ possible.   If action a_3 is chosen at the first stage, there are two more information vectors generated, $(a_3, 1)$, $(a_3, 2)$.   The set D_2 of all possible information vectors for the second stage is then the set of seven vectors

$$D_2 = \{(a_1, 1), (a_1, 2), (a_2, 1), (a_2, 2), (a_2, 3), (a_3, 1)\ (a_3, 2)\}. \quad (3\text{-}2)$$

Note that in Figure 3-2 there are seven nodes where the second decision can be made.   There is one information vector for each such node.   Note also that regardless of what action is taken at the first stage or what the outcome of the first random experiment is, there is an information vector which the decision maker will be using in making a decision at the second stage which summarizes these.

We have noted that there will be an information vector associated with each node in the decision tree where the decision k can be made.   However, there need not be a *different* information vector associated with every such node. Quite possibly two or more nodes will have the same information vector. If a set of nodes T all have the same information vector associated with them, then the decision maker does not know at which of the nodes in T he is at the time the decision is made, since all he knows is the information vector. Situations of this sort arise when the decision maker does not find out enough about the outcome of some experiment to know what branch of the tree he passed along when the experiment was performed. We shall see in more detail in later chapters how such situations can arise. It is often convenient, if one is making explicit use of a decision tree, to label in some manner the sets of nodes having the characteristic that the decision maker does not know at which of the nodes he is.

We might note in general that in $(d_1, \alpha_1, \ldots, d_{k-1}, \alpha_{k-1})$ the possible sets of symbols α_1 will depend on what the action d_1 happened to be, the possible actions d_2 will depend on d_1 and α_1, the possible symbols α_2 will depend on d_1, α_1, and d_2, etc. Thus to obtain the set D_k, we must follow from the initial node in the decision tree along every possible path which leads to a node where the kth decision could be made. Then for any particular information vector in D_k, there is a set of possible actions which the decision maker can select. Let us call these the *allowable actions* for this particular information vector. Suppose that using any rule whatever we associate with each information vector in D_k an allowable action for this vector. This rule defines a function on D_k whose range is a set of allowable actions. This function is called a *decision rule for the kth stage.* A decision rule can then be thought of as a rule which tells the decision maker what action to take for whatever information vector he may be presented with. Stated in still a different way, for each node of the decision tree where the decision maker may be making the kth decision, a decision rule tells the decision maker which of the possible actions associated with that node he should undertake. We can give a formal definition as follows:

DECISION RULE FOR THE kTH STAGE. *Let D_k be the set of information vectors for the kth stage, and consider any function which associates with each information vector in D_k an allowable action. This function is called a decision rule for the kth stage of the decision problem.*

Let us note that in general there will be a very large number of different decision rules for the kth stage. Some may be very poor in that they generally suggest a poor action for the decision maker to take regardless of the node at which he happens to be located. There will be (at least) one best decision rule, however, in the sense that it will be the one that the decision maker should use in making the kth decision. Let us illustrate one of the possible decision rules for the second stage for the problem

illustrated in Figure 3-2. The set D_2 is given by (3-2). We shall illustrate
the function by listing in Table 3-1 the image of each element in D_2, that
is, the action to be associated with each element in D_2. The reader should
check that each action is allowable. How many decision rules are there

TABLE 3-1

ONE DECISION RULE FOR THE SECOND STAGE OF FIGURE 3-2

Element of D_2	Action to be taken
$(a_1, 1)$	b_1
$(a_1, 2)$	b_3
$(a_2, 1)$	b_5
$(a_2, 2)$	b_7
$(a_2, 3)$	b_9
$(a_3, 1)$	b_{11}
$(a_3, 2)$	b_{13}

for the second stage for the example under consideration? It is easy to
determine the number in this case since at each of the seven nodes where
the second decision can be made there are only two actions possible. Thus
there are two actions which can be associated with $(a_1, 1)$. Given any
assignment of an action to $(a_1, 1)$, there are two possible actions that can be
assigned to $(a_1, 2)$, or $2(2) = 4$ combinations of assigning actions to $(a_1, 1)$
and $(a_1, 2)$. Thus in general there are $2^7 = 128$ ways of assigning actions
to the elements of D_2, that is, there are 128 different decision rules for the
second stage of this simple example.

We have discussed above the concept of a decision rule for stage k,
$k \geq 2$, of a decision problem. We can also introduce the notion of a decision rule for the first stage. In this case no information has been generated
by the performance of random experiments or by previous decisions.
Thus the decision rule reduces to saying simply select a particular action.
If there are r different actions available at the first stage, there are r different decision rules for the first stage, the first of these saying take action
a_1, and the sth saying take action a_s. Thus the decision rule for the first
stage is completely specified by writing down the symbol for the action
which that particular rule says to take.

Having introduced the notion of a decision rule for each stage, we shall
now consider a more general concept referred to as a *strategy*. Consider
an n-stage decision problem, and suppose that we have selected a decision
rule for each stage. This set of rules then completely specifies what the
decision maker will do for every possible outcome of each of the random
experiments involved. Such a collection of decision rules is referred to as
a strategy for making decisions in the given situation. More formally:

STRATEGY FOR AN n-STAGE DECISION PROBLEM. *A strategy for a given n-stage decision problem is a set of decision rules, one for each stage in the problem.*

Let us denote symbolically a decision rule for the kth stage of an n-stage problem by R_k. Then a strategy, which we shall symbolize by S, is completely characterized by the specification of a set of decision rules, one for each stage. This can be indicated by writing

$$S = \{R_1, R_2, \ldots, R_n\}. \tag{3-3}$$

We might note that the strategy S in (3-3) can be simplified somewhat. Suppose that R_1 says take action a_i. The only information vectors which can be encountered at stage 2 are then of the form (a_i, α_1). Only the action a_i appears in the first position. Let $\hat{D}_2$ be the subset of D_2 which contains elements of the form (a_i, α_1). Also consider the function which associates with each element in $\hat{D}_2$ the action associated with it by the decision rule R_2. We shall call this the *conditional decision rule* for the second stage, and we shall denote it by $\hat{R}_2$. $\hat{R}_2$ is that part of R_2 which is relevant when R_1 is the rule used for the first stage. For example, if for the problem of Figure 3-2, R_1 is a_1, then $\hat{D}_2 = \{(a_1, 1), (a_1, 2)\}$, that is, if the decision maker takes action a_1 at the first stage, at the second stage he will be confronted only with information vectors for which $d_1 = a_1$. Thus if R_2 is the decision rule given in Table 3-1, $\hat{R}_2$ is the rule which says if the information vector is $(a_1, 1)$ take action b_1, and if it is $(a_1, 2)$ take action b_3. This process can now be continued. Having specified that $d_1 = a_i$ and having derived $\hat{R}_2$ with domain $\hat{D}_2$, consider now R_3. Let $\hat{D}_3$ be that subset of D_3 for which $d_1 = a_i$ and (d_1, α_1) is an element of $\hat{D}_2$. Take $\hat{R}_3$ to be the rule which associates with each element of $\hat{D}_3$ the same action as does R_3. We call $\hat{R}_3$ the conditional decision rule for the third stage. It is that part of R_3 which is relevant, given the selection of the rules R_1 and $\hat{R}_2$. This process can be continued and partial decision rules obtained for each stage. Then S can be represented as

$$S = \{R_1, \hat{R}_2, \ldots, \hat{R}_n\}. \tag{3-4}$$

The only difference between (3-3) and (3-4) is that (3-3) contains in the decision rules $R_2, \ldots, R_n$ information that is irrelevant given the rules selected at the previous stages, whereas all of the information contained in (3-4) is needed.

There will in general be a very large number of different strategies for any given n-stage problem. We can easily determine the number of different strategies for the problem illustrated by Figure 3-2. We have given these in Table 3-2 by giving R_1 and $\hat{R}_2$. In $\hat{R}_2$, to represent the fact that the image of an information vector such as $(a_1, 1)$ is b_1, we use the notation

TABLE 3-2

DIFFERENT STRATEGIES FOR PROBLEM OF FIGURE 3-2

R_1	$\hat{R}_2$
a_1	$(a_1, 1) \to b_1$, $(a_1, 2) \to b_3$
a_1	$(a_1, 1) \to b_2$, $(a_1, 2) \to b_3$
a_1	$(a_1, 1) \to b_1$, $(a_1, 2) \to b_4$
a_1	$(a_1, 1) \to b_2$, $(a_1, 2) \to b_4$
a_2	$(a_2, 1) \to b_5$, $(a_2, 2) \to b_7$, $(a_2, 3) \to b_9$
a_2	$(a_2, 1) \to b_6$, $(a_2, 2) \to b_7$, $(a_2, 3) \to b_9$
a_2	$(a_2, 1) \to b_5$, $(a_2, 2) \to b_8$, $(a_2, 3) \to b_9$
a_2	$(a_2, 1) \to b_6$, $(a_2, 2) \to b_8$, $(a_2, 3) \to b_9$
a_2	$(a_2, 1) \to b_5$, $(a_2, 2) \to b_7$, $(a_2, 3) \to b_{10}$
a_2	$(a_2, 1) \to b_6$, $(a_2, 2) \to b_7$, $(a_2, 3) \to b_{10}$
a_2	$(a_2, 1) \to b_5$, $(a_2, 2) \to b_8$, $(a_2, 3) \to b_{10}$
a_2	$(a_2, 1) \to b_6$, $(a_2, 2) \to b_8$, $(a_2, 3) \to b_{10}$
a_3	$(a_3, 1) \to b_{11}$, $(a_3, 2) \to b_{13}$
a_3	$(a_3, 1) \to b_{12}$, $(a_3, 2) \to b_{13}$
a_3	$(a_3, 1) \to b_{11}$, $(a_3, 2) \to b_{14}$
a_3	$(a_3, 1) \to b_{12}$, $(a_3, 2) \to b_{14}$

$(a_1, 1) \to b_1$. There are in total sixteen different strategies which the decision maker could use, encompassing all the possible ways he could make the pair of decisions. We noted previously, though, that there are 128 different decision rules R_2, and there are three decision rules R_1. If we think of a strategy as $S = \{R_1, R_2\}$, we might reason that for any R_1 there are 128 rules R_2, so that there should be $3(128) = 384$ strategies. It is indeed true that each of these will be a strategy, but they are not all different strategies, because of the redundant information contained in R_2.

For sequential decision problems which cannot be thought of as n-stage problems because the number of decisions to be made can vary depending on how one progresses along the decision tree, it may or may not be useful to introduce the notion of decision rules. However, the important thing to note is that one can always introduce the notion of a strategy. A strategy is simply a prescription which tells the decision maker what action to select at every node that he might reach. We can express this formally as follows:

STRATEGY FOR A SEQUENTIAL DECISION PROBLEM. *If for each node in the decision tree at which a decision maker may find himself, there is prescribed an action to be taken, this is called a strategy.*

A strategy tells the decision maker what to do each time he must make a decision. The definition of a strategy for an n-stage problem is a special case of the general definition of a strategy.

A strategy for a sequential decision problem must, of course, have the characteristic that for any set of nodes T such that the decision maker does not know at which of the nodes he is, the strategy must prescribe that he select the same action for every node in T.

3-4 SOLUTION OF SEQUENTIAL DECISION PROBLEMS

Given the concept of a strategy for a sequential decision problem, we can now show how to solve such problems. To do this, let us consider what happens to the decision tree for a given problem when we select a particular strategy. Let us again refer to Figure 3-2 and suppose that we select the first strategy given in Table 3-2. If we delete from the decision tree in Figure 3-2 all parts of the tree which cannot be passed along when using this strategy, we are reduced to the *sub tree*, as we shall call it, shown in Figure 3-3. Emanating from each node where the decision maker may

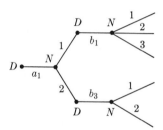

FIGURE 3-3

make a decision, there is only one branch corresponding to the action which the strategy tells him to take. This will be true in general and not merely for the example given, simply because this is the way a strategy is defined. Let us examine in a little more detail the sub tree which is generated by selecting a particular strategy. There are no decisions to be made by the decision maker. The only decisions remaining are those which are to be made by nature. Now recall the notion of a multistage lottery introduced in the previous chapter. The sub tree generated by selecting a particular strategy can be looked on as nothing but a representation of some multi-stage lottery. In particular, Figure 3-3 can be imagined to represent a two stage lottery. At the first stage the roulette wheel has only two numbers on it. If the wheel stops on the number 1, then the decision maker is sent to a single stage lottery in which there are three possible outcomes. If the wheel stops on the number 2, he is sent to a single stage lottery in which there are two possible outcomes. Even a sequential decision problem in which the selection of a strategy does not lead to what initially looks like a tree for a multistage lottery because the number of random experiments differs depending on the path taken, can be converted to a multistage lottery simply by introducing dummy stages in which the roulette wheel has only a single number on it.

Our discussion has shown that the selection of a strategy for a sequential decision problem is equivalent to putting the decision maker into a multistage lottery. There will be a different multistage lottery for each possible strategy. Consider now any given decision problem. Let us suppose that for each of the random experiments involved, the decision maker has in one way or another estimated the probabilities of all the simple events. We can imagine that after the decision maker has made all the decisions and all of the random experiments have been performed, there will be some prize or event that will be awarded to the decision maker. In other words, if we construct a decision tree, then there will be a prize associated with each terminal branch. Let us assume that the decision maker has studied these events or prizes and has determined his utility function (one of his utility functions) defined over this set of events. Suppose also that he has determined every possible strategy and the multistage lottery associated with each. The only problem remaining then for the decision maker is to determine which of the multistage lotteries he most prefers to play. Once he decides what lottery he prefers most (or a set of such lotteries if he is indifferent between two or more most preferred lotteries), he simultaneously determines a strategy (or set of strategies). This strategy (or any of them) is called an *optimal strategy*. He should use this strategy to tell him how to make decisions. An optimal strategy then provides a solution to the sequential decision problem because it tells the decision maker what to do in every situation which he may encounter, and it puts him in the multistage lottery which he prefers most.

Now the theory developed in the last chapter tells us how the decision maker will rank the lotteries in order of preference. From axiom 2 of Section 2-8 we know that he will be indifferent between a multistage lottery and a single stage lottery having the same probabilities of getting the prizes. Suppose then that he determines for each of the multistage lotteries under consideration the probability of getting each prize, and then considers a single stage lottery with these probabilities. From Section 2-8 we know that if he computes the expected utility for each lottery and arranges the single stage lotteries in order of decreasing expected utility, he will have ranked the lotteries in order of preference. However, because he is indifferent between the multistage lottery and the corresponding single stage lottery, this also serves to rank the multistage lotteries in order of preference. Thus to pick the most preferred multistage lottery, the decision maker can simply select the one which yields the largest expected utility.

In the above we have presented a computational procedure which can in principle be used to solve any sequential decision problem which involves only a finite number of decisions. The procedure is as follows. The decision maker determines his utility function over the set of prizes. He estimates the probabilities of the simple events in the random experiments. He determines all the different strategies and the multistage lotteries associated with each. He determines his expected utility for each lottery, and an optimal strategy is the one or ones associated with the lottery or lotteries having the largest expected utility. The optimal strategy or set of such strategies is what he is seeking because it tells him what action to take in each situation where a decision is needed. It should be noted that there might be more than one optimal strategy; this would merely mean that the decision maker is indifferent between several lotteries, each of which has the same largest value of the expected utility.

We shall now point out in more detail why in practice it may be extremely difficult to solve a sequential decision problem in the manner just indicated. Many difficulties can arise, such as that of getting data to estimate a very large number of probabilities in all the random experiments, or obtaining the utility function. However, serious problems would exist even if there were no such data problems. The basic difficulty stems from the fact that frequently there will be incredibly large numbers of different strategies to investigate. The numbers can easily be so large that they are hard to comprehend, for example, numbers like 10^{10}. Even if it took a high speed computer only 0.1 second to determine a strategy and evaluate the expected utility associated with it, more than five years would be required to find the best strategy if there were something like 10^{10} of them. Clearly, a very large fraction of these strategies are normally terrible, in the sense that one could see without even evaluating the expected utility that they should never be used. There are really only a very small number of strategies which need to be investigated in detail. Unfortunately, no general methods have been developed for determining ahead of time which strategies these are without generating all of them and looking at each. This is an important unsolved problem. If it could be solved, then it would become possible to solve many more sequential decision problems. Nevertheless, in spite of these difficulties there are a number of important sequential decision problems which can be solved, and we shall study some of these later. Generally, however, a high speed computer is needed to obtain a numerical solution.

3-5 DISCUSSION

At this point it may be useful to discuss several points concerning what we have done in the previous sections. The first important thing to note is that we did not anywhere specify that at any or every node where the decision maker is to make a decision, every possible action he might take was included. The decision maker is free to include and exclude whatever actions he wishes. We have assumed only that some finite set of actions is associated with each such node, from which the decision maker will choose one. Consequently, it does not necessarily follow that an optimal strategy is the best of all possible strategies which would be generated by considering all possible actions; an optimal strategy is optimal only with respect to the sets of actions represented in the model of the decision problem.

Secondly, it is worth noting that we are always assuming that the decision maker is an individual in the sense that there is a utility function for him and he can assess the needed probabilities. We have not and shall not consider problems where decisions are made by groups of individuals who do not have the same preferences for the prizes and/or do not agree on the probabilities to be used. Furthermore, for most practical problems, it is quite proper to assume that a single individual will make the ultimate decisions. Many persons may be involved in giving advice, facts, and opinions, but generally speaking one individual will have the final say.

Next, note that we are always assuming that the probabilities of the simple events in the various random experiments can be specified. We saw in Chapter 1 that an individual may sometimes have difficulty in specifying a probability, that is, there will be a certain vagueness about what it should be. The theory we have developed treats all probabilities in the same way. It makes no differentiation between probabilities which are known with great accuracy and those which are only very rough estimates. One might feel it would be desirable to have a theory which took account of the reliability of the probabilities. However, no such theories have been developed. The situation here is really no different from situations in the physical sciences or engineering. The probabilities are simply parameters appearing in a mathematical model. Whatever numbers one assigns to these parameters the model uses as if they were the correct values. The mathematical models in physics do not take into account how accurately the physical constants appearing in them have been measured. They simply use whatever numbers are given as if they were the true values of the physical constants. We might mention that some attention has been given to the case where in a single stage decision problem nothing whatever is known about the probabilities of the states of nature. We shall discuss this work briefly in the next chapter. As might be imagined, one tends to be in bad shape if nothing is known about the probabilities of the states of nature.   Our applications of decision theory will be mainly to cases where the probabilities are taken as known.   It should be observed, however, that it is possible to determine how sensitive an optimal solution to a decision problem is to some particular pair of probabilities or set of probabilities.   This can be determined by re-solving the problem for various assumed values of the probabilities and noting how or if the optimal solution changes.   This is referred to as *sensitivity analysis*, and not infrequently one will wish to perform some sort of sensitivity analysis.

It is important to realize that if a decision maker selects an action using the theory we have discussed above, it is not necessarily true that this action will seem like a good one in retrospect after nature has selected the state of nature.   It may turn out to be a very poor action a posteriori. There is no way that the risk introduced by uncertainty can be eliminated without eliminating the causes of uncertainty.   The most we can claim is that the action selected is the best one given the information that the decision maker has available.   If he knew ahead of time which state of nature was going to occur, quite possibly he might choose an entirely different action.

If an action selected can turn out to be wrong in retrospect, what basis do we have for deciding how useful the decision models are in comparison with some other procedure, such as intuition, which the business man might use?   In certain cases, where the decision situation has a frequency interpretation and is encountered repeatedly, one can often verify the value of the theory directly, by considering how things were before the theory was used and how much things have improved on the average after its introduction.   However, for decision situations in which no frequency interpretation is possible, one cannot verify directly that in any given situation a better decision has been made using the theory than would be made without it; but if many decisions are being made, over a period of time one could hope to observe an improvement in performance as compared with what had been happening before the decision theory models were used. In any event, we can at least claim that the models give the decision maker a logical and rational basis for making decisions, which makes explicit the things he would somehow have to take into account at least in a vague way, regardless of how he made the decision.   Since the decision must be made, such a logical procedure should be a valuable aid in making the decision.

Finally, let us make a few observations about sequential decision problems.   In the real world, when we solve a sequential decision problem, normally we are interested only in what action the decision maker should take at the first decision, that is, for the decision he is currently concerned with.   We are not really interested in what rules he should use for later decisions.   The reason for this is that a considerable period of time may pass between the first decision and later decisions, and the entire nature of the problem may change before he gets around to making later decisions. Thus the problem will normally be re-solved, using the most recent information, each time a decision is to be made.   It seems reasonable to ask then why we cannot always treat problems as single stage problems.   The reason is that it is not possible to decide on what the best action is for the first decision without taking into account the courses of action that will be open to the decision maker at later stages.   For example, for the situation discussed in Section 3-2, the best action for the decision maker at the first stage would be quite different if he could not obtain any more units after the first casting.   Thus one is forced to solve the entire sequential problem merely to determine what is the best action to take at the first decision. Given this observation, it will be apparent to the reader that future decisions may in many cases have essentially no influence on the first decision, and because of this, one should in such cases be able to simplify the problem considerably and perhaps even approximate it adequately by a single stage problem.   This is indeed the case and is often a key factor in allowing us to solve complicated problems.   We shall examine these points in more detail later.

PROBLEMS

Section 3-1

1.   Consider the problem referred to in Chapter 1 where a supermarket is trying to decide how much bread should be ordered for a given day.   What is a reasonable definition for the states of nature?

2.   What are the actions for the situation referred to in Problem 1?   What is the random experiment?

3.   A judge is trying to decide if a defendant is guilty and what his sentence should be if so.   Is this a single stage decision problem?   If so, what are the states of nature, and what is the random experiment involved?

4.   A businessman is trying to decide which of ten different gifts he should buy as a Christmas present for his secretary.   Can this be interpreted under certain circumstances as a single stage decision problem?   If so, suggest a definition for the states of nature and describe the random experiment.

5.   A criminal who has just robbed a bank is trying to decide what route he should take to avoid the police.   Is this a single stage decision problem?   Why or why not?

6.   A manufacturer is trying to select a subcontractor to produce parts for a given weapon system the manufacturer is producing.   Might this be interpreted as a single stage decision problem?   If so, what might the states of nature be, and also what would the random experiment be?

7. Solve the single stage problem illustrated in Figure 3-4. The utilities are the numbers indicated on the ends of the terminal branches. The probabilities of the states of nature are indicated on the branches.

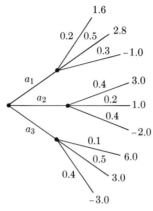

FIGURE 3-4

Section 3-2

1. Make up a description of a two stage decision problem involving some realistic situation.

2. Make up a description of a three stage decision problem involving some realistic situation.

3. Can you think of a sequential decision problem in which the number of decisions depends on the actions selected and the outcomes of the random experiments?

4. Suppose that in the example discussed in this section there was no opportunity after the first casting either to buy additional castings on the outside or to have another batch cast in the foundry. Show that in this case the problem reduces to a single stage decision problem. What are the actions and states of nature? Describe the random experiment. How might the probabilities of the states of nature be determined in each case?

Section 3-3

1. Consider the two stage decision problem shown in Figure 3-5. How many different decision rules are there for the second stage? How many for the first stage? Write down two different decision rules for the second stage and explain in words what each one says. How many different strategies are there for this problem? Write down each of these strategies, and describe in words what each says.

2. List all the decision rules for the second stage in Figure 3-5. Then list all strategies of the form $S = \{R_1, R_2\}$ which use the complete decision rule for the second stage and compare these with the strategies of the form $S = \{R_1, \hat{R}_2\}$ obtained in Problem 1.

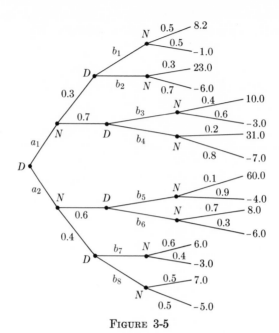

FIGURE 3-5

3. Consider the simplest three stage decision problem in which the decision maker at each stage has only two alternatives to chose from and each random experiment has only two possible outcomes. Draw the decision tree for such a problem. How many decision rules are there for the second stage? How many for the third stage? How many strategies are there?

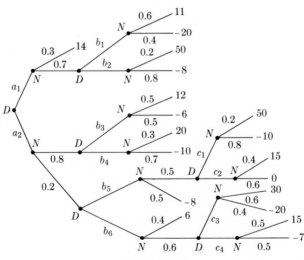

FIGURE 3-6

4. Consider the sequential decision problem illustrated in Figure 3-6. How many strategies are there?   List each of these strategies.

Section 3-4

1. Solve the two stage decision problem given in Figure 3-5.   The probabilities of the simple events are listed on the appropriate branches, and the utilities are indicated at the ends of the terminal branches.

2. Solve the sequential decision problem given in Figure 3-6.   The probabilities of the simple events are listed on the appropriate branches, and the utilities are indicated at the ends of the terminal branches.

CHAPTER 4

SINGLE STAGE DECISION PROBLEMS

Things and actions are what they are, and the consequences of them will be what they will be: why then should we desire to be deceived?

Bishop Joseph Butler, *Fifteen Sermons*

4-1 THE NORMAL FORM

In the previous chapter we showed how any decision problem involving only a finite number of decisions could be solved. In this chapter, and indeed for most of the remainder of the text, we shall study single stage problems. The reason for this emphasis on single stage problems lies in the fact that both the theory and computational problems are much simpler here than for sequential problems. In addition, of course, there are many interesting and important problems which can be adequately represented as single stage decision problems.

What is our mathematical model of a single stage decision problem? To characterize such a problem all we need are symbols for the actions, symbols for the states of nature, symbols for the prizes, a utility function defined over the set of prizes, and a set of functions giving the probabilities of the states of nature for each of the random experiments. Suppose that there are a finite number r of actions which we shall denote by $a_1, \ldots, a_r$. Let $A = \{a_1, \ldots, a_r\}$ so that A is the set of possible actions. Also suppose that there are m states of nature, which we shall denote by $e_1, e_2, \ldots, e_m$, and let $E = \{e_1, \ldots, e_m\}$ so that E is the event set for the random experiments. For a given pair (a_i, e_j) there is a prize Q_{ij}. Let $Q = \{Q_{11}, \ldots, Q_{rm}\}$ be the set of prizes. For each prize Q_{ij} there is a utility U_{ij} of that prize; this defines a function over Q which is $U_{ij} = U(Q_{ij})$. Finally, for each action a_i there is a function $p_{ij} = p_i(e_j)$ which gives the probabilities of the simple events for the random experiment which the decision maker encounters if he takes action a_i. Our mathematical model of a single stage decision problem then consists of nothing but the sets A, E, and Q and the $r + 1$ functions $U_{ij} = U(Q_{ij})$, and $p_{ij} = p_i(e_j)$. One way to illustrate geometrically the character of a single stage decision problem is to use a decision tree like that of Figure 3-1. This is sometimes referred to as the *extensive form* for representing the problem. There is another representation which is also useful sometimes. This is called the *normal form*. The normal form is nothing but a table, or tableau as it is sometimes called, like that shown in Table 4-1. The table illustrated here is frequently referred to as a *payoff table*. Row i of

TABLE 4-1

NORMAL FORM FOR A SINGLE STAGE DECISION PROBLEM

	e_1	e_2	e_3	e_4	$\cdots$	e_m
a_1	p_{11} $\quad U_{11}$	p_{12} $\quad U_{12}$	p_{13} $\quad U_{13}$	p_{14} $\quad U_{14}$	$\cdots$	p_{1m} $\quad U_{1m}$
a_2	p_{21} $\quad U_{21}$	p_{22} $\quad U_{22}$	p_{23} $\quad U_{23}$	p_{24} $\quad U_{24}$	$\cdots$	p_{2m} $\quad U_{2m}$
$\vdots$	$\vdots$					
a_r	p_{r1} $\quad U_{r1}$	p_{r2} $\quad U_{r2}$	p_{r3} $\quad U_{r3}$	p_{r4} $\quad U_{r4}$	$\cdots$	p_{rm} $\quad U_{rm}$

the payoff table describes what can happen if the decision maker selects action a_i. There is a cell in the ith row for every possible state of nature. In the jth cell are placed the numbers p_{ij}, the probability that the state of nature will turn out to be e_j, and U_{ij}, the utility associated with this outcome. To compute the expected utility associated with any action a_i, we multiply together the numbers in each of the cells in the ith row and add up over this row the numbers so obtained. The expected utility associated with each action can be conveniently represented in an additional column. The action the decision maker should take is the one corresponding to the largest expected utility.

From the description just given, it might seem a trivial matter to solve any single stage decision problem. This is by no means true, however. First of all, there may be a very large number of different states of nature, and it may be difficult to list all those which should be included. For certain types of problems there can easily be millions of states of nature.

Then of course, it can be quite an undertaking to determine the probabilities and utilities involved. In this chapter we shall study several rather simple types of problems. Later we shall examine much more complicated problems where a direct determination of all the probabilities and utilities is out of the question, and instead one solves the problem using a large digital computer and a technique called simulation. In the next section we shall present three very simple examples to illustrate the use of the normal form.

4-2 EXAMPLES

1. The simplest of all single stage decision problems are those where only two actions are open to the decision maker, and there are only two states of nature. To illustrate such a problem consider a businessman who is trying to decide which of two projects, call them 1 and 2, to undertake. The profitability of these projects will be strongly influenced by a tax law which Congress is considering. If the law is not passed, project 1 is considerably more favorable than project 2. However, if the law is passed, then project 2 is the more desirable one. The decision maker estimates that the probability of the law being passed is independent of what project he undertakes, and feels that the probability of its being passed is 0.3. If he undertakes project 1, call this action a_1, and if he undertakes project 2, call this action a_2. Denote by e_1 the state of nature that the law will be passed and by e_2 the state of nature that it will not be passed. The decision maker decides, after a comparison of the four possible prizes, that if he undertakes project 1 and the law is passed, his utility is -5; while if the law is not passed, his utility is 20. On the other hand, if he undertakes project 2 and the law is passed, his utility is 4; while if it is not passed, his utility is 15. Note that a utility scale is being used for which the utility of the worst event is -5 and of the best event is 20. The payoff table is then that shown in Table 4-2. In the third column we

TABLE 4-2

PAYOFF TABLE FOR TAX LAW EXAMPLE

	e_1	e_2	Expected utility
a_1	0.3 -5	0.7 20	12.5
a_2	0.3 4	0.7 15	11.7

have given the expected utilities. For example, for action a_1 the expected utility is

$$0.3(-5) + 0.7(20) = -1.5 + 14 = 12.5.$$

The expected utility for action a_1 is the larger of the two, and therefore the businessman should undertake project 1.

2. Consider again the problem introduced in Section 3-1 of the gentleman who is pondering whether to carry his umbrella with him to work. If the umbrella is taken, call this action a_1, and if it is not taken, call this action a_2. Denote by e_1 the state of nature that the sun shines all day, e_2 that it is sunny when the individual is out, but it rains at some other times, e_3 that it rains when the individual is out, but is sunny at some other times, and e_4 that it rains all day. The gentleman estimates on the basis of the weather reports and his observations the following probabilities:

$$p(e_1) = 0.2, \quad p(e_2) = 0.3, \quad p(e_3) = 0.3, \quad p(e_4) = 0.2,$$

which he assumes to be independent of what action he takes. The utilities of the various action state of nature combinations are shown in Table 4-3.

TABLE 4-3

PAYOFF TABLE FOR UMBRELLA EXAMPLE

	e_1	e_2	e_3	e_4	Expected utility
a_1	0.2 −5	0.3 −3	0.3 4	0.2 4	0.1
a_2	0.2 6	0.3 4	0.3 −7	0.2 −6	−0.9

The final column of Table 4-3 gives the expected utilities. The expected utility of action a_1 is the greatest, and thus the gentleman should carry his umbrella.

3. Every Saturday a bakery in a large shopping center stocks a few of a very special and expensive cake which appeals to some of its best customers. Unfortunately, these customers do not necessarily come in every Saturday, nor do they always buy one of these cakes when they are in the bakery. There is no way of finding out ahead of time how many cakes will be demanded. However, over the past two years the owner has kept a record of the number of these cakes demanded on a Saturday. He feels justified in using the historical relative frequencies for probabilities. The historical

data show that the number of cakes demanded on any given Saturday was always less than or equal to five. The relative frequencies give the following probabilities of having j cakes demanded:

$$p(0) = 0.10, \quad p(1) = 0.20, \quad p(2) = 0.20,$$
$$p(3) = 0.30, \quad p(4) = 0.15, \quad p(5) = 0.05.$$

We can then think of the number of cakes demanded as a random variable x, which can take on the values 0, 1, 2, 3, 4, and 5. This random variable can be conveniently used to define a set of states of nature, each state of nature corresponding to the number of cakes demanded. There are therefore six different states of nature, call them $e_0, \ldots, e_5$. The different actions correspond to stocking different numbers of cakes at the beginning of the day. Since no more than five cakes have ever been demanded, the owner will not stock more than five. He may stock any number from 0 to 5, however. There are thus six possible actions, one for each number of cakes stocked, which we shall denote by $a_0, \ldots, a_5$.

For the sums of money involved here, the owner indicates that monetary values reflect his true preferences, and the proper number of cakes to stock can be determined by maximizing the expected profit. Let us then see how to determine the profit when he uses action a_i, and the state of nature turns out to be e_j. The cakes retail for \$5.50 and cost the bakery \$3.50. Any cakes left over on Saturday evening will on Monday morning be placed on a half price counter. All cakes placed on this counter will be sold at half price, i.e., at \$2.75 on Monday. If a customer comes in and requests a cake when the bakery is out of stock, the owner has observed that the customer usually becomes somewhat annoyed, and as a consequence buys less than usual of other things. The owner feels that on the average each time a cake is demanded when he is out of stock costs him about \$2.00. However, the inability to supply a customer's demand has no carry-over effect to future weeks, the owner has observed, since his is the only high quality bakery in the area. Therefore, the only effect of not being able to meet a customer's request for a cake is the two dollar loss on other sales. We can now easily determine the profit if he stocks i cakes and the demand turns out to be j.

When $i > j$, all demands will be met, and he will have $i - j$ cakes left over at the end of the day. If $i = j$, all demands will be met, and there will be no leftovers. If $i < j$, there will be no leftovers, but $j - i$ demands will occur which he cannot fill. The profit in terms of i and j is then

$$
\begin{array}{ll}
5.50j - 3.50i + 2.75(i - j), & i > j; \\
(5.50 - 3.50)i = 2.00i, & i = j; \\
5.50i - 3.50i - 2.00(j - i), & i < j.
\end{array}
\tag{4-1}
$$

The reasoning behind these expressions is the following. If he stocks i cakes, these cost him \$3.50i. If $i > j$, he sells j cakes, the number demanded, and the revenues received from these is $5.50j. In addition, he has $i - j$ left over which bring in an additional revenue of $2.75(i - j)$ on Monday when they are sold at half price. The profit for $i > j$ is then given by the first expression in (4-1). If $i = j$, the demand is for precisely the number stocked and, in this case there are no leftovers and no unfilled demands. The revenues received are $5.50i, while the cost of the cakes is $3.50i. Thus the profit is given by the second expression in (4-1). Finally, if $j > i$, he sells all that he stocked, so that revenues received are $5.50i. Furthermore the cost of the cakes is still $3.50i. Now, however, there is an additional cost to the bakery of $2.00 for every cake demanded which cannot be sold. This cost is then in total $2.00(j - i)$. Thus the profit is that given by the third expression in (4-1). By use of (4-1), we can easily fill the entries in the payoff table. This is done in Table 4-4. Since the probabilities of the states of nature do not depend

TABLE 4-4

PAYOFF TABLE FOR BAKERY'S PROBLEM

	e_0	e_1	e_2	e_3	e_4	e_5	Expected profit
$p(e_j)$	0.10	0.20	0.20	0.30	0.15	0.05	
a_0	0	−2.00	−4.00	−6.00	−8.00	−10.00	−4.70
a_1	−0.75	2.00	0	−2.00	−4.00	− 6.00	−1.175
a_2	−1.50	1.25	4.00	2.00	0	− 2.00	1.40
a_3	−2.25	0.50	3.25	6.00	4.00	2.00	3.025
a_4	−3.00	−0.25	2.50	5.25	8.00	6.00	3.225
a_5	−3.75	−1.00	1.75	4.50	7.25	10.00	2.7125

on the action taken, we have simply listed these in the first row of the tableau. The task of filling out the payoff table is considerably more arduous for this example than for the previous two. The expected profits are shown in the final column. The expected profit for stocking two units is, for example,

$$-1.50(0.10) + 1.25(0.20) + 4.00(0.20) + 2.00(0.30) + 0(0.15)$$
$$- 2.00(0.05) = -0.15 + 0.25 + 0.80 + 0.60 - 0.10 = \$1.40.$$

Since the decision maker can use expected profits as expected utilities, he should select the action which maximizes his expected profit. This is action a_4. In other words, he should stock four cakes. We made no use of discounting in the above computations because for a period of one day no discounting is needed.

Before going on we might observe that in each of the three examples given, the probabilities of the states of nature did not depend on which action was selected.   Very frequently this turns out to be the case.

4-3   THE GENERAL SINGLE STAGE INVENTORY PROBLEM

The last example studied in the previous section is a special case of a general type of problem which arises fairly frequently.   The general problem is referred to as the single stage inventory problem because it is often met in studying various sorts of problems concerning how many units of some item should be stocked.   In this section, we would like to study the general problem of this type.   One of the reasons for doing this is simply because the problem is of interest.   Also, however, we will be able to show how by some additional analysis one can frequently develop greatly simplified procedures for determining optimal actions without ever explicitly constructing a payoff table.

Consider then a situation in which there exists a certain interval of time, which we shall call a period, over which units for some specific item will be demanded.   We shall imagine that the total number of units to be demanded in the period is a random variable x whose probability function will be denoted by $p(x)$.   To meet these demands, an inventory of the item is to be on hand at the beginning of the period.   It is not possible to reorder the item if this inventory is not sufficient.   If the number of units stocked initially is i, then when the demand turns out to be greater than i, some demands cannot be met.   If the demand is less than i, some units will be left over at the end of the period.   If the demand is precisely equal to i, then there will be no leftovers and no unfilled demands.

What we wish to do is determine how many units should be stocked at the beginning of the period.   As in the third example of the previous section, we shall assume that for the sums of money involved, the decision maker's utility function is related by a linear equation to monetary values.   Furthermore, it will be assumed that no factors other than monetary factors are relevant.   Then the decision maker should stock the number of units which maximizes his expected profit.   Let us now consider the various factors which make up the profit.   It will be imagined that the units sell for S dollars each and cost C dollars each.   Any units left over at the end of the period can be sold; the salvage value will be R dollars per unit, where $R < C$, that is, the salvage value is less than the cost.   Let us now examine what happens if the number of units stocked is not sufficient to meet the demand.   We shall assume that if this stocking problem is one that is faced periodically, as was the problem of stocking cakes every Saturday, an inability to meet a customer's demand will not have any carry-over effect to future periods. In particular this means that the customer does not become angry and never return. If this happened, it would have an influence on the probability function for the random variable, and we would be faced with a multistage rather than a single stage decision problem. Nevertheless, it will be assumed that there is a penalty of T dollars for each unit that is demanded and cannot be supplied. Finally, in determining the profit, it will be imagined that the period involved is sufficiently short that discounting is not needed. Thus if it is decided to stock i units, and the state of nature (the demand) turns out to be j, there will be a profit (utility) U_{ij} associated with this action–state of nature pair, which is given by

$$U_{ij} = \begin{cases} Sj - Ci + R(i - j), & j \leq i, \\ Si - Ci - T(j - i), & j > i. \end{cases} \tag{4-2}$$

The reasoning here is precisely the same as that which led to (4-1). We have included the case $i = j$ in the first expression of (4-2). This can be done since $R(i - j) = 0$ when $i = j$.

At this point, we could proceed to construct a payoff table. However, if the demand x could take on a large number of different values, it would be very clumsy to do this. Furthermore, by proceeding in a slightly different way, we shall be led to a much more efficient method of solving the problem. For each number i of units that may be stocked there is determined a unique expected profit. We shall denote the expected profit by $\pi(i)$. This association of an expected profit $\pi(i)$ with each i defines a function over the possible set of i values, and thus we can think of $\pi(i)$ as a function of i. Now $\pi(i)$ is

$$\pi(i) = \sum_{j=0}^{m} U_{ij}p(j), \tag{4-3}$$

where m is taken to be the maximum possible demand. To write out (4-3) more explicitly, we note that the form of U_{ij} differs depending on whether $j \leq i$ or $j > i$. We then split up the summation in this way, writing

$$\pi(i) = \sum_{j=0}^{i} U_{ij}p(j) + \sum_{j=i+1}^{m} U_{ij}p(j), \tag{4-4}$$

when $i < m$ and when $i = m$ (so that $j \leq i$ for all j),

$$\pi(m) = \sum_{j=0}^{m} U_{mj}p(j). \tag{4-5}$$

One would never stock more than m units because a loss would be taken on each one left over. If we now use (4-2), we have

$$\pi(i) = \sum_{j=0}^{i} [Sj - Ci + R(i - j)]p(j)$$

$$+ \sum_{j=i+1}^{m} [Si - Ci - T(j - i)]p(j) \qquad (4\text{-}6)$$

for $i < m$, and

$$\pi(m) = \sum_{j=0}^{m} [Sj - Cm + R(m - j)]p(j). \qquad (4\text{-}7)$$

Here we have obtained an explicit expression for the expected profit when i units are stocked, which could be used directly to compute the expected profit. Of course, (4-6) and (4-7) are precisely what we would obtain by making the computations using the payoff table.

We now wish to show that it is unnecessary to evaluate $\pi(i)$ for each $i = 0, 1, \ldots, m$ and select the largest of these to determine how many units to stock. There is a much simpler procedure one can use. Suppose that we actually did compute $\pi(i)$ for each i and constructed a bar diagram illustrating this function. We would then expect to obtain something like that shown in Figure 4-1. Note that i^* is the optimal number to stock,

FIGURE 4-1

since it corresponds to the largest expected profit. Let us now observe that in starting out with $i = 0$, the expected profit increases when we go to $i = 1$, that is, $\pi(1) - \pi(0) > 0$. Similarly, it increases when we go to $i = 2$, so that $\pi(2) - \pi(1) > 0$. This is true for every i up to i^*; in other words,

$$\pi(i) - \pi(i - 1) > 0, \quad i = 1, \ldots, i^*. \qquad (4\text{-}8)$$

However,

$$\pi(i^* + 1) - \pi(i^*) < 0,$$

and indeed

$$\pi(i) - \pi(i - 1) < 0, \quad i = i^* + 1, \ldots, m. \qquad (4\text{-}9)$$

Thus i^* has the characteristic that it is the value of i where the expected profit stops increasing. In other words, it is the largest value of i for which (4-8) holds.

Note that if we write

$$D(i) = \pi(i) - \pi(i-1), \quad i = 1, \ldots, m, \tag{4-10}$$

then $D(i)$ is a function of i which we can determine directly. $D(i)$ is the change in the expected profit when the number of units stocked is changed from $i - 1$ to i. We have just seen that i^* is the largest value of i for which the function $D(i)$ is positive, that is, $D(i) > 0$. It now occurs to us that if we obtain an explicit expression for $D(i)$ this might lead to a simple way of determining i^*. This does indeed turn out to be the case, as we shall now see.

Note that when we replace i by $i - 1$ in (4-6), we obtain

$$\pi(i-1) = \sum_{j=0}^{i-1} [Sj - C(i-1) + R(i-1-j)]p(j)$$

$$+ \sum_{j=i}^{m} [S(i-1) - C(i-1) - T(j-i+1)]p(j)$$

$$= \sum_{j=0}^{i-1} [Sj - Ci + R(i-j) + C - R]p(j)$$

$$+ \sum_{j=i}^{m} [Si - Ci - T(j-i) + C - S - T]p(j)$$

$$= \sum_{j=0}^{i-1} [Sj - Ci + R(i-j)]p(j) + (C - R)P(i-1)$$

$$+ \sum_{j=i}^{m} [Si - Ci - T(j-i)]p(j)$$

$$- (S + T - C)[1 - P(i-1)], \tag{4-11}$$

where $P(x)$ is the cumulative distribution for x. However,

$$\sum_{j=0}^{i} [Sj - Ci + R(i-j)]p(j)$$

$$= \sum_{j=0}^{i-1} [Sj - Ci + R(i-j)]p(j) + (S - C)ip(i) \tag{4-12}$$

and

$$\sum_{j=i+1}^{m} [Si - Ci - T(j-i)]p(j)$$

$$= \sum_{j=i}^{m} [Si - Ci - T(j-i)]p(j) - (S - C)ip(i). \tag{4-13}$$

Thus if we subtract (4-11) from (4-6), we obtain when using (4-12) and (4-13),

$$D(i) = \pi(i) - \pi(i - 1)$$
$$= (S + T - C)[1 - P(i - 1)] - (C - R)P(i - 1)$$

or

$$D(i) = (S + T - C) - (S + T - R)P(i - 1),$$
$$i = 1, \ldots, m - 1. \quad (4\text{-}14)$$

The reader should check that if we use (4-7) for $\pi(m)$ and (4-6) for $\pi(m - 1)$, then

$$D(m) = (S + T - C) - (S + T - R)P(m - 1). \quad (4\text{-}15)$$

This is precisely what we get from setting $i = m$ in (4-14). Therefore, we can think of (4-14) holding for $i = 1, \ldots, m$.

Now i^* is the largest i for which $D(i) > 0$, i.e., the largest i for which

$$(S + T - C) - (S + T - R)P(i - 1) > 0$$

or

$$(S + T - R)P(i - 1) < S + T - C$$

or since $S + T - R > 0$,

$$P(i - 1) < \frac{S + T - C}{S + T - R}. \quad (4\text{-}16)$$

Here we have a very simple criterion for determining i^*. We look at the cumulative function and determine the largest i for which (4-16) holds. This is a very simple criterion to apply. It is a little inconvenient to remember that it is $P(i - 1)$ and not $P(i)$ that appears in (4-16). We can easily change the criterion to one where $P(i)$ does appear. Not only is i^* the largest i for which $D(i) > 0$, but it also is the smallest i for which $\pi(i + 1) - \pi(i) \leq 0$, that is, $D(i + 1) \leq 0$, as can be seen from Figure 4-1. We write $D(i + 1) \leq 0$ rather than $D(i + 1) < 0$ because it can be true that $\pi(i^* + 1) = \pi(i^*)$, so that the i which gives the maximum profit may not be unique. Now

$$D(i + 1) = (S + T - C) - (S + T - R)P(i),$$
$$i = 0, \ldots, m - 1, \quad (4\text{-}17)$$

and the smallest i for which $D(i + 1) \leq 0$ is the smallest i such that

$$P(i) \geq \frac{S + T - C}{S + T - R}. \quad (4\text{-}18)$$

This is perhaps easier to remember than (4-16). Note that if i^* is the largest i for which (4-16) holds, then i^* must be the smallest i for which (4-18) holds, and conversely. Thus (4-16) and (4-18) are equivalent conditions. In the event that $P(m - 1)$ does not satisfy (4-18), but satisfies (4-16), then $\pi(m) > \pi(m - 1)$, and m units should be stocked.

After some straightforward but slightly tedious manipulation, we have obtained a very simple criterion to determine how many units should be stocked. We compute the positive number

$$\alpha = (S + T - C)/(S + T - R),$$

and then find the smallest value of i for which $P(i) \geq \alpha$. This number is the optimal number to stock. The reader should note how much simpler this criterion is to apply than that of computing the expected profit for each i and seeing which i yields the largest expected profit.

EXAMPLE. Let us use the criterion just developed to solve very simply Example 3 of the previous section. By use of the probability function for x given there, one can immediately obtain the cumulative function. It is illustrated in Figure 4-2. We have $P(0) = 0.10$, $P(1) = 0.30$,

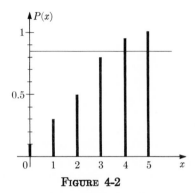

FIGURE 4-2

$P(2) = 0.50$, $P(3) = 0.80$, $P(4) = 0.95$, $P(5) = 1$. Now for the case under consideration $S = 5.50$, $C = 3.50$, $R = 2.75$, and $T = 2.00$. Thus

$$\alpha = \frac{S + T - C}{S + T - R} = \frac{5.50 + 2.00 - 3.50}{5.50 + 2.00 - 2.75} = \frac{4.00}{4.75} = 0.843.$$

We wish to find the smallest i for which $P(i) \geq 0.843$. We see immediately that $i = 4$ is the smallest such i. This is easily determined geometrically if we draw a line parallel to the x-axis through the point 0.843 on the vertical axis as shown in Figure 4-2. We look for the first bar touching or extending above this line. The i corresponding to this bar is i^*. If we used (4-16), we would find the largest $P(i)$ such that $P(i) < \alpha$. This is $P(3)$. Therefore, $i^* - 1 = 3$ or $i^* = 4$. The result we have obtained here is, of course, the same result obtained in the previous section.

We have mentioned above that the optimal quantity to stock may not be unique. It can happen that both i^* and $i^* + 1$ yield the same expected

profit.   As we illustrated things in Figure 4-1, there was only one "hill"
and no "valleys" in the expected profit function.   The reader may now
wonder whether the profit function could look like that in Figure 4-3.

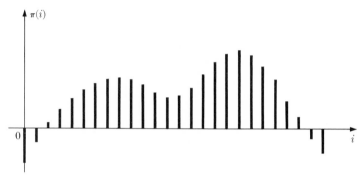

FIGURE 4-3

If it could, it would appear that our rule might not give the correct answer,
because $\pi(i)$ changes from increasing to decreasing twice, and from decreasing to increasing once, i.e., $D(i)$ changes sign three times.   Such behavior
cannot happen with the problem we are discussing when the revenues and
costs have the form we specified.   To see this it is only necessary to look
at $D(i)$.   Recall that as i increases, $P(i)$ cannot decrease.   Therefore,
from (4-14) as we change i to $i + 1$, $D(i)$ can only decrease or remain
unchanged.   Consequently, $D(i)$ can change sign only once, and situations
like those in Figure 4-3 cannot arise, so that our method will always
determine a unique i^* which is an optimal quantity to stock.

4-4 INCREMENTAL ANALYSIS

In the previous section we obtained a very simple criterion for solving
the single stage inventory problem.   This was done by finding an expression for the expected profit $\pi(i)$ when i units were stocked, and then
determining the function $D(i)$ by subtracting from $\pi(i)$ the value $\pi(i - 1)$.
In this section we shall show that there is a much easier way to derive
(4-18).   This new procedure is what economists refer to as incremental
analysis.   Recall that U_{ij} is the profit when i units are stocked and the
demand turns out to be for j units.   Now

$$\Delta_j = U_{i+1,j} - U_{ij}$$

is the difference between the profit when $i + 1$ units are stocked and
i units are stocked, and the demand is j.   The Δ_j can be imagined to be

the values taken on by a random variable Δ. Now the expected value of Δ is

$$\sum_{j=0}^{m} \Delta_j p(j) = \pi(i+1) - \pi(i) = D(i+1), \tag{4-19}$$

so that the expected value of Δ is precisely $D(i+1)$. Therefore $D(i+1)$ is the expected value of the change in the profit when $i+1$ units are stocked instead of i units. This is the difference in the expected profits for stocking $i+1$ and stocking i units, which is in agreement with what we proved in Chapter 1—that the expected value of the difference of two random variables is the difference of the expected values.

Let us now see that it is very easy to compute the expected value of Δ directly. There are two cases to consider. One is that where $j < i+1$ and the other that where $j \geq i+1$. In the first case, the extra unit, unit $i+1$, is not demanded. When this happens the unit will be sold for salvage at the end and then will bring in a sum R. The unit cost is C, so that $\Delta_j = R - C, j < i+1$. Since $R - C < 0$, the profit is decreased in this case. The other case is that where $j \geq i+1$. In this case the unit is sold and brings in S dollars in revenue for an outlay of C dollars. In addition, however, one demand which cannot be supplied is avoided, and this increases the profit by T, so that $\Delta_j = S - C + T$. Consequently,

$$\Delta_j = \begin{cases} R - C, & j < i+1, \\ S - C + T, & j \geq i+1. \end{cases} \tag{4-20}$$

This result can, of course, be obtained by subtracting U_{ij} from $U_{i+1,j}$. Hence on using (4-20),

$$D(i+1) = \sum_{j=0}^{m} \Delta_j p(j) = (R - C) \sum_{j=0}^{i} p(j) + (S - C + T) \sum_{j=i+1}^{m} p(j)$$

$$= (R - C)P(i) + (S - C + T)[1 - P(i)], \tag{4-21}$$

which is (4-17). Equation (4-18) can then be obtained immediately. With this procedure no complicated subtraction of sums is needed. The essence of the incremental analysis method is that we determine directly the values of the random variable giving the change in the profit when we go from stocking i to stocking $i+1$ units, that is, when one extra unit is stocked. This procedure is often very useful to employ in obtaining simplified rules for determining optimal actions. The incremental analysis method does not, however, give us an expression for the expected profit. If it is necessary to compute some particular expected profit, we must determine this separately. If we wished to compute the expected profit for any particular i in the single stage inventory problem, we could use (4-6). This is a rather clumsy expression to use, however. It is easy to convert (4-6) to the much more convenient form

$$\pi(i) = (S - R)\mu_x - (C - R)i - (S + T - R) \sum_{j=i}^{m} (j - i)p(j), \quad (4\text{-}22)$$

where μ_x is the expected demand. We ask the reader to show how to do this in the problems.

Problems which can be phrased as single stage inventory problems arise rather frequently. For example, the decision as to how many Christmas trees a vendor should stock, how many newspapers a boy should carry, how many spares of a given part are to be purchased when a new airliner is procured, illustrate such problems. We shall close our discussion of this type of problem with one final example.

EXAMPLE. Some pieces of equipment produced for the military have the characteristic that the spare parts that may be needed during its lifetime are produced at the same time as the equipment itself. If not enough spares are produced, it may be extremely costly or impossible to obtain them at a later date. There then arises the question of how many spares of each type of part should be produced. The number of spares to be demanded over the lifetime of a piece of equipment cannot be predicted with certainty, but must instead be treated as a random variable. Consider then a typical example of such a situation. A new ship is being constructed for the navy which will have a lifetime of about twenty years. The navy wishes to specify how many spares of a particular very expensive part should be produced when the ship is being constructed. The part might be the shaft and fittings for the screw, for example, or perhaps the rudder mechanism. Let us suppose that each part will cost \$50,000 when produced simultaneously with the ship, but \$150,000 if it must be produced after the ship is launched. After a study of similar ships, the navy decides that no more than six of these spares should ever be needed, and it estimates the probabilities of various numbers of parts being required as:

$$p(0) = 0.2, \quad p(1) = 0.3, \quad p(2) = 0.2, \quad p(3) = 0.1,$$
$$p(4) = 0.1, \quad p(5) = 0.06, \quad p(6) = 0.04.$$

Any parts left over when the ship is scrapped will have a salvage value of \$1000 each. From this information, we would like to determine how many spares should be ordered.

We shall assume that monetary values can be used to represent the navy's utility function. Note that in this problem the navy is not selling the parts, and no revenues are being generated. Thus $S = 0$. Furthermore $C = 50,000$, $R = 1000$, and finally $T = 150,000$ since this is what one must pay for each one that is demanded which cannot be supplied from stock. Then i^*, the optimal number to stock, is the smallest i for which

$$P(i) \geq \frac{150{,}000 - 50{,}000}{150{,}000 - 1000} = \frac{100{,}000}{149{,}000} = 0.670.$$

From the above probability data,

$$P(0) = 0.2, \quad P(1) = 0.5, \quad P(2) = 0.7, \quad P(3) = 0.8,$$
$$P(4) = 0.9, \quad P(5) = 0.96, \quad P(6) = 1.$$

Thus we see that $P(2)$ is the smallest $P(i)$ with $P(i) \geq 0.670$. Therefore two spares should be produced while the ship is being constructed.

4-5 THE SCRAP ALLOWANCE PROBLEM

We would now like to study in some detail a problem somewhat similar to that faced by the manager of the metal working plant in Section 3-2, at each decision he had to make. At the first stage he had the problem of deciding how many units should be cast. This was difficult because he did not know how many castings would turn out defective. The same sort of problem occurred when he made the second decision. Here he was essentially attempting to decide how many units he should have going into the finishing process in order to have finally 1000 good ones. Let us formulate a fairly general type of problem of which that of deciding how many castings are needed at the start of the finishing operation is a special case, and that of deciding how many units to cast initially may also be a special case.

Consider a job shop which makes a variety of products to special order. Usually, a product such as a particular type of gear must undergo operations on several machines such as lathes, drills, and shapers. Jigs are used on each of the machines, and the setup operation can be time consuming and expensive. Often the job on the first machine in the sequence will be completely finished before work is even started on the final operations. Thus it is typical that the jigs on the machines which perform the initial operations will have been torn down, and they will be working on some other job before the finishing operations are started on the job under consideration. Now defectives are occasionally produced during each of the operations. These may be caught at the time they are produced or may not be caught until the final inspection.

The way the job shop operates is as follows. An order for a given number w of some particular part or product will be received. The order is then sent into the shop and is scheduled on each machine involved. The scheduling may be such that after certain operations are finished, the job must wait in in-process inventory for a week or more until the machine used for the next operation becomes available. Finally, the needed raw materials are ordered. The nature of the process is such that even if defectives are discovered when produced there is no way to go back and make extras to replace them without scheduling complete new setups on the machines.   Consequently, more than the final required number w of parts must be scheduled initially.   The question is, how many should be scheduled initially to provide for defectives or scrap? We shall call this a scrap allowance problem.   The answer to the problem depends crucially on the nature of the costs and the relative frequency of defectives.   Let us now examine these aspects.

Consider the generation of defectives by the process.   Imagine that the job is not handled in the manner described above, but that instead we send units through the entire process one at a time.   We then note whether each unit is finished successfully or is defective.   We might then get a sequence such as 111011111101, where a 1 means the unit was successfully completed, while a 0 means that it became a defective at some step in the process.   Let us continue this until we get precisely w good units.   Suppose that j, $j \geq w$ was the actual number of units started through the process to get w good ones, so that $w - 1$ good pieces were obtained from the first $j - 1$ and the wth good one was obtained from the jth piece put through.   Let us repeat this experiment many times and determine the relative frequency of each possible value of j.   The limiting values of these relative frequencies can then be looked upon as the probabilities of the various values which a random variable x can take on.   The random variable x is the number of pieces that must be started to get precisely w good ones.   Denote the probability function for x by $p(x)$.   Let us imagine that the probability function $p(x)$ has been determined.   We shall not concern ourselves at the moment with how this distribution might be determined in practice.   Currently, it probably appears to the reader that it would be extremely difficult to do so.   Interestingly though, as we shall see in the next chapter, it can be rather easy if certain frequently applicable assumptions apply.

The random variable x introduced above does not, at the outset, seem the most natural one to use here.   The most natural one would be y, the number of good pieces obtained if we schedule i units for production. We could indeed use y, but the difficulty is that the distribution of y will change as i is changed, whereas the distribution of x is independent of the number of units scheduled, by the way it is defined.   In order to use x we must assume that the total number of units scheduled in no way influences the occurrence of defectives.   This is quite reasonable for the process described above.   It might not be reasonable at all, however, for the casting operation described in Section 3-2.   We shall find it convenient to use the random variable x in studying the scrap allowance problem.

Let us now turn to the nature of the costs.   Once again it will be assumed that monetary values can be used for utilities.   We shall assume that raw materials costs plus the variable production costs (variable referring to those production costs which change with the number of units produced) amount to C dollars per unit scheduled for production, independently of how many units are scheduled. If any units are produced in excess of the number w ordered, they must be scrapped like defectives. The salvage value for any defectives or unused good units will be R dollars per unit, $R < C$. We now come to consider the most complicated feature of the problem. What happens if the number of units i which are scheduled do not yield w good ones? There are a variety of things which might happen here. We shall study only one of them. It will be imagined that w good units must ultimately be produced, and the way this will be done if less than w are obtained on the normal production run is as follows. Several master machinists will be requested to make the remaining units on a second shift using some special machines and no jigs. We shall now make the very important assumption that the law governing the generation of defectives is precisely the same here as for normal production runs where jigs are used. This means that the probability that precisely j units must be started in order to yield w good units is the same when these men do the work as on a normal production run. It will be imagined that the men always finish a unit before starting another, so that exactly the number of units needed to get the w pieces will be made. No unnecessary good units will be made, although some defectives may be produced in the process of obtaining the required number of good pieces.

The men making the extra pieces must be paid for a full shift regardless of whether they work for the full shift. Furthermore, the number of men who must work is fixed by union regulations, so that a man from one department cannot operate a machine in a different department. Consequently, if only one extra unit must be produced, it is still necessary to pay several men for a full shift. It will be imagined that the possibility that more than a full shift is required to produce the extra units is so remote that it need not be considered. Thus there will be a cost V incurred if any additional units must be produced, and this sum is independent of the number of units to be produced. V is the compensation paid to the workers for overtime plus any additional sums for keeping the shop open. In addition, there will be the raw material and other costs for each extra unit produced. We shall imagine that this unit cost is the same as the cost in the normal production process, i.e., C dollars per unit. Finally, let Q be the sum the customer pays the job shop for the w units.

Having described the problem and the assumptions to be made, we are now ready to determine the optimal size of the initial run. What shall we use for the states of nature? It is convenient to think of these states as the number of units that must be produced to obtain w good pieces. The probabilities of the states of nature will be independent of the action taken, that is, of the number of units i processed in the initial production run. The reason for this is that we assume that the law governing the generation of defectives is the same for a regular run as it is when the units are made by the master machinists on the second shift. We can now write down the profit when the action taken is to schedule i units and the state of nature turns out to be that j units must be produced to obtain w good ones. Let U_{ij} be this profit. It is

$$U_{ij} = \begin{cases} Q - Ci + R(i - w), & j \leq i, \\ Q - Cj + R(j - w) - V, & j > i. \end{cases} \qquad (4\text{-}23)$$

The reasoning is that if w good units are produced among the i which are scheduled, $i - w$ are scrapped either because they are defective or are not needed, and so U_{ij} is given by the first expression in (4-23). If less than w good units are produced, the extra cost V is incurred and $j - i$ additional units must be produced to obtain the w good ones. No extra good units are produced, but the total number of defectives is $j - w$. A total of j units is then started into production.

We shall not compute the expected profit directly. Instead we shall use the incremental analysis approach to determine a simple criterion for computing an optimal number of units to schedule for the production run. Let $\Delta_j = U_{i+1,j} - U_{ij}$, so that Δ_j is the profit when $i + 1$ units make up the production run, and the number of units needed to obtain w good ones is j, less the profit when i units make up the production run and the number of units needed to obtain w good ones is j. When $j \leq i$, then $j < i + 1$ and both $U_{i+1,j}$ and U_{ij} are given by the first expression in (4-23), so that

$$\Delta_j = R - C, \quad j \leq i. \qquad (4\text{-}24)$$

Suppose that $j = i + 1$. Then $j > i$, and U_{ij} is given by the second expression in (4-23). However, $j = i + 1$, and $U_{i+1,j}$ is given by the first expression in (4-23) with i replaced by $i + 1$. Thus

$$\Delta_j = Q - C(i + 1) + R(i + 1 - w) - Q + C(i + 1) - R(i + 1 - w) + V$$
$$= V, \quad j = i + 1. \qquad (4\text{-}25)$$

Finally, if $j > i + 1$, both U_{ij} and $U_{i+1,j}$ are given by the second expression in (4-23) and

$$\Delta_j = 0, \quad j > i + 1. \qquad (4\text{-}26)$$

Thus we can summarize Δ_j as follows:

$$\Delta_j = \begin{cases} R - C, & j < i + 1, \\ V, & j = i + 1, \\ 0, & j > i + 1. \end{cases} \qquad (4\text{-}27)$$

We might note that it is easy to obtain Δ_j directly without ever writing down U_{ij}. If we schedule an extra unit, i.e., go from i to $i + 1$, which is not needed, we incur an extra cost of $C - R$ for the unit which must be scrapped, so that the profit increases by $R - C$, which is a negative number. The extra unit is not needed if $j < i + 1$. If the extra unit scheduled is just the one needed to yield w good units, we save the cost V, that is, the profit increases by V, and nothing else changes. This will occur when $j = i + 1$. If overtime is needed even when the extra unit is scheduled, then the profit is unchanged. The cost V is incurred in both cases, and the same number of defectives is produced in both cases. This happens when $j > i + 1$. Thus (4-27) can be obtained directly. In general, one must be very careful when using an analysis of the type just given. It is easy to make mistakes, and it may be desirable to go through the procedure of determining the profit for the action–state of nature pairs, and then computing the difference directly.

The expected value of the random variable Δ, whose possible values are the Δ_j, is then

$$\sum_{j=w}^{m} \Delta_j p(j) = \sum_{j=w}^{i} (R - C)p(j) + Vp(i + 1) + \sum_{j=i+2}^{m} 0p(j)$$
$$= (R - C)P(i) + Vp(i + 1). \tag{4-28}$$

We have assumed that the decision maker feels that m is the largest possible value of j that could conceivably occur. Note that the smallest possible value of j is w. Now if $\pi(i)$ is the expected profit when i units are scheduled for the production run, then the expected value of Δ is $\pi(i + 1) - \pi(i)$, as we noted in Section 4-4. Therefore,

$$\pi(i + 1) - \pi(i) = (R - C)P(i) + Vp(i + 1). \tag{4-29}$$

Then if the $\pi(i)$ function looked like that in Figure 4-1, i^* is an optimal number to schedule if i^* is the smallest i for which

$$\pi(i + 1) - \pi(i) = (R - C)P(i) + Vp(i + 1) \le 0$$

or

$$Vp(i + 1) \le (C - R)P(i)$$

or

$$\frac{p(i + 1)}{P(i)} \le \frac{C - R}{V}, \tag{4-30}$$

that is, i^* is the smallest i for which (4-30) holds. Equally well, i^* is the largest i for which

$$\frac{p(i)}{P(i - 1)} > \frac{C - R}{V}. \tag{4-31}$$

Note that (4-30) and (4-31) do not involve the revenue Q received from the customer. This criterion is not as easy to apply as (4-18), because we must compute $p(i + 1)/P(i)$ for the various values of i. However, it is easier to apply than computing the expected profit for each i and then selecting the i which yields the largest expected profit.

For the probability functions $p(x)$ of interest in practice, the $\pi(i)$ function will look like that shown in Figure 4-1. However, we cannot prove that it will always look like Figure 4-1. Indeed, there exist probability functions for which $\pi(i)$ looks like Figure 4-3. An example of this is given in the problems. Also, in the problems we ask the reader to show how (4-31) can easily be generalized to handle such situations.

EXAMPLE. Let us now provide a simple example illustrating what has been discussed above. Suppose that a job shop has received an order to produce five high-tolerance helical gears. These will be produced on automatic machines which require essentially no operator attention after the jigs and programs for the machines have been set up. The production cost of each gear is $40, and if a defective is turned out, its scrap value is only $10. If an insufficient number of pieces is scheduled in the production run, three men will have to finish the job on the second shift at an additional cost of $120. It is desired to determine how many gears should be scheduled initially if the probability function for the random variable x is the following:

$$p(5) = 0.56, \quad p(6) = 0.28, \quad p(7) = 0.092,$$
$$p(8) = 0.045, \quad p(9) = 0.015, \quad p(10) = 0.008.$$

For the problem under consideration, $C = 40$, $R = 10$, and $V = 120$. Thus

$$\frac{C - R}{V} = \frac{30}{120} = 0.25.$$

We would like to find the smallest i for which $[p(i + 1)/P(i)] \leq 0.25$. Now $P(5) = p(5) = 0.56$ and for $i = 5$,

$$\frac{p(6)}{P(5)} = \frac{0.28}{0.56} = 0.50,$$

which is not less than or equal to 0.25. Next $P(6) = p(5) + p(6) = 0.84$, and for $i = 6$,

$$\frac{p(7)}{P(6)} = \frac{0.092}{0.84} = 0.109,$$

which is less than 0.25. Thus six units should be scheduled for the run, that is, one extra unit is scheduled as a scrap allowance.

In this section we have discussed the scrap allowance problem for a particular set of assumptions concerning what happens if the scrap allowance is not large enough. It will be clear to the reader that many things could occur in practice other than what we have described. For example, one might schedule another production run using the full setup with jigs. On this run one would once again be faced with the problem of what the scrap allowance should be.   If it turned out not to be enough, still another setup might be required, etc.   Such a procedure yields not a single stage but a sequential decision problem, because it could turn out that several setups might be required.   As still another alternative, one might imagine essentially the same sort of situation as described in this section, except that the men working on overtime would be paid only for the time worked, rather than for a full shift.   In this case instead of a flat cost V, there would be an additional cost T incurred per unit produced on overtime, so that the cost per unit produced on overtime is $T + C$.   We ask the reader to analyze this case in the problems.   It will turn out that here the criterion for determining the optimal i has precisely the same form as for the single stage inventory problem, and indeed in this case the scrap allowance problem can really be thought of as a single stage inventory problem of the type discussed in Section 4-3.   What then is the distinguishing feature which differentiates between the inventory problem as discussed in Section 4-3 and the scrap allowance problem as discussed in this section?   In the inventory problem, we assumed that for each unit demanded which could not be supplied there was a cost T, so that if r units were demanded which could not be supplied the cost was Tr; in other words, the shortage cost was *proportional* to the number of units demanded which could not be supplied.   In the scrap allowance problem, we assumed that if not enough units were scheduled, then a lump sum or fixed cost V was incurred regardless of how many units had to be produced on overtime.   The thing which led to different criteria in the two situations was then the use of a fixed cost of "underage" in this section rather than a proportional cost.   If we had used a proportional cost, then the problems would have been essentially the same.

4-6 THE EXPECTED COST OF UNCERTAINTY

It is often of interest to a decision maker to know what it would be worth to him if all uncertainty could be removed in a given situation.   We would like to study one approach to answering such a question in this section. We shall be assuming that monetary values can be used as utilities.   Now the question as posed above is difficult to answer in a simple way, because the value to the decision maker of determining ahead of time the state which nature is going to select may depend greatly on the particular state nature selects.   It will then be convenient to consider a slightly different situation.   Consider a single stage decision problem for which the set of states of nature is $E = \{e_1, \ldots, e_m\}$ and the probability function for the states of nature is $p_j = p(e_j)$, which we shall assume to be independent of the action selected. Let the set of actions be $A = \{a_1, \ldots, a_r\}$, and the profit be U_{ij} if action a_i is selected and the state of nature turns out to be e_j. Denote by π^* the maximum value of the expected profit over the possible actions in A.

Now suppose that the decision maker encounters this decision problem repeatedly. Suppose further that the long run relative frequency with which nature selects the state e_j is p_j. Imagine, however, that each time that the decision maker encounters this problem, he finds out ahead of time which state of nature is going to be selected. This state will vary from one occasion to the next, but each time the decision maker finds out in advance what it is going to be. If the decision maker knows that the state of nature is going to be e_k, then his profit will be one of the values U_{ik}, and he will select action v for which U_{vk} is the largest of the U_{ik}. Denote by M_k the maximum over i of the U_{ik}. Then when nature selects e_k, and the decision maker knows this ahead of time, his profit will be M_k. Let us now ask: What will be the long run average profit in this situation where the decision maker finds out in advance what state nature will select and nature selects e_j with the long run relative frequency p_j? This long run average profit, which we shall denote by π_c, is

$$\pi_c = \sum_{j=1}^{m} M_j p_j. \qquad (4\text{-}32)$$

The number π_c is called the *expected profit under certainty*. It is the long run average profit if the decision maker always finds out ahead of time what nature is going to do and chooses his action appropriately, and if nature, although not selecting the same action every time, selects e_j with long run relative frequency p_j. The reader should note that π_c has meaning only when the probabilities of the states of nature are independent of the action selected. This is, however, the case normally encountered.

Let us return to the situation where the decision maker does not know in advance what nature is going to do. Let a_s be an optimal action in this case, so that

$$\pi^* = \sum_{j=1}^{m} U_{sj} p_j.$$

Now since M_j is the largest of the U_{ij}, then $M_j \geq U_{sj}$, and since $p_j \geq 0$, $p_j M_j \geq p_j U_{sj}$. The inequality will still hold on summing over j. Hence

$$\sum_{j=1}^{m} M_j p_j \geq \sum_{j=1}^{m} U_{sj} p_j,$$

that is,

$$\pi_c \geq \pi^* \qquad (4\text{-}33)$$

as would be expected, since in determining π_c the decision maker knows what nature is going to do and can choose his action accordingly, while in determining π^* he does not know what will happen.

The number

$$\delta = \pi_c - \pi^* \tag{4-34}$$

is non-negative and is called the *expected cost of uncertainty*. The number δ gives us the long run average amount that the profit per decision could be increased by finding out ahead of time what nature was going to do. Thus δ is simply the maximum amount that the decision maker should be willing to pay to find out ahead of time what state nature is going to select. It is useful to know δ because if δ is small, it would be worth little to try to reduce the uncertainty, whereas if δ is large it would be desirable to try to obtain more information.

The expected cost of uncertainty can be computed from (4-34), regardless of whether the decision situation can be repeated. The number δ is useful to know even when a frequency interpretation is not possible, and it still represents the maximum amount one should be willing to pay to find out what state nature is going to select.

It is usually (but not always) straightforward to compute δ for any particular case of interest. We shall illustrate the procedure for the single stage inventory problem studied in Section 4-3. If the decision maker knew that j units were going to be demanded, he would stock precisely j units and his profit would be

$$M_j = (S - C)j. \tag{4-35}$$

Thus the expected profit under certainty is

$$\pi_c = (S - C) \sum_{j=0}^{m} jp(j) = (S - C)\mu_x, \tag{4-36}$$

where μ_x is the expected demand. Therefore

$$\delta = (S - C)\mu_x - \pi^*, \tag{4-37}$$

where π^* is the optimal value of the expected profit, that is, the expected profit when i^* is stocked.

Let us compute δ for the inventory problem studied in Example 3 of Section 4-2. We saw that $\pi^* = 3.225$. Furthermore,

$$\mu_x = 0(0.10) + 1(0.20) + 2(0.20) + 3(0.30) + 4(0.15) + 5(0.05) = 2.35.$$

Also,

$$S - C = 5.50 - 3.50 = 2.00.$$

Hence

$$\pi_c = (2.00)(2.35) = 4.70,$$

and

$$\delta = 4.70 - 3.225 = \$1.475.$$

The expected cost of uncertainty is \$1.475.

4-7 OPPORTUNITY LOSS

The action that a decision maker would select in a single stage decision problem if he knew what nature was going to do, would in general vary with the state e_j that nature happened to select and would normally be different from the action determined by solving the problem in the manner discussed in Section 4-1.   Let us continue to use the notation and assumptions introduced in the previous section, and imagine that the decision maker selects an arbitrary action a_i.   If the state of nature turns out to be e_j, the profit resulting from the selection of this action will be U_{ij}. If the decision maker knew ahead of time that the state of nature was to be e_j, he could have received a profit M_j, which is the largest of the U_{ij} for the given j.   The non-negative number $M_j - U_{ij}$ is called *the opportunity loss* associated with selecting action a_i when the state of nature turns out to be e_j.   The opportunity loss is the difference between what the profit could have been if he had selected the action most appropriate to e_j, and what it is when action a_i is selected.   Let us write

$$L_{ij} = M_j - U_{ij}, \tag{4-38}$$

so that L_{ij} is the opportunity loss when the action a_i is selected and the state of nature turns out to be e_j.   The opportunity loss is also sometimes referred to as the *regret* on taking action a_i when the state of nature turns out to be e_j.   Regret is a shorter term and conveys the idea quite well, and hence we shall use the word regret more frequently than opportunity loss.   For each action-state of nature pair (a_i, e_j), there is determined a number L_{ij} which is the regret when action a_i is taken and the state of nature turns out to be e_j.   If a_i happens to be the best action to take when e_j is the state of nature, then the regret is 0, $L_{ij} = 0$.   We can thus construct in place of the payoff table a table giving the regrets.   Such a table will be referred to as a *regret table*.   We might observe that we can determine a regret table regardless of whether the utility function for the decision maker is representable by monetary values.   If it is not, however, then the numerical values of the regrets will have no particular meaning.

For a given i, the L_{ij} can be looked on as the values of a random variable L which we shall call the regret or opportunity loss.   Let us denote the expected regret or expected opportunity loss on taking action a_i by $\gamma(i)$.   Then $\gamma(i)$ is the expected value of L for action a_i, and

$$\gamma(i) = \sum_{j=1}^{m} L_{ij} p_j. \tag{4-39}$$

Since L_{ij} is given by (4-38), we have

$$\gamma(i) = \sum_{j=1}^{m} (M_j - U_{ij}) p_j = \sum_{j=1}^{m} M_j p_j - \sum_{j=1}^{m} U_{ij} p_j = \pi_c - \pi(i), \tag{4-40}$$

where π_c is the expected profit under certainty and $\pi(i)$ is the expected profit when action a_i is selected. Now a_k is an optimal action if $\pi(k)$ is the largest of the $\pi(i)$. However, from (4-40), if $\pi(k)$ is the largest of the $\pi(i)$, $\gamma(k)$ is the smallest of the expected regrets $\gamma(i)$. *We have proved therefore that we shall determine an optimal action if we proceed by minimizing the expected regret rather than maximizing the expected utility.* Sometimes it is more convenient to minimize the expected regret than it is to maximize the expected utility, and hence we shall occasionally use this latter criterion. This criterion applies, however, only when the probabilities of the states of nature are independent of the action selected.

One can use incremental analysis to minimize the expected regret just as it could be used to maximize the expected utility. If the function

$$D(i) = \gamma(i) - \gamma(i-1) \qquad (4\text{-}41)$$

changes sign only once, then when i^* is the smallest i for which $D(i+1) \geq 0$, a_{i^*} is an optimal action. We might now make one interesting connection with the material of the last section. Let γ^* be the minimum expected regret. Then we must have

$$\gamma^* = \pi_c - \pi^*, \qquad (4\text{-}42)$$

where π^* is the maximum expected profit. On comparison with (4-34), we see that $\gamma^* = \delta$, that is, the *minimum expected regret is the expected cost of uncertainty.*

EXAMPLE. Consider once again the single stage inventory problem studied in Section 4-3. Let us determine the regret L_{ij} if we stock i units and the demand turns out to be j. If $i = j$, $L_{ij} = 0$ since stocking i units is the best action for this state of nature. If $i > j$, there is a regret of $(C - R)(i - j)$, because for each unit not demanded we suffer a loss of $C - R$. If $j > i$, the regret is $(S - C + T)(j - i)$ because we lose the profit of $S - C$ on each unit demanded which cannot be supplied, and in addition incur a shortage cost of T. Thus

$$L_{ij} = \begin{cases} (C - R)(i - j), & j < i, \\ 0, & j = i, \\ (S - C + T)(j - i), & j > i. \end{cases} \qquad (4\text{-}43)$$

If we plot a bar diagram illustrating L_{ij} as a function of j for a given i, we obtain something like Figure 4-4. When looked at in terms of regrets, the problem of deciding how many units to stock can be imagined as one in which one tries to strike a balance between two costs, a cost of overage and a cost of underage. The cost of overage is $C - R$ per unit not demanded, and the cost of underage is $S - C + T$ for each unit demanded which cannot be supplied. The optimal number of units to stock is that which minimizes the expected value of the sum of these costs.

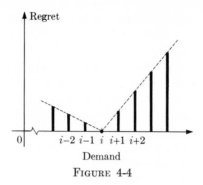

FIGURE 4-4

In the problems, we ask the reader to obtain (4-18) from minimizing regrets.

4-8 PERIODIC REVIEW INVENTORY SYSTEMS

Not infrequently, problems are encountered which at first sight look like multistage decision problems, but which can in fact be solved as single stage problems. We would like to study one such problem in this section. A navy supply depot stocks a very large number of different items which are used at naval bases and on ships of the fleet. Consider a particular spare part which has been used for years and which will continue to be used indefinitely into the future. The supply depot follows a policy of ordering additional stocks of many of the items once a month. A computer is used as an aid in controlling the depot's inventory levels, and once a month the computer will determine how many units were demanded, how many were received and from this, what the current inventory level is. The decision as to how many units should be ordered will be based on the current inventory level. To smooth out the work load for the computer, not all items are considered on the same day of the month. In fact, the computer examines a given item not on the same day every month, but instead after every thirty day period, the work load being spread out so that only about five percent of the items are being examined on any given day. The particular spare part under consideration is one of those whose inventory status is examined once during each thirty-day period, and it is only at these review times that additional stock is ordered.

The depot has maintained records of the number of units of this spare part demanded in each thirty-day period, over a number of years. These data indicate that this demand can be looked upon as a random variable x whose probability function is $p(x)$. There are no noticeable seasonal patterns to the demand.   Neither do there seem to be any long term trends. Thus regardless of what thirty-day period is being considered, the probability that j units will be demanded in that period can be imagined to be $p(j)$.

Let us next consider the costs involved in stocking this spare part.   The depot does not sell the items, and hence no revenues are received as a result of filling demands.   However, the navy must pay for each unit the depot procures from the manufacturer.   We shall suppose that the price, which is determined by a contract between the navy and the manufacturer, is C dollars per unit.   The cost per unit is independent of how many units the depot happens to order in any given month, that is, it does not receive, for example, discounts for ordering in large quantities.   Thus if i units are ordered, the cost of these units is Ci dollars.   In addition to the cost of the units, it costs the navy something to maintain an inventory of the part under consideration.   There are a variety of factors which enter into this cost of carrying inventory, such as insurance, operating costs of the warehouse, loss due to breakage, etc.   In addition, if the navy did not have its money tied up in inventory, it could be used elsewhere, so that an opportunity cost is involved.   We shall not attempt to determine the carrying cost with great accuracy; we shall simply assume that for each unit on hand at the end of the period, just prior to ordering more inventory, a carrying cost of R is incurred.   We are then basing the carrying cost for a thirty-day period on the on-hand inventory at the end of the period. This might seem a very crude way to handle the carrying cost, but it is often adequate in practice.   Thus if j units are on hand at the end of the period, a carrying cost of Rj is incurred for the period.   Finally, let us consider what takes place if the depot is out of stock when a demand for the spare part occurs.   If this happens, the depot takes emergency action and contacts other depots to see if they can supply the unit.   If so, they make a rush shipment directly to the base where the unit is demanded. If no one else can supply the unit, then as a last resort the depot goes directly to the manufacturer.   This latter action is almost never needed, however.   It is hard to estimate precisely the cost of having a demand occur when the depot is out of stock.   However, the depot commander feels it an adequate approximation to assume that a cost T is incurred for each unit demanded which must be obtained by emergency procedures because the depot has no stock on hand.

When at a review time an order is placed for additional stock, it will take some time before this stock is actually shipped from the manufacturer and is in the warehouse ready for use.   This time lag between placement of the order and the time when it is available in the warehouse is called the procurement lead time.   The procurement lead time may be several months or only a day or so.   It will be very convenient in our study of this problem to imagine that the procurement lead time is 0, so that the units are received in the warehouse as soon as the order is placed. For short lead times this may be an adequate approximation to the situation, whereas for longer lead times it will be a very poor approximation. We shall assume a zero lead time simply because it makes the problem much easier to visualize when studying it for the first time.

Let us now study the nature of the problem. At each review time it must be decided how many units of the spare part to order. Between each decision a random experiment is performed which determines the demand for the period. It would appear then that we are dealing with a multistage decision problem, and this is indeed true. The interesting thing, however, is that it can be reduced to a single stage decision problem. To do this it is convenient to imagine that the depot will go on stocking the item forever, so that the process will never terminate. The problem then becomes what we can refer to as an infinite stage decision problem. This might appear to complicate things, but in reality it simplifies them, since through this artifice we eliminate any problems which could arise due to phasing out the item and then ultimately not stocking it any longer. Consequently, regardless of what review time we consider, there are an unending number of decisions yet to be made. In reality then, when the decision maker looks into the future, each review time looks like every other review time.

Consider now the problem the decision maker faces at a review time. Suppose that there are u units of the item in inventory, and the decision maker wants to determine how many additional units to order. If he orders i units, then immediately after placing the order, $h = u + i$ units will be on hand in inventory, since we assume that the procurement lead time is 0. The crucial thing to observe now is that if at some given review time it is optimal to order i units when u units are on hand, then at every review it will be optimal to order i units when the inventory on hand prior to placing the order is u. In other words, if we have a decision rule which tells us how much to order given the amount on hand, which is the optimal one to use at a particular stage, it will be the optimal one to use for all stages. The reason for this lies in the fact that the process is assumed never to terminate, and hence the situation facing the decision maker when u units are on hand is the same regardless of what the stage happens to be. Thus the infinite stage decision problem reduces to one of determining a decision rule which tells how much to order when the on-hand inventory has any value u. This observation alone is sufficient to reduce the problem to a single stage problem. However, before doing so we shall see that the problem can be simplified even more.

We saw that if u units are on hand before ordering and if i units are ordered, then $h = u + i$ units will be on hand immediately after ordering.

Observe next that if at any stage the optimal on-hand inventory after ordering is h, then it should be h after every order is placed regardless of what the size of the order may be. We shall not attempt to prove this rigorously. If quantity discounts were offered, then it would not in general be true that one should always bring the inventory level up to some value h, since there might be advantages to placing large orders. However, when the cost of the order is proportional to the number of units ordered, no order size has an advantage over any other order size. What we are suggesting, but not rigorously proving, is that there is a number h which should always be the inventory level after ordering, that is, if u units are on hand before ordering, one should order $i = h - u$. Thus the problem is reduced to determining an optimal value for h. We shall now see how this can be done.

We shall be assuming, as usual, that monetary values reflect accurately the navy's feelings, so that we can proceed by maximizing the expected profit or by minimizing the expected regret. It will be convenient here to use regrets. But how shall we measure regrets? Since the process takes place over time, we should introduce discounting to take account of the time phasing of the costs. We should then use the expected value of the discounted regret. The regret in period n, when h is specified, will be a random variable which is a function of the demand in the period. If we denote by $L\{n\}$ the random variable representing the regret in period n, then the random variable L representing the discounted regret is related to the $L\{n\}$ by

$$L = \frac{L\{1\}}{1 + i} + \frac{L\{2\}}{(1 + i)^2} + \frac{L\{3\}}{(1 + i)^3} + \cdots. \tag{4-44}$$

However, according to (1-62) the expected value of (1-61) is (1-62), that is, if μ_L is the expected value of L and μ_n is the expected value of $L\{n\}$, then

$$\mu_L = \frac{\mu_1}{1 + i} + \frac{\mu_2}{(1 + i)^2} + \frac{\mu_3}{(1 + i)^3} + \cdots. \tag{4-45}$$

Equation (1-62) holds for an arbitrarily large number of random variables, and hence it will apply to the case under consideration, since in discounting, the terms in the distant future do not contribute significantly to the discounted value. Thus (4-44) and (4-45) can be approximated as closely as we please by a finite sum.

The next thing to observe is that the expected regret per period when we begin the period with h units on hand, is independent of n. Let us denote this number by $\gamma(h)$ so that

$$\mu_n = \gamma(h), \quad \text{all } n,$$

and then

$$\mu_L = \gamma(h)[\rho + \rho^2 + \rho^3 + \cdots], \quad \rho = \frac{1}{1 + i}. \tag{4-46}$$

Now

$$\rho + \rho^2 + \rho^3 + \cdots$$

is just some positive number, call it α. Thus

$$\mu_L = \alpha\gamma(h). \tag{4-47}$$

Since μ_L and $\gamma(h)$ are proportional, that value of h which minimizes the expected discounted regret μ_L will minimize $\gamma(h)$, the expected regret per period, and conversely, if h minimizes $\gamma(h)$ it minimizes μ_L. We have thus proved the interesting result that the same h will be obtained by minimizing the expected regret per period as will be obtained by minimizing the expected discounted regret.

To determine the optimal stock to have on hand after ordering, we only need to minimize $\gamma(h)$, the expected regret per period. The reader will now observe that the problem has been reduced to a single stage decision problem, and in fact, to a single stage inventory problem. We could now apply (4-18) by interpreting the symbols properly. Let us instead, however, derive the criterion directly using incremental regrets. What is the change in the regret if instead of stocking h, we stock $h + 1$ units at the beginning of each period in cases where the demand for the period turns out to be j? If $j < h + 1$, we simply incur a regret of R, the carrying charge for the extra unit stocked. If $j \geq h + 1$, the regret decreases because we save a stockout charge of T, that is, the change in regret is $-T$. Hence if Δ_j is the change in regret on changing from having h to $h + 1$ units on hand in cases where the demand is j, then

$$\Delta_j = \begin{cases} R, & j < h + 1, \\ -T, & j \geq h + 1. \end{cases} \tag{4-48}$$

The expected regret is

$$D(h + 1) = R \sum_{j=0}^{h} p(j) - T \sum_{j=h+1}^{m} p(j) = RP(h) - T[1 - P(h)]. \tag{4-49}$$

The smallest h for which $D(h + 1) \geq 0$ is optimal, that is, if h^* is the smallest h for which

$$P(h) \geq \frac{T}{R + T}, \tag{4-50}$$

then h^* is the optimal number of units to have on hand after ordering and $i^* = h^* - u$ is the optimal quantity to order, where u is the quantity on hand just prior to ordering. We have then solved the inventory problem under consideration. An optimal ordering rule is one in which we order a sufficient quantity to bring the on-hand inventory up to h^* after the order arrives. Note that the cost of the item does not appear explicitly in (4-50). It appears indirectly, however, because the carrying cost R will in general be proportional to the cost of the item. There is nothing in (4-50) which requires that the period between placing orders be thirty days. It can be anything at all. However, as the length of the period changes, then $p(x)$ must be changed accordingly.

EXAMPLE. One item which the navy depot stocks is a large radar tube which costs $500. The carrying cost per month (30-day period) on this tube amounts to $8. If a demand occurs when the depot is out of stock an extra cost of $100 is incurred. The probability function for the demand for this tube in a 30-day period has been estimated to be

$$p(0) = 0.30, \quad p(1) = 0.30, \quad p(2) = 0.20,$$
$$p(3) = 0.10, \quad p(4) = 0.07, \quad p(5) = 0.03.$$

No more than five tubes have ever been demanded in a 30-day period. The cumulative distribution for the demand is then

$$P(0) = 0.30, \quad P(1) = 0.60, \quad P(2) = 0.80,$$
$$P(3) = 0.90, \quad P(4) = 0.97, \quad P(5) = 1.0.$$

Now $R = 8$ and $T = 100$, so $T/(R + T) = 100/108 = 0.925$. The smallest h for which $P(h) \geq 0.925$ is $h = 4$. Therefore, if it is valid to assume that the procurement lead time is very short, a sufficient quantity should always be ordered to bring the on-hand inventory up to four tubes.

The inventory problem discussed in this section is the simplest of all multistage type inventory problems. A number of very restrictive assumptions were made to simplify the situation as much as possible. The problem was not presented to illustrate a realistic inventory model, but instead to illustrate how multistage problems can in certain cases be reduced to a single stage problem. What allowed us to do this was introducing the notion that the system would operate for all future time, and the assumption that the nature of the demand-generating mechanism and the costs did not change with time. Such a situation is referred to as a *steady state* situation. We shall not attempt to modify the model to account for nonzero lead times or to delve much more deeply into inventory theory. A detailed development of inventory models can be found in the text which the author has written in collaboration with T. M. Whitin [2].

*4-9 PROBABILITIES NOT KNOWN

The mathematical model of a single stage decision problem which we have been using assumes that the probabilities of the states of nature are known.

* Starred sections contain material which deviates somewhat from the main line of development. These sections may be omitted without loss of continuity.

The theory does not take into account how vague the decision maker may be about these probabilities, but rather treats the numbers assigned to the probabilities as if they were the correct numbers.   One might ask the question, "What should the decision maker do if he knows absolutely nothing about the probabilities of the states of nature?"   Clearly, in such a case the decision maker is in rather bad shape, and there is a limit to what mathematical analysis can do to help.   There is some question as to whether situations are ever encountered in which the decision maker has no basis whatever for estimating the probabilities.   Nonetheless, it is not unreasonable to study at least briefly such situations.   As a matter of fact, the case where the probabilities of the states of nature are not known has received quite a bit of attention, and a variety of rules have been suggested for selecting an action in such cases.   Unfortunately, none of these rules is very satisfactory.   We shall very briefly survey in this section the five most important rules which have been proposed.

Suppose that we are considering a single stage decision problem with m states of nature and r possible actions, and that the utility of each (a_i, e_j) pair is known.   The probabilities of the states of nature will be assumed to be unknown.   We can then construct a payoff table such as that in Table 4-1, except that no probabilities will appear.   We would like to decide what action the decision maker should take in this case. Clearly the payoff table gives us information which should be useful, and it may make it possible to rule out some actions immediately.   For example, if $U_{ij} \geq U_{kj}$ for each j, then action a_i will be at least as good as action a_k, since regardless of what the state of nature turns out to be, the utility received from action a_i is at least as great as that from action a_k. In such a case we say that action a_i *dominates* action a_k.   Let us then drop all actions which are dominated by other actions.   Once this is done, the situation is more complicated, because one action will be preferred if one state of nature should occur while another will be preferred for a different state.   We shall now consider five possible ways to select an action.   To illustrate each of these as they are discussed, we shall use the decision problem whose payoff table is shown in Table 4-5.

TABLE 4-5

PAYOFF TABLE FOR EXAMPLE

	e_1	e_2	e_3	e_4
a_1	2	5	1	3
a_2	6	4	2	0
a_3	3	1	5	2

1. LAPLACE CRITERION. Laplace, in discussing other matters, suggested a procedure which can be used here. He said that if nothing is known one simply assumes that the states of nature are equally likely, so that if there are m states of nature, one sets $p_j = 1/m$. This is merely a subjective evaluation of the probabilities and reduces the problem to the case we have been considering. Thus one computes

$$\frac{1}{m} \sum_{j=1}^{m} U_{ij} \tag{4-51}$$

for each i and selects the action which yields the largest of these numbers. Now the largest of the numbers (4-51) can be found by selecting the largest of the numbers $\sum_{j=1}^{m} U_{ij}$. It is unnecessary to divide by m. For the example of Table 4-5, if we sum the numbers in each row, we obtain respectively 11, 12, and 11. The number 12 corresponding to row 2 is the largest, and thus according to the Laplace criterion action a_2 would be selected. This rule does not seem especially sound unless one actually has reason to believe that the states are equally likely.

2. MAX-MIN CRITERION. This criterion, which was suggested by the theory of two-person games, is very conservative or pessimistic in the sense that it assumes that nature will do the worst thing possible. Denote by U_i^+ the smallest utility in row i. Then the action to be selected is the one which yields the largest U_i^+. We can say then that we choose the action which maximizes the minimum utility. The U_i^+ for the example of Table 4-5 are respectively 1, 0, and 1. The largest of these numbers is 1, and this occurs for either a_1 or a_3. Thus according to the max-min criterion the decision maker would select either a_1 or a_3. Note that when monetary values can be used as utilities, it follows that the max-min criterion protects one against large losses, but takes no account whatever of possible large profits to be made.

3. MAX-MAX CRITERION. This is a very optimistic criterion. It assumes that the best imaginable outcome will occur. Let U_i^* be the largest of the U_{ij} in row i. Then the action to select is the one which yields the largest of the U_i^*, i.e., the action whose row in the payoff table contains the largest number U_{ij} in the payoff table. For the example in Table 4-5, the U_i^* are respectively 5, 6, and 5. Hence according to the max-max criterion action a_2 should be selected.

4. THE OPTIMISM INDEX. This criterion, suggested by Hurwicz, is a combination of 2 and 3 above. Let U_i^+ be defined as in 2 and U_i^* as in 3. Then consider the numbers

$$\hat{U}_i(\alpha) = \alpha U_i^* + (1 - \alpha)U_i^+, \quad 0 \le \alpha \le 1. \tag{4-52}$$

Now imagine that the decision maker selects a value of α, $0 \le \alpha \le 1$, and computes $\hat{U}_i(\alpha)$ for each i. The action he is to select is then the one corresponding to the largest of the $\hat{U}_i(\alpha)$ values. The number α is called the decision maker's *optimism index*. When $\alpha = 0$, he uses a max-min criterion, and when $\alpha = 1$, he uses a max-max criterion. Thus one can imagine that the larger the value of α he selects, the more optimistic he is. Rather than solving the example of Table 4-5 for a particular α, we shall illustrate geometrically what the situation is for all α. Note that $\hat{U}_i(\alpha)$ can be written

$$\hat{U}_i(\alpha) = U_i^+ + \alpha(U_i^* - U_i^+),$$

and if we plot $\hat{U}_i(\alpha)$ as a function of α, we obtain a straight line. There will be generated a straight line for each value of i, that is, for each action. The three $\hat{U}_i(\alpha)$ functions are

$$\hat{U}_1(\alpha) = 1 + 4\alpha; \quad \hat{U}_2(\alpha) = 6\alpha; \quad \hat{U}_3(\alpha) = 1 + 4\alpha.$$

Note that $\hat{U}_1(\alpha)$ and $\hat{U}_3(\alpha)$ are the same. The resulting two lines are shown in Figure 4-5. The action to be selected is the one with the largest

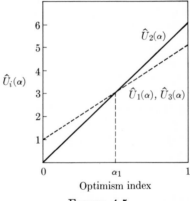

FIGURE 4-5

$\hat{U}_i(\alpha)$. From Figure 4-5 it is seen that for $\alpha < \alpha_1$, a_1 (or a_3) is the action to use. When $\alpha = \alpha_1$, $\hat{U}_1 = \hat{U}_2 = \hat{U}_3$, and any one of the actions can be used. When $\alpha > \alpha_1$, action a_2 is the one to select. We see from Figure 4-5 that the decision maker does not need to determine with great accuracy what he thinks his value of α is, since for any α such that $0 \leq \alpha \leq \alpha_1$, he will select action a_1 (or a_3) while for any α, $\alpha_1 \leq \alpha \leq 1$ he will select a_2. The same sort of thing will apply when there are more actions. There will be a range of α values for which a given action will be the one to be selected. This action will change from one range of α's to another, however.

5. MIN-MAX REGRET. Savage has suggested that instead of using the max-min criterion it might be more appropriate to minimize the maximum regret. Let L_{ij} be the regret when the decision maker selects action a_i and the state of nature turns out to be e_j. Let L_i^+ be the largest of the regrets for action i. Then one selects the action for which L_i^+ is the smallest. Recall that $L_{ij} = M_j - U_{ij}$, where M_j is the largest of the U_{ij} values in column j of the payoff table. A table of regrets for the example of Table 4-5 is given in Table 4-6. We see that the values of

TABLE 4-6

REGRET TABLE FOR EXAMPLE

	e_1	e_2	e_3	e_4
a_1	4	0	4	0
a_2	0	1	3	3
a_3	3	4	0	1

the L_i^+ are respectively 4, 3, and 4. The smallest L_i^+ is 3 and occurs for a_2. Thus a_2 is the action to be selected.

We have now introduced the most important rules which have been suggested to cope with the case when nothing is known about the probabilities of the states of nature. It will be clear to the reader that the rules leave something to be desired. Some specific objections will be considered in the problems. For the simple example used to illustrate the rules, it is notable that each of the three actions seemed appropriate according to at least one of the rules.

4-10 MIXED STRATEGIES

For problems where the probabilities of the states of nature are not known, a decision maker might have considerable difficulty deciding which of two or more actions he really preferred. In desperation, to decide among two competing actions, he might toss a coin and use one action if the coin landed heads up and the other if it landed tails up. This suggests an interesting procedure which could be used to select an action. Instead of deciding what action to take, the decision maker could instead play a game of chance and let the outcome of the game determine the action to be used. It might seem ridiculous to suggest to a businessman that he flip a coin to decide whether to build a plant or not, and indeed normally it is. However, it is interesting to pursue this idea a little further. Consider a single stage lottery in which the prizes are the actions a_i, and the probability of obtaining the prize a_i is q_i. We can then represent this lottery symbolically by

$$\{(q_1, a_1), (q_2, a_2), \ldots, (q_r, a_r)\}. \tag{4-53}$$

One way the decision maker could select an action then is to play this lottery, and the action he would take would be the prize he won. In Section 3-3 we introduced the notion of a strategy for multistage or sequential decision problems. A strategy was a prescription which told the decision maker what action to take each time he had to make a decision. It is convenient to refer to the use of a game of chance to select an action as a particular type of strategy for single stage problems. We shall refer to the game of chance as a *mixed strategy*. A mixed strategy does not tell the decision maker what action to take before playing the game of chance—in this sense it differs from what we called a strategy for multistage problems. It does, however, tell him what action to take for every possible outcome of the game, and in this sense it is similar to a strategy for multistage problems. It also specifies the probability that each action will be taken. When we say that a decision maker is using a mixed strategy, we mean that he does not decide what action to take but plays a lottery whose outcome determines the action to take. The decision maker does not know himself what action will be used until after playing the lottery. We shall refer to a rule which simply says take action a_i as a *pure strategy*. There are r different pure strategies, one for each action, so that the pure strategy i says take action a_i.

To characterize a mixed strategy, it is necessary to specify for each i the probability q_i that a_i will be the action selected by the game of chance. For every different set of probabilities q_i, we obtain a different mixed strategy. There are thus an infinite number of different mixed strategies for the single stage decision problem under consideration. Note that a pure strategy can be looked upon as a special case of a mixed strategy, since the mixed strategy with $q_i = 0$, $i \neq k$, and $q_k = 1$ is equivalent to the pure strategy which says take action a_k. The reason for this is that if $q_k = 1$ we can imagine that the lottery will always say to use action a_k.

The decision maker was originally faced with the problem of selecting one of a finite number of actions. We then suggested that he might not be able to decide what action to take and would let a game of chance decide this for him, that is, he would use a mixed strategy. However, there are an infinite number of different mixed strategies he could use, that is, an infinite number of different lotteries he could play. How does he decide which lottery is most suitable? This would appear to be a more difficult problem than selecting an action. We can then ask the questions:

How should he select a mixed strategy, and what can possibly be gained by introducing mixed strategies?   Let us now examine these questions.

To select a mixed strategy, the decision maker could simply apply one of the rules discussed in the previous section.   We shall not bother to illustrate here how all of these can be generalized to apply to selecting mixed strategies; the procedure will be illustrated only for the max-min criterion, the generalization of the other rules being left to the problems. Note that when a mixed strategy is used, the decision maker does not know what his utility will turn out to be if the state of nature turns out to be e_j, since this will depend on what action the lottery tells him to select.   However, it is possible for him to compute his expected utility if the state of nature turns out to be e_j.   His expected utility is then

$$\sum_{i=1}^{r} q_i U_{ij} = q_1 U_{1j} + \cdots + q_r U_{rj}, \tag{4-54}$$

since the probability that the utility will be U_{ij} is q_i.   The expected utility will depend on the mixed strategy chosen, in other words, on the values of the q_i.   Let us now explain how the max-min criterion can be generalized to treat mixed strategies.   For a given mixed strategy we have an expected utility (4-54) for each state of nature.   Denote by w the smallest of these expected utilities, that is, the minimum of (4-54) over j.   Now w will change as the mixed strategy changes.   Suppose that we find that set of numbers q_i, $i = 1, \ldots, r$ satisfying

$$q_i \geq 0, \quad i = 1, \ldots, r, \quad \sum_{i=1}^{r} q_i = 1,$$

which yields the largest possible value of w.   This set of q_i (which may not be unique) defines a mixed strategy which we shall call the max-min mixed strategy.   This is the way the max-min criterion is generalized to handle mixed strategies.

Let us now see how a max-min strategy can be determined.   When w is the smallest of the m numbers (4-54), it must be true that

$$\sum_{i=1}^{r} q_i U_{ij} \geq w, \quad j = 1, \ldots, m,$$

with the strict equality holding for at least one j.   We wish to find a set of q_i such that w is as large as possible.   In other words, we wish to determine a set of numbers $q_1, \ldots, q_r$ and a number w satisfying

$$\sum_{i=1}^{r} q_i U_{ij} - w \geq 0, \quad j = 1, \ldots, m,$$

$$\sum_{i=1}^{r} q_i = 1, \quad q_i \geq 0, \quad i = 1, \ldots, r, \tag{4-55}$$

such that w has the largest value possible. This is a type of problem referred to as a linear programming problem. Therefore, by solving this linear programming problem, one can determine a max-min strategy. We shall not attempt to illustrate the use of linear programming to determine max-min strategies. Instead, in the next section, we shall illustrate how such strategies can be determined by the use of an interesting type of geometrical analysis in the case where there are only two different states of nature. We shall also examine in the next section the question of what is to be gained by using a mixed strategy.

*4-11 GEOMETRIC INTERPRETATION

Let us consider a single stage decision problem in which there are only two states of nature, e_1 and e_2, and two actions a_1 and a_2. A mixed strategy is then characterized by specifying the probability q that action a_1 will be selected by the lottery, since the probability that action a_2 will be selected is $1 - q$. The expected utilities if the state of nature turns out to be e_1 or e_2 are respectively

$$qU_{11} + (1 - q)U_{21} = U_{21} + q(U_{11} - U_{21}) = x(q), \qquad (4\text{-}56)$$

$$qU_{12} + (1 - q)U_{22} = U_{22} + q(U_{12} - U_{22}) = y(q). \qquad (4\text{-}57)$$

The first of these we have denoted by $x(q)$ and the second by $y(q)$; $x(q)$ and $y(q)$ are, respectively, the expected utility when the state of nature turns out to be e_1 and a_1 is selected with probability q, and the expected utility if the state of nature turns out to be e_2 and a_1 is selected with probability q. Now observe that (x, y) can be plotted as a point in the xy-plane. We shall next show how to illustrate graphically the set of all points $(x(q), y(q))$ generated as q takes on all possible values $0 \le q \le 1$.

Note that for $q = 1$, $x(q) = U_{11}$ and $y(q) = U_{12}$. This mixed strategy is simply the pure strategy which says to take action a_1, that is, the point (U_{11}, U_{12}) in the plane corresponds to the pure strategy a_1. If $q = 0$, $1 - q = 1$ and $x(q) = U_{21}$ and $y(q) = U_{22}$. This mixed strategy is the pure strategy which says to take action a_2, that is, the point (U_{21}, U_{22}) in the plane corresponds to the pure strategy a_2. Next observe that when $0 < q < 1$, $x(q)$ lies between U_{11} and U_{21} and $y(q)$ lies between U_{12} and U_{22}. We can easily relate $x(q)$ and $y(q)$, since if we solve (4-56) for q, we obtain

$$q = \frac{x(q) - U_{21}}{U_{11} - U_{21}},$$

and if we substitute this into (4-57), we have

$$y(q) = \left(\frac{U_{12} - U_{22}}{U_{11} - U_{21}}\right) x(q) + U_{22} - U_{21}\left(\frac{U_{12} - U_{22}}{U_{11} - U_{21}}\right). \qquad (4\text{-}58)$$

Hence $y(q)$ is related to $x(q)$ by a linear equation, and the points $(x(q), y(q))$ must lie on a straight line. Furthermore, since $x(q)$ lies between U_{11} and U_{21} and $y(q)$ lies between U_{12} and U_{22}, the set of points $(x(q), y(q))$ corresponding to all mixed strategies must just be that part of the line (4-58) which joins (U_{11}, U_{12}) to (U_{21}, U_{22}). Let us illustrate this geometrically with an example. Suppose that the payoff table for the two action, two states of nature problem under consideration is that shown in Table 4-7.

TABLE 4-7

	e_1	e_2
a_1	1	3
a_2	5	2

The points corresponding to the pure strategies a_1 and a_2 are then $(1, 3)$ and $(5, 2)$, respectively. These are plotted in Figure 4-6. The set of all points corresponding to all mixed strategies is then the line segment joining these two points as shown in Figure 4-6. In particular, if we choose $q = 0.2$, then from (4-56) and (4-57)

$$x(q) = 5 + 0.2(1 - 5) = 5 - 0.8 = 4.2; \quad y(q) = 2 + 0.2(3 - 2) = 2.2.$$

This point does indeed lie on the line segment and is indicated in Figure 4-6.

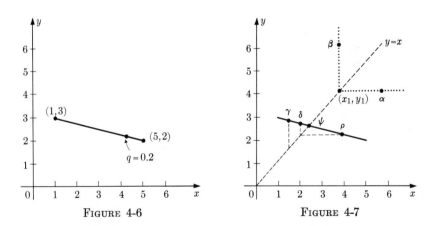

FIGURE 4-6　　　　　　　　　　FIGURE 4-7

We shall now show how a max-min mixed strategy for the example of Table 4-7 can be determined with the aid of Figure 4-6. We wish to find that q for which the smaller of $x(q)$ and $y(q)$ is as large as possible. For any point $(x(q), y(q))$ with $y(q) > x(q)$, then $x(q)$ is the smaller number, whereas if $x(q) > y(q)$, then $y(q)$ is the smaller number. If $x(q) = y(q)$, either one can be looked upon as the smaller. If there is a q for which $x(q) = y(q)$, then this point lies on the line $y = x$ which makes a 45 degree angle with the x-axis. In Figure 4-7 we have reproduced the situation in Figure 4-6 and have also shown the line $y = x$. Consider a particular point (x_1, y_1) on the line $y = x$, and the horizontal and vertical lines emanating from the point as shown in Figure 4-7. Note that any point α on the horizontal line has the form (x, y_1), $x > y_1$, and the minimum of x and y_1 is thus y_1. Similarly, any point β on the vertical line can be written as (x_1, y), $y > x_1$ so that the smaller of x_1 and y is x_1. Consequently, for any point (x, y) on either the horizontal or vertical line emanating from (x_1, y_1), the minimum value of x and y is $x_1 = y_1$.

To determine the optimal max-min mixed strategy, we wish to find that point on the line segment in Figure 4-6 whose smallest coordinate is as large as possible. Let us select a point on this line segment, say the point γ shown in Figure 4-7. Its smallest coordinate is the x-coordinate. Is this point the one on the line segment with its smallest coordinate as large as possible? Clearly not, because the points δ and ρ both have a smallest coordinate which is larger than that of γ. Observe that the x-coordinate is the smallest one for δ and the y-coordinate is the smallest one for ρ. The smallest coordinates have the same value for both of these points, however. It is now clear that the point whose smallest coordinate is as large as possible is the point ψ where the 45° line cuts the line segment under consideration. We can easily find the mixed strategy which yields this point, since it is the point such that $x(q) = y(q)$. For the example under consideration,

$$x(q) = 5 - 4q, \quad y(q) = 2 + q.$$

Hence

$$5 - 4q = 2 + q \quad \text{or} \quad 5q = 3,$$

that is,

$$q = \tfrac{3}{5} = 0.60.$$

The max-min mixed strategy is then unique and is the one which selects action a_1 with probability 0.60.

Let us now ask what is gained by using a max-min mixed strategy rather than by simply selecting the max-min criterion action. If we applied the max-min criterion of the previous section to determine the action to take, it would be a_2 for the example of Table 4-7, and the worst that could result would be a utility of 2 if e_2 occurred. Now if the max-min mixed strategy is used, the expected utility is the same regardless of which state of nature occurs and has the value $y(0.6) = 2 + 0.6 = 2.6$. This is larger than the worst that can happen if the decision maker simply uses a max-min action. Thus by introducing mixed strategies it is possible to increase the expected utility of the worst outcome. Observe carefully, however, that the worst utility the decision maker may actually encounter can be much worse using a max-min mixed strategy rather than a max-min action. Only the expected utility is increased. In particular, for the example under consideration, if the chance mechanism selects a_1 and the state of nature turns out to be e_1, the decision maker will have a utility of 1, whereas using a max-min action the worst he could do would be better than this, a utility of 2.

We have seen how to find the max-min mixed strategy for a particular example. Let us now generalize the procedure so that it can be used to find such a strategy for any two action, two states of nature problem. Denote by X the set of all points $(x(q), y(q))$ generated as q varies between 0 and 1 in (4-56) and (4-57). Suppose that we have represented this set geometrically, and imagine now that it is the line segment shown in Figure 4-8. Consider a collection of right angles with sides vertical and

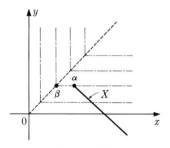

FIGURE 4-8

horizontal and vertices on the line $y = x$ as shown in Figure 4-8. What we wish to do is find that right angle whose vertex has an x-coordinate (or y-coordinate, since $y = x$ at the vertex) which is as large as possible, while the line segments forming the right angle still have at least one point in common with the set X. Thus in Figure 4-8 the right angle which has the largest x-coordinate, while still having a point in common with X, is the one whose vertex is β. Consequently, the point α in X is the point whose smallest coordinate is as large as possible. The point α, as we have shown above, corresponds to a pure strategy, and the max-min mixed strategy in this case is one of the two possible pure strategies.

We can now generalize the preceding geometric interpretation for two-action problems, to problems having r actions. We shall continue to assume, however, that there are only two states of nature. To specify a mixed strategy, one must now specify more than a single probability q; one must specify r probabilities q_i which sum to 1, such that q_i is the probability that the lottery will select action a_i. If U_{i1} and U_{i2} are the utilities when action a_i is taken and the state of nature turns out to be e_1 and e_2, respectively, then the expected utility corresponding to a given mixed strategy when the state of nature turns out to be e_1 is

$$\sum_{i=1}^{r} q_i U_{i1} = x. \qquad (4\text{-}59)$$

Similarly, the expected utility if the state of nature turns out to be e_2 is

$$\sum_{i=1}^{r} q_i U_{i2} = y. \qquad (4\text{-}60)$$

Once again (x, y) can be looked upon as a point in the plane. Denote by X the set of all such points generated by all possible mixed strategies. We shall now show how to represent this set geometrically and also how to determine a max-min mixed strategy. This will be done by use of an example.

Consider the single stage decision problem whose payoff table is that shown in Table 4-8. We shall illustrate for this example the set X referred to above. First let us illustrate the points corresponding to the seven pure strategies. These are the points $(1, 6)$, $(1.5, 5)$, $(7, 0.5)$, $(5, 3)$, $(3, 4)$, $(2.5, 4.5)$, and $(5.5, 2)$, corresponding to the actions a_1 through a_7, respectively. These points are plotted in Figure 4-9. Next observe that

TABLE 4-8

	e_1	e_2
a_1	1	6
a_2	1.5	5
a_3	7	0.5
a_4	5	3
a_5	3	4
a_6	2.5	4.5
a_7	5.5	2

all points on the line segments joining any two of these points must be in the set X. The reason for this is that if we set all $q_i = 0$, except q_u and q_v, then $q_v = 1 - q_u$, and by what we proved for the case where there were only two actions, as q_u varies between 0 and 1 we trace out the line segment joining the point for pure strategy u to that for pure strategy v. Some but not all of these line segments are also shown in Figure 4-9.

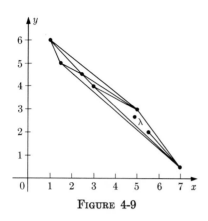

FIGURE 4-9

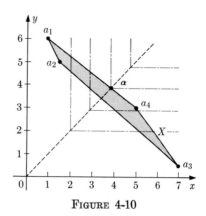

FIGURE 4-10

It remains to consider what happens when more than two q_i are positive. Suppose that $q_1 = 0.3$, $q_3 = 0.5$, and $q_4 = 0.2$, with all other q_i being zero. The point (x, y) corresponding to this mixed strategy is then

$$x = 0.3(1) + 0.5(7) + 0.2(5) = 0.3 + 3.5 + 1.0 = 4.8,$$
$$y = 0.3(6) + 0.5(0.5) + 0.2(3) = 1.80 + 0.25 + 0.60 = 2.65.$$

This is the point λ shown in Figure 4-9. We now claim that the set X is the shaded set of points shown in Figure 4-10, constituting a polygon and its interior. Every mixed strategy will yield one of these points, and each point will correspond to at least one mixed strategy. We shall not attempt to prove this in detail. The reader might convince himself of the truth of the statement by plotting points corresponding to several other mixed strategies. Note that the corners of the polygon correspond to pure strategies. These have been labeled by the action to which they correspond.

The procedure for finding the max-min mixed strategy is now precisely the same as for the case where there were only two actions. We find the right angle with vertex on the line $y = x$ having the coordinates of the vertex as large as possible while still having at least one point of X lying on the lines which form the right angle. From Figure 4-10 we see that the point α corresponds to the max-min mixed strategy. The point α lies on the line segment joining the points corresponding to the pure strategies a_1 and a_4. Hence the mixed strategy has only q_1 and q_4 positive. To determine q_1 (and hence $q_4 = 1 - q_1$), we note that for α, $x = y$, and by (4-59) and (4-60)

$$x = q_1 + 5(1 - q_1), \quad y = 6q_1 + 3(1 - q_1),$$

or on setting $x = y$,

$$q_1 + 5(1 - q_1) = 6q_1 + 3(1 - q_1),$$

that is,

$$7q_1 = 2 \quad \text{or} \quad q_1 = \tfrac{2}{7}, \quad \text{and} \quad q_4 = \tfrac{5}{7}.$$

Hence the max-min mixed strategy is one with $q_1 = \tfrac{2}{7}$, $q_4 = \tfrac{5}{7}$, and all other $q_i = 0$.

Figures 4-11 and 4-12 indicate two other possibilities that could arise in determining the max-min mixed strategy. In Figure 4-11, the max-min mixed strategy is a pure strategy. In Figure 4-12, the max-min strategy

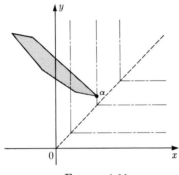

FIGURE 4-11

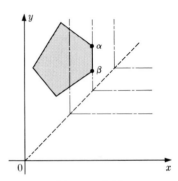

FIGURE 4-12

is not unique, for any point on the line segment joining the points α and β serves to define a max-min strategy. This case is a little bit peculiar, however, since the action corresponding to the pure strategy of the point α dominates the action corresponding to β, and hence there would be no reason to ever include this latter action. This observation brings up a new idea. Just as we could define dominance for actions, we can define dominance for mixed strategies. If we have two mixed strategies S_1 and S_2 which yield the points (x_1, y_1) and (x_2, y_2), and if $x_1 \leq x_2$ and $y_1 \leq y_2$ with strict inequality holding for at least one of the inequalities (so that we are dealing with two different points), then S_2 is said to dominate S_1, and hence S_1 and the point (x_1, y_1) never need be considered in studying mixed strategies. The set of mixed strategies having the property that no mixed strategy in the set is dominated by some other mixed strategy is called the set of *admissible mixed strategies*. The set of admissible strategies generates a set of points Y which is a subset of X. We can easily illustrate the set of points Y when the set X is that shown in Figure 4-10. To do this, it is convenient to note that the set of points corresponding to the mixed strategies which are dominated by the mixed strategy yielding the point (x_1, y_1), is the shaded set in Figure 4-13. By use of this observation, we immediately see that the set Y of points corresponding to mixed strategies which are not dominated by other mixed

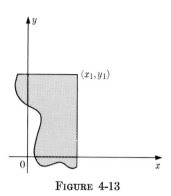

FIGURE 4-13

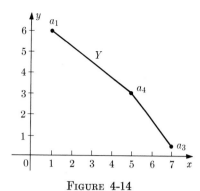

FIGURE 4-14

strategies is that shown in Figure 4-14. Of course, the point corresponding to the max-min mixed strategy is in Y.

When there are three states of nature, one could illustrate the set of points corresponding to all mixed strategies geometrically by a set in three-dimensional space. The geometric representation is much more cumbersome here and not nearly so clear, and we shall not attempt to provide an example. When there are four or more states of nature, we cannot provide any convenient geometric interpretation. Nonetheless, a max-min strategy can always be determined by solving the linear programming problem introduced in the previous section.

*4-12 BAYES STRATEGIES

We observed in the previous section that in the event that nothing is known about the probabilities of the states of nature, a decision maker might feel that it is better to use a max-min mixed strategy than a max-min action. Now, there is nothing to prevent a decision maker from using a mixed strategy even when the probabilities of the states of nature are known. The question then arises in our minds: "Could there be any possible advantage to using a mixed strategy in cases where the probabilities of the states of nature are known?" We have presumably proved in Chapter 2 that when the probabilities of the states of nature are known, the decision maker should simply select that action which maximizes his expected utility. In the proof, however, we implicitly assumed he was going to select an action, and we did not allow for the possibility of mixed strategies. We now wish to investigate whether he can somehow improve his expected utility by use of mixed strategies. We shall continue here to limit our attention to single stage decision problems.

Suppose the decision maker uses a mixed strategy in which the probability of selecting action a_i is q_i. We shall restrict our attention here to cases where the probabilities of the states of nature do not depend on the action selected. Then the probability that the state of nature turns out to be e_j can be denoted by p_j. The decision problem can now be looked on as a random experiment which is a two stage lottery. First a roulette wheel is spun to determine what action will be taken; then another roulette wheel is spun (the same wheel regardless of what action is taken) to determine the state of nature. The prize, however, depends not only on the state of nature but also on the action taken. Thus the probability that the prize is U_{ij} is determined by the probability that at the first stage action i will be taken and at the second stage the state of nature will turn out to be e_j. We showed in Section 2-6 that the probability of this should be $q_i p_j$. We can think of the U_{ij} as being the values of a random variable for the random experiment which is the two stage lottery. The expected utility for the entire random experiment, which we shall denote by Ω, is

$$\Omega = U_{11}q_1p_1 + U_{12}q_1p_2 + \cdots + U_{1m}q_1p_m + U_{21}q_2p_1 + \cdots + U_{2m}q_2p_m$$
$$+ \cdots + U_{r1}q_rp_1 + \cdots + U_{rm}q_rp_m$$
$$= \left(\sum_{j=1}^{m} U_{1j}p_j\right) q_1 + \cdots + \left(\sum_{j=1}^{m} U_{rj}p_j\right) q_r. \tag{4-61}$$

Let us imagine that the decision maker now chooses the mixed strategy so as to maximize Ω. The mixed strategy which maximizes Ω is called a *Bayes' strategy.*

We shall now prove that there is always a pure strategy which is a Bayes' strategy. In other words, the decision maker cannot, by the introduction of mixed strategies, increase his expected utility above that which he can obtain simply by selecting the action which yields the largest value of $\sum_{j=1}^{m} U_{ij}p_j$. Consequently, in cases where the probabilities of the states of nature are known, we need not concern ourselves with mixed strategies. There is no reason why a decision maker should ever consider using one. In other words, it would never be desirable in such cases to tell the decision maker to toss a coin to decide what action to take. The proof is easy to carry out. Let θ be the largest of the numbers $\sum_{j=1}^{m} U_{ij}p_j$. Then

$$\sum_{j=1}^{m} U_{ij}p_j \leq \theta, \quad i = 1, \ldots, r, \tag{4-62}$$

with the strict equality holding for at least one i. However, since $q_i \geq 0$,

$$\left(\sum_{j=1}^{m} U_{ij}p_j\right) q_i \leq \theta q_i, \quad i = 1, \ldots, r. \tag{4-63}$$

Summing (4-63) over i, we obtain

$$\Omega = \left(\sum_{j=1}^{m} U_{1j}p_j\right) q_1 + \cdots + \left(\sum_{j=1}^{m} U_{rj}p_j\right) q_r \leq \theta(q_1 + \cdots + q_r) = \theta, \tag{4-64}$$

since the q_i sum to 1. Thus for any mixed strategy, $\Omega \leq \theta$. Hence, if the strict equality holds in (4-62) for $i = k$, then it is impossible for the decision maker to increase his expected utility above that for taking action a_k by introducing mixed strategies. He can, of course, have $\Omega = \theta$ by using the mixed (and pure) strategy $q_i = 0$, $i \neq k$, $q_k = 1$. This is what we wished to prove, and it relieves us of the necessity of considering mixed strategies in cases where the probabilities of the states of nature are known.

When there are just two states of nature, we can illustrate geometrically the determination of a Bayes' strategy using the same diagrams used in the previous section. To do this, note that we can write

$$\Omega = U_{11}q_1p_1 + U_{21}q_2p_1 + \cdots + U_{r1}q_rp_1 + U_{12}q_1p_2 + \cdots + U_{r2}q_rp_2$$

$$= \left(\sum_{i=1}^{r} q_iU_{i1} \right) p_1 + \left(\sum_{i=1}^{r} q_iU_{i2} \right) p_2 = p_1x + p_2y, \tag{4-65}$$

where x and y are defined by (4-59) and (4-60), respectively. Consider the set of points X of the form (x, y) generated by all possible mixed strategies. Now we wish to select that point in X which yields the largest value of Ω, when Ω is given in terms of x and y by (4-65). Note that in (4-65), p_1 and p_2 are the probabilities of the states of nature and are assumed to be known. Now if we select a particular value of Ω, say Ω_0, the set of points (x, y) in the plane which satisfy the equation

$$\Omega_0 = p_1x + p_2y \tag{4-66}$$

is a straight line. For each different value of Ω we select we get a different straight line. These straight lines so generated will have the interesting

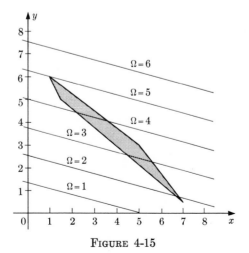

FIGURE 4-15

characteristic that they are all parallel. We wish to determine the particular line having the largest value of Ω which has at least one point in common with the set X. Let us illustrate the situation for the example of Table 4-8. Previously we determined the set X; it is shown in Figure 4-10. Suppose that the probabilities of the states of nature are $p_1 = 0.2$ and $p_2 = 0.8$. In Figure 4-15 we have reproduced the set X and have indicated several of the lines

$$\Omega = 0.2x + 0.8y$$

corresponding to different values of Ω. It is seen that the line with the largest value of Ω which has at least one point in common with X is that for $\Omega = 5$. This line has just one point in common with X, and this is the point $(1, 6)$ which corresponds to the pure strategy a_1. Thus the Bayes' strategy in this case is a pure strategy, as expected.

REFERENCES

1. Blackwell, D., and M. A. Girshick, *Theory of Games and Statistical Decisions.* Wiley, New York, 1954.

     A mathematically advanced text which is concerned with the mathematical theory of games and decision problems. No discussion of practical applications of decision theory is given.

2. Hadley, G., and T. M. Whitin, *Analysis of Inventory Systems.* Prentice-Hall, Englewood Cliffs, N. J., 1963.

3. Schlaifer, R., *Probability and Statistics for Business Decisions.* McGraw-Hill, New York, 1959.

     The first book that attempted to show in some detail how decision theory could be used in solving practical problems. Very little mathematical background is assumed, and mathematics is avoided as much as possible.

4. Thrall, R. M., C. H. Coombs, and R. L. Davis, eds., *Decision Processes.* Wiley, New York, 1954.

5. Weiss, L., *Statistical Decision Theory.* McGraw-Hill, New York, 1961.

PROBLEMS

Sections 4-1 and 4-2

1. Solve the decision problem whose payoff table is

	e_1	e_2	e_3	e_4
a_1	0.2	0.3	0.4	0.1
	-6	3	2	-1
a_2	0.4	0.3	0.2	0.1
	5	0	-2	4
a_3	0.3	0.1	0.2	0.4
	6	-5	1	4

2. A businessman is planning to ship a used machine to his plant in South America where he would like to use it for the next five years. He is trying to decide whether to overhaul the machine before sending it. The cost of overhaul is $2000. If the machine fails when in operation in South America, it will cost him a total of $5000 in lost production and repair costs. He estimates that the probability that it will fail is 0.5 if he does not overhaul it and is 0.1 if he does overhaul it. Neglecting the possibility that the machine might fail more than once in South America, should he overhaul the machine before sending it?

3. What difficulties would be encountered in dealing with Problem 2 if one had to allow for the possibility that the machine might fail more than once?

4. A candy store must decide how many of a large, expensive chocolate rabbit to stock for the Easter season. The rabbit costs $4.00 and sells for $7.50. Any rabbits not sold by Easter can be sold afterward at 30 percent below cost. The owner does not feel that he suffers any loss if a customer demands one of these rabbits when he is out of stock. Over the past five years, the store sold 4, 3, 5, 2, and 4 of these rabbits in the respective Easter seasons. In the three years with the highest sales all rabbits stocked were sold. No records were kept, however, of demands which could not be filled. On the basis of these meager data, the owner feels that the following is his best estimate of the probability function for the demand:

$$p(0) = 0.05, \quad p(1) = 0.10, \quad p(2) = 0.15, \quad p(3) = 0.20,$$
$$p(4) = 0.30, \quad p(5) = 0.15, \quad p(6) = 0.05.$$

Under the assumption that it is impossible to order additional rabbits, how many should be stocked?

5. Re-solve Problem 4 under the assumption that there is a cost to the owner of $2.00 for each rabbit demanded which he cannot supply.

6. An individual is offered the opportunity to invest $10,000 in a wildcat drilling operation in Texas. If the well turns out to produce an average of between 3000 and 5000 barrels per day of crude petroleum for a period of a year, he will be paid $100,000 in return for his investment. If it produces an average of between 1500 and 3000 barrels per day, he will be paid $50,000. If the average is less than 1500 barrels per day, he will be paid nothing and will simply lose his investment. There is no chance that the well will produce an average of more than 5000 barrels per day. If the individual invests $10,000 and gets back $100,000 his utility will be 0.5; if he gets back $50,000 his utility will be 0.4; if he loses the investment his utility will be 0. If he does not invest, and the well produces an average of between 3000 and 5000 barrels per day, his utility will be 0.1; if it produces 1500 to 3000 his utility will be 0.2; and if it produces less than 1500, his utility will be 0.3. He estimates that the probability of an average production of less than 1500 barrels per day is 0.6, of between 1500 and 3000 barrels per day, 0.3, and greater than 3000, 0.1. Should the individual invest or not?

7. A greeting card store is trying to decide how many boxes of a special expensive card to stock. The cards are not sold individually but as a box of 20 cards. These cards cost $8.00 per box and retail for $13.50 per box. Each box not sold during the season can be sold after Christmas at $6.00 per box. There will be no problems due to customers demanding these cards when they are sold out because customers never request a special design, but simply look over the selection and choose from what there is. However, the shop has limited capital and does not like to invest in things that will not sell because it can earn more by not making such mistakes. The owner feels that for each $8.00 invested in a box of these cards which is not sold during the season, he could have earned $2.00 profit by investing it in other cards. The owner estimates the probability function for the number of boxes of these cards that will be demanded as: $p(0) = 0.03$, $p(1) = 0.04$, $p(2) = 0.08$, $p(3) = 0.15$, $p(4) = 0.20$, $p(5) = 0.20$, $p(6) = 0.15$, $p(7) = 0.05$, $p(8) = 0.05$, $p(9) = 0.03$, $p(10) = 0.02$. How many boxes should he stock at the beginning of the season if it is impossible to place re-orders?

8. For many decision problems encountered in the real world, each of the possible states of nature is very complicated and is revealed over a considerable period of time. In such cases the decision maker cannot know what each or even any one of the states of nature really is. Give an example of such a situation and discuss the relevance of the models developed here in such cases. What are some of the procedures often used to try to avoid explaining in detail to the decision maker what each of the states of nature is?

Section 4-3

1. Determine the function $\pi(i)$ for the third example of Section 4-2. Plot a bar diagram of this function. Also determine the function $D(i)$ using the definition (4-10), and plot a bar diagram of $D(i)$. Finally, compute $D(i)$ for each i using (4-14), and show that the same results are obtained as above.

2. Solve Problem 4 for Sections 4-1 and 4-2 using the method developed in this section.

3. Solve Problem 7 for Sections 4-1 and 4-2 using the method developed in this section.

4. Consider the supermarket we have referred to several times, which must decide how much bread to stock on a given Tuesday morning. Each loaf of bread costs the supermarket $0.18 and retails for $0.25. Any loaves not sold by the end of the day will, on Wednesday, be placed on a stale bread counter where the price per loaf will be $0.15. All loaves placed on this counter will be sold. The manager feels that if a customer wants a loaf of this bread when he is out of stock it will cost him $0.50 in lost profits on other sales. However, he does not believe there is any carry-over effect to future days. He believes the demand will always be for some number of loaves in the interval 200 to 299, and feels that each of the values of the random variable x in this interval is equally likely. How many loaves should he stock on Tuesday morning?

5. Verify (4-15). Show that one can avoid making the computation of $D(m)$ a special case simply by imagining that the demand can be as large as $m + 1$, but $p(m + 1) = 0$. Show that this will lead to the correct expression for $D(m)$.

6. For the third example of Section 4-2, suppose that four cakes are stocked. What is the expected number of cakes that will be left over at the end of the day? What is the expected number of demands that will occur which cannot be filled? How is it that both of these expected values can be positive?

7. Suppose in Problem 4 that an optimal number of loaves is stocked. What is the expected number of loaves that will be left over at the end of the day? What is the expected number of demands that will occur when the store is out of stock? What then is the expected cost of shortage?

8. In Problem 4, compute the expected profit when the optimal number of loaves is stocked. Also compute the expected demand. Finally, compute the expected profit if the number of loaves stocked is the smallest integer greater than the expected demand. Hint:

$$\sum_{n=1}^{m} n = \frac{m(m + 1)}{2}.$$

9. Under what conditions can i^* and $i^* + 1$ both be an optimal solution to the single stage inventory problem? Is it possible to have more than two i values which yield an optimal solution?

10. For the general problem discussed in this section, obtain expressions for the expected revenues received from sales during the period, expected revenues received from salvage sales after the period is ended, and the expected cost of shortages when i units are stocked. Then show that the expected profit $\pi(i)$ is the sum of the expected revenues minus the cost of the units minus the expected shortage cost.

11. A dealer in Christmas trees located in Hawaii must place his order with the supplier in Oregon far in advance of the season. The trees procured by this dealer all cost $1.00 each and retail for $2.50. The transportation cost to Hawaii amounts to $0.25 per tree. Any trees left over at the end of the season are a total loss and are burned. The dealer does not believe there is any cost associated with having a demand occur when he is out of stock. After some thought he decides that the probability function he wishes to use for the demand has the following form:

$$p(j) = \begin{cases} a(j - 2000), & 2000 \leq j \leq 2500, \\ a(3000 - j), & 2500 \leq j < 3000, \end{cases}$$

so that the random variable x can take on the values 2000 to 2999. The number a is to be chosen so that the probabilities sum to 1. Determine the optimal number of trees for the dealer to order. Sketch the shape of the functions $p(x)$ and $P(x)$.

12. Re-solve Problem 11 if the dealer must pay \$0.25 for each unsold tree that must be hauled away and burned.

Section 4-4

1. Suppose that the shortage cost for the single stage inventory problem was different from that discussed in the text, in that instead of being proportional to the number of demands which occur when there is no stock, there is a fixed cost V incurred if one or more demands occur when the system is out of stock, and that this cost is independent of how many demands occur when no stock is on hand. Imagine that all other costs are the same as discussed in the text. Use incremental analysis to derive a criterion which must be satisfied by i^*, the optimal number of units to stock.

2. Derive (4-22).

3. For Problem 4 of Sections 4-1 and 4-2, determine the change in the expected profit when the number of units stocked is changed from 3 to 4.

4. For Problem 7 of Sections 4-1 and 4-2, determine the change in the expected profit when the number of units stocked is changed from 7 to 8.

5. For Problem 4 of Section 4-3, determine the change in the expected profit when the number of units stocked is changed from 225 to 226.

6. For Problem 11 of Section 4-3, determine the change in the expected profit when the number of units stocked is changed from 2550 to 2551.

Section 4-5

1. Write down the expected profit for producing a job if i units are scheduled for a production run, given the assumptions made in this section. Show that $\pi(i) = Q - K(i)$, where $K(i)$ is the expected cost. Thus show that the optimal number of units to be scheduled can be determined by minimizing the expected cost. Write down $K(i)$ explicitly.

2. Use the expression for $K(i)$ determined in Problem 1 to compute

$$K(i + 1) - K(i).$$

Relate the expression so obtained to (4-29).

3. A job shop has received an order to produce six huge valve gates for an oil pipeline to be constructed in a foreign country. The variable production cost for each of these amounts to \$200. Each gate requires work in several departments. The setup time on each machine is considerable. If not enough units are scheduled for the initial run, another setup must be made. On the second setup, the units will be passed through one at a time so that no extra good pieces are made. The cost of such an extra setup would be $500. Any good units produced which are not needed are a total loss. The probability function $p(x)$ for the random variable x, the number of units which must be produced to obtain six good units, is $p(6) = 0.50$, $p(7) = 0.35$, $p(8) = 0.10$, $p(9) = 0.05$. How many units should be scheduled for the production run?

4. Suppose that instead of the situation described in the text, if an insufficient number of good units were produced in the production run, the additional units required could be produced by master machinists at an increase in the production cost of T dollars per unit. Formulate the problem for this case. Show that the problem reduces to a single stage inventory problem.

5. Do you have any suggestions as to how the probability function $p(x)$ introduced in the text might be obtained in practice?

6. Consider a problem of the type discussed in the text for which $C = 20$, $R = 5$, $V = 100$, and $Q = 175$. The probability function for x is $p(5) = 0.30$, $p(6) = 0.25$, $p(7) = 0.10$, $p(8) = 0.05$, $p(9) = 0.15$, $p(10) = 0.08$, $p(11) = 0.04$, $p(12) = 0.03$. Determine the expected profit for each value of i, $i = 5, 6, \ldots, 11$, and construct a bar diagram to illustrate the profit function. What troubles are encountered in using (4-30) here? How should (4-30) be modified to handle cases of this type?

7. The value obtained for the scrap allowance will depend on what is included in the production cost C. In addition to the variable costs referred to in the text, one could allocate to each unit and include in C a portion of the fixed costs such as taxes, managerial salaries, etc. Although this is typically done in industry in computing costs, explain why only the variable costs are relevant in determining i^*.

Section 4-6

1. Compute the expected cost of uncertainty for the example given in Section 4-5.

2. Compute the expected cost of uncertainty for Problem 4 of Sections 4-1 and 4-2.

3. Compute the expected cost of uncertainty for Problem 7 of Sections 4-1 and 4-2.

4. Compute the expected cost of uncertainty for Problem 4 of Section 4-3.

5. Compute the expected cost of uncertainty for Problem 11 of Section 4-3.

6. Compute the expected cost of uncertainty for Problem 3 of Section 4-5.

7. What determines whether the expected cost of uncertainty will be large or small?

8. On the same bar diagram plot L_{3j} and L_{5j} as functions of j for the third example of Section 4-2, when L_{ij} is given by (4-43).

Section 4-7

1. Compute a regret table for Example 1 of Section 4-2, and show that minimizing the expected regret yields the same result as maximizing the expected utility.

2. Compute a regret table for Example 2 of Section 4-2, and show that minimizing the expected regret yields the same result as maximizing the expected utility.

3. Compute a regret table for Example 3 of Section 4-2, and show that minimizing the expected regret yields the same result as maximizing the expected utility.

4. Show that solving the single stage inventory problem studied in Section 4-3 can be looked on as solving a sequence of single stage decision problems having only two possible actions and two states of nature. For the ith such problem the actions are (1) stock the ith unit and (2) do not stock the ith unit. The states of nature are (1) the ith unit is demanded and (2) the ith unit is not demanded. Construct a regret table for this problem and derive the criterion that determines which of the two actions is to be preferred. Show that this approach leads in a very simple way to the criterion for determining how many units should be stocked.

5. Show that the scrap allowance problem studied in Section 4-5 can be looked upon as one in which a sequence of single stage decision problems is solved, each of which has only two possible actions and three possible states of nature. The two possible actions for the ith problem are (1) schedule the ith unit to be produced in the production run and (2) do not schedule the ith unit. The states of nature are (1) less than i units are needed to obtain w good ones, (2) precisely i units are needed to obtain w good ones, and (3) more than i units are needed to obtain w good ones. Construct a regret table for this problem and derive the criterion which determines which of the actions is preferred. Show that this leads to the criterion developed in the text for determining the number of units to stock.

6. For the scrap allowance problem studied in Section 4-5, construct a payoff table for the general problem and also a regret table. Note that the regret table has a lot more zeros in it than the payoff table. Could this be helpful in making numerical computations?

7. Construct a regret table for the example given in Section 4-4.

8. Can you provide an intuitive explanation of why the minimum expected regret is equal to the expected cost of uncertainty?

9. For the example of Section 4-5, determine the regret for each e_j when seven units are scheduled for the production run, and construct a bar diagram of the regret variable. Repeat this when six units are scheduled for the production run, and plot this regret variable on the same bar diagram as the previous one.

10. Obtain (4-18) using the criterion that the action to be selected is the one which minimizes the expected regret.

Section 4-8

1. For the example considered in the text, determine the optimal quantity to stock as a function of T, beginning with $T = 0$ and allowing T to become arbitrarily large. Illustrate graphically the optimal quantity to stock as a function of T. Hint: Note that the optimal quantity to stock will change only at a finite number of T values. What determines these values?

2. A small special electric motor stocked by the navy supply depot costs $50 each. If this motor is demanded by a vessel and a unit cannot be supplied, it seriously hampers the operation of the vessel's missile launching equipment, and hence every effort must be made to find one. Generally, this involves sending a plane to pick it up either at the manufacturer or at another depot. It is estimated that such an emergency procedure costs about $500. The procurement lead time from the manufacturer for normal orders is fairly short, being of the order of four days. Assume that the motor is ordered from the manufacturer once every 60 days, and that the probability function for the number of motors demanded in this period is $p(0) = 0.2$, $p(1) = 0.3$, $p(2) = 0.2$, $p(3) = 0.1$, $p(4) = 0.1$, $p(5) = 0.05$, $p(6) = 0.05$. If the approximation is used that the procurement lead time is 0, how many units should be in stock immediately after an order is placed?

3. What difficulties are introduced into the analysis in the text, if quantity discounts are allowed for large order quantities? Can you develop a model to handle this case?

4. What difficulties are introduced into the analysis of the text if the procurement lead time is not 0? Can you develop a model to handle this case given that the procurement lead time is less than the time between reviews? Hint: Let t be a review time, θ the time interval between reviews and τ the procurement lead time. Can you compute the expected number of demands which cannot be supplied from stock that will be incurred over the time period $t + \tau$ to $t + \tau + \theta$? The length of this period is θ and we can associate the expected shortage cost over this interval with the period which begins at time t and ends at time $t + \theta$.

5. A standard vacuum tube stocked by the navy supply depot costs $2.25 each. For each unit which is demanded and cannot be supplied from stock, a cost of $10.00 is incurred. Inventory is replenished once every 90 days and the procurement lead time is seven days. It is believed that the minimum number of tubes that will be demanded in a 90-day period is 300 and the maximum number is 499, with the various possible demands in this interval being equally likely. Under the assumption that the lead time can be approximated by the value 0, what is the optimal number of tubes to have on hand immediately after an order is placed?

6. For the problem discussed in the text, suppose that instead of having a shortage cost of T for each unit which is demanded and cannot be supplied, there is instead a lump sum cost V which is incurred. V is independent of the number of demands that occur when the system is out of stock. If a demand occurs when the system is out of stock, a rush order is sent to the manufacturer for a sufficient number of units so that all demands for the remainder of the period will be filled from this rush order. Then V is the cost of making an emergency procurement. Derive a rule for determining the optimal number of units to have on hand after placing an order at a review time for this case.

7. Re-solve the example given in the text if instead of a shortage cost of $100 for each unit demanded which cannot be supplied from stock, a lump sum cost of $100 is incurred if an emergency order must be placed. Make use of the results of Problem 6 to solve this problem.

8. Re-solve Problem 2 if instead of a shortage cost of $500 for each motor demanded which cannot be supplied from stock, a lump sum cost of $500 is incurred if an emergency order must be placed. Make use of the results of Problem 6 to solve this problem.

9. Re-solve Problem 5 if instead of a shortage cost of $10 for each tube demanded which cannot be supplied from stock, a lump sum cost of $100 is incurred if an emergency order must be placed. Make use of the results of Problem 6 to solve this problem.

10. Consider a problem of the type studied in this section for which $R = 50$ and $T = 150$, and for which the probability function for the demand x in a period is $p(2) = 0.1$, $p(3) = 0.2$, $p(4) = 0.2$, $p(5) = 0.3$, $p(6) = 0.1$, $p(7) = 0.1$. Determine the optimal number of units to have in stock immediately after placing an order. Now, using pennies, construct a random experiment which will generate values of x in accordance with the given probability function. Repeat this experiment 30 times and generate 30 values of x. These numbers can be looked upon as the demands for 30 periods. Compute the cost for each period when the optimal number of units is stocked and when two units more and two units less than the optimal number is stocked. Add up the costs per period in each of these three cases to obtain the total cost for 30 periods, and then obtain the average cost per period over 30 periods in each of the three cases. How do the average costs compare? Is the average cost per period when the optimal number of units is stocked close to the minimum expected cost per period?

Section 4-9

1. Apply each of the five rules discussed in this section to the first example of Section 4-2, and determine the action to be taken in each case. For the optimism index case, determine the action for each possible value of α.

2. Apply each of the five rules discussed in this section to the second example of Section 4-2, and determine the action to be taken in each case. For the optimism index case, determine the action for each possible value of α. Compare the results obtained here with that in Section 4-2.

3. Apply each of the five rules discussed in this section to the third example of Section 4-2, and determine the action to be taken in each case. For the optimism index case, determine the action for each possible value of α. Compare the results obtained here with that in Section 4-2.

4. Consider the single stage decision problem for which the payoff table is the following. Apply each of the five rules discussed in the text and determine the action to be taken in each case. For the optimism index case, determine the action for each possible value of α.

	e_1	e_2	e_3	e_4	e_5	e_6
a_1	15	4	8	-3	0	12
a_2	6	11	-4	2	9	1
a_3	7	6	18	4	-18	7
a_4	-12	9	6	18	10	-2

5. Consider the following payoff table:

	e_1	e_2
a_1	0	100,000
a_2	0.01	0.01

Show that the max-min criterion says to select action a_2. Does this make sense if the numbers represent dollars and the decision maker's utility can be measured in dollars?

6. If one knows nothing about the probabilities of the states of nature, might this sometimes cause difficulties in deciding what the states of nature are, that is, in deciding what events are impossible? Can you provide an example of this?

7. Develop an example which shows the same sort of behavior for the min-max regret criterion as that exhibited in Problem 5 for the max-min criterion.

8. Construct an example where there are four actions and the min-max regret criterion selects action a_3, and where, in addition, if action a_1 is made unavailable, so that only actions a_2, a_3, a_4 remain, then the min-max regret criterion selects action a_2. Explain why this could be considered an undesirable characteristic of a decision rule.

9. Consider the following payoff table for a single stage decision problem.

	e_1	e_2	e_3	e_4	e_5	e_6
a_1	0	1	1	1	1	1
a_2	1	0	0	0	0	0

What does the optimism index criterion say about the action to be selected? Does this seem reasonable?

10. What criticisms can be made of the Laplace criterion?

Section 4-10

1. Consider the single stage decision problem whose payoff table is

	e_1	e_2	e_3	e_4
a_1	4	-2	1	6
a_2	5	7	0	-7
a_3	2	1	8	0

Suppose that the decision maker uses a mixed strategy which selects action a_1 with probability 0.3, action a_2 with probability 0.5, and action a_3 with probability 0.2. What is the decision maker's expected utility if the state of nature turns out to be e_1? What is it if the state of nature turns out to be e_4?

2. For the example of Problem 1, set up, but do not try to solve, the linear programming problem whose solution will yield a max-min mixed strategy for the problem.

3. Show how the problem of generalizing the max-max criterion to max-max mixed strategies can be handled, and formulate a problem whose solution yields a max-max mixed strategy. This is a linear programming problem also.

4. Show how the min-max regret criterion can be generalized to min-max regret mixed strategies, and formulate a problem whose solution will yield a min-max regret mixed strategy. This is another linear programming problem.

5. Show how the optimism index criterion can be generalized to optimism index mixed strategies, and formulate a problem whose solution will yield an optimism index mixed strategy. This is also a linear programming problem.

6. Use the results of Problem 3 to formulate the linear programming problem whose solution yields a max-max mixed strategy for the example of Problem 1.

7. Use the results of Problem 4 to formulate the linear programming problem whose solution yields a min-max regret mixed strategy for the example of Problem 1.

8. Use the results of Problem 5 to formulate the linear programming problem whose solution yields an optimism index mixed strategy for a given α for the example of Problem 1.

Section 4-11

1. Consider the single stage decision problem whose payoff matrix is shown in Table 4-9. Illustrate geometrically the set X of all points $(x(q), y(q))$ generated

TABLE 4-9

	e_1	e_2
a_1	7	1
a_2	3	5

TABLE 4-10

	e_1	e_2
a_1	1	9
a_2	5	7

by all mixed strategies. In particular, determine the points corresponding to $q = 0.2$ and $q = 0.7$. Determine the max-min mixed strategy and illustrate the procedure geometrically.

2. Consider the single stage decision problem whose payoff matrix is shown in Table 4-10. Illustrate geometrically the set of all points $(x(q), y(q))$ generated by all mixed strategies. In particular, determine the points corresponding to $q = 0.3$ and $q = 0.5$. Determine the max-min mixed strategy and illustrate the procedure geometrically.

3. Consider the single stage decision problem whose payoff table is that shown in Table 4-11 below. Illustrate the set of points (x, y) generated by all mixed strategies having only q_2 and q_4 or both different from 0.

TABLE 4-11	e_1	e_2
a_1	1	8
a_2	6	1
a_3	4	2
a_4	3	5
a_5	2	6

TABLE 4-12	e_1	e_2
a_1	3	2
a_2	8	-4
a_3	6	0
a_4	5	1
a_5	4	1.5

TABLE 4-13	e_1	e_2
a_1	2	8
a_2	3	7
a_3	3	5
a_4	2.5	3
a_5	1	6

4. Illustrate geometrically the set X of points (x, y) generated by all mixed strategies for the problem whose payoff table is given in Table 4-11. Determine the max-min mixed strategy for this problem, and illustrate geometrically.

5. Illustrate geometrically the set X of points (x, y) generated by all mixed strategies for the problem whose payoff table is given in Table 4-12. Determine the max-min mixed strategy for this problem, and illustrate geometrically.

6. Illustrate geometrically the set X of points (x, y) generated by all mixed strategies for the problem whose payoff table is given in Table 4-13. In determining X, do not eliminate any pure strategies which are dominated by others. Determine the set of all max-min mixed strategies for this problem and illustrate geometrically.

7. Determine the set of admissible mixed strategies for the problems whose payoff tables are given in Tables 4-11, 4-12, and 4-13, and illustrate geometrically the subsets of X which these represent. Also, show that a max-min mixed strategy is admissible.

8. Prove that a max-min mixed strategy must always be an admissible mixed strategy.

9. Show how the problem of determining a min-max regret mixed strategy can be handled geometrically in the case where there are only two states of nature in precisely the same manner as the determination of max-min mixed strategies. Illustrate by finding the min-max regret mixed strategy for the example of Table 4-9.

10. Determine the min-max regret mixed strategy for the example of Table 4-10 using geometrical analysis.

11. Determine the min-max regret mixed strategy for the problem whose payoff table is given in Table 4-11 above. Use geometrical analysis to do this.

12. Determine the min-max regret mixed strategy for the problem whose payoff table is given in Table 4-12 above. Use geometrical analysis to do this.

13. Determine the min-max regret mixed strategy for the problem whose payoff table is given in Table 4-13 above. Use geometrical analysis to do this.

14. Show how the problem of determining a max-max strategy can be handled geometrically in the case where there are only two states of nature. Illustrate by finding the max-max mixed strategy for the example of Table 4-9.

15. Determine by geometrical analysis the max-max strategy for the problem whose payoff table is given in Table 4-12 above.

16. How should the notion of admissible mixed strategies be defined when using a regret table?

Section 4-12

1. Use geometrical analysis to determine the Bayes' mixed strategy for the example of Table 4-9 for Section 4-11.

2. Use geometrical analysis to determine the Bayes' mixed strategy for the example of Table 4-10 for Section 4-11.

3. Use geometrical analysis to determine the Bayes' mixed strategy for the problem whose payoff matrix is given by Table 4-11 in the problems for Section 4-11.

4. Solve Problem 3 using Table 4-12 instead of Table 4-11.

5. Solve Problem 3 using Table 4-13 instead of Table 4-11.

6. Prove that a Bayes' mixed strategy must be an admissible mixed strategy.

7. Prove that at least one pure strategy will always be a max-max mixed strategy.

8. Show that the generalization of the Laplace criterion to mixed strategies leads to the determination of a Bayes' strategy for the case where if there are m states of nature, each state has the probability $1/m$ of occurring.

CHAPTER 5

ADDITIONAL DEVELOPMENTS
OF
PROBABILITY THEORY

The true logic of this world is in the calculus of probabilities.

James Clerk Maxwell

5-1 DECOMPOSABLE EXPERIMENTS

In our previous discussions we have frequently dealt with random experiments which had the characteristic that they could be imagined to be composed of several parts, each of which could be imagined to be a random experiment. Perhaps the simplest illustration of such an experiment was the example in Section 1-6 of two pennies which were tossed and the number of heads and/or tails turned up was observed. This random experiment can be imagined to consist of two parts each of which is itself a random experiment, since in tossing the two coins we first toss one and then the other, and the tossing of each coin can be considered a random experiment. A two stage, or more generally a multistage lottery provides a more complicated example of the sort of situation we are now considering. The first stage of a two stage lottery is itself a random experiment which determines which of several random experiments will be performed at the second stage. Thus a two stage lottery, which can be considered as a single random experiment, can also be looked upon as built up from, or decomposable into two separate random experiments which are to be performed in sequence. The random experiment to be performed at the second stage, however, will depend on the outcome of the first stage. Note that the situation in this regard is different from that encountered in tossing two pennies, since in the latter case, the second random experiment does not depend on the outcome of the first.

We would like in this chapter and the next to study random experiments which can in one way or another be imagined to be decomposable into simpler random experiments, or equivalently to be built up from simpler random experiments. In particular, we shall be investigating the following problem. Suppose that we have a random experiment with the event set E, which can be imagined to be built up from several random experiments having the event sets $E_1, \ldots, E_n$ say. Suppose in addition that we know the probabilities of the simple events in $E_1, \ldots, E_n$. Can we then determine the probabilities of the simple events in E? We shall see that in a number of cases of practical importance this can indeed be done.

Although we have not done so in the past, it will now be convenient to introduce symbols to represent random experiments and also symbols to represent our mathematical models of these experiments. We shall use the symbol $\Re$ to represent a random experiment. Subscripts on $\Re$ ($\Re_1$, $\Re_2$, etc.) will be used to distinguish between different random experiments. A probability model that we are using to represent $\Re$ mathematically will be denoted by $\mathcal{E}$. Subscripts on $\mathcal{E}$ ($\mathcal{E}_1$, $\mathcal{E}_2$, etc.) will be used to distinguish models for different random experiments.

5-2 PRODUCT MODELS

The decomposable random experiments which are simplest to study have characteristics similar to the experiment involving the tossing of two pennies. In this section we shall give a more precise description of these characteristics and show how the probabilities of the simple events for the random experiment can be determined if the probabilities of the simple events for each of the building blocks are known. Consider a random experiment $\Re$ which can be imagined to consist of the performance of two separate random experiments $\Re_1$ and $\Re_2$, that is, $\Re$ is the random experiment in which $\Re_1$ and $\Re_2$ are performed. Suppose that we have available adequate mathematical models of $\Re_1$ and $\Re_2$, which we shall denote by $\mathcal{E}_1$ and $\mathcal{E}_2$, respectively. Let $\mathcal{E}_1$ have the event set $E_1 = \{f_1, \ldots, f_s\}$ with the probability of the simple event f_i being q_i, and let $\mathcal{E}_2$ have the event set $E_2 = \{e_1, \ldots, e_m\}$ with the probability of e_j being p_j. It is convenient to use different symbols for the simple events and their probabilities in $\mathcal{E}_1$ and $\mathcal{E}_2$. Let us now consider the problem of constructing a mathematical model $\mathcal{E}$ for the random experiment $\Re$.

A suitable means to describe the outcome of $\Re$ is to list the outcomes of each of the random experiments $\Re_1$ and $\Re_2$, that is, to give the symbols for the simple events that were observed respectively when $\Re_1$ and when

$\mathfrak{R}_2$ were performed. If $\mathfrak{R}_1$ yielded f_i and $\mathfrak{R}_2$ yielded e_j, then the pair of symbols $\langle f_i, e_j \rangle$ characterizes the outcome of $\mathfrak{R}$. It is now easily seen that the pair $\langle f_i, e_j \rangle$ serves to define a simple event for $\mathfrak{R}$, since every outcome of $\mathfrak{R}$ is presumably describable in this way, implying that the pairs are collectively exhaustive, and in addition the pairs are mutually exclusive since the elements of E_1 and E_2 are. Let us write $g_{ij} = \langle f_i, e_j \rangle$. Then the symbols g_{ij} define an allowable set of simple events for $\mathfrak{R}$. To determine the number of simple events g_{ij}, note that for each outcome of $\mathfrak{R}_1$ there can be m different outcomes of $\mathfrak{R}_2$. But there are s possible outcomes of $\mathfrak{R}_1$, and hence there must be sm pairs $\langle f_i, e_j \rangle$ or sm simple events g_{ij}. Thus if $\mathcal{E}_1$ has ten simple events and $\mathcal{E}_2$ fifteen, then $\mathcal{E}$ will have 150 simple events g_{ij}. The reader should note that the event set E which we have generated for $\mathfrak{R}$ is not the only possible event set for $\mathfrak{R}$ or even the only one we may be interested in. However, it is *an* event set, and furthermore if E_1 is adequate to treat all events of interest for $\mathfrak{R}_1$ and similarly for E_2, then E should be a satisfactory event set for $\mathfrak{R}$. E is the set of g_{ij}; g_{ij} is the event that f_i is the outcome of $\mathfrak{R}_1$ and, in addition, e_j is the outcome of $\mathfrak{R}_2$.

Consider next the problem of determining the probabilities of the simple events for E when we agree to use E as the event set. We shall denote the probability of g_{ij} by r_{ij}. It will now be shown that if a certain independence condition, as we shall call it, is satisfied, then we can *compute* the r_{ij} from the probabilities of the simple events in $\mathcal{E}_1$ and $\mathcal{E}_2$. Suppose that $\mathfrak{R}$ can be repeated as often as desired. Let us repeat $\mathfrak{R}$ a total of n times, and let n_{ij} be the number of times that the simple event g_{ij} is observed. Then as n becomes arbitrarily large, n_{ij}/n, the relative frequency of g_{ij}, should approach r_{ij}, the probability of g_{ij}. Let n_i be the number of times in n repetitions of $\mathfrak{R}$ that $\mathfrak{R}_1$ yielded the outcome f_i. As n becomes arbitrarily large n_i/n, the relative frequency of f_i, should approach q_i the probability of f_i for $\mathfrak{R}_1$ provided that $\mathfrak{R}_2$ in no way influences the outcome of $\mathfrak{R}_1$. We shall assume this to be the case. Suppose now that $q_i > 0$. Then when n is sufficiently large, we must have $n_i > 0$. But in this case we can write

$$\frac{n_{ij}}{n} = \frac{n_i}{n}\frac{n_{ij}}{n_i}. \tag{5-1}$$

Now as we have seen, n_{ij}/n should approach r_{ij} and n_i/n should approach q_i as n becomes arbitrarily large. What can we say about n_{ij}/n_i? This is the fraction of the number of times when $\mathfrak{R}_1$ yielded f_i that $\mathfrak{R}_2$ yielded e_j. Let us now assume that $\mathfrak{R}_1$ in no way influences the outcome of $\mathfrak{R}_2$. Then for very large n, n_{ij}/n_i should be essentially the relative frequency of e_j when $\mathfrak{R}_2$ is performed alone, i.e., the probability of e_j for $\mathfrak{R}_2$. This probability is p_j. Consequently, when $\Re_1$ has no influence on $\Re_2$ and vice versa, we conclude from (5-1) that it should be the case that

$$r_{ij} = q_i p_j. \tag{5-2}$$

In the above we assumed that $q_i \neq 0$. If $q_i = 0$, then f_i will never occur or almost never occur and g_{ij} will never or almost never occur. Hence the ratio n_{ij}/n will approach 0, i.e., $r_{ij} = 0$. But this is what we would obtain from (5-2) on setting $q_i = 0$. Thus (5-2) holds even if $q_i = 0$, and therefore it holds in every case. We would also reach the conclusion that (5-2) should hold even for experiments which could not be repeated on using the notion of an ensemble relative frequency, provided that neither of the experiments $\Re_1$ and $\Re_2$ had any influence on the other.

By introducing the notion that the experiments $\Re_1$ and $\Re_2$ were independent and did not influence each other, we have seen that the probability of $\langle f_i, e_j \rangle$ for $\Re$ should be $q_i p_j$, which is the product of that probability of f_i in $\mathcal{E}_1$ and the probability of e_j in $\mathcal{E}_2$. Consider now the model $\mathcal{E}$ with the event set E and probabilities of the simple events r_{ij}. $\mathcal{E}$ can then be used as our model of $\Re$. Is $\mathcal{E}$ a realistic model of $\Re$? This depends on how well our assumptions are satisfied. We cannot expect $\mathcal{E}$ to be a realistic model of $\Re$ unless $\mathcal{E}_1$ and $\mathcal{E}_2$ are realistic models of $\Re_1$ and $\Re_2$, respectively, and in addition, unless $\Re_1$ and $\Re_2$ in no way influence each other when performed as required by $\Re$. If these conditions are met, then $\mathcal{E}$ should be a realistic model of $\Re$, i.e., if $\Re$ is performed a large number of times, the relative frequency of g_{ij} should be close to the number r_{ij}. It should be observed that the assignment of the probabilities to the simple events in $\mathcal{E}$ is a personal probability assessment. No experiments need be performed to estimate the r_{ij}. The intuitive notion of independence of the experiments $\Re_1$ and $\Re_2$ operates here in the same way as symmetry did previously, to make it possible to ascertain the probabilities of the g_{ij}.

Before going on, we should prove that the probabilities r_{ij} computed from (5-2) do indeed satisfy the axioms for a probability model. Since $q_i \geq 0$ and $p_j \geq 0$, it follows that each $r_{ij} \geq 0$ as desired. Furthermore, since $q_i \leq 1$ and $p_j \leq 1$, each $r_{ij} \leq 1$. Finally, we can see that the r_{ij} do indeed sum to 1. To see this note that

$$r_{11} + r_{12} + \cdots + r_{1m} + \cdots + r_{sm}$$
$$= q_1 p_1 + \cdots + q_1 p_m + q_2 p_1 + \cdots + q_2 p_m + \cdots + q_s p_1 + \cdots + q_s p_m$$
$$= q_1(p_1 + \cdots + p_m) + \cdots + q_s(p_1 + \cdots + p_m).$$

However, the p_j sum to 1, and so

$$r_{11} + r_{12} + \cdots + r_{sm} = q_1 + \cdots + q_s = 1,$$

since the q_i also sum to 1. Therefore, the probabilities r_{ij} computed from (5-2) do satisfy the axioms for a probability model and do represent a legitimate assignment of probabilities to the simple events in E.

The probability model $\mathcal{E}$ with the event set E and probabilities of the simple events given by (5-2), we shall refer to as the *direct product* of the probability models $\mathcal{E}_1$ and $\mathcal{E}_2$, and we shall write $\mathcal{E} = \mathcal{E}_1 \times \mathcal{E}_2$. In practice, random experiments are often encountered which can be imagined to be representable by direct product models, and this then provides a useful way to construct mathematical models of such experiments. Before generalizing and extending the ideas just introduced, it will be helpful to provide some examples.

5-3 EXAMPLES

1. Consider once again the random experiment $\mathcal{R}$ in which we toss two pennies. Now we can imagine $\mathcal{R}$ to be built up from the two experiments, $\mathcal{R}_1$ in which we toss one penny and $\mathcal{R}_2$ in which we toss the other. Consider the experiment $\mathcal{R}_1$. The event set E_1 for this experiment will consist of only two events, corresponding to whether the penny lands heads or tails up. Let us denote the two simple events by H and T rather than by f_1 and f_2, H denoting a head turning up and T a tail turning up. Then $E_1 = \{H, T\}$. Let us denote the probability of H by q so that the probability of T is then $1 - q$. We shall not necessarily assume that the penny is fair. This defines a model $\mathcal{E}_1$ for $\mathcal{R}_1$. Similarly, we can denote the event set E_2 for $\mathcal{R}_2$ by $E_2 = \{H, T\}$, and let the probability of H in this experiment be p. This defines a model $\mathcal{E}_2$ for $\mathcal{R}_2$. Consider now the model $\mathcal{E}_1 \times \mathcal{E}_2$ defined in the previous section. The event set for $\mathcal{E}_1 \times \mathcal{E}_2$ consists of four simple events which are $\langle H, H \rangle, \langle H, T \rangle, \langle T, H \rangle$, and $\langle T, T \rangle$; where $\langle H, H \rangle$ is the event that both coins land heads up, $\langle H, T \rangle$ the event that the coin of $\mathcal{E}_1$ lands heads, while that of $\mathcal{E}_2$ lands tails, $\langle T, H \rangle$ the event that the coin of $\mathcal{E}_1$ lands tails while that of $\mathcal{E}_2$ lands heads, and $\langle T, T \rangle$ the event that both coins land tails. Let us next return to the experiment $\mathcal{R}$. We indicated in Section 1-6 that the most useful event set for $\mathcal{R}$ is precisely the set of four events which we have just described. Thus the most useful event set for $\mathcal{R}$ is the event set for $\mathcal{E}_1 \times \mathcal{E}_2$.

It is now clear that $\mathcal{E} = \mathcal{E}_1 \times \mathcal{E}_2$ should be a realistic model for $\mathcal{R}$, since the result of tossing one of the pennies should have no influence whatever on tossing the other. This holds true even if we toss the pennies simultaneously. Thus the probabilities of the simple events should be given by (5-2). This leads to the probabilities shown in Table 5-1.

TABLE 5-1

PROBABILITIES OF SIMPLE EVENTS

Simple event	$\langle H, H \rangle$	$\langle H, T \rangle$	$\langle T, H \rangle$	$\langle T, T \rangle$
Probability	qp	$q(1 - p)$	$(1 - q)p$	$(1 - q)(1 - p)$

We have now shown that the experiment $\Re$ which involves the tossing of two pennies can be decomposed into two experiments $\Re_1$ and $\Re_2$ in such a way that if $\mathcal{E}_1$ and $\mathcal{E}_2$ are realistic models for $\Re_1$ and $\Re_2$, then $\mathcal{E}$ should be a realistic model for $\Re$ when $\mathcal{E} = \mathcal{E}_1 \times \mathcal{E}_2$, that is, when $\mathcal{E}$ is the direct product of $\mathcal{E}_1$ and $\mathcal{E}_2$. Suppose that both pennies are fair pennies, so that

$$p = q = 1 - p = 1 - q = \tfrac{1}{2}.$$

Then from Table 5-1 we conclude that the probability of each simple event in $\mathcal{E}$ is $\tfrac{1}{4}$. This is precisely the result that we obtained using the symmetry arguments introduced in Section 1-9. However, our present result is much more general in that we can determine the probabilities of the simple events in $\mathcal{E}$ even if the coins are not fair. This is something we could not accomplish using the symmetry principle. For example, if the first penny has a probability 0.3 of yielding a head and the second penny a probability of 0.6 of yielding a head, then from Table 5-1, the probability of $\langle H, H \rangle$ is 0.18, that of $\langle H, T \rangle$ is 0.12, that of $\langle T, H \rangle$ is 0.42, and that of $\langle T, T \rangle$ is 0.28.

2. Consider an experiment $\Re$ in which first we toss a penny and note whether it lands heads or tails up, and then we select at random a ball from an urn containing one green, three red, and two yellow balls and note the color of the ball obtained. Let a simple event for $\Re$ be characterized by whether the penny landed heads or tails up and by the color of the ball drawn. There are then six simple events which can be characterized by the symbols $\langle H, R \rangle$, $\langle H, Y \rangle$, $\langle H, G \rangle$, $\langle T, R \rangle$, $\langle T, Y \rangle$, and $\langle T, G \rangle$, where H and T mean head and tail, respectively, and R, Y, and G mean red, yellow, and green, respectively. How can we determine the probabilities of these simple events? The symmetry principle does not seem to be applicable here because it is not necessarily true that we can construct an event set in which the simple events are equally likely. (Could this be done if the coin were known to be fair?) Now the color of the ball drawn should in no way be influenced by whether the penny lands heads or tails up. Thus it would seem that a good way to determine the probabilities of the simple events is to try to decompose $\Re$ into two random experiments $\Re_1$ and $\Re_2$ in such a way that $\mathcal{E}$, the model for $\Re$, is the direct product of $\mathcal{E}_1$ and $\mathcal{E}_2$, the models for $\Re_1$ and $\Re_2$, respectively, that is, $\mathcal{E} = \mathcal{E}_1 \times \mathcal{E}_2$. It is quite obvious what the experiments $\Re_1$ and $\Re_2$ are. $\Re_1$ is the experiment in which we toss the penny and note whether it lands heads or tails up and the appropriate event set is $E_1 = \{H, T\}$. We shall not concern ourselves with how the probability of a head is determined but simply assume that it is p. This defines the model $\mathcal{E}_1$ for $\Re_1$. $\Re_2$ is the experiment in which a ball is selected at random from the urn and its color is noted. The appropriate event set is then $E_2 = \{R, Y, G\}$. Consider now the determination of the probabilities of each of these simple events. The urn

contains six balls and one is selected at random. If we imagine a different number painted on each ball and if we use as the event set for $\mathcal{R}_2$ the one with six elements corresponding to the numbers that may appear on the ball drawn, then by symmetry we conclude that each of the six events has the probability $\frac{1}{6}$. Three of these events correspond to a red ball being drawn. Therefore in $\mathcal{E}_2$ it appears that we should take $p(R) = \frac{1}{2}$. Similarly, $p(Y) = \frac{1}{3}$ and $p(G) = \frac{1}{6}$. Now note that the event set of $\mathcal{E} = \mathcal{E}_1 \times \mathcal{E}_2$ is precisely the one we described as being appropriate for $\mathcal{R}$ at the beginning of the example. By (5-2) we can then determine the probability of the simple events in $\mathcal{E}$ to be those given in Table 5-2.

TABLE 5-2

PROBABILITIES OF SIMPLE EVENTS

Simple event	$\langle H, R \rangle$	$\langle H, Y \rangle$	$\langle H, G \rangle$	$\langle T, R \rangle$	$\langle T, Y \rangle$	$\langle T, G \rangle$
Probability	$p/2$	$p/3$	$p/6$	$\frac{1}{2}(1 - p)$	$\frac{1}{3}(1 - p)$	$\frac{1}{6}(1 - p)$

The reader should observe how difficult it would be to try to determine the probabilities of the simple events for $\mathcal{R}$ without using the procedure which we have just developed based on the notion of independence.

5-4 INDEPENDENCE

We would now like to develop in more detail some of the ideas introduced in Section 5-2. We shall begin by defining what we mean by the direct product of two sets $E_1 = \{f_1, \ldots, f_s\}$ and $E_2 = \{e_1, \ldots, e_m\}$. The direct product of E_1 and E_2, written $E_1 \times E_2$, is a set E containing sm elements of the form $\langle f_i, e_j \rangle$. Each element of E is then represented by an ordered pair of elements, the first an element of E_1 and the second an element of E_2. Thus if $E_1 = \{f_1, f_2\}$ and $E_2 = \{e_1, e_2, e_3\}$, then E is the set of six elements

$$E = \{\langle f_1, e_1 \rangle, \langle f_1, e_2 \rangle, \langle f_1, e_3 \rangle, \langle f_2, e_1 \rangle, \langle f_2, e_2 \rangle, \langle f_2, e_3 \rangle\}. \qquad (5\text{-}3)$$

Recall that the elements of a set can be anything at all, and thus we can easily conceive of sets whose elements are ordered pairs of elements of the type indicated. We shall be thinking of E_1, E_2, and E as event sets, and hence the element $\langle f_i, e_j \rangle$ of E will be the event that f_i occurs and that e_j also occurs.

Given any two probability models $\mathcal{E}_1$ and $\mathcal{E}_2$ with event sets E_1 and E_2 respectively, we can always form the mathematical model $\mathcal{E} = \mathcal{E}_1 \times \mathcal{E}_2$. The event set for $\mathcal{E}$ is $E = E_1 \times E_2$ with the probabilities of the simple events in E given by (5-2). We can then ask whether $\mathcal{E}$ is a realistic model of the random experiment $\mathcal{R}$ which consists in performing the two random experiments $\mathcal{R}_1$ and $\mathcal{R}_2$ that are represented by the models $\mathcal{E}_1$ and $\mathcal{E}_2$, respectively. If $\mathcal{E}_1$ and $\mathcal{E}_2$ accurately represent $\mathcal{R}_1$ and $\mathcal{R}_2$, and $\mathcal{R}_1$ and $\mathcal{R}_2$ are performed in such a way that the outcome of one has no influence on the other, then $\mathcal{E}$ should be a realistic model for $\mathcal{R}$.   A random experiment $\mathcal{R}$, which can be decomposed into two random experiments $\mathcal{R}_1$ and $\mathcal{R}_2$ such that if $\mathcal{E}_1$ and $\mathcal{E}_2$ are realistic models of $\mathcal{R}_1$ and $\mathcal{R}_2$ then $\mathcal{E} = \mathcal{E}_1 \times \mathcal{E}_2$ is a realistic model of $\mathcal{R}$, is said to be *composed of, or constructed from, or built up from two independent random experiments* $\mathcal{R}_1$ and $\mathcal{R}_2$.

The probability model $\mathcal{E} = \mathcal{E}_1 \times \mathcal{E}_2$ possesses a number of interesting properties, some of which we shall consider now.   First of all, note that the event f_i for $\mathcal{E}_1$ is also an event for $\mathcal{E}$, that is, it is a subset of E.   It is not true that f_i is one of the simple events for $\mathcal{E}$, however; rather, it is the composite event

$$\{\langle f_i, e_1 \rangle, \langle f_i, e_2 \rangle, \ldots, \langle f_i, e_m \rangle\}, \tag{5-4}$$

since this is the event that f_i occurs and one of the simple events for $\mathcal{E}_2$ occurs.   In other words, it is the event that f_i occurs.   The probability of f_i when f_i is thought of as an event of $\mathcal{E}$ is the sum of the probabilities in (5-4), i.e.,

$$q_i p_1 + q_i p_2 + \cdots + q_i p_m = q_i(p_1 + p_2 + \cdots + p_m) = q_i. \tag{5-5}$$

Hence, as we would expect intuitively, the probability of f_i is q_i, which is the probability of f_i in $\mathcal{E}_1$.   We see therefore that every simple event of $\mathcal{E}_1$ or $\mathcal{E}_2$ is also an event (but not a simple event) of $\mathcal{E}$ and the probability of any such event in $\mathcal{E}$ is the same as its probability in the model for which it is a simple event.

Since each simple event of $\mathcal{E}_1$ is an event of $\mathcal{E}$, *every* event A of $\mathcal{E}_1$, represented by a non-null subset of E_1, is an event of $\mathcal{E}$, since A is the union of one or more simple events from $\mathcal{E}_1$, which are also events of $\mathcal{E}$.   The union of subsets of E gives a subset of E, and hence A is an event of $\mathcal{E}$. Furthermore, the probability of A will be the same whether we find it by adding the probabilities of the simple events in $\mathcal{E}_1$ or by adding the probabilities of the simple events in the subset of E which represents A, since this subset is the union of the subsets representing the simple events of $\mathcal{E}_1$ which represent A, and we have seen that the probability of each simple event f_i of $\mathcal{E}_1$ has the same value regardless of whether we compute it for $\mathcal{E}_1$ or $\mathcal{E}$.   This shows us that any event A of $\mathcal{E}_1$ and, equally well, any event B of $\mathcal{E}_2$ are events of $\mathcal{E}$, and the probabilities of these events are the same in $\mathcal{E}$ as in $\mathcal{E}_1$ or $\mathcal{E}_2$, whichever is appropriate.   What all of this really says is that *in $\mathcal{E}$ each of the models $\mathcal{E}_1$ and $\mathcal{E}_2$ retains its separate identity, and in fact, if we wish to compute the probability of any event A which is an event of $\mathcal{E}_1$, we can use the event set E_1 and the probability function $q_i = q(f_i)$, instead of the more complicated event set E.*   This is an important result which is frequently used in practice.

If A is an event of $\mathcal{E}_1$ and B an event of $\mathcal{E}_2$, then, as we have seen, A and B

are each events of $\mathcal{E}$. Furthermore, $A \cap B$ and $A \cup B$ are events of $\mathcal{E}$, since the intersection or union of subsets of E is a subset of E. $A \cap B$ and $A \cup B$ will not in general be events of either $\mathcal{E}_1$ or $\mathcal{E}_2$ alone, however. Suppose that $A = f_i$ and $B = e_j$. Now when thought of as events for $\mathcal{E}$, f_i is the subset (5-4) of E, and e_j is the subset

$$\{\langle f_1, e_j \rangle, \langle f_2, e_j \rangle, \ldots, \langle f_s, e_j \rangle\}. \tag{5-6}$$

Then the event $A \cap B = f_i \cap e_j$, being the intersection of the sets (5-4) and (5-6), is simply the subset of E containing the single element $\langle f_i, e_j \rangle$, one of the simple events of $\mathcal{E}$. This, of course, is precisely what the result must be, since $\langle f_i, e_j \rangle$ is merely another notation for the event $f_i \cap e_j$. Thus we conclude that $p(f_i \cap e_j)$, the probability of $f_i \cap e_j$, is

$$p(f_i \cap e_j) = q_i p_j = q(f_i)p(e_j)$$

which, of course, must be true since this is the way that the probabilities of the simple events in $\mathcal{E}$ were assigned.

Consider next an arbitrary event A of $\mathcal{E}_1$ and an arbitrary event B of $\mathcal{E}_2$. An analysis like that used in Section 5-2 immediately convinces us that when the outcome of $\mathcal{R}_1$ has no influence whatever on $\mathcal{R}_2$, it should be true that

$$p(A \cap B) = p(A)p(B). \tag{5-7}$$

Now $A \cap B$, A, and B are events of $\mathcal{E}$. Can we verify directly from $\mathcal{E}$ that (5-7) holds? The answer is yes. The proof is a little clumsy because of notational complications, but let us sketch it. Suppose that relative to $\mathcal{E}_1$, A is the event $\{f_{a_1}, \ldots, f_{a_h}\}$ and relative to $\mathcal{E}_2$, B is the event $\{e_{b_1}, \ldots, e_{b_k}\}$. Then relative to $\mathcal{E}$, A and B are, respectively, the events

$$A = \{\langle f_{a_1}, e_1 \rangle, \ldots, \langle f_{a_1}, e_m \rangle, \langle f_{a_2}, e_1 \rangle, \ldots, \langle f_{a_2}, e_m \rangle, \langle f_{a_3}, e_1 \rangle, \ldots, \langle f_{a_h}, e_m \rangle\}, \tag{5-8}$$

$$B = \{\langle f_1, e_{b_1} \rangle, \ldots, \langle f_s, e_{b_1} \rangle, \langle f_1, e_{b_2} \rangle, \ldots, \langle f_s, e_{b_2} \rangle, \langle f_1, e_{b_3} \rangle, \ldots, \langle f_s, e_{b_k} \rangle\}. \tag{5-9}$$

Then $A \cap B$ is the event (the reader should provide the detailed reasoning)

$$A \cap B = \{\langle f_{a_1}, e_{b_1} \rangle, \langle f_{a_2}, e_{b_1} \rangle, \ldots, \langle f_{a_h}, e_{b_1} \rangle, \langle f_{a_1}, e_{b_2} \rangle, \ldots, \langle f_{a_h}, e_{b_2} \rangle,$$
$$\ldots, \langle f_{a_1}, e_{b_k} \rangle, \ldots, \langle f_{a_h}, e_{b_k} \rangle\}. \tag{5-10}$$

The probability of $A \cap B$ is the sum of the probabilities of the simple events in (5-10), i.e.,

$$\begin{aligned} p(A \cap B) &= q_{a_1}p_{b_1} + q_{a_2}p_{b_1} + \cdots + q_{a_h}p_{b_1} + q_{a_1}p_{b_2} + \cdots + q_{a_h}p_{b_2} \\ &\quad + \cdots + q_{a_1}p_{b_k} + \cdots + q_{a_h}p_{b_k} \\ &= (q_{a_1} + \cdots + q_{a_h})p_{b_1} + (q_{a_1} + \cdots + q_{a_h})p_{b_2} + \cdots \\ &\quad + (q_{a_1} + \cdots + q_{a_h})p_{b_k} \\ &= (q_{a_1} + \cdots + q_{a_h})(p_{b_1} + \cdots + p_{b_k}). \end{aligned} \tag{5-11}$$

However, from what we showed above, $p(A)$, the probability of A, can be computed from $\mathcal{E}_1$; and $p(B)$, the probability of B, from $\mathcal{E}_2$. From the definitions of A and B, it then follows at once that

$$p(A) = q_{a_1} + \cdots + q_{a_h}; \quad p(B) = p_{b_1} + \cdots + p_{b_k}. \qquad (5\text{-}12)$$

On using (5-12) in (5-11), we obtain (5-7) which is what we wanted to prove.

In summary, we have proved the following important results concerning the probability model $\mathcal{E} = \mathcal{E}_1 \times \mathcal{E}_2$. *Every event A of $\mathcal{E}_1$ and every event B of $\mathcal{E}_2$ are events of $\mathcal{E}$. Furthermore, the probability of A with respect to $\mathcal{E}$ is the same as the probability of A with respect to $\mathcal{E}_1$, and similarly for B. Finally, $A \cap B$ is an event of $\mathcal{E}$ and $p(A \cap B) = p(A)p(B)$.* The usefulness of these results will be illustrated in the next section.

Let us now generalize our concept of direct products to cases involving more than two building blocks. First we shall define what is meant by the direct product of n sets and simultaneously introduce a convenient notation. Suppose that we have n sets

$$E_i = \{e_{i1}, \ldots, e_{im_i}\}, \quad i = 1, \ldots, n. \qquad (5\text{-}13)$$

The first subscript on the e_{ij} identifies the set and the second the element in the set. The number of elements m_i in E_i can vary with i. We define the direct product of these n sets to be the set E of all ordered n-tuples of the form $\langle e_{1\alpha}, e_{2\beta}, \ldots, e_{n\zeta} \rangle$, the first symbol in the n-tuple being an element of set E_1, the second an element of set E_2, and the nth an element of set E_n. We write

$$E = E_1 \times E_2 \times \cdots \times E_n. \qquad (5\text{-}14)$$

There are $m_1 m_2 \cdots m_n$ elements in E.

Imagine now that we have n probability models $\mathcal{E}_1, \ldots, \mathcal{E}_n$, the ith of which has the event set E_i given by (5-13), and let p_{ij} be the probability of the simple event e_{ij}. Let us now consider the mathematical model $\mathcal{E}$ whose event set is E given by (5-14) and for which the probability of the simple event $\langle e_{1\alpha}, e_{2\beta}, \ldots, e_{n\zeta} \rangle$ is $p_{1\alpha} p_{2\beta} \cdots p_{n\zeta}$. We shall then write

$$\mathcal{E} = \mathcal{E}_1 \times \mathcal{E}_2 \times \cdots \times \mathcal{E}_n \qquad (5\text{-}15)$$

and call $\mathcal{E}$ the *direct product* of the n probability models $\mathcal{E}_i$. If the $\mathcal{E}_i$ represent realistic models for respective random experiments $\mathcal{R}_i$, will $\mathcal{E}$ be a realistic model for the random experiment $\mathcal{R}$ which consists in performing each of the experiments $\mathcal{R}_i$? It will be if the experiments $\mathcal{R}_i$ are performed in such a way that the outcome of any one of them is not in any way influenced by or influences the outcome of any other one. An analysis like that used in Section 5-2 will then show that the probabilities of the simple events in $\mathcal{R}$ are just those given by $\mathcal{E}$. *If a given random experiment $\mathcal{R}$ can be decomposed into n random experiments $\mathcal{R}_i$ in such a way that if $\mathcal{E}$ is the direct product of the models $\mathcal{E}_i$ for the experiments $\mathcal{R}_i$ then $\mathcal{E}$ is a* *suitable model for* $\mathcal{R}$, *we say that* $\mathcal{R}$ *is composed of, or constructed from, or built up from n independent random experiments* $\mathcal{R}_1, \ldots, \mathcal{R}_n$. One often deals with experiments which can be imagined to be built up from a number of independent and noninteracting parts. The material just developed then provides a method for determining the probabilities of the simple events for the experiment of interest. We merely multiply together the probabilities of the simple events $e_{1\alpha}, \ldots, e_{n\zeta}$ which make up the simple event $\langle e_{1\alpha}, \ldots, e_{n\zeta} \rangle$ for the experiment of interest.

The probability model $\mathcal{E} = \mathcal{E}_1 \times \cdots \times \mathcal{E}_n$ has just the same sort of interesting properties that were true in the case where $\mathcal{E} = \mathcal{E}_1 \times \mathcal{E}_2$. In particular, any event A_j of $\mathcal{E}_j$ is also an event of $\mathcal{E}$. Further, the probability of A_j computed using the probability model $\mathcal{E}_j$ is precisely the same as that found using the model $\mathcal{E}$. Next, if A_i is an event of $\mathcal{E}_i$ and A_j is an event of $\mathcal{E}_j$, then for any i and j, $j \neq i$, $A_i \cap A_j$ is an event of $\mathcal{E}$ and

$$p(A_i \cap A_j) = p(A_i)p(A_j). \tag{5-16}$$

Similarly, if A_i is an event of $\mathcal{E}_i$, A_j an event of $\mathcal{E}_j$, and A_k an event of $\mathcal{E}_k$, then $A_i \cap A_j \cap A_k$ is an event of $\mathcal{E}$ and

$$p(A_i \cap A_j \cap A_k) = p(A_i)p(A_j)p(A_k), \tag{5-17}$$

and so forth, so that if we select one event A_j from each $\mathcal{E}_j$, $A_1 \cap \cdots \cap A_n$ is an event of $\mathcal{E}$ and

$$p(A_1 \cap A_2 \cdots \cap A_n) = p(A_1)p(A_2)\cdots p(A_n). \tag{5-18}$$

These results can be proved in the same way as for the case where $\mathcal{E} = \mathcal{E}_1 \times \mathcal{E}_2$, except the notation is now a little more cumbersome. We shall not give the details in the text.

We might note also that if $\mathcal{R}$ can be imagined to be built up from three independent random experiments $\mathcal{R}_1$, $\mathcal{R}_2$, and $\mathcal{R}_3$, and if we define $\mathcal{R}^*$ to be the random experiment in which $\mathcal{R}_1$ and $\mathcal{R}_2$ are performed, then $\mathcal{R}^*$ and $\mathcal{R}_3$ are independent random experiments, and we can also imagine that $\mathcal{R}$ is built up from the two independent experiments $\mathcal{R}^*$ and $\mathcal{R}_3$. Thus if A is an event of $\mathcal{R}^*$ and B is an event of $\mathcal{R}_3$, $A \cap B$ is an event of $\mathcal{R}$ and $p(A \cap B)$ is given by (5-7), where $p(A)$ is computed using the model for $\mathcal{R}^*$ and $p(B)$ using the model for $\mathcal{R}_3$.

It should be observed that when we compute the probabilities of the simple events in $\mathcal{R}$ by imagining $\mathcal{R}$ to be constructed from several independent experiments $\mathcal{R}_i$, the notion of independent experiments is an intuitive one based on our understanding of the real world. It is not something we can prove rigorously by mathematics. Whatever concerns estimating the probabilities of the simple events for a random experiment is not capable of rigorous mathematical proof, since it depends entirely on our understanding of the real world. The only things in probability theory which can be proved rigorously are properties which follow from a given model.   For example, we have proved that if $\mathcal{E}$ is the direct product of n models $\mathcal{E}_j$ and if A_j is an event of $\mathcal{E}_j$, then the probability of $A_1 \cap \cdots \cap A_n$ is given by (5-16) as the product of the probabilities of the individual events.   This could be proved once we had defined $\mathcal{E}$.

We now want to introduce the notion of what we shall call independent events and then relate this to the notion of independent experiments.

INDEPENDENT EVENTS.   *Let $\mathcal{R}$ be a random experiment for which the model $\mathcal{E}$ is being used, and let A and B be two events for $\mathcal{E}$.   The events A and B are said to be independent events if*

$$p(A \cap B) = p(A)p(B). \tag{5-19}$$

A and B are independent events if the probability of the event A and B is the product of the probability of A and the probability of B.   More generally, the events $A_1, \ldots, A_n$ of $\mathcal{E}$ are said to be independent if

$$p(A_1 \cap A_2 \cap \cdots \cap A_n) = p(A_1)p(A_2) \cdots p(A_n) \tag{5-20}$$

holds and, in addition, a similar equation holds for every subset of two or more of the events $A_1, \ldots, A_n$.   In the definition of independent events, $\mathcal{E}$ can be any model whatever.   There is no implication that $\mathcal{E}$ must be the direct product of two or more other models.   The definition of independent events is one that is strictly a mathematical definition.   Given a model $\mathcal{E}$ and any two events A and B, one can determine directly whether or not the events are independent simply by computing $p(A)$, $p(B)$, and $p(A \cap B)$, and determining whether (5-19) holds.   There are no intuitive notions involved here.

Let us now note the connection between the definition of independent events and the intuitive notion of independent experiments.   Generally speaking, our main use of the formula (5-20) will be in cases where $\mathcal{E} = \mathcal{E}_1 \times \cdots \times \mathcal{E}_n$ and the event A_j is an event of $\mathcal{E}_j$.   We shall be thinking of the experiment $\mathcal{R}$ whose model is $\mathcal{E}$ as one constructed from n independent random experiments.   Then we know that when A_j is an event of $\mathcal{E}_j$ the various events A_j are independent and (5-20) applies.   Thus our use of independent events can generally be traced back to the intuitive notion that we are dealing with independent random experiments.

Thus far we have been thinking of decomposing an experiment and using the notion of independent experiments in determining the probabilities of the simple events in the original complex experiment.   The notion of independence and the direct product is useful also in a similar but slightly different context, where rather than decomposing we think of building up an experiment from several others.   Frequently we deal with several random experiments simultaneously, and we are faced with the problem of computing, for example, the probability that one of the experiments will have a given outcome while another will have some other specified out-

come. How do we do this? The first thing to observe is that the probabilities we compute or manipulate must all refer to some one random
experiment. Thus in order to solve problems of the type just contem-
plated, we must construct a mathematical model representing a single
random experiment such that the event set for this model contains as
subsets all the events whose probabilities we wish to compute. Now very
frequently, the individual experiments we are dealing with will appear to
be independent experiments, so that the outcome of one has no influence
on the outcome of the others. Then the single random experiment which
we can use to make computations involving all the experiments simultaneously is simply the one whose mathematical model is the direct product
of the models for the individual experiments involved. The second example of the previous section could easily be interpreted as illustrating this
sort of situation. In the next section some additional examples will be
provided.

5-5 ADDITIONAL EXAMPLES

We are now in a position to solve slightly more difficult probability problems than heretofore, and the following will provide some examples while
also illustrating the material of the previous section.

1. In one box there are 1000 transistors, precisely 14 of which are defective; in another box are 2000 resistors, precisely 16 of which are defective;
and a third box contains 3000 capacitors, precisely 30 of which are defective. An individual selects at random one transistor from the box of
transistors, one resistor from the box of resistors, and one capacitor from
the box of capacitors. We would like to compute the probability that
the transistor selected is defective while the resistor and capacitor are each
good. In order to determine this probability we must construct a mathematical model whose event set contains this event as a subset. Obviously,
we can think of the combined act of selecting one element from each box
as a single random experiment $\Re$, and with the proper choice of the event
set for this random experiment, it is clear that the event we are interested
in will be a subset of the event set.

Let us now construct such a mathematical model of $\Re$. It seems clear
from the description of the problem that the selection of an element from
one box in no way influences or is influenced by the element selected from
either of the other boxes. Thus $\Re$ can be looked upon as being built up
from three independent random experiments $\Re_1$, $\Re_2$, and $\Re_3$, involving the
selection at random of first a transistor from the box of transistors, then
a resistor from the box of resistors, and third a capacitor from the box of
capacitors. Then it seems clear that if $\mathcal{E}_1$, $\mathcal{E}_2$, and $\mathcal{E}_3$ are the models for

these three experiments, the model to use for $\mathcal{R}$ is $\mathcal{E} = \mathcal{E}_1 \times \mathcal{E}_2 \times \mathcal{E}_3$. Consider then the models $\mathcal{E}_1$, $\mathcal{E}_2$, and $\mathcal{E}_3$. Let us imagine that we paint the numbers 1 to 1000 on the 1000 transistors (a different number on each one). As a simple event for $\mathcal{E}_1$ let us use the drawing of a transistor with a given number on it, so that the event i is the drawing of the transistor with the number i on it. There are 1000 simple events. We have assumed that a transistor is selected at random. By definition of random, we are assuming that the drawing of one transistor is as likely as any other, so that the simple events are equally likely, and each has a probability of $1/1000$. This defines $\mathcal{E}_1$. $\mathcal{E}_2$ is defined similarly. We imagine a number painted on each resistor and the simple event j is that the resistor numbered j is drawn. Since a draw is made at random, the simple events are equally likely, and each of the 2000 simple events has a probability of $1/2000$. Finally, to define $\mathcal{E}_3$ we imagine that each capacitor is numbered and that the simple event k corresponds to the drawing of the capacitor numbered k. Since the drawing is made at random, each of the 3000 simple events has a probability $1/3000$. We can now easily characterize $\mathcal{E}$. A simple event in $\mathcal{E}$ can be characterized by the triple of numbers $\langle i, j, k \rangle$ which means that on performing $\mathcal{R}$, transistor i, resistor j, and capacitor k are drawn. There are $(1000)(2000)(3000)$ or six billion simple events. These are equally likely, and each has the very small probability $1/6,000,000,000$.

We can now proceed to determine the probability of interest that the transistor selected is defective while the resistor and capacitor are both good. This can be looked upon as the event $A_1 \cap A_2 \cap A_3$, where A_1 is the event that a defective transistor is selected on performing $\mathcal{R}_1$, A_2 is the event that a good resistor is selected on performing $\mathcal{R}_2$, and A_3 is the event that a good capacitor is selected on performing $\mathcal{R}_3$. Now since $\mathcal{E} = \mathcal{E}_1 \times \mathcal{E}_2 \times \mathcal{E}_3$, and A_1 is an event for $\mathcal{R}_1$, A_2 an event for $\mathcal{R}_2$, and A_3 an event for $\mathcal{R}_3$, we know that

$$p(A_1 \cap A_2 \cap A_3) = p(A_1)p(A_2)p(A_3). \qquad (5\text{-}21)$$

Furthermore, $p(A_i)$ is the probability of A_i computed from the model $\mathcal{E}_i$. Now 14 of the transistors are defective, and hence A_1 consists of 14 simple events in $\mathcal{E}_1$, and therefore $p(A_1) = 14/1000 = 0.014$. There are 16 defective resistors, and thus A_2 consists of 1984 simple events in $\mathcal{E}_2$, and hence $p(A_2) = 1984/2000 = 0.992$. Finally, there are 30 defective capacitors, and thus A consists of 2970 simple events of $\mathcal{E}_3$, and $p(A_3) = 2970/3000 = 0.990$. Consequently, the probability we are seeking is

$$p(A_1 \cap A_2 \cap A_3) = (0.014)(0.992)(0.990) = 0.01379.$$

Whether the relative frequency of $A_1 \cap A_2 \cap A_3$ would actually approach the computed probability if $\mathcal{R}$ were performed a large number of times would, of course, depend on how well our assumptions were approximated in the actual situation. Certainly the independence assumption should be realistic; however, the assumption of selection of units at random is sometimes not as easy to carry out in practice, and special precautions would need to be taken if it is to be even approximately correct.

After having gone through this example in considerable detail, the reader may wonder now why we ever bothered to describe $\mathcal{E}$; $\mathcal{E}$ was never used directly. It is important to note that although we should keep in mind that $\mathcal{E}$ is the model being used in computing the probabilities, we never need to introduce $\mathcal{E}$ explicitly in making the computations. Indeed, some-one familiar with the subject would not even stop to consider $\mathcal{E}$, but would reason as follows. The experiments $\mathcal{R}_1$, $\mathcal{R}_2$, and $\mathcal{R}_3$ are independent, and hence the events A_1, A_2, and A_3 are independent. Thus the probability of $A_1 \cap A_2 \cap A_3$ is given by (5-21). To compute $p(A_i)$, $\mathcal{E}_i$ would auto-matically be used. It is a little dangerous for the beginner to do this without thinking through what is involved. Such an approach is quite satisfactory after one thoroughly understands what he is doing, however.

2. Suppose that for the situation discussed in Example 1 we are asked to compute the probability that either the transistor or the resistor (or both) is defective. We could proceed here to characterize this event as a subset of E and thus to compute its probability. There is a much simpler pro-cedure, however. Let A be the event that a defective transistor is selected on performing $\mathcal{R}_1$ and B the event that a defective resistor is selected on performing $\mathcal{R}_2$. The event whose probability we wish to compute is $A \cup B$. It may not appear to have helped us any to make this observa-tion, but it does, because now we can apply equation (1-26) which reads

$$p(A \cup B) = p(A) + p(B) - p(A \cap B).$$

Furthermore, since $\mathcal{R}_1$ and $\mathcal{R}_2$ are independent experiments,

$$p(A \cap B) = p(A)p(B)$$

by (5-16). Hence to compute $p(A \cup B)$ we need only to evaluate $p(A)$ and $p(B)$. Now from the previous example, $p(A) = 14/1000 = 0.014$ and $p(B) = 16/2000 = 0.008$. Thus

$$p(A)p(B) = (0.014)(0.008) = 0.000112$$
and $\quad\quad p(A \cup B) = 0.014 + 0.008 - 0.000112 = 0.021888.$

It is interesting to note that here, just as in Example 1, it was unnecessary to use explicitly the event set of $\mathcal{E}$ to compute the probability of the event of interest. This was made possible by use of the result obtained in Chapter 1 and serves to illustrate the usefulness of (1-26).

3. Consider once again the situation referred to in Example 1 and suppose that we are asked to compute the probability that at least one of the three elements (transistor, resistor, capacitor) is defective. There is an easy and a difficult way to solve this problem. Let us consider each of them.

Let A be the event that the transistor selected is good and A^c be the event that it is bad, B be the event that the resistor selected is good and B^c be the event that it is bad, and finally let C be the event that the capacitor selected is good and C^c the event that it is defective. The following events of $\mathcal{E}$ then correspond to drawing at least one defective element:

$$D_1 = A^c \cap B \cap C; \quad D_2 = A \cap B^c \cap C; \quad D_3 = A \cap B \cap C^c;$$
$$D_4 = A^c \cap B^c \cap C; \quad D_5 = A \cap B^c \cap C^c; \quad D_6 = A^c \cap B \cap C^c;$$
$$D_7 = A^c \cap B^c \cap C^c. \tag{5-22}$$

Each D_j expresses a way in which at least one defective element can be obtained. Every outcome of $\mathcal{R}$ in which at least one element is defective is represented by one and only one D_j. Hence if D is the event that at least one element is defective, we must have

$$D = D_1 \cup D_2 \cup \cdots \cup D_7. \tag{5-23}$$

Now any pair of the D_j are mutually exclusive events. Hence by applying (1-13) repeatedly as we did in obtaining an expression for the cumulative function, we conclude that

$$p(D) = \sum_{j=1}^{7} p(D_j). \tag{5-24}$$

However, since the experiments $\mathcal{R}_1$, $\mathcal{R}_2$, and $\mathcal{R}_3$ are independent, that is, since $\mathcal{E} = \mathcal{E}_1 \times \mathcal{E}_2 \times \mathcal{E}_3$, $p(D_j)$ is the product of the three probabilities involved. Hence

$$\begin{aligned} p(D) = {} & p(A^c)p(B)p(C) + p(A)p(B^c)p(C) + p(A)p(B)p(C^c) \\ & + p(A^c)p(B^c)p(C) + p(A)p(B^c)p(C^c) + p(A^c)p(B)p(C^c) \\ & + p(A^c)p(B^c)p(C^c). \end{aligned} \tag{5-25}$$

Now using the data and observations made in the first example we see that

$$p(A) = 986/1000 = 0.986; \quad p(A^c) = 0.014;$$
$$p(B) = 1984/2000 = 0.992; \quad p(B^c) = 0.008;$$
$$p(C) = 2970/3000 = 0.990; \quad p(C^c) = 0.010.$$

Hence,

$$\begin{aligned} p(D) = {} & 0.014(0.992)(0.990) + 0.986(0.008)(0.990) + 0.986(0.992)(0.010) \\ & + 0.014(0.008)(0.990) + 0.986(0.008)(0.010) \\ & + 0.014(0.992)(0.010) + 0.014(0.008)(0.010) \\ = {} & 0.01377 + 0.00782 + 0.00975 + 0.00011 + 0.00008 \\ & + 0.00014 + 0.000001 = 0.03167. \end{aligned} \tag{5-26}$$

The procedure just used is an unnecessarily complicated way to compute $p(D)$. For a much simpler way to evaluate $p(D)$, consider the set D^c of $\mathcal{E}$ which contains all simple events in $\mathcal{E}$ which are not in D. Now the event D is that at least one of the elements is defective, and hence D^c is the event that none of the three elements is defective. Thus $D^c = A \cap B \cap C$ and

$$p(D^c) = p(A)p(B)p(C) = 0.986(0.992)(0.990) = 0.96833. \quad (5\text{-}27)$$

We can now very simply compute $p(D)$ by using another result proved in Section 1-9. By (1-27)

$$p(D) = 1 - p(D^c) = 1 - 0.96833 = 0.03167,$$

which is the result obtained above. This example illustrates the usefulness of (1-27).

4. Consider the random experiment $\mathcal{R}^*$ in which we toss a coin and note whether it lands heads or tails up. Then the event set for $\mathcal{R}^*$ can be taken to be $E^* = \{H, T\}$. Let p be the probability that the coin will land heads up. This then defines the mathematical model $\mathcal{E}^*$ for $\mathcal{R}^*$. Consider now the random experiment $\mathcal{R}$ in which we repeat $\mathcal{R}^*$ four times, that is, we toss the same coin four times. Presumably, whether the coin lands heads up or tails up on one toss will have absolutely no influence on what happens on any other toss. Hence $\mathcal{E} = \mathcal{E}^* \times \mathcal{E}^* \times \mathcal{E}^* \times \mathcal{E}^*$ should provide a suitable mathematical model of $\mathcal{R}$. In Table 5-3 we have listed the sixteen simple events for $\mathcal{E}$ and given the probability of each as determined by (5-2). In the table $\langle H, T, H, T \rangle$, for example, means that a head was obtained on the first and third tosses and a tail on the other two tosses.

TABLE 5-3

SIMPLE EVENTS AND THEIR PROBABILITIES FOR FOUR TOSSES OF A COIN

Simple event	Probability	Simple event	Probability
$\langle H, H, H, H \rangle$	p^4	$\langle T, H, T, H \rangle$	$p^2(1-p)^2$
$\langle H, H, H, T \rangle$	$p^3(1-p)$	$\langle T, T, H, H \rangle$	$p^2(1-p)^2$
$\langle H, H, T, H \rangle$	$p^3(1-p)$	$\langle T, H, H, T \rangle$	$p^2(1-p)^2$
$\langle H, T, H, H \rangle$	$p^3(1-p)$	$\langle H, T, T, T \rangle$	$p(1-p)^3$
$\langle T, H, H, H \rangle$	$p^3(1-p)$	$\langle T, H, T, T \rangle$	$p(1-p)^3$
$\langle H, H, T, T \rangle$	$p^2(1-p)^2$	$\langle T, T, H, T \rangle$	$p(1-p)^3$
$\langle H, T, H, T \rangle$	$p^2(1-p)^2$	$\langle T, T, T, H \rangle$	$p(1-p)^3$
$\langle H, T, T, H \rangle$	$p^2(1-p)^2$	$\langle T, T, T, T \rangle$	$(1-p)^4$

It will be observed that the simple events in $\mathcal{E}$ are not in general equally likely; they are equally likely if and only if the coin is a fair coin. By use of the model $\mathcal{E}$ one can answer any question of interest concerning the experiment $\mathcal{R}$. The main questions of interest usually involve the determination of the probability of obtaining a given number of heads or tails. Frequently the sequence in which the heads and tails are obtained is not of interest. To answer such questions it is useful to introduce the random variable x which is the number of heads obtained on performing $\mathcal{R}$. The random variable x can then take on one of the values 0, 1, 2, 3, and 4. To determine the probability function $p(x)$ for x, we select a particular value of x, say 2, and add together the probabilities of all the simple events which yield $x = 2$. This gives $p(2)$. There are six simple events of E which yield $x = 2$, and each of these has the same probability $p^2(1 - p)^2$; hence

$$p(2) = 6p^2(1 - p)^2.$$

The procedure is repeated for each of the five possible values of x. The probability function for x is given in Table 5-4.

TABLE 5-4

PROBABILITY FUNCTION FOR x

j	0	1	2	3	4
$p(j)$	$(1 - p)^4$	$4p(1 - p)^3$	$6p^2(1 - p)^2$	$4p^3(1 - p)$	p^4

Note that if the coin is fair, the probability of getting two heads, for example, is $\frac{3}{8} = 0.375$.

5-6 COMBINATORIAL ANALYSIS

Before going on it will be desirable to examine some simple counting problems. We shall be studying some of the most elementary results from a subject known as combinatorial analysis. Imagine that we have n balls, and that we have numbered these balls from 1 to n by painting a different number on each one. Let us now place these balls in a box. We then select one of the balls from the box, write down the number on it, and place the ball aside (we do not put it back in the box). We now draw out another ball, note the number on it, and place it aside. This process is continued until we have drawn out a total of r balls. The process just described will generate a sequence of r different numbers which we shall symbolize by $a_1, \ldots, a_r$; a_1 gives the number of the first ball drawn and a_r the number of the final one drawn. For example, if there are six balls and four are drawn, the sequence might be 3, 1, 2, 6. Let us now ask the question: How many different sequences of numbers can be generated in this way?

The problem just posed is easily solved. The first ball drawn can have any one of n different numbers on it, so that a_1 can have n different values. Once the first ball has been drawn, there are $n - 1$ balls left. Hence once a_1 is determined, a_2 can have any of $n - 1$ values. Since this is true for each value of a_1, there are $n(n - 1)$ possible sequences for the first two elements. Given a_1 and a_2, there are $n - 2$ balls remaining in the box, and hence a_3 can have $n - 2$ different values. This is true for every pair of values a_1 and a_2. Hence there are $n(n - 1)(n - 2)$ possible sequences for the first three elements. When we are ready to draw out ball r, $r - 1$ have been drawn out previously and $n - r + 1$ remain. Given $a_1, \ldots, a_{r-1}$ there are then $n - r + 1$ possible values that a_r can have, or there is a total of

$$n(n-1)(n-2)\cdots(n-r+1) \qquad (5\text{-}28)$$

different sequences $a_1, \ldots, a_r$ which can be generated.

Suppose that we draw out all the balls, so that $r = n$. Then (5-28) reduces to $n(n-1)\cdots(2)(1)$. We use a special symbol $n!$ to denote this particular product of n numbers. Thus by definition

$$n! = n(n-1)(n-2)\cdots(2)(1). \qquad (5\text{-}29)$$

The symbol $n!$ is read n factorial and is called a factorial symbol. As an example,

$$5! = 5(4)(3)(2)(1) = 120.$$

Note that $n!$ is defined for every natural number n. It is also convenient to introduce the definition

$$0! = 1. \qquad (5\text{-}30)$$

Now observe that (5-29) can be written

$$n! = n(n-1)\cdots(n-r+1)(n-r)\cdots(2)(1)$$
$$= n(n-1)\cdots(n-r+1)(n-r)!, \quad 1 \leq r \leq n.$$

Hence we see that (5-28) can be written using factorial symbols as $n!/(n-r)!$. The number of possible sequences of r numbered balls that can be selected from n balls is called the number of *permutations* of n balls taken r at a time and is sometimes denoted symbolically by P_r^n or $(n)_r$.

EXAMPLES. *1.* Suppose there are three balls in the box, and we draw out two of them. According to (5-28), there are $3(2) = 6$ possible sequences of numbers we could get. These are $(1, 2)$, $(2, 1)$, $(1, 3)$, $(3, 1)$, $(2, 3)$, and $(3, 2)$. If we draw out all three balls, there are $3(2)(1) = 6$ sequences again, which are $(1, 2, 3)$, $(1, 3, 2)$, $(2, 1, 3)$, $(2, 3, 1)$, $(3, 1, 2)$, and $(3, 2, 1)$.

2. Suppose that there are four balls in the box, and we draw out two of them. According to (5-28), there are $4(3) = 12$ possible sequences of numbers we could obtain. These are $(1, 2)$, $(2, 1)$, $(1, 3)$, $(3, 1)$, $(2, 3)$, $(3, 2)$, $(1, 4)$, $(4, 1)$, $(2, 4)$, $(4, 2)$, $(3, 4)$, and $(4, 3)$.

3. A great many different types of problems are mathematically equivalent to the one we have just studied. For example, the number of different ways one could assign r executives to n regional offices, $r \leq n$, and one executive to an office, is given by (5-28), since the first executive can be assigned to any one of n offices and given this assignment, there are $n - 1$ offices to which the next executive can be assigned, etc. The offices correspond to the numbered balls, and the executives serve to define the order of drawing the balls.

In determining the number of permutations of n balls taken r at a time, ordering is important. Thus in the first example above where two balls were drawn, $(2, 3)$ and $(3, 2)$ were different permutations. Let us now study a slightly different problem. Suppose that once again we draw r balls from a box containing n numbered balls. Now, however, we shall concern ourselves only with the numbers on the balls and not with the order in which the numbers appear. We then wish to determine how many different sets of numbers are possible when we do not care about the order of the numbers. When order is irrelevant, $(2, 3)$ and $(3, 2)$ yield the same pair of numbers and would not be considered as different sets. When we draw two balls from a box of three, just three sets of two numbers can be obtained, the first is the pair of numbers 1 and 2, the second is the pair of numbers 1 and 3, and the third is the pair of numbers 2 and 3. The number of sets of numbers generated on selecting r balls from n balls when order is irrelevant is called the number of *combinations* of n balls taken r at a time. To determine the number of combinations all we need to do is determine the number of permutations and then combine all permutations which involve the same set of numbers. For a given set of r different numbers, how many permutations of these r numbers are there? There are precisely $r!$, since any one of the r can be used as the first number, and given this there are $r - 1$ possibilities for the second number, etc. Thus there are $r!$ permutations of r different numbers, that is, for each combination there are $r!$ permutations. Now there are $n!/(n - r)!$ permutations of n numbered balls taken r at a time. Let $C_r{}^n$ be the number of combinations of n balls taken r at a time; then the number of permutations is $C_r{}^n(r!)$, so that we have

$$C_r{}^n = \frac{n!}{r!(n - r)!},\qquad(5\text{-}31)$$

and we have determined $C_r{}^n$, that is, the number of different sets of r numbers that can appear on r balls drawn from n numbered balls. It is often convenient to use yet a different symbolism besides $C_r{}^n$ for $n!/r!(n - r)!$. The following is also frequently used:

$$\binom{n}{r} = \frac{n!}{r!(n - r)!}.$$

The number $C_r{}^n$ is always less than $P_r{}^n$ by a factor $r!$. If n and r are at all large, however, both $C_r{}^n$ and $P_r{}^n$ can be huge, as the following examples will illustrate.

EXAMPLES. *1.* From a box containing five balls numbered 1 through 5, three balls are drawn. How many different combinations of three numbers may be observed on the balls drawn? According to (5-31), this number is

$$C_3{}^5 = \frac{5!}{3!2!} = \frac{5(4)(3)(2)(1)}{3(2)(1)(2)(1)} = 10.$$

Let us list what these are. We shall use a format such as 123. No order is implied here. We are simply listing the numbers observed on the balls. There are the following combinations: 123, 124, 125, 134, 135, 145, 234, 235, 245, 345. There are 60 permutations in this case, since for each combination such as 145, there are six permutations or orders in which the numbers could be obtained. For 145 these are $(1, 4, 5)$, $(1, 5, 4)$, $(4, 1, 5)$, $(4, 5, 1)$, $(5, 1, 4)$, and $(5, 4, 1)$.

2. The reader should note that the results we have obtained are independent of what numbers are painted on the balls, so long as a different number appears on each ball. Thus suppose that we had four balls numbered 2, 5, 7, 9. If we select two of them, the number of combinations of numbers we can observe is $4!/2!2! = 6$. These are 25, 27, 29, 57, 59, 79.

3. Suppose that we have ten numbered balls in a box and draw out six of them. How many combinations of numbers can be observed? Here

$$C_6^{10} = \frac{10!}{6!4!} = \frac{10(9)(8)(7)6!}{(4)(3)(2)6!} = 210,$$

while the number of permutations is $6! = 720$ times 210, or 151,200. If we had 100 balls and selected six of them, the number of combinations would be

$$C_6^{100} = \frac{100!}{6!94!} = 5(33)(49)(97)(16)(95),$$

which is a number larger than 50 million.

Let us now study a problem which looks somewhat different from that studied above, but which will turn out to be mathematically equivalent to it. Consider the random experiment $\mathcal{R}$ which consists in tossing the same coin n times and observing whether the coin lands heads or tails up on each toss. Let us concentrate our attention on those outcomes which yield precisely r heads. How many different sequences of heads and tails are there which yield a total of r heads? If we tossed the coin three times, the following three sequences would yield two heads: $\langle H, H, T \rangle$, $\langle H, T, H \rangle$, and $\langle T, H, H \rangle$, so that the answer is three in this case. We would like to determine an expression from which we can compute this number for any n and r, $r \leq n$. At first glance, this problem may not appear to have any relation to what we have been considering above. Let us examine it in a little more detail, however. Each individual toss of the coin is a random experiment. $\mathcal{R}$ then consists of n random experiments $\mathcal{R}_i$ which we shall number 1 through n. Consider any outcome of $\mathcal{R}$ which yields precisely r heads. If we give the numbers of the experiments $\mathcal{R}_i$ in which a head is obtained, this completely describes the sequence of heads and tails in $\mathcal{R}$, since in all other experiments a tail is obtained. Each set of r numbers selected from the numbers 1 to n will then serve to define a sequence in which r heads are obtained, if we imagine a head being obtained for each experiment in the set of r numbers. Thus if we imagine the experiments to be numbered balls, the number of possible sequences of r heads is the number of combinations of n things taken r at a time and is given by (5-31).

EXAMPLE. A coin is tossed five times. How many different sequences will yield three heads? This was solved in example 1 on p. 240, and the answer is 10. From the combinations listed there we can immediately write down the corresponding sequences. They are $\langle H, H, H, T, T \rangle$, $\langle H, H, T, H, T \rangle$, $\langle H, H, T, T, H \rangle$, $\langle H, T, H, H, T \rangle$, $\langle H, T, H, T, H \rangle$, $\langle H, T, T, H, H \rangle$, $\langle T, H, H, H, T \rangle$, $\langle T, H, H, T, H \rangle$, $\langle T, H, T, H, H \rangle$, and $\langle T, T, H, H, H \rangle$. We have given these in the same order that the combinations were listed on page 241, and the reader should check the correspondence.

We can now generalize the situation just considered to a case where we perform a random experiment n times, which on any trial can have one of m outcomes $e_1, \ldots, e_m$. Consider the single experiment $\mathcal{R}$ which corresponds to performing the experiment n times. Let us focus our attention on outcomes of $\mathcal{R}$ in which each event e_j occurred r_j times and

$$\sum_{j=1}^{m} r_j = n. \tag{5-32}$$

We would like to compute the number of different sequences of the form $\langle \alpha_1, \ldots, \alpha_n \rangle$ where each α_i is one of the e_j, having the property that for each j, e_j appears precisely r_j times. We allow for the possibility that some r_j are 0. For example, we might toss a die ten times and ask how many different sequences there are in which the face with one dot appears three times, that with three dots appears four times, that with five appears twice and that with six appears once, the other faces never appearing. Here, if the event e_j is a face with j dots turning up, $r_1 = 3$, $r_3 = 4$, $r_5 = 2$, and $r_6 = 1$.

To solve this problem we proceed as follows. Consider e_1 which is to appear r_1 times. Imagine as before that the experiments are numbered 1 to n. There are then $n!/r_1!(n - r_1)!$ different ways to assign the event e_1 to the n experiment a total of r_1 times. This is true even if $r_1 = 0$ because then the above formula reduces to 1 which is the correct result, since the one way in which we cannot assign e_1 to any experiment is simply to omit it. Once the r_1 events e_1 have been assigned to experiments, there are $n - r_1$ experiments remaining for the assignment of other events. There are then

$$\binom{n - r_1}{r_2} = \frac{(n - r_1)!}{r_2!(n - r_1 - r_2)!} \tag{5-33}$$

ways to assign the r_2 events e_2 to the remaining $n - r_1$ experiments. For each assignment of the events e_1, the r_2 events e_2 can be assigned in all the ways (5-33), so that in total there are

$$\frac{n!}{r_1!(n - r_1)!}\frac{(n - r_1)!}{r_2!(n - r_1 - r_2)!} = \frac{n!}{r_1!r_2!(n - r_1 - r_2)!} \qquad (5\text{-}34)$$

ways the events e_1 and e_2 can be assigned. Now there are $n - r_1 - r_2$ experiments left, and there are

$$\binom{n - r_1 - r_2}{r_3}$$

ways to assign the r_3 events e_3 to the remaining experiments, or a total of

$$\frac{n!}{r_1!r_2!(n - r_1 - r_2)!}\frac{(n - r_1 - r_2)!}{r_3!(n - r_1 - r_2 - r_3)!}$$

$$= \frac{n!}{r_1!r_2!r_3!(n - r_1 - r_2 - r_3)!} \qquad (5\text{-}35)$$

ways to assign the first three events. By repeating this process we immediately see that the number of ways to assign the m events to the experiments is

$$\frac{n!}{r_1!r_2!\cdots r_m!(n - r_1 - \cdots - r_m)!}.$$

However, by (5-32), $n - r_1 - \cdots - r_m = 0$, and $0! = 1$. The desired number of sequences is then

$$\frac{n!}{r_1!r_2!\cdots r_m!}. \qquad (5\text{-}36)$$

For the die example referred to above, there are then

$$\frac{10!}{3!4!2!} = 12{,}600$$

sequences with the characteristics desired.

Let us conclude the section with a very simple counting problem. Consider the random experiment $\mathfrak{R}$ which consists of repeating independently the random experiment $\mathfrak{R}^*$ a total of n times. Let $\mathcal{E}^*$ be the model of $\mathfrak{R}^*$ and suppose that the event set E^* contains m elements. Consider the model $\mathcal{E}$ which is the direct product of $\mathcal{E}^*$ with itself n times. How many simple events will there be in the event set for $\mathcal{E}$? Each simple event in $\mathcal{E}$ is characterized by an ordered n-tuple $\langle \alpha_1, \ldots, \alpha_n \rangle$, where each α_i is one of the $e_j \in E^*$. Now α_1 can have any of m values corresponding to the m possible outcomes of the first trial. Given α_1, then α_2 can have any of m values corresponding to the m possible outcomes of the second trial. This is true for each α_1. Hence there must be m^2 pairs $\langle \alpha_1, \alpha_2 \rangle$. If we continue this argument, we see that there must be m^ntuples $\langle \alpha_1, \ldots, \alpha_n \rangle$, that is, the event set for $\mathcal{E}$ will contain m^n simple events. In particular, if E^* contains only two events as in tossing a coin, $\mathcal{E}$ will have 2^n simple events.

EXAMPLES.   1.   In Example 4 for Section 5-5 we noted that if a coin is tossed four times, there are 16 simple events in $\mathcal{E}$.   Since $2^4 = 16$ this is in agreement with the formula just obtained.

2.   Consider an urn which contains red, green, and yellow balls.   Suppose that we draw a ball, note its color, replace the ball in the urn, then mix the balls and again draw a ball and note its color.   This experiment $\mathcal{R}$ can be looked upon as one in which the experiment $\mathcal{R}^*$ of drawing a ball from the urn is repeated twice.   Suppose that the event set for $\mathcal{R}^*$ is $E^* = \{R, G, Y\}$, the simple events giving the color of the ball selected. Then $E = E^* \times E^*$ should have $3^2 = 9$ elements, since $m = 3$ and $n = 2$. These are $\langle R, R\rangle, \langle R, G\rangle, \langle R, Y\rangle, \langle G, R\rangle, \langle G, G\rangle, \langle G, Y\rangle, \langle Y, R\rangle, \langle Y, G\rangle$, and $\langle Y, Y\rangle$.

5-7 THE BINOMIAL DISTRIBUTION

In practice one frequently encounters situations where a given random experiment $\mathcal{R}^*$ is repeated a number of times, in such a way that the outcome of the experiment on any given trial neither influences nor is influenced by the outcomes on any other trial.   In these circumstances we refer to the individual performances of $\mathcal{R}^*$ as independent trials.   Consider the random experiment $\mathcal{R}$ which consists of performing n independent trials of $\mathcal{R}^*$.   We know that if $\mathcal{E}^*$ is a suitable mathematical model for $\mathcal{R}^*$, then $\mathcal{E} = \mathcal{E}^* \times \cdots \times \mathcal{E}^*$ should be a suitable mathematical model for $\mathcal{R}$; $\mathcal{E}$ is the direct product of $\mathcal{E}^*$ with itself n times.   In this section we would like to study situations of this type for the very important case where the event set for $\mathcal{E}^*$ is $E^* = \{e_1, e_2\}$, that is, where only two outcomes of $\mathcal{R}^*$ are of interest.   Let p be the probability of e_1 in $\mathcal{E}^*$ and $q = 1 - p$ the probability of e_2.

A simple event for $\mathcal{E}$ will be characterized by an n-tuple $\langle \alpha_1, \ldots, \alpha_n\rangle$ where each α_j is either e_1 or e_2; α_j gives the event of $\mathcal{R}^*$ that occurred on the jth trial.   From what we noted in the previous section there are 2^n simple events in $\mathcal{E}$.   These simple events are in general not equally likely.   The probability of $\langle \alpha_1, \ldots, \alpha_n\rangle$ is $p(\alpha_1)\cdots p(\alpha_n)$.   Now $p(\alpha_j)$ is either p or q, depending on whether α_j is e_1 or e_2.   Suppose that e_1 appears r times in $\langle \alpha_1, \ldots, \alpha_n\rangle$ and e_2 appears $n - r$ times, $r = 0, 1, \ldots, n$.   The probability of $\langle \alpha_1, \ldots, \alpha_n\rangle$ is then $p^r q^{n-r}$.   This holds even if $r = 0$ or $r = n$, if we define $a^0 = 1$ for any number a.   Thus every simple event $\langle \alpha_1, \ldots, \alpha_n\rangle$ in which e_1 appears r times has the probability $p^r q^{n-r}$.   The probabilities of the simple events with different values of r will in general be different.

In studying $\mathcal{R}$, one is frequently interested only in the number of times that the event e_1 (or e_2) appeared in the n trials and not in the particular sequence in which they were obtained. Let us then introduce a random variable x defined over E, which is the number of times that e_1 was observed in the n trials. For every simple event in E for which e_1 appears r times, then $x = r$. The probability function for x can now be determined. Each simple event for which $x = r$ has, as we have shown above, the probability $p^r q^{n-r}$. How many simple events are there with $x = r$? This is just the number of different n-tuples $\langle \alpha_1, \ldots, \alpha_n \rangle$ in which e_1 appears r times. In the previous section we showed that this was C_r^n. Thus $p(r)$, the probability that $x = r$, is

$$p(r) = C_r^n p^r q^{n-r} = \frac{n!}{r!(n-r)!} p^r q^{n-r}. \tag{5-37}$$

The random variable x can assume the $n + 1$ possible values $0, 1, \ldots, n$. The probability function for x is a very important one and is encountered frequently. The interpretation of the random variable x can vary considerably with the circumstances. The probability function $p(x)$ for x is thus given a special name. It is called the *binomial probability function or binomial distribution*, and x is said to have a binomial distribution. We shall also use a special notation for the binomial distribution rather than $p(x)$. We shall write $b(x; n,p)$. Thus by definition

$$b(r; n,p) = \frac{n!}{r!(n-r)!} p^r q^{n-r}, \quad r = 0, 1, \ldots, n. \tag{5-38}$$

The probability function for x clearly depends on how many trials were made, that is, on n, and on the probability p that e_1 will be observed on a given trial. We have indicated this by including the symbols n and p in $b(x; n,p)$ to constantly remind us that the probability function involves these numbers as parameters.

It must be true that

$$\sum_{r=0}^{n} b(r; n,p) = \sum_{r=0}^{n} \frac{n!}{r!(n-r)!} p^r q^{n-r} = 1, \tag{5-39}$$

since $b(x; n,p)$ is a probability function. If we did not know this, it could be proved using the binomial expansion learned in algebra. Recall that the binomial expansion or theorem tells us how to expand $(p + q)^n$ for any p and q as a sum of terms of the form $\beta_r p^r q^{n-r}$. The coefficients β_r of these terms are nothing but the numbers C_r^n, and for this reason the C_r^n are frequently referred to as binomial coefficients. The binomial theorem reads

$$(p + q)^n = \sum_{r=0}^{n} C_r^n p^r q^{n-r}, \tag{5-40}$$

which reduces to (5-39) when $p + q = 1$ since $1^n = 1$. This explains why $b(x; n,p)$ is called the binomial distribution. Each probability $b(r; n,p)$ is a term in the binomial expansion of $(p + q)^n$.

Let us now compute the mean μ and variance σ^2 of the binomial distribution. We omit the subscript x on μ and σ^2 since we are not studying a specific random variable, for which the symbol should be emphasized. By definition,

$$\mu = \sum_{r=0}^{n} rC_r^n p^r q^{n-r} = \sum_{r=1}^{n} rC_r^n p^r q^{n-r}. \tag{5-41}$$

The term with $r = 0$ is 0, and hence one can start the summation with $r = 1$. Now

$$rC_r^n = \frac{r(n!)}{r!(n-r)!} = \frac{n!}{(r-1)!(n-r)!} = \frac{n!}{(r-1)!(n-1-r+1)!}.$$

In the last step we simply added and subtracted 1 in $n - r$ to yield $n - 1 - r + 1$. Thus

$$rC_r^n = n \frac{(n-1)!}{(r-1)!(n-1-r+1)!} = nC_{r-1}^{n-1}.$$

Therefore,

$$\mu = n \sum_{r=1}^{n} C_{r-1}^{n-1} p^r q^{n-r} = np \sum_{r=1}^{n} C_{r-1}^{n-1} p^{r-1} q^{n-1-(r-1)}.$$

If we now write $j = r - 1$, then when $r = 1$, $j = 0$; and when $r = n$, $j = n - 1$. Hence

$$\mu = np \sum_{j=0}^{n-1} C_j^{n-1} p^j q^{n-1-j} = np \sum_{j=0}^{n-1} b(j; n-1, p) = np, \tag{5-42}$$

the last step following from (5-39) with n replaced by $n - 1$. Thus we have proved that the mean of the binomial distribution is $\mu = np$. The above derivation may seem a little complex at first reading, but it is really simple and is the sort of process one encounters frequently.

Consider next σ^2. Precisely the same sort of analysis is employed. It is convenient to use the general result (1-71), which says

$$\sigma^2 = \sum_{r=0}^{n} r^2 b(r; n,p) - \mu^2.$$

The trick we just used to compute μ was to cancel the r in the numerator with the r in $r!$. Here we wish to do the same sort of thing. Now, however, we have an r^2 rather than r. Once one r is canceled, we are left with $(r - 1)!$, so that instead of an r to cancel we need an $r - 1$. We can arrange things so that there is an $r - 1$ by writing

$$r^2 = r(r - 1) + r.$$

Thus

$$\sum_{r=0}^{n} r^2 b(r;n,p) = \sum_{r=0}^{n} r(r-1)b(r;n,p) + \sum_{r=0}^{n} rb(r;n,p). \qquad (5\text{-}43)$$

Now the second sum on the right in (5-43) is μ. In the first sum on the right in (5-43), both $r = 0$ and $r = 1$ give terms which are 0, and hence the summation can be started at $r = 2$ rather than $r = 0$. Thus

$$\sigma^2 = \sum_{r=2}^{n} r(r-1)b(r;n,p) + \mu - \mu^2. \qquad (5\text{-}44)$$

Next observe that

$$r(r-1)C_r^n = n(n-1)\frac{(n-2)!}{(r-2)!(n-2-r+2)!} = n(n-1)C_{r-2}^{n-2}, \qquad (5\text{-}45)$$

and

$$\sum_{r=2}^{n} r(r-1)b(r;n,p) = n(n-1)p^2 \sum_{r=2}^{n} C_{r-2}^{n-2} p^{r-2} q^{n-2-(r-2)}$$

$$= n(n-1)p^2 \sum_{j=0}^{n-2} C_j^{n-2} p^j q^{n-2-j} = n(n-1)p^2, \qquad (5\text{-}46)$$

the last step following from (5-39) with n replaced by $n - 2$. Hence on using (5-46) in (5-44) along with $\mu = np$, we have

$$\sigma^2 = n(n-1)p^2 + np - n^2 p^2 = n^2 p^2 - np^2 + np - n^2 p^2$$
$$= np(1-p) = npq. \qquad (5\text{-}47)$$

Therefore, the variance of the binomial distribution is $\sigma^2 = npq$, and the standard deviation is then

$$\sigma = \sqrt{npq}. \qquad (5\text{-}48)$$

The reader might be concerned that the above derivation only holds for $n \geq 2$, since in (5-44) the summation begins with $r = 2$. Note, however, that if $n = 1$, the largest value of r is 1 and the first summation in (5-44) disappears, that is, it is 0. But this is what we obtain from (5-46) when $n = 1$. Thus the expression for σ^2 holds for all natural numbers n. Later we shall see that there is a much easier way to compute μ and σ for the binomial distribution. This latter method will not have the general applicability to other distributions of the method introduced here, however.

The binomial distribution involves as parameters n and p. It is useful to keep in mind how the bar diagram for $b(x;n,p)$ changes with p for a given n. We have illustrated this in Figures 5-1, 5-2, and 5-3 by plotting the bar diagrams for $p = 0.1, 0.45,$ and 0.83 in the case where $n = 10$. The means np of the distributions for these cases are then 1, 4.5, and 8.3, respectively. These values have not been indicated on the figures. The three bar diagrams have quite different appearances. As one might expect intuitively, if p is small then the events with the highest probabilities are

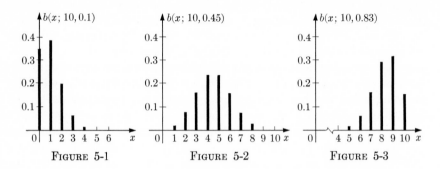

FIGURE 5-1   FIGURE 5-2   FIGURE 5-3

those corresponding to small values of x, while just the reverse is true if p is close to 1. In Figure 5-1 no bars are shown for $x = 5$ through 10; $b(x; 10, 0.1)$ is actually positive for these values, but is so small that the bars could not be shown on the figure. The same holds for $x = 0$, 9, and 10 in Figure 5-2, and $x = 0$ through 4 in Figure 5-3.

The range of possible values of x in each of the bar diagrams is 0 to 10, and the midpoint of the range is then 5. The bar diagram in Figure 5-1 has the characteristic that the values of x with the largest probabilities lie to the left of the midpoint of the range, while in Figure 5-2 they are more or less symmetrically spaced about it, and in Figure 5-3 they lie to the right of the midpoint. The distributions whose bar diagrams are those of Figures 5-1 and 5-3 are called *skewed*. We can make this notion more precise for any probability function $p(x)$ as follows. *A distribution $p(x)$ is said to be symmetric with ξ as a point of symmetry if whenever $\xi + u$ is a possible value of the random variable x, so is $\xi - u$ and $p(\xi + u) = p(\xi - u)$.* A distribution which is not symmetric is said to be *skewed*. The distribution in Figure 5-3 is said to be skewed to the right and that in Figure 5-1 is said to be skewed to the left. The closer p comes to 0.5, the closer $b(x; n, p)$ comes to being symmetric; the distribution is symmetric when $p = 0.5$.

For any probability function $p(x)$, the value of x (which is not necessarily unique) where $p(x)$ takes on its largest value is called the mode of the distribution. Thus $x = 9$ is the mode of $b(x; 10, 0.83)$ shown in Figure 5-3. In Figure 5-2, it appears that both $x = 4$ and $x = 5$ are modes. However, the probability is slightly greater for $x = 4$ than for $x = 5$, and hence 4 is the mode. As one would expect intuitively, the mode of $b(x; n, p)$ tends to increase with p for a given n, and for small p the mode lies to the left of the midpoint of the range, while for large p it lies to the right of the midpoint of the range.

It is very clumsy to make by hand numerical computations which involve the binomial distribution, since it is very laborious to evaluate $C_r^n p^r q^{n-r}$. It is even somewhat complicated to do this on a computer. This would suggest that tables of the binomial distribution could be useful to eliminate the need for such computations. However, it is also difficult to tabulate the binomial distribution. The reason for this is that $b(x; n,p)$ involves two parameters n and p, and for each n and p there are $n + 1$ values of x possible. Thus covering the entire range of n and p values which might be of interest leads to tables which fill a very large volume. Two well-known tables of this type have been computed and references are given to them at the end of the chapter. However, it is not very convenient to use such a large volume of tables if one can avoid it. Fortunately, for most purposes, one can avoid ever using the binomial distribution directly. This is accomplished by approximating $b(x; n,p)$ by functions which are easier to work with. There are two approximations which serve rather well to handle most situations one encounters in practice. One of these will be considered in Section 5-9 and the other in Chapter 7.

Before giving some examples illustrating the usefulness of the binomial distribution, it is desirable to point out one other feature of $b(x; n,p)$ which is often useful in making computations. Note that $b(r; n,p)$ is not only the probability that e_1 occurred r times in n trials, it is also the probability that e_2 occurred $n - r$ times in the n trials, since if e_1 occurs r times, e_2 must occur $n - r$ times. However, the probability that e_2 occurs $n - r$ times is $b(n - r; n,q)$. Thus

$$b(r; n,p) = b(n - r; n,q). \tag{5-49}$$

This can be verified directly without the above reasoning, since

$$b(n - r; n,q) = \frac{n!}{(n - r)!(n - n + r)!} q^{n-r} p^{n-n+r} = b(r; n,p). \tag{5-50}$$

Because of (5-49), it is never necessary to tabulate $b(r; n,p)$ for $p > 0.5$, since to compute any such probability it is only necessary to use (5-49) and compute instead $b(n - r; n, 1 - p)$ and $1 - p < 0.5$. For this reason the tables of the binomial distribution normally do not show values for $p > 0.5$. To illustrate what tables are like for the binomial probability function $b(x; n,p)$, we have given some very brief tables (Tables A and B) at the end of the text. Although we have not included one, tables for the cumulative function, which we shall denote by $B(x; n,p)$, are also frequently useful to avoid the necessity for summing entries in the tables for $b(x; n,p)$.

5-8 EXAMPLES

1. Consider the production process for some given item. The part may be a plastic part which is made on an extrusion molding machine, it might be a metal part which is stamped out of sheet metal, it could be a helical gear which requires operations on a number of machines, or it could be a radio produced on an assembly line. We need not be concerned what the precise nature of the production process is. Once an item is produced, it will either meet specifications and be classified as good, or it will not meet specifications and be classified as defective. In general, the process will not invariably produce good units. For a variety of reasons, defectives will be produced now and then. The process of manufacturing one unit of the product can be looked upon then as a random experiment with only two outcomes, one being that the unit produced is good, and the other being that the unit is defective. Now, can the production of the units one after another be looked upon as independent trials of this experiment? Generally not. Frequently, defectives will be produced in batches and it will be found that there is some assignable cause for the defectives, such as a drop in the temperature in the plastic molding process. However, even when the process is operating properly, defects can still be produced occasionally due to the interplay of a variety of small chance effects. When this is the case, the production process behaves almost as if each unit produced represents an independent trial of the random experiment referred to. Suppose that the process is behaving in such a way that the production of each unit represents an independent trial of a random experiment. From our notion of probability as a long run relative frequency, the probability that a given unit will be defective is the long run fraction defective. Denote this probability by p. Let us now select in any way we wish (without examining the units) n units produced by the process. The probability that precisely r of these are defective is then the binomial probability $b(r; n,p)$.

When a production process operates in such a way that the production of each unit represents an independent trial of a random experiment in which the probability of a defective is p, the process is said to be in *statistical control*. When the process is in statistical control we say that defects are generated at random. Here we encounter still another and different use of the word random. Statistical control is an idealized concept, and it is not possible to prove whether or not any given real process is in statistical control. Nonetheless, the concept is very helpful in that it is used as a standard to judge whether the process is deviating from the standard sufficiently that one should investigate to see if there is some assignable cause of the defectives being generated. Note that the concept of statistical control does not imply anything about the defective fraction produced. A process could be in statistical control while producing a very high fraction defective and not in statistical control when producing a low fraction defective. What quality control personnel and industrial engineers attempt to do, of course, is keep the process in control while producing the lowest possible fraction defective.

The sort of procedure generally used for monitoring the production process is the following. Periodically, perhaps once every ten minutes or every hour or every day, a sample of n units will be selected from the period's production. The number r of defectives in the sample will be determined. Then a decision is made either to let the process continue as is, or to investigate to see if something is wrong with it. Which action will be selected depends on the value of r. If r is too large, this will be taken as an indication that something has gone wrong. Now it can also be useful to look at the process if r is exceptionally small, since then the process is doing better than expected and an investigation might lead to an improvement in the process. Thus the procedure followed might be to do nothing if $\alpha_1 \leq r \leq \alpha_2$, and to investigate the process if $r < \alpha_1$ or $r > \alpha_2$.

The problem we have been discussing is a statistical decision problem, and the values chosen for α_1 and α_2 should depend on the costs involved. The present problem is a rather complicated type of decision problem, as we shall see in more detail later. The general practice followed in industry uses a much simpler procedure to determine α_1 and α_2. The values employed are

$$\alpha_1 = \mu - 3\sigma = np - 3\sqrt{npq}, \quad \alpha_2 = \mu + 3\sigma = np + 3\sqrt{npq}, \quad (5\text{-}51)$$

so that if r is more than three standard deviations away from the expected number of defectives in the sample, action is taken. Although there is no detailed theoretical justification for the use of these values for α_1 and α_2, they have been found to work out quite well in practice.

One can easily maintain a graphical record of the behavior of the process over time using a chart, called a *control chart*, an example of which is shown in Figure 5-4. Each time a sample is taken, one plots on this chart at the time when the sample was taken, the number of defects in the sample. Through the points np, α_1, and α_2 on the vertical axis we draw horizontal lines. The line through np is called the center line, the one through α_1 is

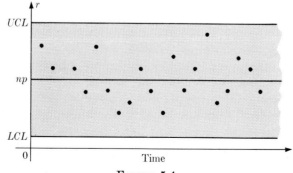

FIGURE 5-4

called the lower control limit, abbreviated LCL, and the one through α_2 is called the upper control limit, abbreviated UCL.   As long as the points lie inside the control limits no action is taken.   However, if a point falls outside the control limits, then action is taken.   Control charts, of which the one just described is one particular type, are widely used in industry and are very useful for controlling processes.

2.   Seventeen women are in the maternity ward of a hospital awaiting the birth of children.   What is the probability that precisely eight will have girls and the remainder boys?   Let us assume for our model that there will be no multiple births, so that seventeen children will be born. Historical data show that the relative frequency of girl babies is about 0.49.   It then seems reasonable to imagine the situation as seventeen independent trials of a random experiment which leads to the birth of a girl or a boy with the probability of a girl being 0.49.   Then the probability of precisely eight girls is $b(8; 17,0.49)$.   This probability is 0.1885.

3.   The air force has 50 Minuteman missiles sitting in readiness at a given launch site with their electronic systems always operating.   These missiles are all checked periodically by electronic checkout equipment, perhaps once per day, to determine if any failures have occurred in the electronic systems.   Suppose that the probability that any given missile fails in the period between tests is 0.01.   What is the probability that two or more missiles fail in a given period?   If we make the reasonable assumption that a failure in one missile in no way influences the others, then the probability is $1 - B(1; 50,0.01) = 0.0894$.

5-9   THE POISSON APPROXIMATION

In many cases where one is making use of the binomial distribution, it happens to be true that p is quite small, say less than 0.1, and n is fairly large, say 50 or more, so that the mean μ is a number between 1 and 25. For example, in dealing with a sample taken from a production process, the probability that a given unit is defective may be 0.02 or even less, while the sample size may be 100 or more (the sample is generally chosen to be large enough so that the expected number of defectives in the sample is at least 1).   In this section we wish to derive a function which offers a good approximation to the binomial distribution in such cases and is quite a bit easier to work with numerically.   To obtain this function, we shall examine what happens to $b(r; n,p)$ as n gets larger and larger, while the mean remains constant.   To keep the mean constant, p must get closer and closer to 0 as n is increased, since $\mu = np$.   Let us hold the mean constant at the value β, that is, $\beta = np$.   Then for any given value of n, we must have $p = \beta/n$. Now if we substitute β/n for p in $b(r; n,p)$, we obtain

$$b(r; n,p) = \frac{n!}{r!(n-r)!}\left(\frac{\beta}{n}\right)^r\left(1 - \frac{\beta}{n}\right)^{n-r}, \tag{5-52}$$

which depends only on n for a fixed r and β. Now

$$\left(\frac{\beta}{n}\right)^r = \frac{\beta^r}{n^r}; \quad \left(1 - \frac{\beta}{n}\right)^{n-r} = \frac{\left(1 - \dfrac{\beta}{n}\right)^n}{\left(1 - \dfrac{\beta}{n}\right)^r}.$$

Thus

$$b(r; n,p) = \frac{\beta^r}{r!}\left[\frac{n(n-1)\cdots(n-r+1)}{n^r}\right]\frac{\left(1 - \dfrac{\beta}{n}\right)^n}{\left(1 - \dfrac{\beta}{n}\right)^r}$$

$$= \frac{\beta^r}{r!}\left[1\left(1 - \frac{1}{n}\right)\left(1 - \frac{2}{n}\right)\cdots\left(1 - \frac{r-1}{n}\right)\right]\frac{\left(1 - \dfrac{\beta}{n}\right)^n}{\left(1 - \dfrac{\beta}{n}\right)^r}. \tag{5-53}$$

Let us next consider what happens when we increase n unendingly while keeping r fixed. As n gets larger and larger, $1 - (a/n)$ gets closer and closer to 1 for any value of a. Therefore, we conclude that as n becomes arbitrarily large,

$$\left(1 - \frac{1}{n}\right)\left(1 - \frac{2}{n}\right)\cdots\left(1 - \frac{r-1}{n}\right)$$

approaches 1 and $[1 - (\beta/n)]^r$ approaches 1. We might be tempted to say that $[1 - (\beta/n)]^n$ also approaches 1. However, the situation is different now in that the power to which $1 - (\beta/n)$ is raised increases as n increases. We must be more careful here. To study the behavior of this expression as n becomes very large, it is a little more convenient to reintroduce p and study what happens as p gets close to 0. Now since $\beta/n = p$, we have

$$\left(1 - \frac{\beta}{n}\right)^n = (1 - p)^{\beta/p} = [(1 - p)^{1/p}]^\beta. \tag{5-54}$$

In Table 5-5 we have given the value of $(1 - p)^{1/p}$ for various values of p.

TABLE 5-5

VALUES OF $(1 - p)^{1/p}$

p	$(1 - p)^{1/p}$	p	$(1 - p)^{1/p}$
0.1	0.3486	0.001	0.3673
0.01	0.3660	0.0001	0.3677

These were computed using an accurate table of logarithms. It seems clear that $(1 - p)^{1/p}$ is not approaching 1, but is approaching a number whose value is roughly 0.367. This is indeed the case. If one is familiar with the use of the methods of the calculus, one can easily prove, see [5] for example, that the limit of $(1 - p)^{1/p}$ as p approaches 0 is a unique number whose value is approximately 0.36787944. This number is the reciprocal of a very well-known number in mathematics which is always denoted by e and which serves as the base for the system of natural logarithms; e has the approximate value 2.71828182. Hence $(1 - p)^{1/p}$ approaches e^{-1}, and therefore $(1 - p)^{\beta/p}$ or $[1 - (\beta/n)]^n$ approaches the number $e^{-\beta}$, which is not 1, in general, and which depends on β. On replacing the factors in (5-53) by their limiting values we conclude that when $np = \beta$, $b(r; n,p)$ approaches, as n becomes arbitrarily large, a number which we shall denote by $p(r; \beta)$ which is

$$p(r; \beta) = \frac{\beta^r}{r!} e^{-\beta}. \tag{5-55}$$

The number $p(r; \beta)$ is the limit of $b(r; n,p)$ as n becomes arbitrarily large while maintaining $np = \beta$. Since r can take on every integral value from 0 to n, we see that as n becomes arbitrarily large, r can take on every non-negative integral value. Thus for every non-negative integer r we can compute a number $p(r; \beta)$ given by (5-55). This association with each non-negative integer a number $p(r; \beta)$ describes a function whose domain is the set of all non-negative integers. The image of the integer r is $p(r; \beta)$. This function is called the Poisson function, and it will be of considerable interest to us.

Now originally, we started looking for a function that would provide a good approximation for $b(r; n,p)$ when p was small and n reasonably large. At the moment, we have no reason in the world to believe that the Poisson function (5-55) is such a function, since it was obtained as a limit in which n became arbitrarily large and p arbitrarily close to 0. It does not necessarily follow at all that it will yield a good approximation for small p and moderately large n. The only convenient way to determine whether it does yield a good approximation is by making numerical comparisons in a large number of cases. Interestingly enough, the Poisson function turns out to be extremely good for approximating $b(r; n,p)$ when p is small. It does much better than one might reasonably expect to be the case. How do we approximate $b(r; n,p)$ by the Poisson function? In place of $b(r; n,p)$ we simply compute $p(r; \beta)$ where $\beta = np$ is the mean of the distribution $b(x; n,p)$, i.e., we use $p(r; np)$ in place of $b(r; n,p)$. Now it is not much easier to compute numerically $p(r; np)$ than it is to compute $b(r; n,p)$. What have we gained then if we are approximating $b(r; n,p)$ by another function which is almost as difficult to compute? The great advantage gained is that $p(r; \beta)$ involves only a single parameter β rather than the two parameters n and p which appear in $b(r; n,p)$. Thus $p(r; \beta)$

can be tabulated much more compactly than $b(r; n,p)$. Rather complete
tables of the Poisson function require only a small volume, while those
for $b(r; n,p)$ require a large volume or several volumes. Indeed, very
useful tables of $p(r; \beta)$ can be given in just a few pages. Two extensive
tables of $p(r; \beta)$ have been published and references are given to them at
the end of this chapter. In Table C at the end of the text is given a very
brief table of $p(r; \beta)$.

Even though a considerable amount of numerical work has been done
in comparing $p(r; np)$ and $b(r; n,p)$ for various values of r, n, and p, it is
not easy to give precise rules as to when $p(r; np)$ can be used in place of
$b(r; n,p)$. The accuracy of the approximation depends not only on n and p
but also on r. If considerable accuracy is required, then one must use care
in approximating $b(r; n,p)$ by $p(r; np)$. For most computations of the
sort one usually makes, however, great accuracy is not needed, and in
fact, an error of five percent or so in the probabilities is acceptable for
probabilities in the range 0.1 to 1, and often an even larger error is acceptable if the probability is less than 0.1. Roughly speaking then two
significant figures are more than adequate, and an error of two or three in
the second significant figure may be quite acceptable. In such situations
a good general rule is that the Poisson function can be used if $p \leq 0.1$ and
$np \geq 5$, and the Poisson function may be quite adequate even if np is of
the order of 1 or 2. The Poisson function often gives a remarkably good
approximation even for small values of n. To illustrate this we used the
tables given at the end of the text to determine $b(r; n,p)$ and $p(r; np)$ for
$n = 10$ and the two values of p, $p = 0.10$ and 0.05. The comparison is
given in Table 5-6. Observe that $p(r; np)$ yields a rather good approximation in both cases, in spite of the fact that n is only 10.

TABLE 5-6

COMPARISON OF $b(r; 10, p)$ AND $p(r; 10p)$

	$p = 0.10$			$p = 0.05$	
r	$b(r; 10, 0.10)$	$p(r; 1)$	r	$b(r; 10, 0.05)$	$p(r; 0.5)$
0	0.3487	0.3679	0	0.5987	0.6065
1	0.3874	0.3679	1	0.3151	0.3033
2	0.1937	0.1839	2	0.0746	0.0758
3	0.0574	0.0613	3	0.0105	0.0126
4	0.0112	0.0153	4	0.0010	0.0016
5	0.0015	0.0031	5	0.0001	0.0002
6	0.0001	0.0005	6	0.0000	0.0000

5-10 THE POISSON DISTRIBUTION

The Poisson function was obtained from the binomial distribution by a
special form of limiting process. Now if one sums $b(r; n,p)$ from $r = 0$

to $r = n$, the result is 1 for every value of n and p. Thus we feel intuitively that this should still hold true in the limit as n becomes arbitrarily large, while p approaches 0 in such a way that $\beta = np$. In other words, we feel that if we add up all the values $p(r; \beta)$ for $r = 0, 1, 2, \ldots$, we should obtain 1, i.e.,

$$p(0; \beta) + p(1; \beta) + p(2; \beta) + \cdots = 1. \qquad (5\text{-}56)$$

Recall that $p(r; \beta)$ is defined for every non-negative integer. Thus (5-56) is the sum of an infinite number of terms. Such summations are considered in calculus and are called infinite series. Infinite series can sum to a finite number. When this happens the series is said to converge. The series (5-56) can easily be represented using the summation notation, where to indicate that there is no upper limit on r we use the symbol ∞ on top of the summation sign and write the right-hand side of (5-56) as $\sum_{r=0}^{\infty} p(r; \beta)$, which is read the sum from r equal 0 to infinity of $p(r; \beta)$.

The reader familiar with infinite series will not need to rely on our intuitive argument to convince himself of the truth of (5-56). It can easily be proved as follows. The Taylor's expansion, see [5], of e^β about the origin is an infinite series which converges to e^β for all β, and it has the form

$$e^\beta = 1 + \beta + \frac{\beta^2}{2!} + \frac{\beta^3}{3!} + \cdots = \sum_{r=0}^{\infty} \frac{\beta^r}{r!}. \qquad (5\text{-}57)$$

Now recall that if $\sum_{r=0}^{\infty} a_r$ converges to a, then $\sum_{r=0}^{\infty} (\alpha a_r)$ converges to αa for any number α. If we take $\alpha = e^{-\beta}$ and apply this result to (5-57), we conclude that $\sum_{r=0}^{\infty} \beta^r e^{-\beta}/r!$ converges to $e^{-\beta}e^\beta = e^0 = 1$. But from (5-55) this is precisely (5-56). This then proves that (5-56) is true. From (5-56), since $p(r; \beta) > 0$ if $\beta > 0$, it follows that $p(r; \beta) < 1$ for all r.

We have shown that when $\beta > 0$, $0 < p(r; \beta) < 1$ for all r and that in addition $\sum_{r=0}^{\infty} p(r; \beta) = 1$. Intuitively then, it would appear that the Poisson function with $\beta > 0$ can be looked upon as the probability function for a random variable x which can take on every non-negative integral value. It is very useful to think of things in this way. To do so, however, requires some generalization of our previous ideas because if we take as the event set in this case the set X of possible values which x can take on, there are an infinite number of elements in the event set. There is no reason why originally we could not have considered event sets of the form $E = \{e_0, e_1, e_2, \ldots\}$ where there was a simple event corresponding to each non-negative integer or for every integer. Everything that we have done remains unchanged. Once again, every subset of E can be considered to be an event. Now, however, there are composite events which consist of an infinite number of simple events, and in such cases, (1-12) must be reinterpreted as an infinite series. Thus, intuitively, nothing is changed by making this generalization. However, a rigorous development in this case requires an understanding of infinite series. Now we mentioned in Chapter 1 that the number of events in any real world situation will always be finite. Thus any mathematical model whose event set contains an infinite number of simple events will be only an approximation to the real world situation. However, it not infrequently turns out to be a very convenient approximation to make. In the future we shall on a number of occasions find it convenient to deal with event sets like $E = \{e_0, e_1, e_2, \ldots\}$ which contain an infinite number of elements.

Given the above discussion we see that it is indeed legitimate to think of the Poisson function with $\beta > 0$ as the probability function for a random variable which can assume all non-negative integral values. We shall do this in the future, and we shall then refer to $p(x; \beta)$ as the *Poisson probability function or Poisson distribution, and any random variable x whose probability function is $p(x; \beta)$ will be said to have a Poisson distribution.* We have obtained the Poisson distribution as a result of looking for a way to approximate the binomial distribution. The Poisson distribution is, however, a very important distribution in its own right, not merely as an approximation to the binomial distribution. The Poisson distribution arises in many important areas, and we shall illustrate some of these in Chapter 10 when studying the so-called Poisson process.

We can easily compute the mean μ and variance σ^2 of the Poisson distribution just as we did for the binomial distribution. By definition

$$\mu = \sum_{r=0}^{\infty} rp(r; \beta) = \sum_{r=1}^{\infty} rp(r; \beta). \tag{5-58}$$

However,

$$rp(r; \beta) = \frac{\beta^r}{(r-1)!} e^{-\beta} = \beta \frac{\beta^{r-1}}{(r-1)!} e^{-\beta} = \beta p(r-1; \beta), \tag{5-59}$$

so

$$\mu = \sum_{r=1}^{\infty} \beta p(r-1; \beta) = \beta \sum_{u=0}^{\infty} p(u; \beta) = \beta \tag{5-60}$$

by (5-56). Thus the mean of the Poisson distribution is the number β. Recall that to approximate $b(r; n,p)$ we use $p(r; np)$, that is, we use for β the mean of the binomial distribution. However, β is also the mean of $p(x; \beta)$. Thus in approximating $b(x; n,p)$ we use a Poisson distribution with the same mean.

The variance of $p(x; \beta)$ is

$$\sigma^2 = \sum_{r=0}^{\infty} r^2 p(r; \beta) - \mu^2 = \sum_{r=2}^{\infty} r(r-1)p(r; \beta) + \mu - \mu^2. \tag{5-61}$$

Now

$$\sum_{r=2}^{\infty} r(r-1)p(r; \beta) = \beta^2 \sum_{r=2}^{\infty} p(r-2; \beta) = \beta^2 \sum_{u=0}^{\infty} p(u; \beta) = \beta^2;$$

hence

$$\sigma^2 = \beta^2 + \beta - \beta^2 = \beta = \mu, \qquad (5\text{-}62)$$

and we have obtained the interesting result that the variance of the Poisson distribution is equal to its mean in numerical value (the physical dimensions are different, however).

For every non-negative integer r, $p(r;\beta) > 0$ when $\beta > 0$. However, for r values which lie more than about three standard deviations to the right of β, the values of $p(r;\beta)$ are so close to zero that nothing would be changed for all normal computations if we set them equal to 0. What this implies then is that even though we must, if we are to be rigorous, imagine that the event set for a random variable x, which has a Poisson distribution, contains an infinite number of elements; in practice x behaves as if it can take only a finite number of values because the probabilities of very large values of x are so small that we can safely treat them as impossible for most computations. This is precisely what we want, of course, because in the real world it is not possible for any random variable to take on arbitrarily large values. There is always some upper limit (perhaps very large) on the magnitude of x. A mathematical model which yields a random variable which can take on arbitrarily large values is only an approximation to any real world situation, and to be realistic, the probabilities that the variable can be greater than some upper limit must be essentially 0.

5-11 THE PASCAL DISTRIBUTION

We have seen in Section 5-7 that the probability of obtaining r heads in n tosses of a coin, when the probability of a head on any given toss is p, is $b(r; n,p)$. Suppose now that someone asks us what is the probability that the coin must be tossed a total of n times in order to obtain r heads. In more general terms consider an experiment $\mathcal{R}^*$ with the mathematical model for $\mathcal{R}^*$ being $\mathcal{E}^*$. Suppose that the event set for $\mathcal{E}^*$ contains only two simple events e_1 and e_2 with the probability of e_1 being p and that of e_2 being $q = 1 - p$. We shall assume that $p > 0$. What is the probability that precisely n independent trials of $\mathcal{R}^*$ must be performed in order to obtain r occurrences of e_1? Note that if precisely n trials are required to obtain r occurrences of e_1, then e_1 must occur on the nth trial and must have in addition occurred $r - 1$ times in the first $n - 1$ trials. Now we can think of the process of repeating $\mathcal{R}^*$ a sufficient number of times to obtain r occurrences of e_1 as a random experiment $\mathcal{R}$. Let us examine the nature of the event set for $\mathcal{R}$. As a simple event we shall use the number of trials needed to obtain r occurrences of e_1. It is impossible to obtain e_1 a total of r times in less than r trials of $\mathcal{R}^*$. Thus the event set for $\mathfrak{R}$ must be the set of numbers $Y = \{r, r + 1, r + 2, \ldots\}$. The interesting thing is that this event set does not contain a finite number of elements. An arbitrarily large number of trials may be needed to obtain e_1 a total of r times. Here then we have another example of the sort of event set introduced in the previous section.

What probability shall we assign to the simple event n that n trials are needed to obtain r occurrences of e_1? To answer this, consider the random experiment which consists of performing $\mathfrak{R}^*$ precisely n times, and let $\mathcal{E} = \mathcal{E}^* \times \cdots \times \mathcal{E}^*$ be the event set for this experiment. Let us compute the probability that e_1 occurs a total of r times and in addition e_1 occurs on the final trial. The set of simple events corresponding to this event will be of the form $\langle \alpha_1, \ldots, \alpha_{n-1}, e_1 \rangle$, where e_1 appears $r - 1$ times in $\alpha_1, \ldots, \alpha_{n-1}$. The probability of each such simple event is $p^r q^{n-r}$. How many such simple events are there? This is just the number of different sequences in which one can obtain e_1 a total of $r - 1$ times in $n - 1$ trials, i.e., C_{r-1}^{n-1}. Thus the desired probability is

$$C_{r-1}^{n-1} p^r q^{n-r} = \binom{n-1}{r-1} p^r q^{n-r}. \tag{5-63}$$

Since this is the probability that e_1 will be observed r times in n trials with the additional stipulation that e_1 appears on trial n, it should be the probability that precisely n trials are needed to obtain r occurrences of e_1, and it seems appropriate to use (5-63) as the probability of the simple event n.

Now since the event set Y we are using is a set of numbers, we can imagine these to be the possible values which a random variable y can take on; y is the number of trials needed to obtain r occurrences of e_1. Thus the probability that $y = n$, which we shall denote by the special symbol $b_P(n; r,p)$, is from (5-63)

$$b_P(n; r,p) = \frac{(n-1)!}{(r-1)!(n-r)!} p^r q^{n-r}. \tag{5-64}$$

Then $b_P(y; r,p)$ is the probability function for y. This probability function is given a special name. It is called the *Pascal probability function or Pascal distribution*.

There is clearly a close connection between the Pascal and the binomial distributions. To make explicit what it is, all we need to do is replace $n - r$ in (5-64) by $n - 1 - (r - 1)$. Then it becomes immediately obvious that

$$b_P(n; r,p) = p b(r - 1; n - 1, p). \tag{5-65}$$

Thus we see that $b_P(n; r,p)$ can easily be evaluated from tables for the binomial distribution.

We are now in a position to answer a problem considered in Section 4-5 in the discussion of the scrap allowance problem. We introduced there a probability function for a random variable y which was the number of units that had to be scheduled to obtain w good pieces. We did not indicate how to obtain such a probability function. This can now be done, however. If we assume that the process is in statistical control with the probability p that any unit will be good, the probability function desired is precisely the Pascal distribution $b_P(y; w,p)$.

To prove that $b_P(y; r,p)$ is a legitimate probability function, it is only necessary to show that

$$\sum_{n=r}^{\infty} b_P(n; r,p) = \sum_{n=r}^{\infty} \binom{n-1}{r-1} p^r q^{n-r} = 1, \qquad (5\text{-}66)$$

since then, inasmuch as $b_P(n; r,p) > 0$, it must be true that $b_P(n; r,p) \leq 1$. To verify (5-66), the reader familiar with calculus will note that

$$\sum_{n=r}^{\infty} \binom{n-1}{r-1} p^r q^{n-r} = p^r \sum_{j=0}^{\infty} \binom{j+r-1}{r-1} q^j.$$

However, on using the binomial theorem for negative exponents, see [5], we have for $0 < q < 1$,

$$(1-q)^{-r} = \sum_{j=0}^{\infty} \binom{j+r-1}{r-1} q^j, \qquad (5\text{-}67)$$

or since $1 - q = p$,

$$p^r(1-q)^{-r} = 1 = p^r \sum_{j=0}^{\infty} \binom{j+r-1}{r-1} q^j = \sum_{n=r}^{\infty} b_P(n; r,p), \qquad (5\text{-}68)$$

which is what we wished to prove. Given (5-66), it is easy to obtain μ the mean and σ^2 the variance of the Pascal distribution. These are

$$\mu = \frac{r}{p}, \quad \sigma^2 = \frac{rq}{p}\left(1 + \frac{q}{p}\right); \qquad (5\text{-}69)$$

and the reader is asked to obtain them in the problems.

5-12 SAMPLING AND THE HYPERGEOMETRIC DISTRIBUTION

In Section 5-6 we studied the problem of determining the number of different ways that r numbered balls could be drawn from n balls in a box. We now wish to study random experiments which essentially involve this sort of operation. Consider a box containing N balls which are numbered 1 to N (with just a single number assigned to each ball). Let us now mix the balls thoroughly, and without looking at the balls selected draw out n balls from the box (the reasons for changing the notation to N and n rather than the n and r used in Section 5-6 will appear shortly). We then ask what is the probability that the n balls drawn will have painted on them a specified set of numbers $\alpha_1, \ldots, \alpha_n$, where the numbers are all different and all selected from the set of numbers $1, \ldots, N$. To answer this question, we must be a little bit more specific about what we mean, because two interpretations are possible. First we can imagine that the n balls are drawn out one at a time and we look at the number on each as it is drawn, and we wish to know the probability of getting $\alpha_1, \ldots, \alpha_n$ in the specific sequence written down. The other interpretation is that, regardless of whether the balls are drawn out one at a time or all together, we do not care about the sequence but only about the numbers which appear on the balls.

Let us then consider each interpretation. Suppose that we wish to compute the probability of obtaining the numbers in a given order. To construct an event set for this experiment, it seems natural to use as a simple event the event that a given set of n numbers is obtained in a given sequence. The number of simple events is then $(N)_n$, the number of permutations of N numbers taken n at a time. What probability should be assigned to each simple event? If the balls are well mixed, etc., then by symmetry it would appear that any one sequence is just as likely to be obtained as any other sequence, and therefore the simple events should be equally likely. Under this assumption the probability of each simple event is $1/(N)_n$, and this then is the probability that we were seeking to determine. If the balls are drawn from the box in such a way that the simple events are equally likely, then we say that the sample of n balls is drawn *at random*. Let us denote by E_1 the event set containing the $(N)_n$ simple events, each simple event corresponding to obtaining n specified numbers in a given sequence; and let $\mathcal{E}_1$ be the probability model with the event set E_1, the probability of each simple event being $1/(N)_n$.

If the balls are selected at random, then $\mathcal{E}_1$ serves equally well to compute the probability of the event where we obtain n specified numbers, but are not concerned about the order. There are $n!$ orders possible for the n numbers, and hence the probability of obtaining n numbers without regard to order should be $n!/(N)_n$. Now

$$\frac{(N)_n}{n!} = \frac{N!}{n!(N-n)!} = C_n{}^N,$$

so that the desired probability is $1/C_n{}^N$. When order is not important we can use a simpler event set in which a simple event is the obtaining of a given set of n numbers on the balls. From Section 5-6 we know that there are $C_n{}^N$ such simple events, since this is the number of combinations of N numbers taken n at a time. Denote this event set by E_2. We have just seen that the probability of each simple event in E_2 is $1/C_n{}^N$. Thus the simple events in E_2 are equally likely also. Denote by $\mathcal{E}_2$ the probability model with the event set E_2 and having the probability of each simple event being $1/C_n^N$. We have shown that if the events in E_1 are equally likely, then the events in E_2 must also be equally likely. This result seems reasonable intuitively, since by symmetry we feel that drawing one set of n numbers is just as likely as drawing any other set. For problems that will be of interest to us, the order of the balls in the sample drawn will not be relevant, and hence we shall use $\mathcal{E}_2$ as our mathematical model of a random experiment in which n balls are drawn at random from a box containing N balls. Many interesting problems can be characterized by a random experiment of this type.

Let us next imagine that each of the N balls in the box falls into one of two categories. To be specific suppose that M of the balls, say those numbered 1 through M, are painted red and the remaining $N - M$ are painted blue. We shall now proceed to compute the probability that when n balls are selected at random from the box precisely r of them will turn out to be red. To determine this probability, we must first compute the number of simple events in E_2 which have this characteristic. Every simple event for which exactly r of the balls have numbers from the set of numbers 1 through M will be an event in which precisely r red balls were drawn, and no other simple events have this characteristic. There are C_r^M ways to select r numbers from M numbers, and this is the number of different ways to select r red balls from the set of M red balls. However, for each such selection there are C_{n-r}^{N-M} ways to select the remaining $n - r$ numbers from the numbers $M + 1$ through N, i.e., there are C_{n-r}^{N-M} ways to select $n - r$ blue balls from the $N - M$ blue balls. Consequently, there must be $C_r^M C_{n-r}^{N-M}$ simple events which yield the event that r of the n balls drawn are red. Since each simple event has the probability $1/C_n^N$, the probability that precisely r of the balls drawn will be red is $C_r^M C_{n-r}^{N-M}/C_n^N$.

Now we can think of the number of red balls obtained in the sample of size n drawn from the box of N balls as being a random variable x defined over E_2. The random variable x can then take on the values $0, 1, \ldots, n$, if $n \leq M$, or otherwise $0, 1, \ldots, M$. The probability function for x will be denoted by $h(x; n,M,N)$, and from what we have just shown

$$h(r; n,M,N) = \frac{C_r^M C_{n-r}^{N-M}}{C_n^N} = \frac{\dbinom{M}{r} \dbinom{N - M}{n - r}}{\dbinom{N}{n}}$$

$$= \frac{\dfrac{M!}{r!(M - r)!} \dfrac{(N - M)!}{(n - r)!(N - M - n + r)!}}{\dfrac{N!}{n!(N - n)!}}. \qquad (5\text{-}70)$$

The probability function $h(x; n,M,N)$ is called the *hypergeometric proba-bility function or hypergeometric distribution*, and x is said to have a *hyper-geometric distribution*.

The hypergeometric distribution is an important one in practice, espe-cially in quality control. However, it is much more difficult to make computations using the hypergeometric distribution than it was with the binomial distribution. Furthermore, whereas the binomial distribution involved two parameters, the hypergeometric involves three, n, M, and N. Thus if it takes a large volume to give fairly complete tables of the bino-mial, it would almost take such a volume for each N for the hypergeometric distribution. It is thus out of the question to tabulate the hypergeometric distribution for every combination of the parameters which might be of particular interest. One large volume devoted to tables of the hyper-geometric distribution has been published [6], but it goes only to $N = 50$. To actually use the hypergeometric distribution in practice then, unless one always wants to make use of a large digital computer, it is necessary to approximate $h(x; n,M,N)$ by functions which are easier to compute. We shall now investigate in part how this can be done.

First we shall show that for large N the hypergeometric distribution can be approximated by the binomial. In order to do this it is convenient to write $p = M/N$ and $q = (N - M)/N$ so that p is the fraction of red balls and q is the fraction of blue balls. Note that p and q are not prob-abilities here. Then, instead of writing $h(x; n,M,N)$, we shall write $h(x; n,p,N)$, and

$$h(r; n,p,N) = \frac{\binom{pN}{r}\binom{qN}{n-r}}{\binom{N}{n}}. \tag{5-71}$$

Now observe that we can write (5-71) as follows:

$$h(r; n,p,N) = \frac{n!}{r!(N-n)!}\left(\frac{pN}{N}\right)\left(\frac{pN-1}{N-1}\right)\cdots\left(\frac{pN-r+1}{N-r+1}\right) \times$$
$$\left(\frac{qN}{N-r}\right)\left(\frac{qN-1}{N-r-1}\right)\cdots\left(\frac{qN-n+r+1}{N-n+1}\right). \tag{5-72}$$

We can next note that

$$\frac{pN-j}{N-j} = \frac{p(N-j)+pj-j}{N-j} = p + \frac{j(p-1)}{N-j}, \tag{5-73}$$

and as N becomes large holding p fixed (that is, the fraction of red balls fixed), this term approaches p. Thus as N becomes large,

$$\left(\frac{pN}{N}\right)\left(\frac{pN-1}{N-1}\right)\cdots\left(\frac{pN-r+1}{N-r+1}\right)$$

approaches p^r. Similarly, the product of the $n - r$ factors involving q approaches q^{n-r}, and $h(r; n,p,N)$ approaches $b(r; n,p)$. Thus as we allow N to become very large while keeping the fraction of red balls in the box constant, $h(r; n,p,N)$ becomes very close to $b(r; n,p)$ for all r, n, and p. Let us provide an intuitive interpretation of this result. Suppose that we had a box with N balls having p as the fraction of the balls which are red. Consider a random experiment in which we select at random one ball and note its color. The probability that the ball is red is then p. Suppose that we now put the ball drawn back into the box again, mix them and repeat the experiment. Let us do this n times. We then have n independent experiments and the probability that a red ball will be selected precisely r times is $b(r; n,p)$. The difference between the situation just described and the one where we simply select n balls and note their color is that for the experiment just described we replace the ball drawn before making another draw. If we did not replace the ball drawn, the experiments would not be independent and the probability of drawing a red ball would change from one trial to the next. This is precisely the situation when we draw out n balls because we can imagine that they are drawn out one at a time, but each one drawn is not put back before the next is drawn. Now if N is very large, $M = pN$, the number of red balls will be large. In this case, if the total number n of balls drawn out is small compared to N, it does not make much difference whether we replace the balls drawn out before drawing the next one. The probability of drawing a red one will not change much. In such a case, drawing out n balls is essentially equivalent to n independent trials of the experiment in which one ball is drawn out, and hence the probability that r balls are red is essentially $b(r; n,p)$.

From what we have just shown, it seems reasonable that when N is fairly large, say 500 to 1000 or more, and the sample size is small with respect to N, say one tenth of N or less, and if r is considerably less than $M = pN$ while $n - r$ is considerably less than qN, then we can approximate $h(r; n,p,N)$ by $b(r; n,p)$. In practice one essentially always makes this sort of approximation if any amount of computation involving the hypergeometric distribution is involved. However, the approximation procedure is usually carried further, since the binomial distribution is not easy to work with either. For most applications, the fraction of red balls will be small, and the sample size n will be chosen large enough so that the expected number of red balls in the sample is at least 2. However, in such cases, the Poisson distribution can be used to approximate the binomial, and hence to approximate the hypergeometric distribution also. Very frequently then, it turns out that one can use $p(r; np)$ as a suitable approximation for $h(r; n,p,N)$.

Since $h(x; n,p,N)$ is the probability function for x, we must have

$\sum_{r=0}^{n} h(x; n,p,N) = 1$.   This can also be proved directly using (5-70) or (5-71).   Given this result one can compute the mean μ and variance σ^2 of $h(x; n,p,N)$ in the same way as for the other distributions studied.   The results are

$$\mu = np; \quad \sigma^2 = npq\left(\frac{N-n}{N-1}\right). \tag{5-74}$$

We ask the reader to derive these results in the problems.   Note that the mean of $h(x; n,p,N)$ is the same as that for $b(x; n,p)$ and is independent of N, while the variance is smaller by the factor $(N-n)/(N-1)$.   On noting that $\mu = np$ and that when approximating $h(r; n,p,N)$ we use $b(r; n,p)$ or $p(r; np)$, we see that we approximate $h(x; n,p,N)$ by a binomial or Poisson distribution having the same mean as $h(x; n,p,N)$.

5-13 EXAMPLES

1.   Two senators are chosen at random from the 100 senators in the United States Senate.   What is the probability that neither is from Pennsylvania?   This situation can be imagined as one in which a sample of two balls is chosen at random from a box containing 100 balls, 2 of which are red.   We want the probability that neither ball is red.   This number is $h(0; 2,2,100)$ when we use the symbolism $h(r; n,M,N)$, i.e.,

$$\frac{\binom{2}{0}\binom{98}{2}}{\binom{100}{2}} = \frac{\dfrac{2!}{2!}\dfrac{98!}{2!96!}}{\dfrac{100!}{2!98!}} = \frac{98(97)}{100(99)} = 0.960.$$

Here $p = 2/100 = 0.02$, and $np = 0.04$.   If we used $b(0; 2,0.02)$ to approximate the probability, we would obtain 0.960 to three decimal places, which to this accuracy is precisely the same as the exact answer.

Suppose that instead we wished to compute the probability that both senators are from Pennsylvania.   This is $h(2; 2,2,100)$, i.e.,

$$\frac{\binom{2}{2}\binom{98}{0}}{\binom{100}{2}} = \frac{1(1)}{\dfrac{100!}{2!98!}} = \frac{1}{50(99)} = 0.000202.$$

If we use the binomial approximation $b(2; 2,0.02)$, we obtain 0.0004 which although of the right order of magnitude is off by a factor of two.   The reason the error is so high here is that we are computing the probability that all red balls are removed.   Since there are only two, when one is removed, the probability of drawing a red ball on the second trial is drastically changed.   It reduces the probability, and thus as expected the correct probability is less than that estimated from $b(2; 2,0.02)$.

We might note in passing that to select two senators at random all we need to do is assign each a number and then select at random two numbered balls from a box containing 100 such balls. The senators having the numbers on the balls drawn are then the ones selected.

2. In one box are 100 transistors, 5 of which are defective. In another box are 100 diodes, 6 of which are defective. Two transistors are selected at random from the box of transistors and one diode from the box of diodes. What is the probability that exactly two of the three elements selected are defective? The random experiment $\Re$ which consists of selecting the two transistors and one diode can be looked upon as built up from two independent random experiments $\Re_1$ and $\Re_2$, where $\Re_1$ involves selecting two transistors at random from the box of transistors and $\Re_2$ involves the selection at random of one diode from the box of diodes. Let A be the event of $\Re$ in which two defective elements are obtained. Now two defective elements are obtained if both transistors are defective and the diode is good, call this the event A_1, or if precisely one of the transistors is defective and the diode is defective, call this event A_2. Thus $A = A_1 \cup A_2$, and A_1 and A_2 are exclusive events. Thus by (1-13)

$$p(A) = p(A_1) + p(A_2).$$

Now let A_3 be the event that two bad transistors are drawn, and A_4 the event that the diode drawn is good. Then $A_1 = A_3 \cap A_4$. In addition, let A_5 be the event that precisely one transistor is defective, and A_6 the event that the diode is defective. Then $A_2 = A_5 \cap A_6$. Inasmuch as $\Re_1$ and $\Re_2$ are independent experiments,

$$p(A_1) = p(A_3)p(A_4); \quad p(A_2) = p(A_5)p(A_6).$$

Furthermore, the probabilities of A_3 and A_5 can be computed using the model for $\Re_1$ and those of A_4 and A_6 by using the model for $\Re_2$.

The probabilities of drawing two defective transistors and one defective and one good transistor are, respectively,

$$p(A_3) = \frac{\binom{5}{2}\binom{95}{0}}{\binom{100}{2}} = \frac{5(2)}{50(99)} = 0.00202,$$

$$p(A_5) = \frac{\binom{5}{1}\binom{95}{1}}{\binom{100}{2}} = \frac{5(95)}{50(99)} = 0.096.$$

The probabilities of drawing a good and drawing a defective diode are, respectively,

$$p(A_4) = \frac{94}{100} = 0.94; \quad p(A_6) = \frac{6}{100} = 0.06.$$

Hence

$$p(A_1) = 0.00202(0.94) = 0.00189; \quad p(A_2) = 0.096(0.06) = 0.00575.$$

Therefore, the desired probability is

$$p(A) = 0.00189 + 0.00575 = 0.00764.$$

3.   Many manufacturers purchase parts from suppliers in lots of 1000 or more.   Normally, it is necessary for the manufacturer to maintain a check on the quality of the material received from any given supplier.   This could perhaps be done by checking every unit received.   However, the cost of such a procedure is often inordinately high.   In addition, there are cases where testing a unit destroys it, and therefore it would not be possible to check every unit.   To avoid these problems, a typical procedure used is to select at random from each lot a sample of n units.   Each unit in this sample is checked to see whether it is good or defective.   Based on the number of defectives in the sample a decision is then made whether to accept the entire lot (implying that the quality appears to be satisfactory) or to reject the lot (implying that the quality does not seem to be satisfactory).   We shall not concern ourselves with what happens if a lot is rejected (it might be returned to the supplier, for example), but will concentrate our attention on the procedure used to check lots.   The process of checking materials received from suppliers is called *incoming inspection*.   The process of selecting a sample of n units from a lot and then accepting it or rejecting it based on the number of defectives in the sample is referred to as a *single sampling plan*.

The way a single sampling plan operates is as follows.   First the sample size n is selected.   Next a number c called the *acceptance number* is chosen.   Then a sample is selected at random (we shall not consider in detail what precautions must be taken to approximate the notion of randomness), and the number r of defectives in the sample is determined.   If $r \leq c$ the lot is accepted, and if $r > c$ the lot is rejected.   The value selected for c will determine how "tight" the sampling plan is.   If c is very small this means that high quality is desired.   Let us now ask, what is the probability that a lot having a fraction defective of p will be accepted?   Normally, one will be dealing with situations where the sample size is small compared to the lot size and the fraction defective is small.   Then the Poisson distribution can be used to approximate the hypergeometric in making these computations, and $p(r; np)$ is the probability that there will be precisely r defectives in the sample.   The probability that the lot will be accepted is the probability that $r \leq c$.   This is nothing but $P(c; np)$, the cumulative Poisson distribution evaluated at c.   Denote by $P_a(p)$ the probability of accepting the lot when the lot fraction defective is p.   Thus $P_a(p) = P(c; np)$.   One can then for a given n and c plot a curve giving $P_a(p)$ as a function of p.   This curve is called the *operating characteristic curve for*

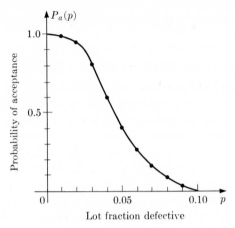

FIGURE 5-5

the sampling plan. An example of such a curve for $n = 100$ and $c = 4$ is shown in Figure 5-5. For small p the probability that the lot will be accepted is high while for large p it is very small. The reader can check the points on this curve using the Poisson table at the end of the text.

REFERENCES

The texts dealing with probability theory given in the references for Chapter 1 are also suitable references for this chapter. In addition, the following are of interest.

1. Burington, R. S., and D. C. May, *Handbook of Probability and Statistics with Tables.* Handbook Publishers, Sandusky, Ohio, 1953.
   A rather popular handbook which contains a somewhat more extensive collection of tables than is given at the end of this text.

2. Fisz, M., *Probability Theory and Mathematical Statistics,* 3rd. ed. Wiley, New York, 1963.
   A good text which covers a wide variety of topics at a moderately advanced level. A knowledge of calculus is assumed.

3. General Electric Co., *Tables of the Individual and Cumulative Terms of Poisson Distribution.* Van Nostrand, Princeton, N. J., 1962.

4. Krickeberg, K., *Probability Theory.* Addison-Wesley, Reading, Mass., 1965. An advanced treatment of the mathematical theory. Applications are not discussed.

5. Kuratowski, K., *Introduction to Calculus.* Addison-Wesley, Reading, Mass., 1961.
   A good reference for the calculus of one variable. Beginning on p. 185 the

Taylor's expansion is considered, on p. 192 the binomial theorem for negative arguments is derived, and on pp. 95 and 167 techniques for finding the limit as p approaches 0 of $(1 - p)^{1/p}$ are considered.

6. Lieberman, G. J., and D. B. Owen, *Tables of the Hypergeometric Probability Distribution*. Stanford University Press, Stanford, Calif., 1961.

7. Molina, E. C., *Poisson's Exponential Binomial Limit (Tables)*. Van Nostrand, Princeton, N. J., 1942.

8. *Table of the Cumulative Binomial Probabilities*. Ordnance Corps Pamphlet ORDP 20-1, 1952. (577 pages)

9. *Tables of the Cumulative Binomial Probability Distribution*. Harvard University Press, Cambridge, Mass., 1955.

10. Yaglom, A. M., and I. M. Yaglom, *Challenging Mathematical Problems with Elementary Solutions*, Vol. 1. Holden-Day, San Francisco, 1964.
This translation of a well-known Russian problem book contains a number of interesting probability problems.

PROBLEMS

Sections 5-2 and 5-3

1. Two fair dice are tossed, and it is observed which face turns up on each. Set up a mathematical model for this random experiment and determine what seems to be a proper estimate of the probability of each simple event.

2. For the situation outlined in Problem 1, consider the random variable x, which is the sum of the number of points on the faces turned up. Determine the probability function for x.

3. Two loaded dice are tossed, and it is observed what face turns up on each. Set up a mathematical model for this random experiment if the probabilities that the various faces will turn up for each of the individual dice are those given in the following table.

Points on face turned up	1	2	3	4	5	6
Probability for die 1	0.10	0.20	0.25	0.05	0.30	0.10
Probability for die 2	0.20	0.10	0.20	0.10	0.20	0.20

4. For the situation outlined in Problem 3, consider the random variable x, which is the sum of the number of points on the faces turned up. Determine the probability function for x.

5. Note that we can construct a physical model of a biased coin which has a probability $\frac{1}{3}$ of landing head up when tossed by placing three balls (or coins) numbered 1, 2, and 3, in a box, shaking them well, drawing one, and considering it to be a head if ball number 1 is drawn and a tail, otherwise. Use this artifice to construct an experiment in which a coin with probability $\frac{1}{3}$ of yielding a head is tossed and, in addition, a fair coin is tossed, and it is then noted how each one lands. Repeat this experiment 50 times and determine the relative frequency of each of the four events in Table 5-1. Do the relative frequencies agree fairly well with the probabilities determined according to the formulas given in Table 5-1?

6. One box contains three red, two green, and five yellow balls while another box contains five red, three green, and four yellow balls. Let $\Re$ be the random experiment in which one ball is selected at random from each box. Set up a mathematical model for $\Re$. What is the probability that both balls are red? What is the probability that one is red and one is green? What is the probability that one is red and one is yellow?

7. Two mothers who have recently had babies meet on the street and begin to discuss their children. What is the probability that both had girls, if the historical data show that about 0.49 of births are girls? Construct a suitable model by which the computation can be made.

8. An examination contains two multiple choice questions, the first having two alternatives and the second four alternatives. If a student selects at random the answer to each question, what is the probability that he will get both correct? Construct a suitable model by which the computation can be made.

9. One roulette wheel has five equally spaced numbers on it (the numbers 1 through 5). Another roulette wheel has ten equally spaced numbers on it (the numbers 1 through 10). Each roulette wheel is spun, and the number on which it stops is observed. Construct a mathematical model of the random experiment. A casino operates a game using these two roulette wheels which is of the form: If both roulette wheels stop on the same number, the player receives $50. If they stop on different numbers, he pays the casino $10.50. What is the player's expected winnings per trial?

Sections 5-4 and 5-5

1. Let $E_1 = \{3, 5, 7, 9\}$ and $E_2 = \{2, 4, 6\}$. Determine the set $E = E_1 \times E_2$. Plot the numbers in E_1 on a horizontal axis and the numbers in E_2 on a vertical axis. Then illustrate geometrically the elements of E.

2. Let $E_1 = \{f_1, f_2, f_3\}$ and $E_2 = \{e_1, e_2, e_3, e_4, e_5\}$. Determine the set $E = E_1 \times E_2$.

3. Consider two probability models $\mathcal{E}_1$ and $\mathcal{E}_2$ whose mathematical representation is the following:

	E_1				E_2				
Simple event	f_1	f_2	f_3	f_4	e_1	e_2	e_3	e_4	e_5
Probability	0.2	0.4	0.3	0.1	0.1	0.3	0.2	0.3	0.1

Construct the model $\mathcal{E} = \mathcal{E}_1 \times \mathcal{E}_2$ and show that the probabilities of the simple events satisfy the axioms for a probability model.

4. For the situation outlined in Problem 3, characterize the simple event f_3 of $\mathcal{E}_1$ as an event of $\mathcal{E}$. Show that the probability of f_3 in $\mathcal{E}$ is the same as in $\mathcal{E}_1$.

5. For the situation outlined in Problem 3, characterize the event $A = \{f_1, f_3\}$

of $\mathcal{E}_1$ as an event of $\mathcal{E}$. Show that the probability of A in $\mathcal{E}$ is the same as the probability of A in $\mathcal{E}_1$.

6. For the situation outlined in Problem 3, characterize the event $B = \{e_2, e_4, e_5\}$ of $\mathcal{E}_2$ as an event of $\mathcal{E}$. Show that the probability of B in $\mathcal{E}$ is the probability of B in $\mathcal{E}_2$.

7. Consider the events A and B defined in Problems 5 and 6 as events of $\mathcal{E}$. Determine the simple events in $\mathcal{E}$ which represent $A \cap B$, and determine $p(A \cap B)$ by summing the probabilities of these simple events. Show that (5-7) holds, where $p(A)$ and $p(B)$ are computed with respect to $\mathcal{E}_1$ and $\mathcal{E}_2$, respectively.

8. Consider the three probability models whose mathematical representation is the following:

	$\mathcal{E}_1$		$\mathcal{E}_2$			$\mathcal{E}_3$		
Simple event	e_{11}	e_{12}	e_{21}	e_{22}	e_{23}	e_{31}	e_{32}	e_{33}
Probability	0.3	0.7	0.2	0.5	0.3	0.4	0.1	0.5

Construct the model $\mathcal{E} = \mathcal{E}_1 \times \mathcal{E}_2 \times \mathcal{E}_3$ and show that the probabilities of the simple events do satisfy the axioms for a probability model.

9. For the situation outlined in Problem 8, characterize the simple event e_{12} of $\mathcal{E}_1$ as an event of $\mathcal{E}$ and show that the probability of e_{12} computed for $\mathcal{E}$ is the same as that in $\mathcal{E}_1$.

10. For the situation outlined in Problem 8, characterize the event $A = \{e_{11}, e_{12}\}$ of $\mathcal{E}_1$ as an event of $\mathcal{E}$. Show that the probability of A in $\mathcal{E}$ is the same as the probability of A in $\mathcal{E}_1$.

11. For the situation outlined in Problem 8, characterize the event $B = \{e_{21}, e_{23}\}$ of $\mathcal{E}_2$ as an event of $\mathcal{E}$. Show that the probability of B in $\mathcal{E}$ is the same as the probability of B in $\mathcal{E}_2$.

12. For the situation outlined in Problem 8, characterize the event $C = \{e_{32}, e_{33}\}$ of $\mathcal{E}_3$ as an event of $\mathcal{E}$. Show that the probability of C in $\mathcal{E}$ is the same as the probability of C in $\mathcal{E}_3$.

13. Consider the event $B \cap C$ where B and C are defined in Problems 11 and 12, respectively. Characterize $B \cap C$ as an event of $\mathcal{E}$ and determine $p(B \cap C)$ by adding up the probabilities of the appropriate simple events. Then show that $p(B \cap C) = p(B)p(C)$ where $p(B)$ and $p(C)$ are computed with respect to $\mathcal{E}_2$ and $\mathcal{E}_3$, respectively.

14. Consider the event $A \cap B \cap C$ where A, B, and C are defined in Problems 10, 11, and 12, respectively. Characterize $A \cap B \cap C$ as an event of $\mathcal{E}$ and determine its probability by summing the probabilities of the appropriate simple events and show that $p(A \cap B \cap C) = p(A)p(B)p(C)$, where $p(A)$, $p(B)$, and $p(C)$ are computed with respect to $\mathcal{E}_1$, $\mathcal{E}_2$, and $\mathcal{E}_3$, respectively.

15. Suppose that $\mathcal{E} = \mathcal{E}_1 \times \mathcal{E}_2 \times \mathcal{E}_3$ and that $\mathcal{E}_4 = \mathcal{E}_2 \times \mathcal{E}_3$. Then prove that $\mathcal{E} = \mathcal{E}_1 \times \mathcal{E}_4$.

16. Prove (5-16). Hint: To do this consider the performance of all $\mathcal{R}_u$, $u \neq i$ or j as a single experiment $\mathcal{R}$ containing a single simple event. Why and how can this be done?

17.   Prove (5-17), using the same procedure used in Problem 16.

18.   A box contains 1000 vacuum tubes, 150 of which are defective. Another box contains 100 resistors, 3 of which are defective. A third box contains 500 capacitors, 30 of which are defective. Suppose that we select at random a vacuum tube, a resistor and a capacitor. By construction of a suitable mathematical model, compute the probability that none of the three elements selected is defective.

19.   For the situation described in Problem 18, what is the probability that at least one of the three elements selected is defective?

20.   For the situation described in Problem 18, what is the probability that the vacuum tube or the resistor is defective?

21.   For the situation described in Problem 18, what is the probability that the resistor or the capacitor is defective?

22.   For the situation described in Problem 18, what is the probability that the resistor and the capacitor are defective?

23.   One urn contains two red, three green, and four yellow balls. A second urn contains three red, one green, and two yellow balls. A third urn contains five red, six green, and one yellow balls. Consider a random experiment $\Re$ in which one ball is selected at random from each of the three urns and the color of each ball so obtained is noted. Let a simple event be one which gives the color of the ball obtained from each of the three urns. List all the simple events and determine the probability of each.

24.   For the situation described in Problem 23, what is the probability that two of the balls are green and the other is yellow?

25.   For the situation described in Problem 23, what is the probability that one ball is red, one is green, and one is yellow?

26.   For the situation described in Problem 23, what is the probability that at least one ball is red?

27.   For the situation described in Problem 23, what is the probability that precisely two different colors appear on the three balls drawn?

28.   For the situation described in Problem 23, what is the probability that no yellow ball is drawn?

29.   Consider a random experiment $\Re$ in which a coin having a probability p of landing heads up is tossed three times. Construct a mathematical model for $\Re$. Let x be the random variable which gives the number of heads obtained on the three tosses. Determine the probability function for x.

30.   Consider the random experiment $\Re$ in which a fair die is tossed three times. Describe an event set for $\Re$ in which all the simple events are equally likely. How many simple events are there? Do not attempt to list them. Can you determine the probability function for the random variable x which gives the sum of the number of points obtained on the three tosses?

31.   Many electronic systems now used in missiles and space exploration work contain thousands of elements such as transistors, resistors, etc. Each of these elements must perform satisfactorily if the whole system is to do so. The reliability of a system (or element) is defined to be the probability that it will perform in a satisfactory way during a complete mission, the mission being specified. Suppose that a given system contains 1000 elements. A mission can then be characterized so far as success or failure of the system goes as a random experiment consisting of the performance of 1000 random experiments, the ith of which has two outcomes, that is, the ith element fails or it does not fail. Let us imagine, as is often done in practice, that these experiments are independent. If each element has the same reliability p, what value must p have if the reliability of the system is to be 0.95? The system will be assumed to fail if any one of the elements fails.

Section 5-6

1. A box contains five balls numbered 1 through 5. List the possible sequences, i.e., permutations obtainable when three balls are drawn from the box. Show that this number is $(5)_3$.

2. Re-solve Problem 1 when the balls are numbered 2, 5, 7, 8, 9. Thus show that in this case the number of permutations does not depend on the particular set of five numbers printed on the balls.

3. List the possible permutations of the numbers 1, 2, 3, 4.

4. Show that the number of possible permutations of n numbered balls taken $n-1$ at a time is the same as the number of permutations when the balls are taken n at a time. Why is this?

5. For the situation described in Problem 1, determine how many different combinations of numbers there are; list each one. Show that this number is $C_3{}^5$.

6. For the situation described in Problem 2, determine how many different combinations of numbers there are; list each one. Show that this number is $C_3{}^5$.

7. In how many ways may five boys and four girls be seated in a row of nine chairs? What is the answer if boys and girls must alternate?

8. A coin is tossed six times. List each possible sequence of heads and tails for the case where two heads are obtained. Show that the number of sequences is $C_2{}^6$.

9. Roughly estimate the number of combinations of 100 numbered balls there are when 50 are selected at a time.

10. An urn contains three red, two green, and one yellow balls. Suppose that these balls are drawn out of the urn one at a time. How many different sequences of colors are possible? List each one, and show that the number obtained is that given by (5-36).

11. Suppose that we have n balls, numbered 1 through n, and m boxes. Show that there are m^n ways to place the balls in the boxes when any number of balls can be placed in a given box.

12. Assume that over a considerable period, the number of births on any given day of the year is about the same as on any other day. There are 20 people in a room, none of whose birthdays you know and none of whom are related. What would be your estimate of the probability that precisely two people were born on the same day of the year? What does the probability mean in this case?

13. An absent-minded individual wrote three letters and sealed them without writing the addresses on the envelopes. Having forgotten which letter he had put in which envelope, he wrote the three addresses on the envelopes at random. What is the probability that at least one of the letters was addressed correctly?

Sections 5-7 and 5-8

1. A fair coin is tossed five times. Compute the probability that on three of these tosses it lands heads up.

2. A fair coin is tossed ten times. Compute the probability that on five of these tosses it will land heads up.

3. Use the table at the rear of the text to obtain a bar diagram for $b(x; 7,0.3)$.

4. Use the table at the rear of the text to obtain a bar diagram for $b(x; 7,0.1)$.

5. Use the table at the rear of the text to obtain a bar diagram for $b(x; 9,0.2)$.

6. Use the table at the rear of the text to obtain a bar diagram for the cumulative binomial distribution $B(x; 10,0.2)$.

7. A fair coin is tossed seven times. What is the expected number of heads? Give an intuitive meaning to this expected value. What is the standard deviation? Give an intuitive meaning to the standard deviation.

8. Use the table at the end of the text to compute directly the mean of $b(x; 5,0.1)$ without using (5-42). Thus verify (5-42) in this case.

9. Show that

$$\frac{b(r+1; n,p)}{b(r; n,p)} = \left(\frac{n-r}{r+1}\right)\frac{p}{q}, \qquad r = 0, \ldots, n-1.$$

Thus prove that $b(r+1; n,p) > b(r; n,p)$ when $r+1 < (n+1)p$, and $b(r+1; n,p) < b(r; n,p)$ when $r+1 > (n+1)p$. Let $m = (n+1)p = \mu + p$. When m is not an integer, show that $b(x; n,p)$ increases up to the largest integer less than m, which will be denoted by $[m]$, and then decreases for larger values. Thus the mode of the distribution is unique and is $[m]$. If m is an integer, then show that $b(m; n,p) = b(m-1; n,p)$ so that the mode is not unique, but m and $m-1$ can be considered to be modes. In either case, show that the mode cannot be more than a distance of one unit of x away from the mean. Illustrate by an example a case where the mode is greater than the mean and a case where the mode is less than the mean. This shows that the mode and the mean are always close together, never being separated by more than one unit of x.

10. Illustrate the results of Problem 9, using $b(x; 9, 0.2)$. Actually, compute each ratio, m, $[m]$, np, and the mode and verify the results in this special case.

11. Consider the behavior of $b(r; n,p)$ as n increases. Show that regardless of what value of r is selected, and whatever the value of p, $0 < p < 1$, then $b(r; n,p)$ gets smaller and smaller as n is increased.

12. Use the table in the rear of the text to evaluate $b(6; 7,0.8)$, $b(8; 10,0.9)$, and $b(9; 9,0.7)$.

13. When a particular process is in statistical control, past history indicates that the long run fraction defective is 0.1. To control the process, a sample of ten units is selected once per hour, and the number of defectives is plotted on a control chart. What are the control limits and center line for the control chart? At least how many defectives must there be in the sample if the sample point lies above the upper control limit?

14. For the situation discussed in Problem 13, suppose that the process suddenly changes to producing a fraction defective of 0.2. What is the probability that on the first sample taken after the shift occurs, the number of defectives in the sample will be outside the control limits so that an investigation will be made?

15. For the situation described in Problem 13, show how to compute the probability that if the process is producing a fraction defective of p and the control limits appropriate to a fraction defective of 0.1 are used, that the number of defectives r in any particular sample will be inside the control limits. Denote this probability by $P_a(p)$. This is the probability that it will be assumed that things are normal and no action will be taken. For each p, a probability $P_a(p)$ can be determined. Then one can plot $P_a(p)$ as a function of p. The resulting curve is called the operating characteristic curve for the control chart. Determine this curve for the situation under consideration.

16. Let 0.2 be the fraction of a large number of light bulbs tested which failed after burning continuously for two weeks. An apartment building installs seven of these bulbs in hall lights, which burn continuously. What is the probability that five of the bulbs will be burned out at the end of two weeks?

17. Let x be a random variable whose probability function is $b(x; n,p)$. Consider now the new random variable $y = x/n$. Show that the expected value of y is p and the variance of y is pq/n. If $p(y)$ is the probability function for y, show that $p(y) = b(ny; n,p)$. What are the possible values that y can take on? Intuitively, y is the fraction of the time that e_1 was observed in n independent trials.

18. Consider the random variable x whose probability function is $b(x; 10,0.2)$. Plot a bar diagram of the probability function for the random variable $y = x/n$ introduced in Problem 17.

19. The type of control chart which we described in the text is not often used in industry. One reason for this is that telling a production manager the number of defectives in the sample does not convey much to him since he does not always keep in mind what the sample size is. Thus instead of using the number of defectives r, one plots r/n, the fraction defective in the sample. This has immediate significance to the manager. What are the upper and lower control limits and the center line for a control chart on which we plot the fraction defective, given that the process produces a fraction defective of p when under control? Hint: Use the results of Problem 17.

20. Consider any random experiment $\mathfrak{R}^*$ and let the event A have the probability p. Then one can construct a model for $\mathfrak{R}^*$ in which there are only two simple events A and A^c. Let $\mathfrak{R}$ be the random experiment in which n independent trials of $\mathfrak{R}^*$ are performed, and let x be the random variable giving the number of times A occurred in the r trials. Show that x has the binomial distribution $b(x; n,p)$.

21. In developing a probability model, we were guided by the intuitive notion that probabilities are equal to long run relative frequencies. We are now in a position to show that our model says, as it should, that a probability can be given a frequency interpretation. Let us now make precise the way in which it does this. Suppose that A is an event of $\mathfrak{R}^*$ to which our model assigns a probability p. Consider the experiment $\mathfrak{R}$ which consists of performing n independent trials of $\mathfrak{R}^*$, and let x be the number of occurrences of A. Consider the random variable x/n which is the relative frequency of A in the n trials of $\mathfrak{R}^*$. If y is the random variable

$$y = \left| \frac{x}{n} - p \right|,$$

prove that $p(y \geq \epsilon)$, the probability that $y \geq \epsilon$, satisfies the inequality

$$p(y \geq \epsilon) \leq pq/n\epsilon^2.$$

Hint: Apply Chebyschev inequality of Problem 19 for Section 1-17 to the case under consideration.

22. For the situation described in Problem 21, how large must n be if we want the probability that $y \geq 0.001$ to be less than 0.0001 when $p = 0.3$?

23. Eight passengers board a train consisting of three cars. Each passenger selects at random which car he will sit in. What is the probability that there will be three people in the first car?

24. A man buys two boxes of matches and places them in his pocket. Every time he has to light a match, he selects at random one of the two boxes. After some time the man takes one of the boxes from his pocket and on opening it finds it empty. Observe that this statement implies that at the point in time when the individual used the last match in this box, he did not throw it away, but instead put it back in his pocket. What is the probability that there are at the moment k matches left in the other box if each box originally contained n matches and we assume that this is the first time that he has encountered an empty box? This is a famous problem which is referred to as Banach's match box problem after the Polish mathematician of the same name.

25. Suppose that the probability that a batter gets a hit whenever he comes up to bat is $\frac{1}{5}$. Some people feel this implies that he is sure to get at least one hit in five times at bat. What is the probability of at least one hit in five times at bat? What is the expected number of hits in five times at bat? Why does the expected value not imply that he gets one hit in five?

26. Consider an electronic system which consists of n parts. Suppose that each part has the same probability p of failing when the system is used for a given mission. Assume that whether or not a given part fails is independent of what happens to other parts. What is the probability that the system does not fail, i.e., that no part fails? The following argument is often given to obtain this probability. Since the probability that any one part fails is p, the probability that at least one part fails is np, and hence the probability that the system does not fail is $1 - np$. Show that the reasoning and resulting probability are incorrect. Even though the probability of successful operation is not $1 - np$, there are certain conditions under which the number $1 - np$ is very close to the probability of successful operation. Explain what these conditions are, and why things work out this way.

27. Two ground to air missiles are fired simultaneously at a target aircraft. If the probability that a given missile hits the target is $\frac{1}{3}$, what is the probability that at least one of the missiles hits the target. What is the probability of a hit if three missiles are fired?

Section 5-9

1. Make a table comparing $b(r; 9,0.1)$ and $p(r; 0.9)$ for $r = 0, \ldots, 9$.

2. Make a table comparing $b(r; 10,0.2)$ and $p(r; 2)$ for $r = 0, \ldots, 10$.

3. Make a table comparing $b(r; 8,0.1)$ and $p(r; 0.8)$ for $r = 0, \ldots, 8$.

4. Use a Poisson approximation to estimate $b(10; 100,0.05)$ and $b(5; 1000,0.001)$.

5. Use a Poisson approximation to estimate $b(15; 500,0.02)$ and $b(8; 200,0.05)$.

6. When a given process is operating properly, it yields a fraction defective of 0.02. The process is controlled by twice a day taking a sample of 100 units from the production and determining how many are defective. What are the upper and lower control limits and the center line for a control chart to be used in controlling this process. If the process suddenly changes to producing a fraction defective of 0.04, what is the probability that the number of defectives in the first sample taken after this occurs lies outside the upper control limit?

7. Determine and plot the operating characteristic curve for the control chart of Problem 6. For a definition of an operating characteristic curve, see Problem 15 of the previous section.

8. Note that when $b(r; n, p)$ is approximated by $p(r; np)$, $p(r; np) > 0$ for every non-negative number while $b(r; n,p)$ is defined only for integers in the range 0 to n. Thus while $b(r; n,p)$ sums to 1 as r ranges from 0 to n, $p(r; np)$ sums to a number less than 1 as r ranges from 0 to n. Thus the probabilities determined from the approximation $p(r; np)$ do not precisely satisfy the axioms for a probability model. Could this cause any problems?

Section 5-10

1. Verify that the sum over r of $p(r; 0.2)$ is unity to the accuracy given in the table at the end of the text.

2. Construct a histogram for $p(x; 0.4)$, and indicate the expected value of x on this diagram.

3. Construct a histogram for $p(x; 4)$, and indicate the expected value of x on this diagram.

4. Show that
$$\frac{p(r + 1; \beta)}{p(r; \beta)} = \frac{\beta}{r + 1}, \quad r = 0, 1, 2, \ldots,$$
so that $p(r + 1; \beta) > p(r; \beta)$ when $r + 1 < \beta$, i.e., $r + 1 < \mu$ and $p(r + 1; \beta) < p(r; \beta)$ when $r + 1 > \mu$. Thus show that the mode of $p(x; \beta)$ is unique when β

is not an integer and the mode is $[\mu]$, where $[\mu]$ is the largest integer less than μ. If μ is an integer, the mode is not unique but is taken on at μ and $\mu - 1$. Consequently, just as with the binomial distribution, the mode cannot differ by more than one unit of x from the mean. Show that in this case the mode is never greater than the mean.

5. Verify numerically each of the results of Problem 4 for $p(x; 9)$.

6. Show that for $r \geq 1$, $rp(r; \beta) = \beta p(r - 1; \beta)$.

7. Let h be any non-negative integer greater than or equal to 2. Show that

$$\sum_{r=h}^{\infty} (r - h)p(r; \beta) = \beta - h + hP(h - 1; \beta) - \beta P(h - 2; \beta)$$

where $P(x; \beta)$ is the cumulative Poisson distribution.

Section 5-11

1. Show how one can evaluate $b_P(n; r,p)$ using tables for the binomial distribution. Illustrate by constructing a bar diagram for $b_P(y; 3,0.4)$.

2. Construct a bar diagram for $b_P(y; 2,0.2)$.

3. Derive the mean of the Pascal distribution.

4. Derive the variance of the Pascal distribution.

5. What is the probability that exactly seven tosses of a fair coin will be required to obtain two heads?

6. A certain production process is such that the probability that any given unit turned out will be defective is 0.1. Assuming that the process is in statistical control, what is the probability that at least five pieces will have to be turned out to obtain three good ones?

7. Show that

$$\frac{b_P(n + 1; r,p)}{b_P(n; r,p)} = \frac{nq}{n + 1 - r}, \quad n = r, r + 1, \ldots,$$

so that $b_P(n + 1; r,p) > b_P(n; r,p)$ if $n + 1 < \mu - (q/p)$, and $b_P(n + 1; r,p) > b_P(n; r,p)$ if $n + 1 > \mu - (q/p)$. If $\mu - (q/p)$ is not an integer, then the mode is unique and is the largest integer less than $\mu - (q/p)$. If $\mu - (q/p)$ is an integer m, then the mode is taken on at m and $m - 1$. Unlike the situation for the binomial and Poisson distributions, the mode for the Pascal is not necessarily within one unit of y from the mean. Show that the mode is always less than the mean and indicate the conditions under which it may be a considerable distance away from the mean. What would be the mode if $r = 3$ and $p = 0.2$?

8. Instead of using the random variable y which gives the number of trials necessary to obtain r occurrences of e_1, it is sometimes convenient to introduce a new random variable $z = y - r$, so that z is the number of trials over and above r trials that is needed to obtain r occurrences of e_1. The random variable z is said to have a *negative binomial distribution*. Note that if $b_n(z; r,p)$ is the probability function for z, then $b_n(z; r,p) = b_P(r + z; r,p)$. Thus write down the functional form of $b_n(z; r,p)$. Show that the bar diagram for $b_n(z; r,p)$ can be obtained

from that for $b_P(y; r,p)$ by translating the latter r units to the left. Derive the mean and variance of the variable z.

9. Determine the probability that precisely $k + 1$, $k = 0, 1, 2, \ldots$, tosses of a coin having a probability p of landing heads up when tossed will be required before the first head is obtained. The probability function $p(k)$ is referred to as the geometric distribution. Determine the mean and variance of this distribution, and construct bar diagrams for it in the case where $p = 0.1, 0.5$, and 0.7.

Sections 5-12 and 5-13

1. A box contains five balls numbered 1 to 5, the first three of which are red and the remaining two are blue. Three balls are drawn from the box. List all of the ordered sequences which correspond to two red balls being drawn. Show that if order is disregarded the number of possibilities is $C_2{}^3 C_1{}^2$.

2. A box contains ten balls numbered 1 to 10. Five of the balls are selected at random from the box. What is the probability that the number 1 appears on one of the balls drawn?

3. Consider the situation outlined in Problem 2. What is the probability that one ball drawn is numbered 1 and that another ball drawn is numbered 2?

4. Consider the situation outlined in Problem 2. What is the probability that the balls numbered 1, 2, and 3 are drawn?

5. Consider the situation outlined in Problem 2. What is the probability that the balls numbered 1, 2, 3 and 4 are drawn?

6. Consider the situation outlined in Problem 2. What is the probability that the balls numbered 1, 2, 3, 4 and 5 are drawn?

7. One box contains ten balls numbered 1 to 10, and another box contains eight balls numbered 1 to 8. Consider the random experiment in which we select at random five balls from the first box and select at random three balls from the second box. What is the probability that two balls drawn are numbered 1?

8. For the situation described in Problem 7, what is the probability that at least one of the balls drawn is numbered 1?

9. For the situation described in Problem 7, what is the probability that two balls numbered 1 and two balls numbered 2 were drawn?

10. For the situation described in Problem 7, what is the probability that at least one ball is numbered 1 and at least one ball is numbered 2?

11. For the situation described in Problem 7, what is the probability that the balls numbered 1 and 2 appear precisely once (and are not repeated)?

12. For the situation described in Problem 7, what is the probability that a ball numbered 1 does not appear?

13. Suppose that there are n balls in an urn, m of which are red. One ball is now selected at random. Show that according to (5-70) the probability that the ball selected is red is m/n, as would be expected in this case.

14. Two students are selected at random from a group of ten students, six of whom are boys and four of whom are girls.   What is the probability that one boy and one girl will be selected?

15.   Answer Problem 14 in the case where there are 100 students, 60 of which are boys.   Can you explain intuitively the reason for the difference in the answers?

16.   An urn contains six red and five blue balls.   Four balls are selected at random. What is the probability that precisely two of them are red?

17.   For the situation described in Problem 16, what is the probability that at least one red ball is obtained?

18.   For the situation described in Problem 16, what is the probability that there are precisely two red balls or three blue balls?

19.   For the situation described in Problem 16, what is the probability that two or less red balls are drawn or two or more blue balls?

20.   An urn contains six red, four blue, and three yellow balls.   Four balls are selected at random from the urn.   What is the probability that precisely two of the balls drawn are red?

21.   For the situation described in Problem 20, what is the probability that two red and two blue or two red and two yellow balls are obtained?

22.   For the situation described in Problem 20, what is the probability that two red and one blue or two red and one yellow balls will be obtained?

23.   A box contains 1000 transistors, 25 of which are defective.   A sample of four transistors is selected at random from the lot.   Compute the exact probability that none of those selected is defective, and also compute the Poisson approximation for this.

24.   A box contains 1000 transistors, 50 of which are defective.   A sample of 100 transistors is selected at random from the lot.   Use the Poisson approximation to estimate the probability that 9 of the transistors in the sample are defective.

25.   A box contains 1000 transistors, 500 of which are defective.   A sample of 20 transistors is drawn at random from the box.   Use the binomial approximation to estimate the probability that eight transistors in the sample are defective.

26.   An urn contains three red, two green, and three yellow balls.   Another urn contains two red, two green, and one yellow balls.   Consider the random experiment in which three balls are selected at random from the first urn and two balls are selected at random from the second urn.   What is the probability that two red balls were drawn from the first urn and one red ball from the second urn?

27.   For the situation described in Problem 26, what is the probability that two of the five balls selected are red?

28.   For the situation described in Problem 26, what is the probability that at least one of the five balls drawn is red?

29.   For the situation described in Problem 26, what is the probability that one of the five balls drawn is red and one of them is green?

30.   For the situation described in Problem 26, what is the probability that precisely one yellow or precisely one blue ball (or both) will be in the five balls selected?

31. Consider the single sampling plan whose operating characteristic curve is shown in Figure 5-5. Five lots, each of which has a fraction defective of 0.02, are sampled. What is the probability that all five lots will pass inspection?

32. A radio manufacturer purchases resistors in lots of 10,000 from several suppliers. The manufacturer would like to reject with high frequency any lots having a fraction defective of 0.05 or more, but would prefer not to reject lots having a fraction defective of 0.02 or less. A single sampling plan of the following type is used currently. A sample of 200 resistors is selected. The lot is accepted if five or less are defective and is rejected otherwise. Determine the operating characteristic curve for this plan. Does it appear to satisfy the manufacturer's requirements?

CHAPTER 6

CONDITIONAL PROBABILITY MODELS
AND
JOINT DISTRIBUTIONS

For we know in part, and we prophesy in part.

I Corinthians 13, 9.

6-1 CONDITIONAL PROBABILITY MODELS

Consider some random experiment $\mathcal{R}$ and let $\mathcal{E}$ be a suitable mathematical model for $\mathcal{R}$. We shall suppose that the event set for $\mathcal{E}$ is $E = \{e_1, \ldots, e_m\}$ and that $p_j = p(e_j)$ is the function which gives the probabilities of the simple events. Suppose now that $\mathcal{R}$ is performed, and either while $\mathcal{R}$ is taking place or after $\mathcal{R}$ is completed, we are given some information about how $\mathcal{R}$ is turning out or has turned out, but that we are not given complete information about the outcome of $\mathcal{R}$, that is, we are not told which simple event will or has occurred. Given this additional information, our original probability model may be an inappropriate one to use in making any additional computations which remain to be done. The question then arises as to how we can proceed to develop a new model $\mathcal{E}_c$ which will incorporate the additional information about the outcome of $\mathcal{R}$. The new model will be called a *conditional probability model*. The word conditional is used because $\mathcal{E}_c$ makes use of information about what has actually happened on performing $\mathcal{R}$. We shall show that it is normally possible to construct the model $\mathcal{E}_c$ in a straightforward way from $\mathcal{E}$. No new investigations have to be made to determine the probabilities of the simple events in $\mathcal{E}_c$. They can be computed directly from the probabilities of the simple events in $\mathcal{E}$. Before going on with the theory, however, let us illustrate with some examples the manner in which information about $\mathcal{R}$ can be obtained.

EXAMPLES. *1*. Consider the experiment $\mathcal{R}$ in which a ball is selected at random from an urn containing ten balls numbered 1 through 10. Suppose that balls 1, 2, and 3 are red, while the others are blue. The event set for $\mathcal{R}$ can be imagined to consist of ten simple events, the jth of which is the event that ball j is drawn. Suppose now that $\mathcal{R}$ is performed and we are not told the number of the ball that was drawn, but we are told that it is red. Once we know that a red ball was drawn, it follows that the number on the ball must be 1, 2, or 3, and if any additional computations are to be made, we should use an event set containing just three simple events, corresponding to whether the ball drawn was 1, 2, or 3.

2. Let us next give an example where information is generated as $\mathcal{R}$ is performed. Consider a two stage lottery. Once the spin of the first roulette wheel has determined to which single stage lottery the player goes, the probability to be assigned to his getting any given prize e_j will in general be different from what it was before the spin of the first wheel. Similarly, for an n-stage lottery, additional information is generated at each stage, and after every spin of a roulette wheel, the probabilities of getting the various prizes will in general change.

3. Mortality tables will tell us what the probability is that a new-born baby will die in his jth year. However, if this baby lives for $j - 1$ years, the probability that he will die in his jth year of life is different from what it was at the time of his birth. To express the same thing with a different example, one can determine before launching a space vehicle, the probability of a successful soft landing on the moon; this probability of success will increase, however, if the vehicle completes the flight to the vicinity of the moon.

4. Suppose that a geologist is searching for likely oil bearing formations, and he comes upon a promising looking structure. Now not all likely looking structures contain oil. We can imagine that whether oil is present depends on the outcome of a random experiment which was performed millions of years ago. From his previous experience and the experience of others, the geologist can assign a personal probability that producible quantities of oil are present. To gain more information on what the outcome of the random experiment was, the geologist can perform certain experiments, such as a seismic test. Although such tests will not tell him definitely whether oil is present, the additional information gained may modify drastically his original probability estimate.

Let us now return to the general problem of seeing how to construct the conditional probability model $\mathcal{E}_c$ from the given model $\mathcal{E}$. The first step in doing this is to characterize the type of information made available on the outcome of $\mathcal{R}$. The important thing to note is that the only kind of information which can be made available is that which rules out some of the simple events in E. The information will be of a form which says that some event A of $\mathcal{R}$ has occurred. Now A is a subset of E, and the information that A has occurred means that the simple event of $\mathcal{R}$ which has occurred or will occur is one of the simple events in A. Thus the appropriate event set to use for $\mathcal{E}_c$ is nothing but the set A. The set A should be a suitable event set for $\mathcal{E}_c$, since it contains the simple events from E which can occur. We have thus seen how to obtain the event set for $\mathcal{E}_c$.

Let us next turn to the question of what probability should be assigned to the simple events in A. Suppose that the simple event $e_k \in A$. Assume now that $\mathcal{R}$ is an experiment which can be repeated over and over again. Imagine that $\mathcal{R}$ has been performed a large number of times n. Denote by n_A the number of times that A occurred and by n_k the number of times that e_k occurred. Now the probability of e_k in $\mathcal{E}_c$ is the long run fraction of the time that e_k is the simple event observed when A occurred. But this should be just the limit of n_k/n_A as n becomes arbitrarily large. Denote the probability of e_k in $\mathcal{E}_c$ by $p(e_k|A)$. Now

$$\frac{n_k}{n_A} = \frac{n_k}{n}\frac{n}{n_A} = \frac{n_k/n}{n_A/n}, \tag{6-1}$$

and as n becomes arbitrarily large n_k/n becomes p_k and n_A/n becomes $p(A)$, the probability of A, which we shall assume to be different from 0 since A has occurred. Thus from (6-1) it appears that we should take $p(e_k|A)$ to be

$$p(e_k|A) = p_k/p(A), \quad e_k \in A. \tag{6-2}$$

The same conclusion would be reached even if $\mathcal{R}$ could not be repeated, on using the notion of an ensemble relative frequency. This is what we shall do then. For $\mathcal{E}_c$ we shall use A as the event set and the probabilities of the simple events in A will be given by (6-2). We might note that the probability assignment (6-2) does satisfy the axioms for a probability model, since first $p(e_k|A) \geq 0$. Furthermore, if one sums the probabilities p_k of the simple events $e_k \in A$ one obtains $p(A)$. Thus if one sums the $p(e_k|A)$, one obtains $p(A)/p(A)$ or 1 as desired. From what we have just said, it follows that $p_k \leq p(A)$, and therefore it is also true that $p(e_k|A) \leq 1$. Hence both axioms are satisfied, and (6-2) represents an allowable assignment of probabilities to the event set A. The probability $p(e_k|A)$ is given a special name. It is called *the conditional probability of e_k given that the event A has occurred*. Sometimes we abbreviate this and simply say the conditional probability of e_k when it is understood that this is conditional on the event A having occurred.

EXAMPLES. *1.* Consider the first example given at the beginning of this section. Before performing the experiment, we would say that the probability of drawing ball 1 is $\frac{1}{10}$. Let us now determine the probability that ball 1 is drawn when we know that a red ball is drawn. To do this we must construct a suitable conditional probability model $\mathcal{E}_c$. If a red ball is drawn, then the ball drawn must have the number 1 or 2 or 3 painted on it, that is, $A = \{1, 2, 3\}$ if we use as the symbols for the simple events the numbers on the balls. Now A is the event set that we use for $\mathcal{E}_c$. The probability of each simple event is given by (6-2). In (6-2), p_k and $p(A)$ are probabilities computed for the original model so that $p_k = \frac{1}{10}$ and $p(A) = \frac{3}{10}$. Hence $p(e_k|A) = \frac{1}{3}$ for each of the simple events in A. We now have the model $\mathcal{E}_c$. It is a model with the event set A and having the probability of each simple event being $\frac{1}{3}$. We can then easily determine the probability that ball 1 was drawn. This event is one of the simple events of $\mathcal{E}_c$ and has the probability $\frac{1}{3}$. This is, of course, what we would expect intuitively, since if a red ball is selected, the events that the ball selected is 1, 2, or 3 should be equally likely. If we asked for the probability that the ball selected has either the number 1 or 2 on it, this is simply the event $\{1, 2\}$ and its probability is $\frac{2}{3}$.

2. Let us next turn to Example 3 given at the beginning of this section, but instead of considering things on a year by year basis use a much simpler treatment. Suppose we determine from historical data the fraction of males who die before they are 20, who die between 20 and 40, who die between 40 and 60, who die between 60 and 80, and who die after the age of 80. We can use these five ranges as the simple events for a random experiment, and the relative frequencies of death in each of these periods are the probabilities that a new-born male baby will die in each given period. Denote the periods by e_1, e_2, e_3, e_4, and e_5. Historical data then suggest that $p(e_1) = 0.077$, $p(e_2) = 0.054$, $p(e_3) = 0.191$, $p(e_4) = 0.480$, $p(e_5) = 0.198$. Here we have a model for predicting the probability that a new-born male baby will die in any one of the specified periods. Suppose now, however, that we wish to compute the probability that a young man just turned 20 will die in one of the periods e_2 through e_5. We can imagine this to be a situation in which information about the progress of a random experiment has been given to us. The information given us is that the individual has lived to the age of 20, i.e., the event A has occurred that he will die after the age of 20. Thus $A = \{e_2, e_3, e_4, e_5\}$ and this is the event set for the conditional probability model. Now $p(A) = 0.923$, and hence according to (6-2)

$$p(e_2|A) = \frac{0.054}{0.923} = 0.059; \quad p(e_3|A) = \frac{0.191}{0.923} = 0.206;$$

$$p(e_4|A) = \frac{0.480}{0.923} = 0.520; \quad p(e_5|A) = \frac{0.198}{0.923} = 0.215;$$

and these are the probabilities of the simple events for $\mathcal{E}_c$. Note that at the time of birth the probability of dying between 40 and 60 is 0.191, while if the individual survives until the age of 20 this probability increases to 0.206.

6-2 CONDITIONAL PROBABILITY

In the previous section we saw how to modify a probability model $\mathcal{E}$ for some random experiment $\mathfrak{R}$ if certain partial information is made available about the outcome of $\mathfrak{R}$. This yielded a new model $\mathcal{E}_c$, which was called a conditional probability model. The probabilities of the simple events in $\mathcal{E}_c$ are given by (6-2) when A is the event set for $\mathcal{E}_c$. Let us now note that we did not prove in a rigorous mathematical sense that the probabilities (6-2) are the probabilities of the simple events in $\mathcal{E}_c$. Recall that there is no way we can prove mathematically that an assignment of probabilities to the simple events is correct. We used our intuitive understanding of the meaning of probability to obtain (6-2). One could verify that $\mathcal{E}_c$ was consistent with the real world by performing $\mathfrak{R}$ a large number of times and observing that the frequency of each e_k relative to A was close to the number given in (6-2), but this does not represent a mathematical proof. The situation here is similar to the introduction of the notion of independent random experiments. We could not prove in that case either that our method of computing the probabilities of the simple events from those of the independent experiments into which $\mathfrak{R}$ could be decomposed was correct. We did, however, introduce into the mathematical model the notion of independent events, and given any two events of the model we can rigorously determine whether they are independent. We then related the intuitive notion of independent experiments to the rigorous definition of independent events. We shall now proceed in a similar manner here. We are going to define in $\mathcal{E}$ what we shall call conditional probabilities, and this will then be related to what was discussed in the previous section.

CONDITIONAL PROBABILITY OF B GIVEN A. *Let $\mathcal{E}$ be a mathematical model of some random experiment $\mathfrak{R}$ and let A and B be any two events such that $p(A) \neq 0$. The number $p(A \cap B)/p(A)$ we shall call the conditional probability of B given A, and write it $p(B|A)$, so that*

$$p(B|A) = \frac{p(A \cap B)}{p(A)}. \tag{6-3}$$

We do not define $p(B|A)$ when $p(A) = 0$. For any two events A and B, it is straightforward to determine the number which we have called the conditional probability of B given A. We compute in $\mathcal{E}$ the probabilities $p(A \cap B)$ and $p(A)$, and then $p(B|A)$ is given by (6-3). Note that by (6-3), $p(B|A) \geq 0$, and inasmuch as $A \cap B \subseteq A$, $p(A \cap B) \leq p(A)$, so that $p(B|A) \leq 1$, as must be true if $p(A|B)$ is to be used as a probability.

Let us now provide an intuitive interpretation of $p(B|A)$. Suppose that in the performance of $\Re$ we find that A has occurred. According to our discussion of the last section, if we wish to make additional computations concerning $\Re$ we should modify $\mathcal{E}$ to obtain a conditional probability model $\mathcal{E}_c$ whose event set is A and for which the probabilities of the simple events are given by (6-2). Let us now ask, what is the probability of B computed from our new model $\mathcal{E}_c$? To compute the probability of B in $\mathcal{E}_c$, we determine those simple events in B which are also in A. This set of simple events is $A \cap B$. We then add up the probabilities (6-2) for the simple events in $A \cap B$. However, if we sum the p_k for simple events in $A \cap B$ we get $p(A \cap B)$. Thus the probability of B in $\mathcal{E}_c$ is $p(A \cap B)/p(A)$, i.e., $p(B|A)$. This is the probability that B will occur or has occurred when we know that A has occurred. Therefore, intuitively $p(B|A)$ is the probability of B that we would compute from the conditional probability model $\mathcal{E}_c$ which has A for an event set.

Note that we can write (6-3) as

$$p(A \cap B) = p(B|A)p(A). \tag{6-4}$$

Equation (6-4) is often a useful one to remember; it always holds when $p(A) \neq 0$ (by definition). Recall that previously we defined two events A and B to be independent if

$$p(A \cap B) = p(A)p(B). \tag{6-5}$$

On equating the expressions for $p(A \cap B)$ in (6-5) and (6-4), we see that when A and B are independent, $p(A)p(B) = p(B|A)p(A)$, or since $p(A) \neq 0$

$$p(B|A) = p(B). \tag{6-6}$$

What we have just shown is that if A and B are independent then (6-6) must hold. However, if (6-6) holds then the events are independent. *Therefore, the events A and B with $p(A) \neq 0$ are independent if and only if the conditional probability of B given A is the probability of B, in other words, if a knowledge that A has occurred does not change our estimate of the probability of B.* This, of course, is what we mean intuitively by independent events.

Just as we can define $p(B|A)$ when $p(A) \neq 0$, we can define $p(A|B)$ when $p(B) \neq 0$ by writing

$$p(A \cap B) = p(A|B)p(B), \tag{6-7}$$

and $p(A|B)$ is the probability of A when B is known to have occurred. If we equate the expressions for $p(A \cap B)$ in (6-4), we obtain when $p(A) \neq 0$ and $p(B) \neq 0$,

$$p(B|A)p(A) = p(A|B)p(B). \tag{6-8}$$

Equation (6-8) provides an interesting connection between the probability of B that one would compute from a conditional probability model whose event set is A, and the probability of A one would compute from a conditional probability model whose event set is B. Let us note from (6-8) that if $p(B|A) = p(B)$, so that A and B are independent, then $p(A|B) = p(A)$, provided that $p(A) \neq 0$ and $p(B) \neq 0$. Intuitively this says that if the occurrence of A has no influence on our estimate of the probability of B, then the occurrence of B will not modify our estimate for the probability of A.

We shall delay giving examples illustrating conditional probabilities until after the next section has been covered, since they are mainly of use in studying models of the type to be discussed there.

6-3 TWO STAGE AND MULTISTAGE PROBABILITY MODELS

We have already seen that the notion of a multistage lottery is very important in decision theory. Many random experiments can really be looked upon as multistage lotteries even though the experiment may be phrased in an entirely different terminology. In this section we would like to study multistage probability models. As in our discussion of lotteries, we shall concentrate our attention on what we shall call a two stage random experiment. Let $\mathcal{R}_1$ be a random experiment and assume $\mathcal{E}_1$ is a suitable mathematical model of $\mathcal{R}_1$. Suppose that the event set for $\mathcal{E}_1$ is $E_1 = \{f_1, \ldots, f_s\}$, and let the probability of f_i be q_i. Next imagine that we have s additional random experiments $\mathcal{R}_{i2}$, $i = 1, \ldots, s$, with a suitable mathematical model for $\mathcal{R}_{i2}$ being $\mathcal{E}_{i2}$. Each model $\mathcal{E}_{i2}$ will be imagined to have the same event set $E = \{e_1, \ldots, e_m\}$. However, the probabilities of the simple events can change from one model to another, that is, with i. Let p_{ij} be the probability of e_j in $\mathcal{E}_{i2}$. Consider now the random experiment $\mathcal{R}$ which first consists in performing $\mathcal{R}_1$, and then, if the outcome of $\mathcal{R}_1$ is f_i, the random experiment $\mathcal{R}_{i2}$ is performed. We shall call the random experiment $\mathcal{R}$ a two stage random experiment. It is possible to represent diagramatically the two stage experiment $\mathcal{R}$ by a tree like that shown in Figure 6-1.

We can note that a two stage lottery is a special case of what we have defined to be a two stage random experiment. We can note also that just as in our discussion of lotteries there is no real restriction implied in assuming that all of the experiments $\mathcal{R}_{i2}$ have the same event set, since if e_k is impossible in $\mathcal{R}_{u2}$ we simply set $p_{uk} = 0$. The notion of a two stage random experiment is much more general than it might appear at first glance, and many important random experiments can be thought of as two stage random experiments. It is now clear that we could introduce the notion of

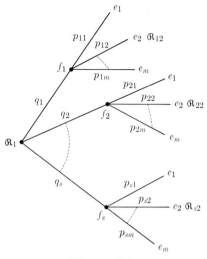

FIGURE 6-1

multistage random experiments just as we did multistage lotteries. However, we shall see that we can handle all problems of interest just using
the notion of a two stage random experiment. Hence we shall not attempt
to develop in detail models of n-stage random experiments for $n \geq 3$.

We would now like to show how we can develop a mathematical model
$\mathcal{E}$ for the two stage random experiment $\mathcal{R}$ from a knowledge of the models
for $\mathcal{R}_1$ and the $\mathcal{R}_{i2}$. Consider first the characterization of the simple events
for $\mathcal{R}$. As a simple event for $\mathcal{R}$ we shall use the ordered pair $\langle f_i, e_j \rangle$ which
gives the simple event f_i obtained on performing $\mathcal{R}_1$ and the simple event
e_j obtained on performing $\mathcal{R}_{i2}$. There are sm such simple events. In discussing lotteries we used only the e_j, i.e., the prizes obtained on playing
the lottery. In general, however, the outcome of $\mathcal{R}_1$ may be very important, and in setting up the simple events for $\mathcal{R}$ we shall indicate what happened at each stage. We shall denote by E the set containing the sm
simple events $\langle f_i, e_j \rangle$.

Let us next determine the probabilities r_{ij} of the simple events $\langle f_i, e_j \rangle$.
If $\mathcal{R}$ is performed a large number of times n, let n_{ij} be the number of times
that $\mathcal{R}_1$ yields the outcome f_i and $\mathcal{R}_{i2}$ yields the outcome e_j. Then as n
becomes arbitrarily large, n_{ij}/n becomes r_{ij}. However, if n_i is the number
of times that $\mathcal{R}_1$ yields outcome f_i, we can write

$$\frac{n_{ij}}{n} = \left(\frac{n_i}{n}\right)\left(\frac{n_{ij}}{n_i}\right). \tag{6-9}$$

We shall assume that each $q_i > 0$, so that for n sufficiently large we expect that $n_i > 0$ and hence we can divide by n_i in (6-9). Observe that as n becomes larger and larger, the ratio n_i/n approaches q_i. Now n_{ij}/n_i is the fraction of the time that the performance of $\Re_{i2}$ yields the event e_j. This must approach p_{ij} as n becomes larger and larger. The argument just given then suggests that r_{ij}, the probability of $\langle f_i, e_j \rangle$, should be assigned the value

$$r_{ij} = q_i p_{ij}. \tag{6-10}$$

We would reach the same conclusion even if $\Re$ could not be repeated, by use of the ensemble notion. Furthermore, it might be noted that (6-10) holds even if $q_i = 0$, since then $r_{ij} = 0$, which is what (6-10) yields in this case. We shall then use (6-10) for the probabilities of the simple events for $\Re$. The probability assignment (6-10) does satisfy the axioms for a probability model. To see this, note that $0 \leq r_{ij} \leq 1$ since $0 \leq q_i \leq 1$ and $0 \leq p_{ij} \leq 1$. Furthermore, if we add up all the r_{ij} we obtain

$$q_1 p_{11} + \cdots + q_1 p_{1m} + q_2 p_{21} + \cdots + q_2 p_{2m} + \cdots + q_s p_{s1} + \cdots + q_s p_{sm}$$
$$= q_1(p_{11} + \cdots + p_{1m}) + q_2(p_{21} + \cdots + p_{2m}) + \cdots + q_s(p_{s1} + \cdots + p_{sm})$$
$$= q_1 + q_2 + \cdots + q_s = 1,$$

as desired. For our model $\mathcal{E}$ of $\Re$ then we shall use as the event set E, the set of ordered pairs $\langle f_i, e_j \rangle$ with the probability of each simple event being given by (6-10).

We shall next find it of interest to investigate some of the characteristics of the model $\mathcal{E}$. It is instructive to compare $\mathcal{E}$ here with the model $\mathcal{E}$ obtained in Section 5-2 for the case where $\Re$ was built up from two independent random experiments. The event sets are of precisely the same form. The reason for this is that we assumed that all the experiments $\Re_{i2}$ had the same event set. Furthermore, the equations (6-10) and (5-2) for the probabilities of the simple events look quite similar. They are not the same, however, since in (5-2) a p_j appears which is independent of i, while in (6-10) a p_{ij} appears. This is the crucial difference between the situation studied in Section 5-2 and that considered here. Now the probabilities of the outcomes of the experiment performed at the second stage will depend on the outcome at the first stage. Thus we see that a two stage experiment of the type we have been considering here will reduce to the case of two independent experiments if and only if each $\Re_{i2}$ is the same experiment, call it $\Re_2$, that is, if the p_{ij} do not depend on i.

The probability of the simple event f_i of $\Re_1$ is q_i in $\mathcal{E}_1$, the model for $\Re_1$. Now f_i is also an event of $\Re$; it is the event $\{\langle f_i, e_1 \rangle, \ldots, \langle f_i, e_m \rangle\}$. The probability of the event f_i in $\mathcal{E}$ is then

$$q_i p_{i1} + \cdots + q_i p_{im} = q_i(p_{i1} + \cdots + p_{im}) = q_i. \tag{6-11}$$

Therefore, f_i has the same probability in $\mathcal{E}$ as in $\mathcal{E}_1$. This is what we would desire intuitively, because adding a second stage does not influence the probability of f_i in $\Re_1$.

The event e_j is a simple event for each of the experiments $\Re_{i2}$ and is the event $\{\langle f_1, e_j \rangle, \ldots, \langle f_s, e_j \rangle\}$ of $\mathcal{E}$.   The probability of e_j in $\mathcal{E}$ is then

$$q_1 p_{1j} + \cdots + q_s p_{sj} = \sum_{i=1}^{s} q_i p_{ij}. \tag{6-12}$$

This is precisely the same result as we obtained in a somewhat different way in Section 2-6.   Consider next the event $f_i \cap e_j$.   This is nothing but the simple event $\langle f_i, e_j \rangle$ of $\mathcal{E}$, and its probability is $q_i p_{ij}$.   In $\mathcal{E}$ let us next compute the conditional probability of e_j given that the outcome of $\Re_1$ is f_i, i.e., $p(e_j | f_i)$.   By the definition of conditional probability,

$$p(e_j | f_i) = \frac{p(f_i \cap e_j)}{p(f_i)} = \frac{q_i p_{ij}}{q_i} = p_{ij}. \tag{6-13}$$

Thus $p(e_j | f_i) = p_{ij}$.   This is what we would expect intuitively, since if the outcome of $\Re_1$ is f_i, the experiment $\Re_{i2}$ is performed at the second stage and the probability that e_j is the outcome of $\Re_{i2}$ is p_{ij}.

Very frequently one has occasion to study random experiments $\Re$ where it is very convenient to think of the experiment as a two stage experiment. In such cases one is often interested in determining the probability of either an event which in our above notation turns out to be $\langle f_i, e_j \rangle$ or an event e_j.   We have seen above how to find the probabilities of each of these events in terms of the probabilities determined from the models for the individual stages.   This can be a very helpful way to determine the probabilities of interest.   While it is by no means true that the second stage experiments will always have the same event sets, as we have already noted, this in no way influences the above analysis.   The next section will provide some examples to illustrate the usefulness of the material just developed.

It is worthwhile to observe that the events e_j introduced above as the simple events for the second stage experiment do not necessarily refer solely to what happens in the second stage.   It may be convenient or necessary to include in the description of the e_j some aspect of the first stage experiment.   Thus, for example, the e_j could describe the final outcome of both stages combined.   The first example of Section 6-6 will illustrate a situation where the e_j have this interpretation.

6-4 EXAMPLES

1.   An urn contains five red balls, four blue balls, and seven yellow balls. Two balls are selected at random, one after the other, from the urn.   Let us determine the probability that the first ball selected was red and the second selected was yellow.   We can think of the random experiment $\Re$ involved here as a two stage experiment in which at the first stage we perform the experiment $\mathcal{R}_1$ where we select at random one ball from an urn containing 16 balls, and at the second stage select at random one of the remaining 15 balls. Let us use as the event set for $\mathcal{R}_1$ the set $E = \{R, B, Y\}$, where R stands for a red ball being drawn, B for a blue ball, and Y for a yellow ball. Since all balls have the same probability of being drawn and since five are red, we conclude that the probability of a red ball is $p(R) = \frac{5}{16}$. Similarly, $p(B) = \frac{1}{4}$ and $p(Y) = \frac{7}{16}$. The event set E will also serve as an event set for the second stage experiment. The probabilities of the simple events depend, however, on the color of the ball drawn at the first stage. We are concerned only with the case where a red ball was drawn. In this case, there are 15 balls remaining of which four are red, four blue, and seven yellow. Given that a ball is selected at random, the probability that a yellow one is drawn should be $\frac{7}{15}$. Thus from (6-10), the probability that the first ball drawn is red and the second ball drawn is yellow is $\frac{5}{16}(\frac{7}{15}) = \frac{7}{48} = 0.146$. In terms of the discussion of the previous section, what we have done here is to compute the probability of one of the simple events for $\mathcal{R}$.

Suppose that instead of being asked for the probability that the first ball is red and the second yellow, we ask for the probability that one ball drawn is red and the other yellow. The event now of interest consists of two simple events for $\mathcal{R}$, i.e., $\langle R, Y \rangle$, $\langle Y, R \rangle$, since we must get either a red then a yellow or a yellow then a red ball. We have already computed the probability of $\langle R, Y \rangle$. Now the probability of getting a yellow on the first draw is $\frac{7}{16}$, and the probability of getting a red on the second draw, given that a yellow was obtained on the first is $\frac{5}{15}$, so that the probability of $\langle Y, R \rangle$ is $\frac{7}{16}(\frac{5}{15}) = \frac{7}{48} = 0.146$, which is precisely the same as that for $\langle R, Y \rangle$. Thus the probability of one red and one yellow ball is $2(0.146)$ or 0.292. In solving problems of the type just considered, once one understands the theory it is unnecessary to construct in detail a model for $\mathcal{R}$. One simply determines $p(R)$ and then $p(Y|R)$, the conditional probability of a yellow on the second draw given a red on the first, and multiplies these numbers together to obtain the probability of $\langle R, Y \rangle$.

2. Consider the same situation as in Example 1, except that now three balls are drawn out at random one after the other, and we ask what the probability is that the first is red, the second yellow, and the third blue. We could quite correctly think of this as a three stage random experiment. A very convenient way to solve the problem is to think of it as involving a two stage experiment $\mathcal{R}$, the first stage of which, $\mathcal{R}_1$, can itself be looked upon as a two stage experiment. We can imagine that $\mathcal{R}_1$ is the experiment in which we draw out the first two balls, and this can be decomposed into one experiment in which we draw out the first ball and another experiment in which we draw out the second ball. Now in Example 1 we computed the probability that the first ball drawn will be red and the second

yellow. This is 0.146 and is the probability that $\mathfrak{R}_1$ yields the event $\langle R, Y \rangle$. Given that a red and yellow ball have been drawn out, there are 14 balls left, four of which are blue. The probability that the second stage of $\mathfrak{R}$ (i.e., the third draw) yields a blue ball is then $\frac{4}{14} = 0.286$. Hence the probability that the first ball is red, the second yellow, and the third blue is $0.146(0.286) = 0.0418$.

3. A lot containing N resistors is such that pN of them are defective, i.e., the lot fraction defective is p, and qN of them are good. A sample of n resistors is selected at random from the lot. What is the probability that precisely r of these are defective? We have seen how to solve this problem in Section 5-12. We shall now show how the result can be obtained using conditional probabilities and the notion of two stage experiments. We can imagine that the n resistors are drawn out one at a time. Now the experiment in which we select n resistors can be looked on as a two stage experiment in which we first select $n - 1$ of them and then the nth. However, the experiment in which one selects $n - 1$ resistors can be looked at as a two stage experiment in which we first select $n - 2$ and then the $n - 1$st one, etc. Let us begin by computing the probability that the first r resistors selected are defective and the last $n - r$ are good. The probability that the first one is defective is $pN/N = p$. Given that the first is defective, there are $N - 1$ resistors left in the lot, $pN - 1$ of which are defective. The conditional probability that the second is defective given that the first is, is then $(pN - 1)/(N - 1)$, so that the probability that the first two are defective is

$$\frac{pN}{N} \left(\frac{pN - 1}{N - 1} \right).$$

Given that the first two resistors selected are defective, $N - 2$ resistors remain in the lot, $pN - 2$ of which are defective. Thus the conditional probability that the third is defective given that the first two are, is $(pN - 2)/(N - 2)$. Continuing this we see that the probability that the first r are defective is

$$\frac{pN}{N} \left(\frac{pN - 1}{N - 1} \right) \cdots \left(\frac{pN - r + 1}{N - r + 1} \right).$$

Given that the first r resistors selected are defective, there remain $N - r$ resistors, qN of which are good. The probability that resistor $r + 1$ is good is then $qN/(N - r)$, etc. Therefore, the probability that the first r resistors are defective and the last $n - r$ are good is

$$\frac{pN}{N} \left(\frac{pN - 1}{N - 1} \right) \cdots$$

$$\left(\frac{pN - r + 1}{N - r + 1} \right) \left(\frac{qN}{N - r} \right) \cdots \left(\frac{qN - n + r + 1}{N - n + 1} \right). \quad (6\text{-}14)$$

We can next note that the probability of obtaining precisely r defectives in any order is (6-14). The reason for this is that the denominators in the probability expression will always be $N, N - 1, \ldots, N - n + 1$ in this order, while the numerators will be some permutation of those in (6-14), so that when the product is computed the same number is obtained as in (6-14). Now the number of different orders in which r defectives can be obtained is $C_r{}^n$. Therefore, the probability that precisely r resistors in the sample will be defective is

$$\frac{n!}{r!(n-r)!}\left[\frac{pN}{N}\left(\frac{pN-1}{N-1}\right)\cdots\right.$$
$$\left.\left(\frac{pN-r+1}{N-r+1}\right)\left(\frac{qN}{N-r}\right)\cdots\left(\frac{qN-n+r+1}{N-n+1}\right)\right]. \quad (6\text{-}15)$$

On comparison with (5-72), we see that (6-15) is $h(r; n, p, N)$, the hypergeometric probability function.

The present derivation of $h(r; n, p, N)$ permits us to obtain a very clear understanding of why and under what conditions $h(r; n, p, N)$ can be approximated by the binomial distribution $b(r; n, p)$. If $(pN - k)/(N - j)$ is very close to p, then the probability of drawing out a defective resistor on the $(j + 1)$st draw is essentially independent of what happened on the first j draws; and similarly if $(qN - k)/(N - j)$ is very close to q, the probability of drawing out a good resistor on the $(j + 1)$st draw is independent of what happened on the first j draws. Under such circumstances the various draws correspond to independent random experiments and the probability of r defectives in n trials will be essentially $b(r; n, p)$. Now these conditions will be satisfied if for all allowable j, $N - j$ is essentially equal to N, and $pN - k$ and $qN - k$ are essentially equal to pN and qN, respectively. This will be true when the sample size is small with respect to the lot size, r is small compared to the number of defectives, and $n - r$ is small compared to the number of good units.

4. A type of probability problem one frequently encounters in textbooks is a version of the following. One of two drawers in a desk contains one gold and one silver coin. The other drawer contains one gold and two silver coins. An individual selects one of the two drawers at random, opens the drawer, and without observing the coins, selects at random one of the coins there. What is the probability that he will select a gold coin? We can think of this random experiment $\Re$ as a two stage experiment where he selects in the first stage a drawer, and in the second stage a coin in the drawer. Let the simple events for $\Re$ be $\langle 1, G \rangle$, $\langle 1, S \rangle$, $\langle 2, G \rangle$, $\langle 2, S \rangle$ where $\langle 1, G \rangle$ means that drawer 1 was selected and the gold coin in drawer 1 was selected, and so forth for the others. We wish to compute the probability of the event that he obtains a gold coin, i.e., the event $\{\langle 1, G \rangle, \langle 2, G \rangle\}$. Now the probability of selecting either drawer is $\frac{1}{2}$. The probability of

selecting the gold coin in drawer 1 is $\frac{1}{2}$, so that the probability of $\langle 1, G \rangle$ is $\frac{1}{4}$. The probability of selecting a gold coin if drawer 2 is selected is $\frac{1}{3}$, so that the probability of $\langle 2, G \rangle$ is $\frac{1}{6}$. Therefore the probability of selecting a gold coin is

$$\tfrac{1}{4} + \tfrac{1}{6} = 0.250 + 0.167 = 0.417.$$

All we are really doing here is illustrating an application of (6-12). It should be observed that the chances of selecting any one of the five coins are not equal, so that the probability of a gold coin is not $\frac{2}{5} = 0.4$, even though this is close to the correct probability.

5.   We have indicated previously that a production process which is operating properly often behaves to a good approximation as if defectives are generated at random. In other words, the production of each unit can be imagined to be an independent trial of a random experiment in which the probability of a defective is p. The probability that r of n units produced will be defective is then the binomial probability $b(r; n, p)$. Let us go on to consider a slightly more complicated situation.

Suppose that a given item is not produced continuously, but instead is produced periodically in lots of size n. The process of producing a lot of the given item involves setting up several machines and making a production run of n units. The jigs are then torn down and some other product is run. Past experience has indicated that during the production run the process generally behaves as if defectives are turned out at random. However, the probability that any given unit will be defective is not always the same. This probability varies depending on how the jigs are aligned. To simplify matters, imagine that the probability of a defective takes on a finite number of possible values $p_1, \ldots, p_s$, and let us imagine that the probability that it will be p_i is q_i. Suppose now that we are asked to compute the probability that on the next setup r defectives will be produced in the run of n units. We can imagine the random experiment involved to be a two stage experiment. In the first stage, when the setup is carried out, a random experiment is performed which determines the probability p_i that any given unit produced in the run will be defective. Once this is done, the second stage involves making the production run of n units. This second stage experiment corresponds to n independent trials of a random experiment in which the probability of generating a defective in any trial is p_i. The probability of obtaining r defectives in the production run, given that the probability of a defective on each trial is p_i, is the binomial probability $b(r; n, p_i)$. The probability that the nature of the setup at the first stage will yield p_i as the probability of a defective is q_i. Therefore, by (6-12), the probability of obtaining r defectives is

$$q_1 b(r; n, p_1) + \cdots + q_s b(r; n, p_s) = \sum_{i=1}^{s} q_i b(r; n, p_i). \qquad (6\text{-}16)$$

This shows how we can take account of the fact that the probability of a defective is not known ahead of time but is itself the result of a random experiment.

6-5 BAYES' LAW

Two stage experiments will be of great interest to us in Chapter 8. The two stage experiments that will concern us there will be of a somewhat different type than we have emphasized thus far. In Chapter 8 we shall be interested in cases where the first stage of the two stage experiment has been performed, but we do not know what the outcome of it is. The second stage then will be an experiment designed to give us information about the outcome of the first stage. This no doubt sounds confusing to the reader, so let us provide a realistic example, which has already been discussed in part as Example 4 on p. 283. Recall that a geologist was investigating a likely looking structure trying to decide on the chances that it contained oil in producible quantities. To obtain additional information, he performs a seismic experiment which involves observing how sound waves are reflected from the structure. This experiment does not definitely tell whether oil is present or not, but does give additional information. The seismic experiment can be looked upon as the second stage of a two stage random experiment. The first stage was completed millions of years ago when nature decided whether or not to put oil in the structure, and, if so, how much. The outcome of the seismic experiment will depend on the outcome of the first stage. What the geologist would like to compute are the probabilities of the various outcomes of the first stage given the outcome of the seismic experiment.

Having this concrete example to illustrate what we have in mind, let us turn to studying the general case. Suppose that $\Re$ is a two stage random experiment of the type discussed in Section 6-3. Assume that $\Re$ is performed and at the end of the second stage the event e_k is observed. The outcome of the first stage is not known. We would like to compute the probability that the outcome of the first stage was f_i given that the outcome of the second stage is e_k, that is, we wish to compute the conditional probability $p(f_i|e_k)$ of f_i, given e_k. By (6-3)

$$p(f_i|e_k) = \frac{p(f_i \cap e_k)}{p(e_k)}. \qquad (6\text{-}17)$$

Note that $p(f_i \cap e_k) = q_i p_{ik}$ since $f_i \cap e_k$ is the simple event $\langle f_i, e_k \rangle$. Also, from (6-12) $p(e_k) = \sum_{u=1}^{s} q_u p_{uk}$. It is convenient to use u as the summation index here because i appears elsewhere. Hence

$$p(f_i|e_k) = \frac{q_i p_{ik}}{\displaystyle\sum_{u=1}^{s} q_u p_{uk}}. \tag{6-18}$$

This rule for computing the conditional probability $p(f_i|e_k)$ is called *Bayes' law or Bayes' formula*, and it is a result which we shall use very frequently in the future.

It will be instructive to examine (6-18) in a little more detail. Recall that q_i is the probability of the event f_i occurring when the first stage experiment is performed. However, $p(f_i|e_k)$ is also a probability of f_i, which is in general different from q_i. How can we have two different probabilities for the same event? The answer lies in the interpretation of these probabilities. By definition, q_i is the probability that we assign to the outcome f_i before the experiment $\Re$ is performed or before we know what the outcome of the second stage is. On the other hand $p(f_i|e_k)$ is the probability we would assign to f_i after both stages of $\Re$ are completed and we know that the second stage yielded the event e_k. The number q_i is the long run relative frequency with which the event f_i would be observed if $\Re$ was repeated unendingly. The number $p(f_i|e_k)$ is the long run relative frequency of the event f_i for those cases where the second stage experiment yielded the event e_k. Observe that these will in general be different relative frequencies. It is convenient to use different names to refer to these two probabilities. We shall refer to q_i as the *prior or a priori probability*, since it refers to the probability of f_i prior to performing the experiment, and the conditional probability $p(f_i|e_k)$ will be referred to as *posterior or a posteriori probability*, since it refers to the probability of f_i after the second stage experiment has been performed.

We can write (6-18) in another form, which is especially useful, by noting that $q_i = p(f_i)$ and $p_{ik} = p(e_k|f_i)$. Then we have

$$p(f_i|e_k) = \frac{p(e_k|f_i)p(f_i)}{\displaystyle\sum_{u=1}^{s} p(e_k|f_u)p(f_u)}. \tag{6-19}$$

It is by use of one of the forms of Bayes' law (6-17), (6-18), or (6-19) that we can revise the prior probabilities of the events f_i and compute the posterior probabilities based on the results of the second stage experiment. It is important to note that in order to compute the posterior probabilities $p(f_i|e_k)$ we must make use of the prior probabilities $p(f_i) = q_i$. What this means in terms of the geologist's problem referred to earlier, is that before he can use the results of the seismic experiment to obtain a new estimate of the probability that the structure under consideration has oil in producible quantities, he must have made some original prior probability estimates for the various possible states of nature.   These may have been based on historical data or on personal probabilities.

6-6 EXAMPLES ILLUSTRATING BAYES' LAW

We shall now give some very simple examples illustrating Bayes' law. The subject will be treated in much more detail in Chapter 8, and therefore, these examples are only of an introductory character.

1.   An individual tosses a fair coin three times and tells us that he obtained one head in the three times.   What is the probability that he obtained a head on the first toss?   We can think of the first toss as the first stage of a two stage random experiment with the second stage representing the remaining two tosses.   The simple events for the first stage will just be H or T corresponding to whether a head or tail is obtained.   The simple events for the second stage will be taken to be the number of heads obtained on the three tosses.   Note that with this definition they do not refer to the outcome of the second stage only, but actually describe the outcome of both stages combined.   The situation can then be represented by the tree shown in Figure 6-2.   Since the coin is fair, $q_1 = q_2 = \frac{1}{2}$, that is, the prior

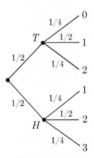

FIGURE 6-2

probability of a head or a tail in $\frac{1}{2}$ as shown in Figure 6-2.   If the coin lands heads up on the first toss, the total number of heads on the three tosses can only have the values 1, 2, or 3.   If one head is obtained, this means that two tails were obtained on tosses 2 and 3.   The probability of this is $\frac{1}{4}$.   The other probabilities for the second stage experiment are determined in the same way.   Note that the event sets are not the same for the two second stage experiments.   This does not matter at all.   We wish to compute $p(H|1)$, the conditional probability of a head on the first

toss given that one head was obtained in three tosses. Then according
to (6-19),

$$p(H|1) = \frac{p(1|H)p(H)}{p(1|H)p(H) + p(1|T)p(T)}.$$

On substituting in the numbers from Figure 6-2, we see that

$$p(H|2) = \frac{\frac{1}{4}(\frac{1}{2})}{\frac{1}{4}(\frac{1}{2}) + \frac{1}{2}(\frac{1}{2})} = \frac{1}{3}.$$

Thus, if the experiment of tossing a coin three times is repeated a very large
number of times, the fraction of the cases in which one head was obtained
which also yielded a head on the first toss, would then be close to $\frac{1}{3}$. Since
only one head is obtained in three tosses, the posterior probability of a
head on the first toss is reduced from the prior probability of $\frac{1}{2}$ to the value
of $\frac{1}{3}$.

2. A manufacturer buys ball bearings from a supplier in lots of 10,000.
Usually, the fraction defective in the lot is 0.001.   However, occasionally
something goes wrong with the supplier's production process, and the
fraction defective in the lot jumps to 0.02.   For simplicity, we shall suppose that every lot the manufacturer receives has a lot fraction defective of
0.001 or 0.02.   The supplier has indicated, and this is confirmed by the
manufacturer's records, that the probability of receiving a lot having a
fraction defective of 0.02 is 0.05.   The manufacturer attempts to check
on the quality of the supplier's lot by selecting at random a sample of 500
ball bearings from the lot and determining the number of defective bearings
in the sample.   On checking a particular lot, it is found that there are
five defective ball bearings in the sample.   What are the posterior probabilities that the lot fraction defective is 0.001 and 0.02?

We can think of the situation just described as a two stage random
experiment.   The first stage was carried out at the supplier's factory where
the lot fraction defective was determined.   The second stage involves
taking a sample of 500 ball bearings from the lot and noting the number
defective.   We wish to compute the conditional probabilities $p(0.001|5)$
and $p(0.02|5)$ that the lot fraction defective is 0.001 or 0.02, given that five
defectives were found in the sample.   By (6-19),

$$p(0.001|5) = \frac{p(5|0.001)p(0.001)}{p(5|0.001)p(0.001) + p(5|0.02)p(0.02)}.$$

Now by assumption, the prior probabilities are $p(0.001) = 0.95$ and
$p(0.02) = 0.05$.   Consider next the conditional probabilities $p(5|0.001)$
and $p(5|0.02)$.   The probability $p(5|0.001)$ is the probability that 5 defec-
tive ball bearings will be found in a sample of 500 selected from a lot of
10,000 ball bearings having a fraction defective of 0.001.   We studied
such problems in Section 5-12 and showed that this probability is the

hypergeometric probability $h(5; 500, 0.001, 10,000)$. Since the sample size is small with respect to the lot size, and r is not large with respect to the total number of defectives, and p is very small, we can approximate this probability by the Poisson probability $p(5; np)$. Since $n = 500$ and $p = 0.001$, np must be 0.5. From the table of Poisson probabilities at the end of the text, we see that $p(5; 0.5) = 0.0002$. Thus $p(5|0.001) = 0.0002$. Using the same arguments we see that $p(5|0.02)$ can be approximated by the Poisson probability $p(5; 10) = 0.0378$. Hence

$$p(0.001|5) = \frac{0.0002(0.95)}{0.0002(0.95) + 0.0378(0.05)}$$

$$= \frac{0.00019}{0.00019 + 0.00189} = \frac{0.00019}{0.00208} = 0.09.$$

Thus as a result of taking the sample, our estimate of the probability that the lot fraction defective is 0.001 changed from 0.95 to 0.09. The probability $p(0.02|5) = 0.91$, since it is merely $1 - p(0.001|5)$. Note that we could not compute $p(0.001|5)$ with great accuracy here. To do so, we would have required more accurate tables.

6-7 JOINT DISTRIBUTIONS

We noted in Chapter 1 that when studying a random experiment $\mathcal{R}$ we must frequently deal with several different random variables associated with the experiment. We noted there that if we are dealing only with a random variable x and other random variables which are functions of x, then X, the set of different values which the random variable x can take on, may be used as an event set in the probability model for $\mathcal{R}$. In this case, $p(x)$ the probability function for x becomes the function which assigns probabilities to the simple events. We would now like to generalize these ideas to cases where we are dealing with two or more random variables, but it is not necessarily true that one is a function of the other or that all but one are functions of the remaining one.

Consider some random experiment $\mathcal{R}$, and let $\mathcal{E}$ be a suitable model for $\mathcal{R}$ such that the event set for $\mathcal{E}$ is $E = \{e_1, \ldots, e_m\}$, with the probability of e_j being p_j. Suppose now that we have two random variables x and y defined over E by the functions $\xi_j = x(e_j)$ and $\zeta_j = y(e_j)$, respectively. Thus when the outcome of $\mathcal{R}$ is e_j, the value ξ_j of x and also the value ζ_j of y will be determined. Let $X = \{x_1, \ldots, x_k\}$ be the set of different values which x can take on. We shall assume as in Chapter 1 that $x_1 < x_2 < \cdots < x_k$. Similarly, let $Y = \{y_1, \ldots, y_s\}$ be the set of different values that y can take on. We shall now form the set $W = X \times Y$; W is the direct product of X and Y. The set W contains ks elements of the form $\langle x_u, y_v \rangle$, which is an ordered pair of numbers, the first from X and the second from Y. Now observe that when $\Re$ is performed, one and only one element of W will be observed. The reason for this is that W contains every possible pair of values of x and y. No two elements of W can be observed simultaneously, because only one value of x and one value of y can be observed. The elements of W thus provide a way of subdividing the outcomes of $\Re$ into a set of mutually exclusive and collectively exhaustive events, and thus W could be used as the event set for a mathematical model for $\Re$.

We can easily see how to compute the probability of the event $\langle x_u, y_v \rangle$. Let S_{uv} be the set of all simple events e_j from E such that $\xi_j = x_u$ and $\zeta_j = y_v$. Then the probability of $\langle x_u, y_v \rangle$ is the sum of the probabilities of the simple events in S_{uv}. Now it may turn out that S_{uv} is empty, i.e., there is no simple event e_j such that $\xi_j = x_u$ and $\zeta_j = y_v$. In this case we assign the probability of 0 to $\langle x_u, y_v \rangle$. Let us denote by $p(x_u, y_v)$ the probability of $\langle x_u, y_v \rangle$. We shall denote the function which associates with each element $\langle x_u, y_v \rangle \in W$ the probability $p(x_u, y_v)$ symbolically by $p(x, y)$. This is the usual notation in mathematics for a function of two variables. We shall call the function of $p(x, y)$ the *joint probability function* or *joint distribution* for the random variables x and y. The joint probability function $p(x, y)$ is a generalization of the notion of a probability function $p(x)$ for a single random variable x to two random variables.

It may now be observed that any computations which we wish to make involving only the random variables x and y can be made using W as the event set for $\Re$ and $p(x, y)$ as the function which assigns probabilities to the simple events. The reason for this is that every event involving x and y must be some subset of W, since every possible pair of values of x and y which can be observed is represented by a simple event in W. Denote by $p_1(x)$ and $p_2(y)$ the probability functions for x and y, respectively. We use subscripts 1 and 2 on the functions to differentiate between them, since if we did not do this, we would not know whether $p(2)$ is the probability that $x = 2$ or the probability that $y = 2$. When we are simultaneously considering the joint probability function $p(x, y)$ and the probability functions $p_1(x)$ and $p_2(y)$, it is helpful, in order to avoid confusion as to which probability function we are referring to, to introduce another adjective to refer to $p_1(x)$ and $p_2(y)$. We shall refer to $p_1(x)$ as the *marginal probability function* or *marginal distribution* of x and $p_2(y)$ as the marginal probability function or marginal distribution of y. The marginal distribution of x is simply the probability function for x, but we introduce the word marginal to make clear the distinction from the joint distribution of x and y.

If one knows the joint distribution $p(x, y)$ of x and y, it is straightforward to determine the marginal distributions $p_1(x)$ and $p_2(y)$. The event that $x = x_i$ is the following subset of W

$$\{\langle x_i, y_1 \rangle, \langle x_i, y_2 \rangle, \ldots, \langle x_i, y_s \rangle\}.$$

Therefore $p_1(x_i)$, the probability that $x = x_i$, is the sum of the probabilities of the simple events in the subset, i.e.,

$$p_1(x_i) = \sum_{v=1}^{s} p(x_i, y_v), \quad i = 1, \ldots, k. \tag{6-20}$$

Equation (6-20) then provides the rule for determining the marginal distribution $p_1(x)$ from the joint distribution $p(x, y)$. We simply sum over y. This can be indicated symbolically for the entire function $p_1(x)$ by writing

$$p_1(x) = \sum_{v=1}^{s} p(x, y_v), \tag{6-21}$$

and $p(x, y_v)$ can be thought of as the symbol for the function which assigns to each element $\langle x_i, y_v \rangle$ of the set $\{\langle x_1, y_v \rangle, \ldots, \langle x_k, y_v \rangle\}$ the number $p(x_i, y_v)$. Precisely similar results hold for obtaining the marginal distribution of y. Thus

$$p_2(y_j) = \sum_{u=1}^{k} p(x_u, y_j), \quad j = 1, \ldots, s, \tag{6-22}$$

and

$$p_2(y) = \sum_{u=1}^{k} p(x_u, y). \tag{6-23}$$

If we make the reasonable assumption that no $p_2(y_v) = 0$, then by definition of conditional probability we can write

$$p(x_i, y_v) = p_1(x_i|y_v)p_2(y_v), \tag{6-24}$$

since $p(x_i, y_v)$ is the probability of $x_i \cap y_v$. Thus (6-20) can be written

$$p_1(x_i) = \sum_{v=1}^{s} p_1(x_i|y_v)p_2(y_v). \tag{6-25}$$

We can write (6-25) even if for one or more values of y_v, $p_2(y_v) = 0$, since we simply omit these v from the summation. The reason we can do this is that if $p_2(y_v) = 0$, then $p(x_u, y_v) = 0$, and this term makes a zero contribution in (6-20). We can also write in place of (6-21)

$$p_1(x) = \sum_{v=1}^{s} p_1(x|y_v)p_2(y_v), \tag{6-26}$$

where $p_1(x|y_v)$ can be considered the symbolic representation of the conditional probability function for x, given that y_v has occurred. The function $p_1(x|y_v)$ would be the probability function for x in the conditional probability model $\mathcal{E}_c$, whose event set consisted of the simple events for which $y = y_v$. By precisely the same arguments as those just used, we can convert (6-22) and (6-23) to

$$p_2(y_j) = \sum_{u=1}^{k} p_2(y_j|x_u)p_1(x_u) \tag{6-27}$$

and
$$p_2(y) = \sum_{u=1}^{k} p_2(y|x_u)p_1(x_u). \qquad (6\text{-}28)$$

Note that in the above we used the same subscripts on the conditional probability functions as on the marginal functions.

Usually, but not always, our interest in the joint distribution of two random variables will be in situations where $\mathcal{R}$ can be imagined either to be composed of two independent random experiments or where $\mathcal{R}$ is a two stage random experiment. In such cases one of the random variables will refer to one of the independent experiments or to the first stage, while the other random variable will refer to the other random experiment or the second stage.

It is of interest to study the case where $\mathcal{R}$ is composed of two independent random experiments $\mathcal{R}_1$ and $\mathcal{R}_2$ for which suitable mathematical models are $\mathcal{E}_1$ and $\mathcal{E}_2$, respectively. Let the random variables be defined x with respect to the event set for $\mathcal{E}_1$ and y with respect to the event set for $\mathcal{E}_2$. Then the event that $x = x_u$ is an event of $\mathcal{E}_1$, and $y = y_v$ is an event of $\mathcal{E}_2$. These are independent events because the experiments are assumed to be independent. Thus since the probability of $x_u \cap y_v$ is $p(x_u, y_v)$, we must have by (5-19)

$$p(x_u, y_v) = p_1(x_u)p_2(y_v) \qquad (6\text{-}29)$$

for every value of u and v. In other words, the joint distribution function is equal to the product of the marginal distribution functions. We can indicate this using the symbols for the functions by writing

$$p(x, y) = p_1(x)p_2(y), \qquad (6\text{-}30)$$

and by (6-30) we mean that (6-29) holds for each u and each v. This is an interesting and important result. It says that when x and y refer to different independent random experiments, we can easily determine the joint distribution of x and y using (6-30). It then seems natural to generalize our previous definition of independent events to define what we shall call *independent random variables*. This will be done as follows.

INDEPENDENT RANDOM VARIABLES. *Let $\mathcal{R}$ be a random experiment which is being represented by the probability model $\mathcal{E}$ with the event set E. Let x and y be two random variables whose domain is E, and let $p_1(x)$ and $p_2(y)$ be the probability functions for x and y. Then x and y are said to be independent random variables if the joint probability function $p(x, y)$ for x and y is given by the product of the marginal probability functions $p_1(x)$ and $p_2(y)$, i.e., (6-30) holds.*

Note that the definition of independent random variables is such that we can verify rigorously for any two random variables whether they are independent or not. We determine $p(x, y)$, $p_1(x)$, and $p_2(y)$ and see if (6-30) holds. Note that the notion of independent random experiments does not appear in the above definition. However, from our previous discussion, we know that if $\Re$ is made up of two independent random experiments and if x refers to one of these and y to the other, then x and y will be independent random variables.

We have used the random variables x and y to define the event set W with the simple events $\langle x_u, y_v \rangle$. Suppose now that we associate with each element $\langle x_u, y_v \rangle$ of W a number θ_{uv}. This rule defines a function over W and hence defines a new random variable z which can take on the values θ_{uv}. Instead of writing $\theta_{uv} = z(\langle x_u, y_v \rangle)$, which is clumsy, we shall use the standard notation for a function of two variables and write

$$\theta_{uv} = z(x_u, y_v). \tag{6-31}$$

Now the random variable z can be looked upon as a function of the random variables x and y, and we can indicate this by writing $z = z(x, y)$. The expected value of z, μ_z, is

$$\mu_z = \theta_{11}p(x_1, y_1) + \cdots + \theta_{1s}p(x_1, y_s) + \theta_{21}p(x_2, y_1) + \cdots + \theta_{ks}p(x_k, y_s)$$

$$= z(x_1, y_1)p(x_1, y_1) + \cdots + z(x_1, y_s)p(x_1, y_s) + \cdots + z(x_k, y_s)p(x_k, y_s)$$

$$= \sum_{v=1}^{s} z(x_1, y_v)p(x_1, y_v) + \sum_{v=1}^{s} z(x_2, y_v)p(x_2, y_v)$$

$$+ \cdots + \sum_{v=1}^{s} z(x_k, y_v)p(x_k, y_v)$$

$$= \sum_{u=1}^{k} \left[\sum_{v=1}^{s} z(x_u, y_v)p(x_u, y_v) \right] = \sum_{v=1}^{s} \left[\sum_{u=1}^{k} z(x_u, y_v)p(x_u, y_v) \right]. \tag{6-32}$$

The expected value of z is computed, as always, by multiplying the value of z for each simple event by the probability of the simple event and then adding over all simple events.

In the above definition z can be anything we like. In particular, we can set $z = x$ so that $\theta_{uv} = x_u$, and the number associated with $\langle x_u, y_v \rangle$ is x_u. We would hope that the expected value of x computed according to (6-32) would be the same as that obtained using the marginal probability function for x, $p_1(x)$. Let us now see that this is true. According to (6-32) when $z = x$,

$$\mu_x = x_1p(x_1, y_1) + \cdots + x_1p(x_1, y_s) + x_2p(x_2, y_1) + \cdots + x_2p(x_2, y_s)$$

$$+ \cdots + x_kp(x_k, y_1) + \cdots + x_kp(x_k, y_s)$$

$$= x_1 \sum_{v=1}^{s} p(x_1, y_v) + x_2 \sum_{v=1}^{s} p(x_2, y_v) + \cdots + x_k \sum_{v=1}^{s} p(x_k; y_v). \tag{6-33}$$

However, by (6-25)

$$p_1(x_i) = \sum_{v=1}^{s} p(x_i, y_v), \tag{6-34}$$

so that on using (6-34) in (6-33)

$$\mu_x = x_1 p_1(x_1) + \cdots + x_k p_1(x_k) = \sum_{u=1}^{k} x_u p_1(x_u), \qquad (6\text{-}35)$$

which is what we desire.

Note also that if $z = x + y$,

$$\mu_z = \sum_{u=1}^{k} \left[\sum_{v=1}^{s} (x_u + y_v)\, p(x_u, y_v) \right]$$

$$= \sum_{u=1}^{k} \left[\sum_{v=1}^{s} x_u p(x_u, y_v) \right] + \sum_{u=1}^{k} \left[\sum_{v=1}^{s} y_v p(x_u, y_v) \right]$$

$$= \mu_x + \mu_y, \qquad (6\text{-}36)$$

so that the expected value of z is the sum of the expected values of x and y. Here we have obtained in a slightly different way a result obtained in Chapter 1.

Everything we have been discussing above for two random variables can easily be generalized to any number of random variables. For example, if we started out with three random variables x, y, and z defined over the event set E for $\Re$, and if X, Y, and Z are the sets of different values which these random variables can take on, then $W = X \times Y \times Z$ can be used as an event set for $\Re$, and the simple events of W will have the form $\langle x_u, y_v, z_w \rangle$. The probability of each such simple event can be denoted by $p(x_u, y_v, z_w)$, and the function $p(x, y, z)$ represented by all such values is called the joint distribution of the random variables x, y, and z. The random variables x, y, and z are said to be independent if

$$p(x, y, z) = p_1(x) p_2(y) p_3(z), \qquad (6\text{-}37)$$

where $p_1(x)$, $p_2(y)$, and $p_3(z)$ are the probability functions for x, y, and z, respectively, i.e., the marginal probability functions for x, y, and z.

6-8 EXAMPLES OF JOINT DISTRIBUTIONS

We shall now provide some examples of the material developed in the previous section.

1. Consider a random experiment $\Re$ and let us denote our model of $\Re$ by $\mathcal{E}$. Suppose that E, the event set for $\mathcal{E}$, contains ten simple events whose probabilities are given in Table 6-1. Let two random variables x and y be defined by the values given in Table 6-1. The set of possible values which x can take on is then $X = \{-1, 0, 2, 3\}$, and the set of possible values which y can take on is $Y = \{2, 5\}$. The set $W = X \times Y$ then contains eight elements of the form $\langle x_u, y_v \rangle$. These are listed in Table 6-2 along with their probabilities $p(x_u, y_v)$. To determine the probability of $\langle x_u, y_v \rangle$,

TABLE 6-1

DATA FOR EXAMPLE

e_j	e_1	e_2	e_3	e_4	e_5	e_6	e_7	e_8	e_9	e_{10}
$p_j = p(e_j)$	0.05	0.15	0.10	0.20	0.02	0.08	0.10	0.04	0.06	0.20
$\xi_j = x(e_j)$	−1	3	2	3	−1	0	2	0	2	−1
$\zeta_j = y(e_j)$	2	5	2	5	2	2	5	5	2	2

we find all the simple events e_j in E for which $\xi_j = x_u$ and $\zeta_j = y_v$, and we add together the probabilities of these simple events. Thus the simple events e_1, e_5, and e_{10} have $\xi_j = -1$ and $\zeta_j = 2$, so that the probability of $\langle -1, 2 \rangle$ is 0.05 plus 0.02 plus 0.20, i.e., 0.27 as shown in Table 6-2. Note

TABLE 6-2

JOINT DISTRIBUTION OF x AND y

$\langle x_u, y_v \rangle$	$\langle -1, 2 \rangle$,	$\langle -1, 5 \rangle$,	$\langle 0, 2 \rangle$,	$\langle 0, 5 \rangle$,	$\langle 2, 2 \rangle$,	$\langle 2, 5 \rangle$,	$\langle 3, 2 \rangle$,	$\langle 3, 5 \rangle$
$p(x_u, y_v)$	0.27	0	0.08	0.04	0.16	0.10	0	0.35

that there is no simple event with $\xi_j = -1$ and $\zeta_j = 5$. Hence the probability of $\langle -1, 5 \rangle$ is assigned a value of 0, since it cannot occur. The probabilities of the other elements in W are obtained in the same manner. Table 6-2 then gives us explicitly the joint distribution $p(x, y)$ of the random variables x and y.

The probability function $p_1(x)$ for x, i.e., the marginal probability function for x, can be obtained in two ways. We can go to Table 6-1 and determine $p_1(x_i)$ by adding together the probabilities of all the simple events for which $\xi_j = x_i$. Alternatively, we can go to Table 6-2 and use (6-20) to obtain $p_1(x_i)$. Let us illustrate the use of (6-20).

$$p_1(-1) = p(-1, 2) + p(-1, 5) = 0.27 + 0 = 0.27 \qquad (6\text{-}38)$$

$$p_1(0) = p(0, 2) + p(0, 5) = 0.08 + 0.04 = 0.12 \qquad (6\text{-}39)$$

$$p_1(2) = p(2, 2) + p(2, 5) = 0.16 + 0.10 = 0.26 \qquad (6\text{-}40)$$

$$p_1(3) = p(3, 2) + p(3, 5) = 0 + 0.35 = 0.35 \qquad (6\text{-}41)$$

Equations (6-38) through (6-41) give the function $p_1(x)$. The reader should go back to Table 6-1 and see that the same function is obtained. Similarly, for $p_2(y)$ we have by (6-27)

$$p_2(2) = p(-1, 2) + p(0, 2) + p(2, 2) + p(3, 2)$$
$$= 0.27 + 0.08 + 0.16 + 0 = 0.51; \qquad (6\text{-}42)$$

$$p_2(5) = p(-1, 5) + p(0, 5) + p(2, 5) + p(3, 5)$$
$$= 0 + 0.04 + 0.10 + 0.35 = 0.49. \qquad (6\text{-}43)$$

Equations (6-42) and (6-43) give $p_2(y)$.

We can now note that the random variables x and y in this example are not independent. To see this, note that $p_1(-1)p_2(5) = 0.27(0.49) = 0.132$ while $p(-1, 5) = 0$. Thus $p(-1, 5)$ is not equal to $p_1(-1)p_2(5)$, and (6-29) is not satisfied for this pair of x and y values. For two random variables to be independent, (6-29) must hold for *every* pair of values that x and y can take on.

We saw in Chapter 1 that the probability function for a random variable can be clearly represented graphically by use of a bar diagram in the plane. It is not possible to give such a useful geometric representation of the joint probability function $p(x, y)$ of two random variables x and y. One can, however, represent $p(x, y)$ using a perspective three dimensional diagram of the type shown in Figure 6-3. We represent $\langle x_u, y_v \rangle$ by a point in the

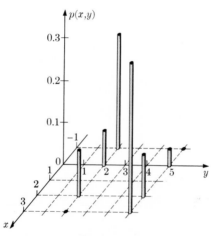

FIGURE 6-3

plane, and at this point one erects a bar whose height is $p(x_u, y_v)$. Figure 6-3 represents the joint distribution of Table 6-2. We shall never use diagrams such as that of Figure 6-3, since they are not especially helpful for most purposes.

2. Consider the random experiment $\Re$ in which a fair coin is tossed and a fair die is rolled, and we note whether the coin lands heads or tails up and the number of dots on the face of the die which turns up. Let x be a random variable which has the value 1 if the coin lands heads up and 0 if it lands tails up, and let y be a random variable representing the number of dots on the face of the die which turns up. Now $\Re$ can be thought of as made up of two independent random experiments $\Re_1$ and $\Re_2$, $\Re_1$ being that in which the coin is tossed, and $\Re_2$ that in which the die is tossed, and thus a suitable model for $\Re$ should be the direct product of the models for each of the individual experiments. The set of values which x can take on is $X = \{0, 1\}$, and the set of values y can take on is $Y = \{1, 2, 3, 4, 5, 6\}$. Now X is a suitable event set for $\mathcal{E}_1$, the model for $\mathcal{R}_1$, and Y is a suitable event set for $\mathcal{E}_2$, the model for $\mathcal{R}_2$. The events in X are equally likely and each has probability $\frac{1}{2}$, and those in Y are also equally likely and each has probability $\frac{1}{6}$. The probability function for x is one that says $p_1(0) = p_1(1) = \frac{1}{2}$. The probability function for y is $p_2(j) = \frac{1}{6}$ for every value j of y. According to the material developed in Section 5-2, $W = X \times Y$ should be a suitable event set for the model $\mathcal{E}$ of $\mathcal{R}$. The elements of W have the form $\langle x_u, y_v \rangle$. According to (5-2) we should compute the probability of $\langle x_u, y_v \rangle$ by multiplying the probability of x_u times that of y_v, i.e.,

$$p(x_u, y_v) = p_1(x_u)p_2(y_v) = \tfrac{1}{2}(\tfrac{1}{6}) = \tfrac{1}{12}. \qquad (6\text{-}44)$$

When the simple events in $\mathcal{E}_1$ and $\mathcal{E}_2$ can be looked upon as the values of random variables, then (5-2) simply reduces to a rule for computing the joint probability distribution of the two random variables from the marginal probability functions. It says that $p(x_u, y_v)$ is computed according to (6-44). But by the definition of independent random variables, $\mathcal{E}$ is constructed in such a way that the random variables x and y are independent. This is, of course, what we want since our previous discussion has shown that they should be in this case. This example has then shown the connection of the material developed in Section 5-2 with that developed in the previous section.

6-9 THE MULTINOMIAL AND MULTIPLE HYPERGEOMETRIC DISTRIBUTIONS

In Section 5-7 we studied a random experiment $\mathcal{R}$ which consisted of performing n independent trials of a random experiment $\mathcal{R}^*$. The mathematical model $\mathcal{E}^*$ used for $\mathcal{R}^*$ had an event set in which there were only two simple events e_1 and e_2, e_1 having a probability p. We proved in Section 5-7 that the random variable x giving the number of occurrences of e_1 in n trials of $\mathcal{R}^*$ had a binomial distribution. We would now like to generalize Section 5-7 to consider a random experiment $\mathcal{R}$ which consists in performing n independent trials of a random experiment $\mathcal{R}^*$, where the mathematical model $\mathcal{E}^*$ for $\mathcal{R}^*$ uses the event set $E = \{e_1, \ldots, e_m\}$ and the probability of e_j is p_j. The difference between the situation now being considered and that considered in Section 5-7 is that we are now allowing $\mathcal{R}^*$ to have more than two outcomes.

We can imagine that associated with $\mathcal{R}$ are m random variables. Since m may be large, we shall refer to these as $x\{1\}, \ldots, x\{m\}$ rather than x, y, z, and $x\{j\}$ is the number of times that e_j is observed. Each $x\{j\}$

can take on the values 0, 1, 2, ..., n. However, if when $\mathfrak{R}$ is performed $x\{1\} = r_1, \ldots, x\{m\} = r_m$, it must be true that

$$r_1 + r_2 + \cdots + r_m = n, \qquad (6\text{-}45)$$

since on a given trial of $\mathfrak{R}^*$ only one simple event e_j can be observed. Let us now ask, what is the probability that e_1 will be observed precisely r_1 times, e_2 precisely r_2 times, ..., and e_m precisely r_m times, where the r_j satisfy (6-45)? The probability of observing e_1 on the first r_1 trials of $\mathfrak{R}^*$, e_2 on trials $r_1 + 1, \ldots, r_1 + r_2$, etc., is

$$p_1^{r_1} p_2^{r_2} \cdots p_m^{r_m}. \qquad (6\text{-}46)$$

This is also the probability for any given sequence in which e_j is observed r_j times. How many different sequences are there? We answered this problem in Section 5-6 and the answer is given by (5-36). The reader should at this point review the material that led to (5-36). Thus if $p_m(r_1, \ldots, r_m)$ is the probability that e_1 will be observed r_1 times, e_2 will be observed r_2 times, etc., then

$$p_m(r_1, \ldots, r_m) = \frac{n!}{r_1! r_2! \cdots r_m!} p_1^{r_1} p_2^{r_2} \cdots p_m^{r_m}, \qquad (6\text{-}47)$$

where the r_j also satisfy (6-45). Now (6-47) is nothing but the representation of the joint distribution of the m random variables $x\{1\}, \ldots, x\{m\}$. We can represent this function symbolically by $p_m[x\{1\}, \ldots, x\{m\}]$, and this joint distribution of m random variables is called the *multinomial distribution*. It represents the generalization of the binomial distribution to situations where there can be more than two outcomes on a given trial of $\mathfrak{R}^*$.

EXAMPLE. Defects in units produced by a given production process are classified as major or minor defects. A given item coming off the production line will either be classified as good, as having a minor defect, or as having a major defect. When the process is under control, it behaves as if each item produced is the result of an independent trial of a random experiment in which the probability that the item is good is 0.60, the probability that it has a minor defect is 0.30, and the probability that it has a major defect is 0.10. Suppose now that a sample of five units is selected from recent production. If the process is in control, what is the probability that three of these will be good, one will have a minor defect, and one a major defect? If we think of $x\{1\}$ as a random variable giving the number of good units, $x\{2\}$ a random variable giving the number of minor defects, and $x\{3\}$ the number with the major defects, we then wish to determine the probability that $x\{1\} = 3$, $x\{2\} = 1$, and $x\{3\} = 1$. According to (6-47) this is

$$p_m(3, 1, 1) = \frac{5!}{3!1!1!}(0.60)^3(0.30)(0.10) = 20(0.216)(0.03) = 0.124.$$

Having obtained the generalization of the binomial distribution, let us now obtain the corresponding generalization of the hypergeometric distribution. Consider a box containing N balls, N_1 of which are painted a particular color, call it color 1, N_2 of which are of color 2, . . ., and N_m of which are color m. Thus there are balls of m different colors in the box. We now select at random n balls from the box and ask what is the probability that precisely r_1 have color 1, r_2 color 2, etc., and r_m color m, where $\sum_{j=1}^{m} r_j = n$. To construct a model of this random experiment $\Re$, we can imagine that we number the balls from 1 to N. Then there are C_n^N combinations of numbers which could be drawn on selecting n balls. We feel that all these are equally likely events. Let us then use as an event set E, one which gives the numbers, without regard to order, on the balls drawn. Each of these simple events has probability $1/C_n^N$. Now N_1 of the balls have color 1, and there are $C_{r_1}^{N_1}$ different sets of r_1 numbered balls which can be selected from the N_1 balls of color 1. For any given set of numbers for color 1, there are $C_{r_2}^{N_2}$ sets of r_2 numbered balls which can be selected from the N_2 balls of color 2. Thus we see that the number of simple events in E which correspond to the event of interest is

$$\binom{N_1}{r_1}\binom{N_2}{r_2}\cdots\binom{N_m}{r_m},$$

and $p_h(r_1, r_2, \ldots, r_m)$, the probability that r_1 of the balls have color 1, r_2 color 2, etc., is

$$p_h(r_1, r_2, \ldots, r_m) = \frac{\binom{N_1}{r_1}\binom{N_2}{r_2}\cdots\binom{N_m}{r_m}}{\binom{N}{n}}. \qquad (6\text{-}48)$$

We can imagine that associated with $\Re$ there are m random variables $x\{1\}, \ldots, x\{m\}$ such that $x\{j\}$ is the number of balls of color j drawn. Then the probability that $x\{j\} = r_j, j = 1, \ldots, m$ is given by (6-48), and thus (6-48) can be looked upon as the joint probability function for these random variables. We shall call this joint probability function the *multiple hypergeometric distribution*, and we can represent it symbolically as $p_h[x\{1\}, \ldots, x\{m\}]$.

EXAMPLE. A lot of 100 vacuum tubes contains three with a defective heating element, five with a defective grid, and two in which both the heating element and grid are defective. The remainder are good. Five tubes are selected at random from the lot. What is the probability that one has a defective heating element, one a bad grid, and one has both a bad grid and a defective heating element, the other two being good? This probability is

$$p_h(1, 1, 1, 2) = \frac{\binom{3}{1}\binom{5}{1}\binom{2}{1}\binom{90}{2}}{\binom{100}{5}}$$

$$= \frac{3(5)(2)(90)(89)(5)(4)(3)(2)}{2(100)(99)(98)(97)(96)} = 0.00161.$$

The reader should try to obtain the same result using the conditional probability approach.

6-10 LINEAR COMBINATIONS OF RANDOM VARIABLES

Let x and y be two random variables associated with some random experiment $\Re$, and let $p(x, y)$ be the joint probability function for these random variables. Suppose that we now form a new random variable z by writing $z = ax + by$. We shall refer to z as a *linear combination* of x and y. If x can take on the values x_u, $u = 1, \ldots, k$, and y the values y_v, $v = 1, \ldots, s$, then the expected value of z is

$$\mu_z = \sum_{u=1}^{k}\left[\sum_{v=1}^{s}(ax_u + by_v)p(x_u, y_v)\right] = a\sum_{u=1}^{k}\left[\sum_{v=1}^{s}x_u p(x_u, y_v)\right]$$

$$+ b\sum_{u=1}^{k}\left[\sum_{v=1}^{s}y_v p(x_u, y_v)\right] = a\mu_x + b\mu_y, \qquad (6\text{-}49)$$

which is the same as the result obtained in Chapter 1.

Next let us determine the variance of z. The variance of z is the expected value of $(z - \mu_z)^2$. However,

$$(z - \mu_z)^2 = (ax + by - a\mu_x - b\mu_y)^2 = [a(x - \mu_x) + b(y - \mu_y)]^2$$
$$= a^2(x - \mu_x)^2 + b^2(y - \mu_y)^2 + 2ab(x - \mu_x)(y - \mu_y). \qquad (6\text{-}50)$$

Hence, σ_z^2 the variance of z is given by

$$\sigma_z^2 = a^2\sum_{u=1}^{k}\left[\sum_{v=1}^{s}(x_u - \mu_x)^2 p(x_u, y_v)\right] + b^2\sum_{u=1}^{k}\left[\sum_{v=1}^{s}(y_v - \mu_y)^2 p(x_u, y_v)\right]$$

$$+ 2ab\sum_{u=1}^{k}\left[\sum_{v=1}^{s}(x_u - \mu_x)(y_v - \mu_y)p(x_u, y_v)\right],$$

or

$$\sigma_z^2 = a^2\sigma_x^2 + b^2\sigma_y^2 + 2ab\sigma_{xy}, \qquad (6\text{-}51)$$

where σ_x^2 and σ_y^2 are the variances of x and y, respectively, and σ_{xy} is a new quantity which we have not studied before. The number σ_{xy} is the expected value of the random variable $(x - \mu_x)(y - \mu_y)$ and is called the *covariance of x and y* and is given by

$$\sigma_{xy} = \sum_{u=1}^{k} \left[\sum_{v=1}^{s} (x_u - \mu_x)(y_v - \mu_y)p(x_u, y_v) \right]. \quad (6\text{-}52)$$

In a rough way, σ_{xy} is an indication of the tendency of x and y to vary together, i.e., if x tends to be large when y is large and small when y is small, then σ_{xy} will be a relatively large number. If x can take on both large and small values for any given value of y, say y_v, then $x - \mu_x$ will be positive in some cases where y_v occurs and negative in others, and the various terms in the sum (6-52) will tend to cancel, giving a value of σ_{xy} close to zero.

Let us see what can be said about σ_{xy} in the case where x and y are independent random variables. In this case x and y have no tendency to vary together, and from what we have just said above σ_{xy} should have a value close to zero. *We shall prove that when x and y are independent random variables* $\sigma_{xy} = 0$, so that σ_{xy} is always exactly 0 in this case. To prove this, we recall that when x and y are independent, $p(x, y) = p_1(x)p_2(y)$, where $p_1(x)$ and $p_2(y)$ are the marginal probability functions for x and y. Then when we write out (6-52) in detail, it becomes in this case

$$\begin{aligned}\sigma_{xy} =\ & (x_1 - \mu_x)(y_1 - \mu_y)p_1(x_1)p_2(y_1) + (x_2 - \mu_x)(y_1 - \mu_y)p_1(x_2)p_2(y_1) \\ & + \cdots + (x_k - \mu_x)(y_1 - \mu_y)p_1(x_k)p_2(y_1) \\ & + (x_1 - \mu_x)(y_2 - \mu_y)p_1(x_1)p_2(y_2) \\ & + \cdots + (x_k - \mu_x)(y_2 - \mu_y)p_1(x_k)p_2(y_2) \\ & + \cdots + (x_k - \mu_x)(y_s - \mu_y)p_1(x_k)p_2(y_s), \quad (6\text{-}53)\end{aligned}$$

or

$$\sigma_{xy} = (y_1 - \mu_y)p_2(y_1) \sum_{u=1}^{k} (x_u - \mu_x)p_1(x_u)$$

$$+ \cdots + (y_s - \mu_y)p_2(y_s) \sum_{u=1}^{k} (x_u - \mu_x)p_1(x_u). \quad (6\text{-}54)$$

However, $\sum_{u=1}^{k} (x_u - \mu_x)p_1(x_u)$ is the expected value of $x - \mu_x$, and we proved in Chapter 1 that the expected value of this random variable is 0. Thus each term in (6-54) is 0, and hence $\sigma_{xy} = 0$, which is what we wished to prove. We have proved that when x and y are independent then $\sigma_{xy} = 0$. However, it is not necessarily true that x and y are independent when $\sigma_{xy} = 0$. It is possible that $\sigma_{xy} = 0$ even if x and y are not independent.

When x and y are independent and $\sigma_{xy} = 0$, we see from (6-51) that σ_z^2 can be computed from the variance of x and y. It is

$$\sigma_z^2 = a^2\sigma_x^2 + b^2\sigma_y^2, \quad x \text{ and } y \text{ independent.} \quad (6\text{-}55)$$

In particular, if $z = x + y$, so that z is the sum of x and y, and if x and y are independent random variables, then

$$\sigma_z{}^2 = \sigma_x{}^2 + \sigma_y{}^2, \quad x \text{ and } y \text{ independent,} \qquad (6\text{-}56)$$

and of course, in this case $\mu_z = \mu_x + \mu_y$. This latter relation, however, does not require that x and y be independent.

We have shown above how to determine the mean and variance of $z = ax + by$. To determine the probability function for z, we first compute the value of z, and call it θ_{uv}, for each $\langle x_u, y_v \rangle$ pair. We determine from the θ_{uv}, the set $Z = \{z_1, \ldots, z_t\}$ of possible values that z can take on. To compute $p(z_i)$, we find all $\langle x_u, y_v \rangle$ for which $\theta_{uv} = z_i$. Then $p(z_i)$ is the sum of the $p(x_u, y_v)$ for which $\theta_{uv} = z_i$.

We can easily generalize the discussion of the above paragraphs to the case where we have a linear combination of any finite number of random variables. Let $x\{1\}, \ldots, x\{w\}$ be the random variables associated with some random experiment $\mathfrak{R}$, and let us form the new random variable

$$z = a_1 x\{1\} + a_2 x\{2\} + \cdots + a_w x\{w\}. \qquad (6\text{-}57)$$

Again z will be called a linear combination of the random variables $x\{1\}$, $\ldots, x\{w\}$. From Chapter 1 we know that the expected value of z is

$$\mu_z = a_1 \mu_1 + a_2 \mu_2 + \cdots + a_w \mu_w, \qquad (6\text{-}58)$$

where μ_i is the expected value of $x\{i\}$. Let us next determine the variance of z. The variance of z is the expected value of $(z - \mu_z)^2$. However, from (6-57) and (6-58)

$$(z - \mu_z)^2 = \left[\sum_{i=1}^{w} a_i(x\{i\} - \mu_i) \right]^2$$

$$\begin{aligned}
= \; & a_1{}^2(x\{1\} - \mu_1)^2 + \cdots \\
& + a_w{}^2(x\{w\} - \mu_w)^2 + 2a_1 a_2(x\{1\} - \mu_1)(x\{2\} - \mu_2) + \cdots \\
& + 2a_1 a_w(x\{1\} - \mu_1)(x\{w\} - \mu_w) \\
& + 2a_2 a_3(x\{2\} - \mu_2)(x\{3\} - \mu_3) + \cdots \\
& + 2a_2 a_w(x\{2\} - \mu_2)(x\{w\} - \mu_w) + \cdots \\
& + 2a_{w-1} a_w(x\{w-1\} - \mu_{w-1})(x\{w\} - \mu_w). \qquad (6\text{-}59)
\end{aligned}$$

Thus, the random variable $(z - \mu_z)^2$ is a linear combination of random variables of the form $(x\{i\} - \mu_i)^2$ and $(x\{i\} - \mu_i)(x\{k\} - \mu_k)$. Consequently applying (6-58), the expected value of $(z - \mu_z)^2$, i.e., $\sigma_z{}^2$ is $a_1{}^2$ times the expected value of $(x\{1\} - \mu_1)^2$ plus, $\ldots$, plus $a_1 a_2$ times the expected value of $(x\{1\} - \mu_1)(x\{2\} - \mu_2)$ plus etc. However, the expected value of $(x\{i\} - \mu_i)$ is $\sigma_i{}^2$, the variance of $x\{i\}$. Similarly, the expected value of $(x\{i\} - \mu_i)(x\{k\} - \mu_k)$ is σ_{ik}, the covariance of $x\{i\}$ and $x\{k\}$. Consequently, the variance of z is

$$\sigma_z{}^2 = a_1{}^2 \sigma_1{}^2 + \cdots + a_w{}^2 \sigma_w{}^2 + 2a_1 a_2 \sigma_{12} + \cdots$$
$$+ 2a_1 a_w \sigma_{1w} + \cdots + 2a_{w-1} a_w \sigma_{w-1,w}. \qquad (6\text{-}60)$$

Suppose now that the $x\{i\}$ are independent random variables, so that the joint distribution for all of them is the product of the marginal distributions for each of them. In this case, the joint distribution of $x\{u\}$ and $x\{v\}$ is the product of the marginal distributions for $x\{u\}$ and $x\{v\}$. Hence, from what we have proved above, $\sigma_{uv} = 0$ for each such u and v. Thus when the random variables are independent, (6-60) reduces to

$$\sigma_z{}^2 = \sum_{i=1}^{w} a_i{}^2 \sigma_i{}^2. \tag{6-61}$$

Therefore, if z is the sum of w independent random variables, so that $z = \sum_{i=1}^{w} x\{i\}$, then the variance of z is the sum of the variances of the $x\{i\}$, i.e.,

$$\sigma_z{}^2 = \sigma_1{}^2 + \cdots + \sigma_w{}^2. \tag{6-62}$$

This is a very useful result.

In general, it is not a simple matter to determine the probability function for z, when z is a linear combination of a number of random variables $x\{i\}$, from the joint distribution of the $x\{i\}$, since one must find all possible combinations of the $x\{i\}$ values which yield a given value of z and then sum the probabilities for all these combinations. There are certain cases where this can be done easily, however, and we shall illustrate two of these in the next section.

6-11 EXAMPLES

Let us now provide several examples illustrating various aspects of the theory developed in the previous section.

1. Consider the random experiment and the random variables x and y described in Table 6-1. Let us define a new random variable z by $z = 3x - 5y$. Then from Table 6-1,

$$z(e_1) = -13, z(e_2) = -16, z(e_3) = -4, z(e_4) = -16, z(e_5) = -13,$$
$$z(e_6) = -10, z(e_7) = -19, z(e_8) = -25, z(e_9) = -4, z(e_{10}) = -13,$$

If we write $\theta_j = z(e_j)$, then μ_z the expected value of z is

$$
\begin{aligned}
\mu_z = \sum_{j=1}^{10} \theta_j p_j = &-13(0.05) - 16(0.15) - 4(0.10) - 16(0.20) - 13(0.02) \\
&- 10(0.08) - 19(0.10) - 25(0.04) - 4(0.06) - 13(0.20) \\
= &-[0.65 + 2.40 + 0.40 + 3.20 + 0.26 + 0.80 + 1.90 \\
&\qquad\qquad\qquad + 1.00 + 0.24 + 2.60] = -13.45.
\end{aligned}
$$

The reader can quickly determine from Table 6-1 that $\mu_x = 1.30$ and $\mu_y = 3.47$. But

$$3\mu_x - 5\mu_y = -13.45 = \mu_z,$$

and thus (6-49) is verified in this special case.

Next, σ_z^2, the variance of z is given by

$$\sigma_z^2 = \sum_{j=1}^{10} \theta_j^2 p_j - \mu_z^2 = 169(0.05) + 256(0.15) + 16(0.10) + 256(0.20)$$
$$+ 169(0.02) + 100(0.08) + 361(0.10) + 625(0.04) + 16(0.06)$$
$$+ 169(0.20) - 180.9025 = 25.9875.$$

Let us now evaluate σ_x^2 from (6-51) and see that the same result is obtained. From Table 6-1 and the values of μ_x and μ_y given above, we see that

$$\sigma_x^2 = 1(0.05) + 9(0.15) + 4(0.10) + 9(0.20) + 1(0.02) + 4(0.10)$$
$$+ 4(0.06) + 1(0.20) - 1.69 = 2.77;$$

$$\sigma_y^2 = 4(0.05) + 25(0.15) + 4(0.10) + 25(0.20) + 4(0.02) + 4(0.08)$$
$$+ 25(0.10) + 25(0.04) + 4(0.06) + 4(0.20) - 12.0409 = 2.2491.$$

It is somewhat clumsy to compute σ_{xy} from the definition (6-52). However, one can easily convert (6-52) to a form which is much easier to handle computationally, just as one did for the variance. Observe that the random variable $(x - \mu_x)(y - \mu_y)$ can be written

$$(x - \mu_x)(y - \mu_y) = xy - \mu_y x - \mu_x y + \mu_x \mu_y. \tag{6-63}$$

Then, by (1-61) the expected value of $(x - \mu_x)(y - \mu_y)$ is the expected value of xy minus μ_y times the expected value of x minus μ_x times the expected value of y plus $\mu_x \mu_y$. Thus if we denote the expected value of xy by μ_{xy}, we have

$$\sigma_{xy} = \mu_{xy} - \mu_y \mu_x - \mu_x \mu_y + \mu_x \mu_y = \mu_{xy} - \mu_x \mu_y, \tag{6-64}$$

since the expected value of x is μ_x and the expected value of y is μ_y. In other words,

$$\sigma_{xy} = \sum_{u=1}^{k} \left[\sum_{v=1}^{s} x_u y_v p(x_u, y_v) \right] - \mu_x \mu_y, \tag{6-65}$$

or if $\xi_j = x(e_j)$, $\zeta_j = y(e_j)$ and $p_j = p(e_j)$, where $E = \{e_1, \ldots, e_m\}$ is the event set being used for $\Re$, we have

$$\sigma_{xy} = \sum_{j=1}^{m} \xi_j \zeta_j p_j - \mu_x \mu_y. \tag{6-66}$$

Applying this last formula, we have from Table 6-1

$$\sigma_{xy} = -2(0.05) + 15(0.15) + 4(0.10) + 15(0.20) - 2(0.02) + 10(0.10)$$
$$+ 4(0.06) - 2(0.20) - 4.511 = 1.839.$$

Finally, according to (6-51)

$$\sigma_z^2 = 9\sigma_x^2 + 25\sigma_y^2 - 30\sigma_{xy} = 9(2.77) + 25(2.2491) - 30(1.839)$$
$$= 24.93 + 56.2275 - 55.17 = 25.9875,$$

which is precisely the same result obtained by computing σ_z^2 directly. This verifies (6-51) in this particular case.

2. Consider a random experiment $\mathcal{R}$ which consists in performing n independent trials of a random experiment $\mathcal{R}^*$, $\mathcal{R}^*$ having only two outcomes e_1 and e_2, with the probability of e_1 being p. In Section 5-7 we showed that the random variable x representing the number of occurrences of e_1 had the binomial distribution $b(x; n, p)$. Let us now introduce n random variables $y\{j\}$, where $y\{j\}$ is the number of occurrences of e_1 on the jth trial, i.e., $y\{j\} = 1$ if e_1 occurs and $y\{j\} = 0$ if e_1 does not occur. These are the only possible values that each $y\{j\}$ can take on. The probability that $y\{j\} = 1$ is p, and the probability that $y\{j\} = 0$ is q. Thus μ_j, the expected value of $y\{j\}$, is

$$\mu_j = 1p + 0q = p, \tag{6-67}$$

and σ_j^2, the variance of $y\{j\}$, is

$$\sigma_j^2 = 1p + 0q - p^2 = p - p^2 = p(1 - p) = pq. \tag{6-68}$$

We can now note that the random variable x giving the number of occurrences of e_1 on n trials is the sum of the $y\{j\}$, i.e.,

$$x = y\{1\} + \cdots + y\{n\}. \tag{6-69}$$

Note that since the trials are independent and different $y\{j\}$ refer to different trials, the $y\{j\}$ are independent random variables. Hence μ, the expected value of x, is the sum of the μ_j, i.e.,

$$\mu = \mu_1 + \cdots + \mu_n = p + \cdots + p = np, \tag{6-70}$$

and σ^2, the variance of x, is the sum of the σ_j^2, i.e.,

$$\sigma^2 = \sigma_1^2 + \cdots + \sigma_n^2 = pq + \cdots + pq = npq. \tag{6-71}$$

Here we have derived the mean and variance of the binomial distribution in a much simpler way than by the method used in Section 5-7.

The experiment $\mathcal{R}$ in which we perform n independent trials of $\mathcal{R}^*$ can be looked upon as built up from two independent experiments $\mathcal{R}_1$ and $\mathcal{R}_2$, where in $\mathcal{R}_1$ we perform n_1 independent trials of $\mathcal{R}^*$ and in $\mathcal{R}_2$ we perform n_2 independent trials of $\mathcal{R}^*$, $n_1 + n_2 = n$. Let $x\{1\}$ be the number of occurrences of e_1 in $\mathcal{R}_1$, and $x\{2\}$ the number of occurrences of e_1 in $\mathcal{R}_2$. Thus $x\{1\}$ is a random variable with the binomial distribution $b(x\{1\}; n_1, p)$ and $x\{2\}$ is a random variable with the binomial distribution $b(x\{2\}; n_2, p)$. The mean and variance of $x\{1\}$ are $\mu_1 = n_1 p$ and $\sigma_1^2 = n_1 pq$, and the mean and variance of $x\{2\}$ are $\mu_2 = n_2 p$ and $\sigma_2^2 = n_2 pq$. Now x, the random variable giving the number of occurrences of e_1 in $\mathcal{R}$, is $x = x\{1\} + x\{2\}$, and $x\{1\}$ and $x\{2\}$ refer to different independent random experiments and are independent random variables. Thus it should be true that μ and σ^2, the mean and variance of x, are

$$\mu = \mu_1 + \mu_2 = n_1 p + n_2 p = (n_1 + n_2)p, \tag{6-72}$$

and

$$\sigma^2 = \sigma_1^2 + \sigma_2^2 = n_1 pq + n_2 pq = (n_1 + n_2)pq, \tag{6-73}$$

which is indeed correct when one uses $n = n_1 + n_2$. Note that our above discussion has shown the following. If $x\{1\}$ and $x\{2\}$ are independent random variables having the distributions $b(x\{1\}; n_1, p)$ and $b(x\{2\}; n_2, p)$, then $x = x\{1\} + x\{2\}$ has the binomial distribution $b(x; n_1 + n_2, p)$.

3. Suppose that x and y are independent random variables associated with some experiment $\mathfrak{R}$, and that the probability function for x is the Poisson distribution $p(x; \beta_1)$, while the probability function for y is the Poisson distribution $p(y; \beta_2)$. We shall now determine the probability function for the random variable $z = x + y$.

Since x and y are independent, the joint probability function for x and y is

$$p(x, y) = p(x; \beta_1)p(y; \beta_2),$$

so the probability $p(i, j)$ that $x = i$ and $y = j$ is

$$p(i, j) = \left(\frac{\beta_1{}^i}{i!}\right)\left(\frac{\beta_2{}^j}{j!}\right) e^{-\beta_1} e^{-\beta_2} = \left(\frac{\beta_1{}^i}{i!}\right)\left(\frac{\beta_2{}^j}{j!}\right) e^{-(\beta_1 + \beta_2)}. \tag{6-74}$$

Note that the set of values z can take on is the set of all non-negative integers, since z can be 0 when $x = y = 0$, z can be 1 when $x = 1$, and $y = 0$, etc. Next let us determine all pairs $\langle i, j \rangle$ for which $z = r$. Then $r = i + j$ or $j = r - i$. For any i, $i = 0, 1, 2, \ldots, r$, there is a j for which $r = i + j$. There are thus $r + 1$ pairs $\langle i, j \rangle$ for which $z = r$. They are $\langle 0, r \rangle, \langle 1, r - 1 \rangle, \ldots, \langle r, 0 \rangle$. If $p(r)$ is the probability that $z = r$, then

$$p(r) = p(0, r) + p(1, r - 1) + \cdots + p(r, 0) = \sum_{i=0}^{r} p(i, r - i), \tag{6-75}$$

or on using (6-74),

$$p(r) = e^{-(\beta_1 + \beta_2)} \sum_{i=0}^{r} \frac{1}{i!(r - i)!} \beta_1{}^i \beta_2{}^{r-i}. \tag{6-76}$$

However, by the binomial theorem (5-40),

$$(\beta_1 + \beta_2)^r = \sum_{i=0}^{r} \frac{r!}{i!(r - i)!} \beta_1{}^i \beta_2{}^{r-i}, \tag{6-77}$$

so

$$\sum_{i=0}^{r} \frac{1}{i!(r - i)!} \beta_1{}^i \beta_2{}^{r-i} = \frac{(\beta_1 + \beta_2)^r}{r!}, \tag{6-78}$$

and

$$p(r) = \frac{(\beta_1 + \beta_2)^r}{r!} e^{-(\beta_1 + \beta_2)} = p(r; \beta_1 + \beta_2). \tag{6-79}$$

Thus we have proved the interesting result that if x and y are independent random variables having Poisson distributions with means β_1 and β_2, respectively, $z = x + y$ has a Poisson distribution with mean $\beta_1 + \beta_2$. The reader should note that the variance of z is the sum of the variance of x and the variance of y.

We can easily generalize the result just obtained. Suppose that we have w independent random variables $x\{1\}, \ldots, x\{w\}$ such that $x\{j\}$ has a Poisson distribution with mean β_j. Then if we form the new random variable, $x = \sum_{j=1}^{w} x\{j\}$, it follows that x has a Poisson distribution with mean $\sum_{j=1}^{w} \beta_j$. The proof of this follows easily from what we have just shown above, since first of all $y\{2\} = x\{2\} + x\{1\}$ has a Poisson distribution with mean $\beta_1 + \beta_2$. Now $x\{3\}$ and $y\{2\}$ are independent random variables as we ask the reader to demonstrate in the problems. Hence $y\{3\} = x\{3\} + y\{2\}$ has a Poisson distribution with mean $\beta_1 + \beta_2 + \beta_3$. Continuing this process, we conclude that x has a Poisson distribution with mean $\sum_{j=1}^{w} \beta_j$.

4.　Consider some project which will take place over a period of w years. Let $x\{j\}$ be the net return for year j. This will be the revenues received in year j less all costs incurred in year j. We shall imagine that the $x\{j\}$ are random variables. The discounted profit from the project is then a random variable z which is a linear combination of the $x\{j\}$, i.e.,

$$z = a_1 x\{1\} + \cdots + a_w x\{w\}, \quad a_j = \frac{1}{(1 + i)^j} \tag{6-80}$$

The expected value of z is then given by (6-58) and the variance of z by (6-60). If the $x\{j\}$ are independent random variables, then the variance of z is given by (6-62). When the $x\{j\}$ are independent, the variance of x can be expressed in terms of the variances of the $x\{j\}$. If the $x\{j\}$ are not independent, then the covariances must be known to obtain the variance of z. This example shows that linear combinations of random variables can arise in very natural ways, and that the material in the previous section can be useful in analyzing such situations.

REFERENCES

The references dealing with probability theory given in Chapters 1 and 5 are also appropriate here. Some others are

1. Goldberg, S., *Probability: An Introduction*. Prentice-Hall, Englewood Cliffs, N. J., 1960.

2. Mosteller, F., *Fifty Challenging Problems in Probability with Solutions*. Addison-Wesley, Reading, Mass., 1965.

3. Uspensky, J. V., *Introduction to Mathematical Probability.* McGraw-Hill, New York, 1937.

4. Wadsworth, G. A., and J. G. Bryan, *Introduction to Probability and Random Variables.* McGraw-Hill, New York, 1960.

PROBLEMS

Section 6-1

1. A fair die is tossed and we are told that a face with an even number of dots turns up. Develop a conditional probability model which could be used for making any additional computations concerning this random experiment. What is the probability that the face with two dots on it turned up?

2. An urn contains eight red and six blue balls. Four of the red balls and three of the blue balls have a gold dot painted on them. A ball is selected at random. We are not told its color, but we are told that it has a gold dot on it. Set up a conditional probability model which could be used for making additional computations concerning this random experiment. What is the probability that the ball drawn was red?

3. Reconsider Problem 2, under the assumption that two balls are drawn at random and we are told that both have a gold dot on them. What is the probability that both are red? What is the probability that one is red and one is blue?

4. A lot of vacuum tubes contains 1000 tubes 10 of which have a defective grid and no other defects, and 20 of which have both a defective grid and a defective heating element. A tube is drawn at random from the lot and we are told that it has a defective grid. What is the probability that it also has a defective heating element? What model did you use in computing this probability?

5. If the data given in Example 2 on p. 285 apply, what is the probability that an individual who has lived to age 40 will die after the age of 60? What is this probability at the time of the individual's birth?

6. Consider a random experiment $\mathcal{R}$ for which we are using the mathematical model $\mathcal{E}$ having the event set $E = \{e_1, \ldots, e_{10}\}$, with $p(e_1) = 0.05$, $p(e_2) = 0.10$, $p(e_3) = 0.20$, $p(e_4) = 0.07$, $p(e_5) = 0.03$, $p(e_6) = 0.15$, $p(e_7) = 0.12$, $p(e_8) = 0.08$, $p(e_9) = 0.14$, $p(e_{10}) = 0.06$. Imagine that $\mathcal{R}$ is performed, and we are told that the event $A = \{e_1, e_6, e_8, e_{10}\}$ has occurred. Construct a conditional probability model that would be appropriate for making additional computations about $\mathcal{R}$.

Section 6-2

1. If $p(A) = 0$, why is it not meaningful to introduce conditional probabilities $p(B|A)$? In other words, show that there is no definition of $p(B|A)$ in terms of probabilities in $\mathcal{E}$ for this case that would seem appropriate. Hint: If $p(A) = 0$, can we construct a conditional probability model $\mathcal{E}_c$ from $\mathcal{E}$, or if A occurs when $p(A) = 0$ in $\mathcal{E}$, does this mean that $\mathcal{E}$ is completely irrelevant and we must start over to obtain a model $\mathcal{E}_c$?

2. Consider the situation outlined in Problem 6 for Section 6-1. Compute $p(B|A)$ when $B = \{e_6, e_8, e_9\}$.

3. Consider the situation outlined in Problem 6 for Section 6-1. Let $B = \{e_6, e_8, e_9\}$. Construct a conditional probability model for the case where B is known to have occurred. Compute $p(A|B)$ using this model, and from the results of Problem 6 compute $p(B|A)$. Thus verify that (6-8) holds.

4. Re-solve Problem 3 computing $p(A|B)$ and $p(B|A)$ using $\mathcal{E}$ and the definition (6-3) rather than applying the conditional probability model $\mathcal{E}_c$.

5. Consider the random experiment $\mathfrak{R}$ in which three independent trials of the experiment $\mathfrak{R}^*$ are performed, $\mathfrak{R}^*$ having only two possible outcomes e_1 and e_2 with the probability of e_1 being p. Take as the model for $\mathfrak{R}$, the model $\mathcal{E} = \mathcal{E}^* \times \mathcal{E}^* \times \mathcal{E}^*$, where $\mathcal{E}^*$ is the model for $\mathfrak{R}^*$. Let A be the event that on trials 1 and 2 the event e_1 was observed. From the definition (6-3) compute the conditional probability that e_1 will be observed on the third trial given A and show that this probability is p, so that the outcome on the third trial is independent of A.

6. Let $\mathfrak{R}$ be a random experiment which consists in performing two independent random experiments $\mathfrak{R}_1$ and $\mathfrak{R}_2$ and let the probability model for $\mathfrak{R}$ be $\mathcal{E} = \mathcal{E}_1 \times \mathcal{E}_2$, where $\mathcal{E}_1$ and $\mathcal{E}_2$ are the models for $\mathfrak{R}_1$ and $\mathfrak{R}_2$, respectively. Let A be an event of $\mathcal{E}_1$ and B an event of $\mathcal{E}_2$. Prove that $p(B|A) = p(B)$ using the definition (6-3).

7. Consider the random experiment $\mathfrak{R}$. Suppose that as $\mathfrak{R}$ progresses it is observed that the event A has occurred. We can then modify the model $\mathcal{E}$ for $\mathfrak{R}$ to obtain probability model $\mathcal{E}_c$. Now imagine that as $\mathfrak{R}$ continues the event B is also observed. Then $\mathcal{E}_c$ can be modified to give a new conditional probability model $\mathcal{E}_c'$, appropriate to the event $A \cap B$ having been observed. Alternatively, one can obtain $\mathcal{E}_c'$ directly from $\mathcal{E}$. Go through both of these processes to find an expression for $p(C|A \cap B)$ and show that

$$p(A \cap B \cap C) = p(C|A \cap B)p(B|A)p(A).$$

Also show that

$$p(A \cap B \cap C) = p(B \cap C|A)p(A),$$

so that

$$p(B \cap C|A) = p(C|A \cap B)p(B|A).$$

Interpret this last result intuitively.

8. From the definition (6-3) of conditional probability, prove the following when the quantities involved are defined:

$$p(A \cap B \cap C) = p(A \cap C|B)p(B) = p(A|B \cap C)p(C|B)p(B)$$
$$p(A \cap B \cap C) = p(B \cap C|A)p(A) = p(C|A \cap B)p(A|B)p(B)$$
$$p(A|B \cap C)p(C|B) = p(C|A \cap B)p(A|B).$$

Interpret the last of these results intuitively.

9. If A and B are mutually exclusive events for some random experiment and $p(A \cup B) \neq 0$, then show that

$$p(A|A \cup B) = \frac{p(A)}{p(A) + p(B)}.$$

Sections 6-3 and 6-4

1. An urn contains five balls numbered 1 through 5. Consider the random experiment $\Re$ in which one ball is selected at random from the urn and then a second one is selected. Construct a model for $\Re$ treating $\Re$ as a two stage experiment, i.e., by first constructing a model $\mathcal{E}_1$ and then models $\mathcal{E}_{i2}$. What is the probability that the balls numbered 2 and 3 will be drawn?

2. Two boxes are placed on a table. In the first box are four red and three green balls. In the second box are two red and six green balls. Consider the random experiment $\Re$ in which first a box is selected at random and then one of the balls in the box is selected at random. Construct a mathematical model for $\Re$. What is the probability that a red ball is drawn?

3. A desk contains three drawers. In the first are one gold and one silver coin. In the second are one gold and two silver coins and in the third are two gold and one silver coin. Consider the random experiment $\Re$ in which one first selects a drawer at random and then selects at random one of the coins in the drawer. Construct a mathematical model for $\Re$. What is the probability that the coin selected is gold?

4. An urn contains six red and three blue balls. Someone draws out at random one of the balls but does not tell us what color it was. We now select at random one of the remaining eight balls. What is the probability that it is red? How do you explain the result obtained?

5. In a box are fifty light bulbs, ten of which are defective. One bulb is selected at random from the box and then a second one is. What is the probability that the first bulb selected is defective and that the second one selected is not?

6. Show that (6-14) is a special case of the general result

$$p(A_1 \cap A_2 \cap \cdots \cap A_n) = p(A_n|A_1 \cap \cdots \cap A_{n-1})p(A_{n-1}|A_1 \cap \cdots \cap A_{n-2})$$
$$\cdots p(A_2|A_1)p(A_1).$$

Prove this general result.

7. An urn contains five red and four green balls. Two balls are selected at random. Use conditional probabilities to determine the probability that one of the balls selected is red and the other is green.

8. An urn contains six red, four green, and three yellow balls. Three balls are selected at random from the urn. What is the probability that one is red, one green, and one yellow?

9. A jeweler receives a lot of fifty watches, five of which have a defective gear, three of which have a defective mainspring, and one of which has both a defective gear and a bad mainspring. The jeweler selects three watches at random to sell to a customer. What is the probability that at least one watch is defective?

10. For the situation described in Problem 9, what is the probability that one watch will have a defective mainspring (and no other defect) and that the other two watches will be good?

11. For the situation described in Problem 9, what is the probability that one watch will have a defective mainspring while the other two will not have a defective mainspring?

12. For the situation described in Problem 9, what is the probability that one watch will have a defective mainspring, and another watch (perhaps the same one) a defective gear, so that there are two defects in the watches selected?

13. A production run of a seldom used very expensive spare part is normally for only five units of the part. If the setup is made correctly, the probability that any given unit produced will be defective is 0.05, but if it is not, the probability that any given unit will be defective is 0.15. Setups are made correctly 90 per cent of the time. In either case, the process behaves as if each unit produced is the result of an independent trial of a random experiment. What is your estimate of the probability that no defectives will be produced on any given production run?

14. Seven cards having printed on them the letters A, G, H, J, M, N, O, one letter per card, are shuffled thoroughly and then the first four cards are turned face up and placed side by side in the order in which they were drawn. What is the probability that they will spell out the name JOHN?

15. Seven cards, four of which have the number 3 painted on them and three of which have the number 2 painted on them are shuffled thoroughly, and then the first four cards are turned face up and placed side by side in the order in which they were drawn. What is the probability that the resulting number will be 3232? What is the probability that the resulting number will be 3332?

16. An individual wishes to call a friend from a public phone booth. The friend has an unlisted number. The individual can remember all but the last digit of his friend's number, but unfortunately cannot recall the final digit. He has two dimes in his pocket. He decides to select the last digit at random, and if it is wrong he will select another digit at random from the unused digits. What is the probability that he will dial the correct number before running out of dimes?

17. Re-solve Problem 16 under the assumption that the individual has three dimes.

18. Consider a two stage experiment of the type described in the text. Let x be a random variable associated with this experiment, and suppose that if the simple event $\langle f_i, e_j \rangle$ occurs the value ξ_{ij} of x is observed. Show that

$$\mu_x = \sum_{j=1}^{s} \sum_{j=1}^{m} \xi_{ij} q_i p_{ij} = \sum_{i=1}^{s} \bar{\xi}_i q_i,$$

where

$$\bar{\xi}_i = \sum_{j=1}^{m} \xi_{ij} p_{ij}.$$

Show that $\bar{\xi}_i$ is the expected value of x given that the outcome of the first stage is f_i. This result is frequently useful. Generalize this result to three and n-stage lotteries in such a way that associated with every stage there is an expected value of x for the remaining stages given the outcomes of the earlier stages. Show the connection between the expected values at two successive stages.

19. An urn contains n red balls and n green balls, or $2n$ balls in total. Each of n individuals selects at random two balls from the urn. The balls drawn out are not replaced, so that when the nth individual makes the selection only two balls remain. What is the probability that each individual selected one red and one green ball?

20. For the situation discussed in Problem 19, what is the probability that each individual selected two balls of the same color?

21. An antiaircraft gun crew is about to fire at a target aircraft. The probability of hitting the aircraft on the first shot is 0.25. If the aircraft is not hit on the first shot, the gun can be reloaded and fired again. The probability of a hit on the second shot is 0.15 (the probability is lower since the aircraft is now in a more unfavorable position). If the second shot is also a miss, the gun can be reloaded once again and a third shot fired. The probability of a hit on the third shot is 0.07. There is no possibility of firing a fourth shot because the plane will be out of range. What is the probability that the target will be hit?

Sections 6-5 and 6-6

1. Solve Problem 2 for Section 6-1 using Bayes' law. Describe the two stage experiment in which Bayes' law is being applied.

2. Solve Problem 3 for Section 6-1 using Bayes' law.

3. Solve Problem 4 for Section 6-1 using Bayes' law. Describe the two stage experiment in which Bayes' law is being applied.

4. Two urns stand on a table. The first contains five red and three green balls and the second contains two red and six green balls. One of the urns is selected at random and then a ball is selected at random from that urn. Suppose that we are not told what urn was selected, but are told that a red ball was drawn. What is the probability that the first urn was selected? Solve this problem using Bayes' law.

5. Re-solve Problem 4 by constructing a model for the random experiment and next determining a conditional probability model, and then finally the desired probability.

6. A manufacturer receives lots containing 10,000 Phillips head screws from a supplier who is usually very reliable. Occasionally, however, the supplier's production process gets out of control and a bad lot is shipped out before the out of control condition is caught. Normally, the fraction defective in a lot is about 0.01 while if the process gets out of control it will be about 0.10. On the average, approximately one lot in 100 comes from an out of control process. A sample of 100 screws is taken from a particular lot, and it is found that three are defective. What is the posterior probability that the lot fraction defective is 0.01?

7. Consider the geologist who is concerned with the question of whether or not a particular structure contains oil in producible quantities. He assigns a prior probability of 0.20 that it does. A seismic experiment is now performed. Imagine, for simplicity (although this is far from realistic), that there are only two outcomes of the seismic experiment. One is that it says there is oil, and the other is that it says that there is no oil. The seismic experiment does not always give the correct indication of what the true situation is, however. If there is oil in producible quantities, the probability that the seismic experiment will say that there is oil is 0.7 and if there is no oil the probability that it will say there is is 0.3. A seismic experiment is performed and it says that there is oil. What is the posterior probability that there is oil present in producible quantities? Draw a tree to indicate the nature of the two stage random experiment which is being hypothesized here.

8. A fair coin is tossed four times, and three heads are obtained. What is the probability that a head was obtained on each of the first two tosses?

9. A fair coin is tossed five times and three heads are obtained. What is the probability that a head and a tail were obtained on the first two tosses (in either order)?

10. A fair die is rolled twice, and the sum of the number of points obtained on the two tosses is ten. What is the probability that the face with five dots on it turned up on the first toss? Draw a tree indicating the nature of the two stage experiment involved here.

11. A production process which turns out transistors has a long run fraction defective of 0.005. A testing device is used to check each transistor produced. It has been found that the device always indicates that a defective is indeed defective, but for about 1 in every 100 good transistors it indicates that a good transistor is defective. If the device indicates that a given resistor is defective, what is the probability that it is actually defective? Describe carefully the model you are using.

12. A slip of paper is given to George who either marks it with a plus or a minus sign. The probability that George writes a plus is $\frac{1}{4}$. The slip is then passed from George to Harry, to Chris, and finally to Maury. Each individual may either leave the sign unchanged or change it. Assume that Harry, Chris and Maury each have a probability $\frac{3}{4}$ of changing the sign. If the final sign is a plus, what is the probability that George originally wrote a plus sign? This is often referred to as the problem of four liars because it can be formulated as follows. Suppose that George makes a statement and then Maury says that Chris says that Harry says that George was telling the truth. What is the probability that George was actually telling the truth? Problems of this sort are of practical interest in data transmission systems where errors can be introduced at various stages in the transmission process.

Sections 6-7 and 6-8

1. Consider the random experiment $\mathcal{R}$ for which we are using the model described in Table 6-3. Let x and y be two random variables also described in Table 6-3. Determine the probability functions $p_1(x)$ and $p_2(y)$ directly from Table 6-3. Also determine the joint probability function $p(x, y)$. Next determine $p_1(x)$ from $p(x, y)$ using (6-20) and verify that the same function is obtained as above. In a similar way evaluate $p_2(y)$.

2. For the situation described in Problem 1, compute μ_x and μ_y directly from

TABLE 6-3

DATA FOR PROBLEM

e_j	e_1	e_2	e_3	e_4	e_5	e_6	e_7	e_8	e_9
$p_j = p(e_j)$	0.07	0.08	0.20	0.10	0.15	0.05	0.10	0.13	0.12
$\xi_j = x(e_j)$	-3	0	6	2	0	6	-3	2	0
$\zeta_j = y(e_j)$	5	1	1	5	0	1	5	0	1

Table 6-3. Also compute μ_x from (6-33) and show that the same number is obtained. Do the same for μ_y.

3. From Table 6-3 determine the set $W = X \times Y$ referred to in the text. Is the event e_1 a subset of W? Is e_2 a subset of W?

4. Given the joint distribution $p(x, y)$ for two random variables x and y, show how to compute the variance of x. Illustrate by computing the variance of x defined in Table 6-3.

5. Determine a three dimensional bar diagram such as that shown in Figure 6-3 for the joint distribution of the random variables x and y defined in Table 6-3.

6. For the situation described by Table 6-3 determine the conditional probability function $p(x|5)$, i.e., the conditional probability function for x given that $y = 5$.

7. Use (6-25) and the results of Problems 1 and 6 to determine $p_1(x)$.

8. Are the random variables of Table 6-3 independent? Prove whatever statement you make.

9. Consider the random variable $z = xy$. Compute μ_z using the joint probability function $p(x, y)$ determined in Problem 1.

10. Consider the random variable $z = x^2 + y^2$. Compute μ_z using the joint probability function $p(x, y)$ determined in Problem 1.

11. Consider the random experiment $\Re$ for which we are using the model described in Table 6-4. Let x and y be two random variables also described in Table 6-4.

TABLE 6-4

DATA FOR PROBLEM

e_j	e_1	e_2	e_3	e_4	e_5	e_6	e_7	e_8	e_9
$p_j = p(e_j)$	0.10	0.05	0.15	0.05	0.10	0.15	0.20	0.15	0.05
$\xi_j = x(e_j)$	2	0	-2	0	2	-2	5	5	0
$\zeta_j = y(e_j)$	-1	2	-1	-1	2	2	-1	2	-1

Determine the probability functions $p_1(x)$ and $p_2(y)$ directly from Table 6-4. Also determine the joint probability function $p(x, y)$. Next determine $p_1(x)$ from $p(x, y)$ using (6-20), and verify that the same function is obtained as above.

12. For the situation described in Problem 11, compute μ_x and μ_y directly from Table 6-3. Also compute μ_x from (6-33) and show that the same number is obtained.

13. From Table 6-3 determine the set $W = X \times Y$ referred to in the text. Is the event e_1 a subset of W? Is the event e_4 a subset of W?

14. Use the joint distribution $p(x, y)$ to compute the variance of the random variable x described in Table 6-4.

15. Determine a three dimensional bar diagram such as that shown in Figure 6-3 for the joint distribution of the random variables x and y defined in Table 6-4.

16. For the situation described by Table 6-4 determine the conditional probability function $p(x|-1)$, i.e., the conditional probability function for x given that $y = -1$.

17. Are the random variables of Table 6-4 independent? Prove whatever statement you make.

18. Consider the random variable $z = 1/y$, y being defined in Table 6-4. Compute μ_z using the joint probability function $p(x, y)$ determined in Problem 11.

19. A fair coin is tossed three times. Let x be the number of heads obtained on the first two tosses and y the number of heads obtained on the three tosses. Determine the joint probability function $p(x, y)$. Are x and y independent random variables? Prove whatever statement you make. What is the intuitive reason for your answer?

20. A fair coin is tossed four times. Let x be the number of heads obtained on the first two tosses and y the number of heads obtained on the last two tosses. Determine the joint probability function $p(x, y)$. Are x and y independent random variables? Prove whatever statement you make. What is the intuitive reason for your answer?

21. An urn contains three balls numbered 1, 2, and 3. Two balls are selected at random and are drawn out one after the other. Let x be the number on the first ball and y the number on the second ball. Determine the joint probability function $p(x, y)$. Are x and y independent random variables? Prove whatever statement you make.

Section 6-9

1. A fair die is tossed three times. What is the probability that in the three tosses, a face with one dot on it, a face with three dots, and a face with six dots on it turn up (the order in which these are obtained being irrelevant)?

2. A fair die has one of its faces painted red, another blue, another green, another yellow, another black, and the remaining one white. The die is tossed four times. What is the probability that the red face turns up once, the green face twice, and the white face once?

3. A lot of ten watches which was damaged in shipment contains two with broken crystals, three with a broken mainspring and one with a defective bearing. The remainder are good. Three watches are selected at random from the lot. What is the probability that one has a broken crystal, one a broken mainspring, and the other is not defective?

4. Out of ten cars coming off an assembly line, two have a defective rear axle, one has a defective transmission, and one has both a defective transmission and a defective axle. The others are not defective. Four cars out of these ten are selected at random and sent to a dealer. What is the probability that one has a defective axle (and no other defect), one has a defective transmission (and no other defect), and the other two are not defective?

5. For the situation outlined in Problem 4, what is the probability that one of the cars will have a defective axle and one (perhaps the same one) a defective transmission (there is a total of two defects in the three cars sent to the dealer)?

6. For the situation described in Problem 4, what is the probability that the car with a defective axle and a defective transmission is sent to the dealer?

7. For the situation described in Problem 4, what is the probability that two cars will have a defective axle (the condition of the other car being unspecified)?

8. For the situation described in Problem 4, what is the probability that at least two cars will have a defective axle?

Sections 6-10 and 6-11

1. Let x and y be the random variables defined by Table 6-3. Consider the random variable $z = 2x + 6y$. Determine μ_z and σ_z^2 by determining directly from Table 6-3 the probability function for z. Next compute these quantities using (6-49) and (6-51). What is σ_{xy} in this case?

2. Let x and y be the random variables defined by Table 6-4. Consider the random variable $z = 5x - y$. Determine μ_z and σ_z^2 by determining directly from Table 6-4 the probability function for z. Next compute these quantities using (6-49) and (6-51). What is σ_{xy} in this case?

3. Compute σ_{xy} for the random variables x and y introduced in Problem 19 for Sections 6-7 and 6-8.

4. Compute σ_{xy} for the random variables x and y introduced in Problem 20 for Sections 6-7 and 6-8.

5. Compute σ_{xy} for the random variables x and y introduced in Problem 21 for Sections 6-7 and 6-8.

6. If x and y are two random variables, prove that

$$a^2\sigma_x^2 + 2a\sigma_{xy} + \sigma_y^2 \geq 0$$

for every real number a.

7. Prove that for random variables x and y,

$$\sigma_{xy}^2 \leq \sigma_x^2\sigma_y^2.$$

Hint: From the result of Problem 6, the quadratic equation

$$y = a^2\sigma_x^2 + 2a\sigma_{xy} + \sigma_y^2$$

in the variable a cannot have two different real roots. Alternatively, set $a = -\sigma_{xy}/\sigma_x^2$ in the expression of Problem 6.

8.   From the results of Problem 7 show that

$$-\sigma_x\sigma_y \leq \sigma_{xy} \leq \sigma_x\sigma_y,$$

and hence

$$-1 \leq \sigma_{xy}/\sigma_x\sigma_y \leq 1, \quad \sigma_x \neq 0, \sigma_y \neq 0.$$

The number $\rho = \sigma_{xy}/\sigma_x\sigma_y$ is called the *correlation coefficient or dimensionless covariance for x and y*.   Note that if x and y are independent, then $\rho = 0$.   Whenever $\rho = 0$, the variables x and y are said to be uncorrelated.   Explain the intuitive meaning of a value of ρ close to 1 and a value of ρ close to -1.   What is ρ when $y = x$ and $y = -x$?

9.   Construct an example where $\sigma_{xy} = 0$, but x and y are not independent random variables.

10.   Let x, y, and z be three independent random variables.   Prove that any two of these, say x and y, are then independent.

11.   Let $x\{1\}$, $x\{2\}$, and $x\{3\}$ be independent random variables, and let $y = x\{1\} + x\{2\}$.   Prove that y and $x\{3\}$ are independent random variables.   Show that the result holds true if y is any function of $x\{1\}$ and $x\{2\}$.

12.   Suppose that a fair die is tossed twice.   Let x be the random variable giving the sum of the number of points on the faces turned up.   Determine the probability function for x.   Also determine the mean and variance of x by two different methods.

13.   Let x have the binomial distribution $b(x; n, p)$, so that x can be imagined to be the number of occurrences of e_1 on n independent trials of a random experiment $\mathfrak{R}^*$ in which the probability of e_1 is p.   Imagine that one more trial of $\mathfrak{R}^*$ is performed and let $y = 1$ if e_1 occurs and $y = 0$ otherwise.   Consider the random variable $z = y + x$.   Prove that z has the distribution $b(z; n + 1, p)$.

14.   Note that when z is a sum of n independent random variables $x\{j\}$, it is the variances which add, not the standard deviations.   Suppose that each $x\{j\}$ has the same variance σ^2.   Show that $\sigma_z = \sigma\sqrt{n}$, so that the standard deviation of z is less than n times σ.

15.   We suggested in Chapter 1 that we might try to determine approximately the expected value of some random variable x by repeating the experiment involved a number of times and then determining the arithmetic average of the values of x observed.   Consider then some random variable x associated with an experiment $\mathfrak{R}^*$.   Let $\mathfrak{R}$ be the random experiment in which n independent trials of $\mathfrak{R}^*$ are performed.   Let $x\{j\}$ be the random variable representing x on the jth trial of $\mathfrak{R}^*$.   Then $x\{1\}, \ldots, x\{n\}$ are independent random variables each of which has the same expected value μ and variance σ^2.   Why is this true?   Now let us form the new random variable

$$\bar{x} = \frac{1}{n}\sum_{j=1}^{n} x\{j\}.$$

Prove that $\mu_{\bar{x}} = \mu$ and $\sigma_{\bar{x}}^2 = \sigma^2/n$.   Interpret intuitively these results.   Note that the variance of $\bar{x}$ is less than x, but is proportional to the variance of x, and that it decreases with increasing n.   Explain these facts intuitively.   Since $\sigma_{\bar{x}}^2$

gets closer and closer to 0 as n increases, this means that the average fluctuation of the observed values of $\bar{x}$ about μ become less and less, and hence on the average our estimate of μ should become better and better with increasing values of n.

16. Let x be a random variable which can take on the values $0, 1, 2, \ldots, n$ or all non-negative integral values. We can include cases where x can only take on the values $r, r + 1, \ldots$, simply by imagining that x can take on all non-negative values but $p(0) = 0, \ldots, p(r - 1) = 0$. Denote the probability function of x by $p(x)$. Consider now the function of a new variable θ (θ is not a random variable)

$$\Upsilon(\theta) = p(0) + p(1)\theta + \cdots + p(n)\theta^n,$$

or

$$\Upsilon(\theta) = p(0) + p(1)\theta + p(2)\theta^2 + \cdots$$

depending on whether x takes on the values $0, 1, \ldots, n$ or all non-negative values. In the first case $\Upsilon(\theta)$ is a polynomial. In the second $\Upsilon(\theta)$ is the sum of an infinite series. The function $\Upsilon(\theta)$ is called the *generating function* or sometimes the *z-transform* for $p(x)$. Generating functions are useful in studying sums of independent random variables. Show that if x has the binomial distribution $b(x; n, p)$, then $\Upsilon(\theta) = (p\theta + q)^n$. Similarly, show that if x has a Poisson distribution $p(x; \beta)$, then $\Upsilon(\theta) = e^{\beta(\theta-1)}$. Finally, show that if x has the negative binomial distribution $b_N(x; r, p)$, then $\Upsilon(\theta) = p^r/(1 - \theta q)^r$ (see Problem 8 of Section 5-11 for a definition of the negative binomial distribution). The reader familiar with calculus will note that since the Taylor's expansion of a function about the origin is unique, a knowledge of $\Upsilon(\theta)$ is as good as a knowledge of $p(x)$, because $p(x)$ can be found from the Taylor's expansion of $\Upsilon(\theta)$. The reader should also explain the relation between $p(j)$ and the jth derivative of $\Upsilon(\theta)$. Finally, the reader familiar with calculus should explain why μ_x is the first derivative of $\Upsilon(\theta)$ evaluated at $\theta = 1$. He should similarly explain how $\sigma_x{}^2$ may be determined from $\Upsilon(\theta)$.

17. Let x and y be two independent random variables each of which can take on all non-negative integral values. We can include in this random variables which take on only the values $0, 1, \ldots, n$ by simply imagining that all non-negative integral values can be taken on except $p(n + 1) = 0$, $p(n + 2) = 0$, etc. Denote the generating functions for x and y by $\Upsilon_x(\theta)$ and $\Upsilon_y(\theta)$, respectively, where the notion of a generating function is that introduced in Problem 16. Thus

$$\Upsilon_x(\theta) = \sum_{j=0}^{\infty} p_1(j)\theta^j; \quad \Upsilon_y(\theta) = \sum_{j=0}^{\infty} p_2(j)\theta^j,$$

where $p_1(x)$ and $p_2(y)$ are the probability functions for x and y. Consider now

$$\Upsilon_x(\theta)\Upsilon_y(\theta) = \left(\sum_{j=0}^{\infty} p_1(j)\theta^j\right)\left(\sum_{j=0}^{\infty} p_2(j)\theta^j\right)$$

$$= \sum_{j=0}^{\infty} p_1(j)\theta^j[p_2(0) + p_2(1)\theta + \cdots].$$

Thus show that $\Upsilon_x(\theta)\Upsilon_y(\theta) = \sum_{r=0}^{\infty} p(r)\theta^r$, and by collecting in the above all terms which involve θ^r, show that

$$p(r) = \sum_{j=0}^{r} p_1(j)p_2(r-j).$$

Next show that $p(z)$ is the probability function for the random variable $z = x + y$, so that $\Upsilon_x(\theta)\Upsilon_y(\theta)$ is the generating function for z, i.e.,

$$\Upsilon_{x+y}(\theta) = \Upsilon_x(\theta)\Upsilon_y(\theta),$$

when x and y are independent random variables. Frequently the probability function for $x + y$ is called the *convolution* of the probability functions for x and y. Generalize the above to show that the generating function for the sum of n independent random variables is the product of the n generating functions for the individual random variables. Use the result just obtained to provide a proof that if x and y are independent random variables having Poisson distributions $p(x; \beta_1)$ and $p(y; \beta_2)$, then $z = x + y$ has the Poisson distribution $p(z; \beta_1 + \beta_2)$.

18. We have shown in Section 5-11 that the random variable y representing the number of independent trials of a random experiment $\Re^*$ needed to obtain precisely r occurrences of the event e_1 has a Pascal distribution. Now we can imagine that $y = \sum_{i=1}^{r} x\{i\}$, where $x\{i\}$ is the number of trials after the occurrence of e_1 for the $(i-1)$st time that are needed before e_1 occurs again. Are the variables $x\{i\}$ independent? Why? What is the probability function for $x\{i\}$? Compute the generating function defined in Problem 16 for each $x\{i\}$, and use the results of Problem 17 to determine the generating function for y. Is it the generating function for the Pascal distribution?

19. For the situation described in Problem 18, compute the mean and variance of each $x\{i\}$ and hence the mean and variance of y.

20. Conclude from Problem 18 that the random experiment $\Re$ referred to there can be looked upon as the performance of r independent trials of an experiment $\Re^+$, where $\Re^+$ is the experiment in which we make a sufficient number of independent trials of $\Re^*$ to obtain e_1 precisely once.

21. Let x and y be independent random variables, and let $z = xy$. Show that $\mu_z = \mu_x\mu_y$. What can be said about $\sigma_z{}^2$?

22. Show that

$$\sum_{u=1}^{k}\left[\sum_{v=1}^{s} a_{uv}\right] = \sum_{v=1}^{s}\left[\sum_{u=1}^{k} a_{uv}\right]$$

so that the order of summation can be interchanged. Use this result to write (6-52) in a different form.

23. A real estate developer plans to bid on n different parcels of land at a given auction. Assume that if he bids a sum x_j on parcel j, there is a probability $p_j(x_j)$ that he will win the bid. If he wins the bid he pays x_j for the parcel, and if he loses the bid he pays nothing. Let y be the total sum that the developer will have to pay as a result of the n bids. Note that y is a random variable. Write y as a linear combination of n random variables, and determine μ_y and $\sigma_y{}^2$ under the assumption that what is bid on one parcel has no influence whatever on the outcome of the other bids.

CHAPTER 7

CONTINUOUS RANDOM VARIABLES

Little drops of water, little grains of sand,
Make the mighty ocean, and the pleasant land.
So the little minutes, humble though they be,
Make the mighty ages of eternity.

Julia Carney, *Little Things*

7-1 THE NORMAL APPROXIMATION

The binomial distribution is frequently encountered in practice. We noted in Chapter 5, however, that it is difficult to evaluate numerically binomial probabilities, and it is also difficult to tabulate the binomial distribution in a compact form convenient for general use. We developed in Chapter 5 the Poisson approximation to the binomial which is applicable when p is small and n is moderately large. At present, we have no way of approximating the binomial distribution for p values in the range 0.1 to 0.5. We now wish to introduce another approximation to the binomial distribution which is especially good for p values close to 0.5, even for small values of n, but which can be used for any value of p if n is sufficiently large. The new approximating function to be introduced is called the *normal density function*, and when using this function to approximate the binomial distribution, we say that we are using the normal approximation. It turns out that the normal density function is useful not only in approximating the binomial distribution, but it is also employed to approximate the Poisson, hypergeometric, and Pascal distributions. It is a remarkable fact that a very large percentage of the frequently occurring probability functions can be approximated by the normal density function, and for this reason alone, the normal density function would be very important in probability theory. However, it also turns out as we shall see below that the normal density function is of great importance in its own right, not merely as an approximation to other probability functions. All things considered then, the normal density function turns out to be one of the most important, if not the most important function in probability and statistics. For the moment we shall only concern ourselves with a study of the way in which this function can be usefully employed to approximate the binomial distribution and some of the other probability functions which we have studied.

The process by which $b(r; n,p)$ (or $p(r; \beta)$ or $h(r; n,p,N)$ or $b_P(n; r,p)$) is approximated by the normal density function requires the introduction of some new ideas, which we shall now proceed to study. The *standardized normal density function*, which will be denoted symbolically by $\varphi(t)$, is the function

$$\varphi(t) = \frac{1}{\sqrt{2\pi}} e^{-t^2/2}, \tag{7-1}$$

where e is the same number introduced in Section 5-9. Its value is approximately 2.718. The number pi, π, is the number encountered in geometry. Its value is approximately 3.14159. For every real number t one can compute a positive value of $\varphi(t)$. The domain for $\varphi(t)$ thus consists of all real numbers. The graph of $\varphi(t)$ is shown in Figure 7-1. If one examines Figures 5-1 through 5-3, which illustrate some histograms for the binomial distribution, there appears to be no similarity whatever between them and Figure 7-1. Let us then proceed to see what the connection is.

First let us consider the bar diagram for $b(x; 10, 0.5)$ shown in Figure 7-2. Suppose that we introduce rectangles as illustrated. There is a rectangle associated with each of the eleven possible values of x, and the height of the rectangle corresponding to $x = r$ is $b(r; 10, 0.5)$. The base of this rectangle extends from $r - 0.5$ to $r + 0.5$, and hence the base has length 1. Let us now remove the bars and retain the rectangles to obtain Figure 7-3. In Figure 7-3 the probability that x takes on a particular value, say $x = 4$, is the altitude of the rectangle centered about 4. However, the probability that $x = 4$ is also the area of this rectangle, i.e., the area of the shaded rectangle in Figure 7-3, since the area is numerically equal to the altitude, inasmuch as the length of the base is 1. If we wanted the probability of the event $2 \leq x \leq 5$, we could add up the altitudes of the rectangles corresponding to $x = 2$, $x = 3$, $x = 4$, and $x = 5$, or we could add up the areas of these four rectangles. The area of these four rectangles is simply the shaded area shown in Figure 7-4. Now it often turns out to be convenient to represent a probability function graphically, using a diagram in which probabilities are measured by areas rather than a bar diagram where the probability that $x = r$ is the height of a bar, and the probabilities of compound events such as $r_1 \leq x \leq r_2$ are found by adding together the heights of the appropriate bars. Diagrams in which prob-

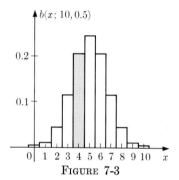

FIGURE 7-1

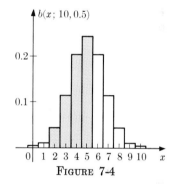

FIGURE 7-2

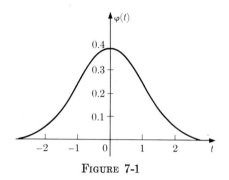

FIGURE 7-3

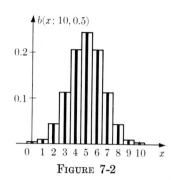

FIGURE 7-4

abilities are represented by areas are called *histograms*. At the moment, the reader may feel that the change from a bar diagram to a histogram is a trivial one since the heights of the rectangles in the histogram are simply the probabilities. This is not true in general, however. It was true in the example that we started out with only because the base of the rectangle had length 1. The reason that the base of each rectangle had length 1 was that x took on integral values only. Let us next study a case where heights of the rectangles in a histogram are not probabilities.

Consider any random variable x with expected value μ_x and variance σ_x^2. Consider now the new random variable t, where

$$t = \frac{x - \mu_x}{\sigma_x} = \frac{1}{\sigma_x} x - \frac{\mu_x}{\sigma_x}. \tag{7-2}$$

By (1-64), μ_t, the expected value of t, is

$$\mu_t = \frac{1}{\sigma_x} \mu_x - \frac{\mu_x}{\sigma_x} = 0. \tag{7-3}$$

The variance of t is the expected value of t^2 since $t - \mu_t = t$. However,

$$t^2 = \frac{1}{\sigma_x^2} (x - \mu_x)^2,$$

and hence the expected value of t^2 is $1/\sigma_x^2$ times the expected value of $(x - \mu_x)^2$. However, the expected value of $(x - \mu_x)^2$ is σ_x^2. Therefore $\sigma_t^2 = \sigma_x^2/\sigma_x^2 = 1$, i.e.,

$$\sigma_t^2 = 1. \tag{7-4}$$

We have thus proved that if we have any random variable x and define a new random variable t by (7-2), then t has a mean of 0 and a variance of 1.

Let us now return to the random variable x with the binomial distribution $b(x; 10, 0.5)$. The random variable t for this case is then

$$t = \frac{x - np}{\sqrt{npq}} = \frac{x - 5}{1.5625} = 0.641\, x - 3.21. \tag{7-5}$$

Since x can take on the values 0, 1, $\ldots$, 10, t can take on the eleven values

$$-3.21, -3.21 + 0.641 = -2.57, \ldots, 2.57, 3.21.$$

Note that there are just as many different values of t as there are values of x. Thus if we think of the x values as representing simple events, there will be a different t value associated with every simple event and the probability that $t = t_i$ is the probability of that value of x which, when substituted into (7-5), yields t_i. Since $x = 0$ yields $t = -3.21$, the probability that $t = -3.21$ is the probability that $x = 0$. If x has the binomial distribution $b(x; n,p)$, and if t is related to x by (7-2), then we say that t has a *standardized binomial distribution*, and the probability function for t will be denoted by $b_s(t; n,p)$. The value of i of x which yields t_i is, on solving (7-2) for x, with $x = i$,

$$i = \sigma_x t_i + \mu_x, \tag{7-6}$$

so that $b_s(t_i; n,p)$ can be computed from $b(x; n,p)$ using

$$b_s(t_i; n,p) = b(\sigma_x t_i + \mu_x; n,p). \tag{7-7}$$

In Figure 7-5 we have shown the bar diagram for the probability function $b_s(t; 10, 0.5)$ for the random variable t when x has the binomial distribution $b(x; 10, 0.5)$. Let us now return to the idea introduced in Figure 7-2 of inscribing rectangles about the bars. The spacing between successive values of t is 0.641 rather than 1 as in Figure 7-2, and the base of the rectangle for t_i will extend from $t_i - 0.3205$ to $t_i + 0.3205$ (0.3205 being $0.641/2$) and will have length 0.641. Note that in this case the area of the rectangle corresponding to t_i so obtained does not have area $b_s(t_i; 10, 0.5)$, but instead has area $0.641\, b_s(t_i; 10, 0.5)$. Consequently, if we want to construct a histogram for t where probabilities are represented by areas, we must have the heights of the rectangles be not $b_s(t_i; 10, 0.5)$, but instead

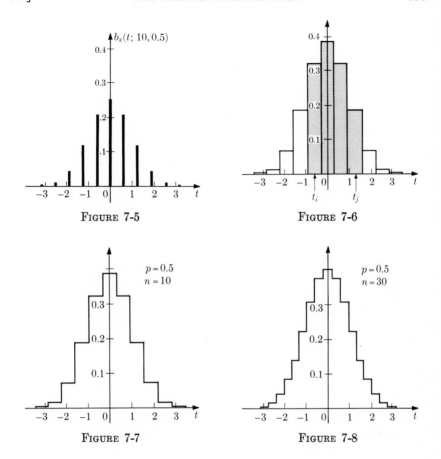

FIGURE 7-5

FIGURE 7-6

FIGURE 7-7

FIGURE 7-8

this value divided by 0.641, that is, $b_s(t_i; 10, 0.5)/0.641$. Now $0.641 = 1/\sigma_x$, so that in general the probabilities of t_i must be multiplied by σ_x to obtain a histogram for t. This diagram is shown in Figure 7-6. In Figure 7-6 the height of the rectangle associated with t_i is $\sigma_x b_s(t_i; 10, 0.5)$; and the area of this rectangle is $b_s(t_i; 10, 0.5)$. The probability that $t_i \leq t \leq t_j$ is the sum of the areas of the rectangles for $t_i, t_{i+1}, \ldots, t_j$. Equally well, it is the area of the shaded region which extends from $t_i - 0.3205$ to $t_j + 0.3205$, as shown in Figure 7-6. Given the histogram for t, we can easily make computations involving the original random variable x since if we wish the probability that $i \leq x \leq j$, we compute

$$t_i = \frac{i - \mu_x}{\sigma_x}; \quad t_j = \frac{j - \mu_x}{\sigma_x} \tag{7-8}$$

and determine the area lying between $t_i - 0.3205$ and $t_j + 0.3205$. However, $0.3205 = 1/2\sigma_x$. Therefore, if

$$\hat{t}_i = \frac{i - \frac{1}{2} - \mu_x}{\sigma_x}; \quad \hat{t}_j = \frac{j + \frac{1}{2} - \mu_x}{\sigma_x}, \tag{9-7}$$

then the probability that $i \leq x \leq j$ is the area of the histogram for t lying in the interval $\hat{t}_i \leq t \leq \hat{t}_j$.

In general then, we have shown that if x has the binomial distribution $b(x; n,p)$, and if we introduce the new random variable t which has a standardized binomial distribution, we can construct a histogram for t such that the rectangle to be associated with t_i has an altitude of $\sigma_x b_s(t_i; n,p)$ and whose base has length σ_x^{-1} and extends from $t_i - (2\sigma_x)^{-1}$ to $t_i + (2\sigma_x)^{-1}$. The area of this rectangle is $b_s(t_i; n,p)$, that is, is the probability of t_i. It is also the probability of x_i, where x_i is the value of x which yields t_i. Furthermore, to compute the probability that $i \leq x \leq j$, we compute the numbers $\hat{t}_i$ and $\hat{t}_j$ given by (7-9) and determine the area of the histogram for t lying between t_i and t_j. Precisely this same procedure applies for any random variable x which takes on only integral values. It is not necessary that it have a binomial distribution. Thus the same procedure could be used for a random variable x with a Poisson or Pascal or hypergeometric distribution, for example.

We are at last ready to introduce the normal approximation to the binomial distribution. Let x have the binomial distribution $b(x; n,p)$ and consider the histogram for the random variable t which has the standardized binomial distribution $b_s(t; n,p)$. We would now like to investigate the behavior of this histogram as n gets larger and larger, p remaining fixed at a given value. In Figure 7-7 we have shown the outline of the histogram for $n = 10$ and $p = 0.5$, which is obtained from Figure 7-6, and in Figure 7-8 the outline of the histogram for $n = 30$ and $p = 0.5$. As n increases, the spacing $1/\sigma_x$ between successive t values decreases since $\sigma_x = \sqrt{npq}$ increases. Interestingly, the height of the histogram at any particular t value, which is $\sigma_x b_s(t; n,p)$, becomes more and more nearly constant as n increases. This is clearly indicated in Figures 7-7 and 7-8. Furthermore, the outline of the histogram gets closer and closer to a smooth curve, since the steps become smaller and smaller. *In fact, as n gets larger and larger, the outlines of the histograms come closer and closer to being the smooth curve which is the graph of $\varphi(t)$, the standardized normal density function.* This happens to be true regardless of the value of p. However, for p close to 0.5 the outlines of the histograms approach $\varphi(t)$ much more quickly than for p values close to 0 or 1. In Figure 7-9 we have shown on the same graph the outline of the histogram for $n = 10$, $p = 0.5$, and $\varphi(t)$. Note that the outline of the histogram is approximated very well by $\varphi(t)$ even for n as small as 10 in this case. There are theoretical reasons why the histograms for t should behave in this way, which we shall refer to later. Having made this observation, we can now see how

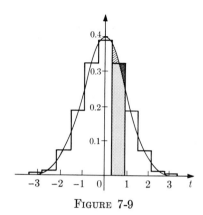

FIGURE 7-9

the normal density function can be used to compute probabilities involving $b(x; n,p)$. Instead of determining areas in the histogram for t, we shall determine the area between $\varphi(t)$ and the t-axis for the corresponding values of t. Thus if one wanted to evaluate the probability that $i \leq x \leq j$, one would compute $\hat{t}_i$ and $\hat{t}_j$ from (7-9) and evaluate the area of the shaded region shown in Figure 7-10. This would give the normal approximation to

$$\sum_{r=i}^{j} b(r; n,p) = B(j; n,p) - B(i - 1; n,p), \tag{7-10}$$

where $B(x; n,p)$ is the symbol for the cumulative binomial distribution.

Let us now investigate the question of how we can evaluate areas between $\varphi(t)$ and the t-axis, such as the shaded region shown in Figure 7-10. To see how to do this, consider Figure 7-11. The lightly shaded region is the area between the $\varphi(t)$ curve and the t-axis lying to the left of t_1. For every value of t, there is a number call it $\Phi(t)$ which is the area between the $\varphi(t)$ curve and the t-axis lying to the left of the specified value of t. This association with each real number t the number $\Phi(t)$ defines a function

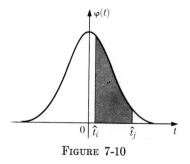

FIGURE 7-10

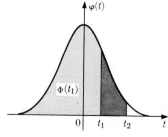

FIGURE 7-11

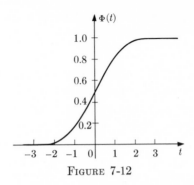

FIGURE 7-12

whose domain is the set of all real numbers. We can then look on $\Phi(t)$ as a function of t. It is possible to draw a graph showing $\Phi(t)$. This is shown in Figure 7-12. It is not possible to give a formula for $\Phi(t)$ in terms of functions we are familiar with, as it was for $\varphi(t)$. The function $\Phi(t)$ is a new function which is not expressible in terms of familiar functions. Hence there is no formula into which one can substitute t and compute the exact value of $\Phi(t)$. The value of $\Phi(t)$ can, however, be computed as accurately as desired by numerical methods. We shall not consider these numerical methods since tables of $\Phi(t)$ are available, and one is given at the end of the text in Table E. Note that as t gets larger and larger, $\Phi(t)$ gets closer and closer to 1. Thus the entire area between the $\varphi(t)$ curve and the t-axis has the value 1. Note also that $\Phi(0) = 0.5$. Hence that part of the area lying to the left of $t = 0$ is precisely half the total area under the $\varphi(t)$ curve. Observe, furthermore, that if $t_2 > t_1$, then $\Phi(t_2) > \Phi(t_1)$ since $\Phi(t_2)$ is $\Phi(t_1)$ plus the area lying between t_1 and t_2.

Once we have a table of $\Phi(t)$ it is very easy to determine the area of the darkly shaded region in Figure 7-11. Note that $\Phi(t_2)$ is $\Phi(t_1)$ plus the area of the darkly shaded region. Therefore, the area of the darkly shaded region is simply $\Phi(t_2) - \Phi(t_1)$. In the table for $\Phi(t)$ we look for t_1 in the t column and read the value of $\Phi(t_1)$ in the $\Phi(t)$ column, and similarly for t_2. Now it may turn out that t_1 is not one of the tabulated values in the table, but instead t_1 lies between two tabulated values of t, say t_u and t_v. To determine $\Phi(t_1)$, it is convenient to imagine that between t_u and t_v the graph of $\Phi(t)$ is given by a straight line. Then one uses linear interpolation, and $\Phi(t_1)$ as given by

$$\Phi(t_1) = \Phi(t_u) + \left[\frac{\Phi(t_v) - \Phi(t_u)}{t_v - t_u} \right] (t_1 - t_u). \tag{7-11}$$

On examining Table E for $\Phi(t)$ at the end of the text, the reader will note that only values of $t \geq 0$ are tabulated. How then do we determine $\Phi(t)$ when $t < 0$? This can easily be done using the table and the following property of $\Phi(t)$. Let t_1 be positive, and let $\Phi^*(t_1)$ be the area under the graph of $\varphi(t)$ lying to the *right* of t_1. Then

$$\Phi(t_1) + \Phi^*(t_1) = 1 \qquad (7\text{-}12)$$

since the total area is 1. However, it happens to be true that the area to the right of t_1 is the same as the area to the left of $-t_1$, i.e., $\Phi(-t_1) = \Phi^*(t_1)$. Thus from (7-12)

$$\Phi(-t_1) = 1 - \Phi(t_1). \qquad (7\text{-}13)$$

To compute $\Phi(-t_1)$, where $-t_1 < 0$, we subtract from 1 the value of $\Phi(t_1)$. For example, to compute $\Phi(-0.32)$ we look up $\Phi(0.32)$ in Table E, which is 0.6255, so that $\Phi(-0.32) = 1 - 0.6255 = 0.3745$.

Suppose now that we wish to approximate $b(r; n,p)$ using the normal approximation. This probability is the area of the histogram for t lying between $t_r - (1/2\sigma_x)$ and $t_r + (1/2\sigma_x)$, where $t_r = (r - \mu_x)/\sigma_x$. Thus if

$$t_- = \frac{r - \frac{1}{2} - np}{\sqrt{npq}}; \quad t_+ = \frac{r + \frac{1}{2} - np}{\sqrt{npq}}, \qquad (7\text{-}14)$$

the probability desired is the area of the histogram from t_- to t_+. But the normal approximation to this area is $\Phi(t_+) - \Phi(t_-)$. Consequently,

$$b(r; n,p) \doteq \Phi\left(\frac{r + \frac{1}{2} - np}{\sqrt{npq}}\right) - \Phi\left(\frac{r - \frac{1}{2} - np}{\sqrt{npq}}\right), \qquad (7\text{-}15)$$

where $\doteq$ means approximately equal. Next consider the case where we wish to compute approximately the probability that $x \leq r$, i.e., $B(r; n,p)$. This probability is the area of the histogram for t lying to the left of t_+, t_+ being defined by (7-14). The normal approximation to this area is $\Phi(t_+)$. Therefore,

$$B(r; n,p) \doteq \Phi\left(\frac{r + \frac{1}{2} - np}{\sqrt{npq}}\right). \qquad (7\text{-}16)$$

From (7-15) and (7-16) one can determine any other approximation of interest. For example, if one desired the probability that $i \leq x \leq j$, this is (7-10), and (7-16) is then used to approximate each cumulative probability.

It is now of interest to ask under what conditions the normal approximation to the binomial distribution will give a satisfactory result. Just as with the Poisson approximation, this is hard to answer. The accuracy of the approximation depends on n, p, and r. Generally speaking, for ordinary sorts of computations where two significant figure accuracy is more than adequate, the normal approximation can always be used if np, the mean of the binomial distribution, is greater than 25. This is true regardless of the value of p. However, for p values close to 0.5, the approximation can be quite satisfactory for np as low as 5 or 6, that is, for n as small as 10 or 12. The reader should keep in mind that the accuracy of the approximation will vary with r and p for a given np, and for $np = 25$, the error may be less than 5 percent in some cases and up to 20 percent or so if the probabilities are very small. Errors of this magnitude are often tolerable, and this is the basis for saying that the normal approximation is adequate for $np > 25$ for ordinary uses. If high accuracy is required, then one must be very careful in using the normal approximation to be sure that it does provide sufficient accuracy.

As we mentioned at the beginning of this section, the normal density function can be used to approximate the Poisson, Pascal, and hypergeometric distributions as well as the binomial. The procedure used to approximate any one of these is the same as that for the binomial distribution. To approximate the probability function for any one of these distributions, we use (7-15) replacing $b(r; n,p)$ by the appropriate probability to be approximated and np and $\sqrt{npq}$ by the mean and standard deviation, respectively, for the probability function of interest. Similarly, to approximate the cumulative function for any one of these distributions one uses (7-16) replacing $B(r; n,p)$ by the cumulative probability of interest and np and $\sqrt{npq}$ by the mean and standard deviation, respectively, for the probability function of interest. Let us then consider the conditions under which the normal approximation will suffice for these distributions. Once again, of course, this depends on the accuracy desired, and the accuracy in turn depends on all the parameters. However, for the usual case where two significant figure accuracy is more than adequate, the normal approximation can be used for the Poisson distribution when β, the mean, is greater than 25. One is essentially forced to use the normal approximation when $\beta > 100$ if computations are being made by hand since even the best tables stop at about $\beta = 100$. For the Pascal distribution recall that

$$b_P(n; r,p) = pb(r - 1; n - 1,p),$$

so that one should be able to use the normal approximation for $b_P(n; r,p)$ whenever the normal approximation can be used for $b(r - 1; n - 1, p)$, i.e., for $(n - 1)p > 25$. The normal approximation can be used for the hypergeometric distribution whenever it is suitable to approximate it by the binomial and whenever the normal approximation is a suitable approximation to the binomial. This should be true when $n/N \leq 0.1$ and $np > 25$, p being fraction defective in the lot or the fraction of the N units having the particular characteristic of interest.

7-2 EXAMPLES

Let us now give some numerical examples which illustrate the applicability of the normal approximation.

1. Let us estimate $b(6; 10, 0.5)$ using the normal approximation. The mean of $b(x; 10, 0.5)$ is $np = 5$, and the standard deviation we determined previously to be 1.5625. We use (7-15) in making the normal approximation with $r = 6$. Now

$$\frac{6 + 0.5 - 5}{1.5625} = \frac{1.5}{1.5625} = 0.961; \qquad \frac{6 - 0.5 - 5}{1.5625} = \frac{0.5}{1.5625} = 0.321,$$

so that

$$b(6; 10, 0.5) \doteq \Phi(0.961) - \Phi(0.321).$$

The value of $\Phi(t)$ is not given for $t = 0.961$, but is given for 0.96 and 0.97. From Table E, $\Phi(0.96) = 0.8315$; $\Phi(0.97) = 0.8340$. Using the linear interpolation formula (7-11),

$$\Phi(0.961) = \Phi(0.96) + \frac{\Phi(0.97) - \Phi(0.96)}{0.01} (0.001)$$

$$= 0.8315 + 0.0002 = 0.8317.$$

Similarly, $\Phi(0.321) = 0.6255 + 0.0004 = 0.6259$, and

$$b(6; 10, 0.5) \doteq 0.8317 - 0.6259 = 0.2058.$$

From Table B the correct value of $b(6; 10, 0.5)$ is 0.2051. In this case the normal approximation gives a remarkably close approximation. The situation is illustrated geometrically in Figure 7-9. The lightly shaded area plus the darkly shaded area is $b(6; 10, 0.5)$, while the normal approximation yields the lightly shaded area plus the crosshatched area. The crosshatched area is about the same as the darkly shaded area, and thus the normal approximation yields a result which is quite close to being correct.

We might note also as a result of the computation just made that since usually one is interested in no more than two significant figure accuracy, it is unnecessary to bother with interpolation in Table E. One simply uses the closest tabulated value of t.

2. Let us estimate $B(6; 10, 0.5)$ using the normal approximation. We use (7-16) here with $r = 6$. Thus from the results of the previous example, we see that $B(6; 10, 0.5) \doteq \Phi(0.961) = 0.8317$. If we add up the values of $b(r; n, p)$ in Table B from $r = 0$ to 6, we obtain the correct value of 0.8282. Thus the normal approximation again yields a value very close to the correct value.

3. Let us next estimate $B(1; 10, 0.1)$ using the normal approximation. We use (7-16) with $r = 1$. Now $np = 1$ and $\sqrt{npq} = \sqrt{0.9} = 0.947$. Thus

$$t_+ = \frac{1 + 0.5 - 1}{0.947} = \frac{0.5}{0.947} = 0.529.$$

Hence $B(1; 10, 0.1) \doteq \Phi(0.53) = 0.7019$. The correct value can be found from Table A by adding the values of $b(r; 10, 0.1)$ for $r = 0$ and 1. This yields 0.7361. Thus the normal approximation does not do quite as well in this case. The reason is that p is far from 0.5, and the histogram for t is skewed and its outline does not resemble the normal curve very closely. The outline of the histogram for t in this case is shown in Figure 7-13.

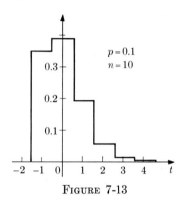

FIGURE 7-13

4. In a production run of a particular item 10,000 units are manufactured. Assume that the process is in statistical control when the run is made and that the probability that any given unit will be defective is 0.005. Let us estimate the probability that the number of defectives in the lot will be 40 or less. The probability we desire to estimate is $B(40; 10,000, 0.005)$. It would be difficult to evaluate this directly because no table goes up to $n = 10,000$ for the binomial distribution. However, $\mu = np = 50$ and $\sigma = \sqrt{49.8} = 7.02$. We should, therefore, be able to estimate this probability with reasonable accuracy using the normal approximation and (7-16). Now

$$t_+ = \frac{40 + 0.5 - 50}{7.02} = -\frac{9.5}{7.02} = -1.35.$$

Thus by (7-13)

$$B(40; 10,000; 0.005) \doteq \Phi(-1.35) = 1 - \Phi(1.35) = 1 - 0.9115 = .0885.$$

Hence the desired probability is approximately 0.089, and the probability of getting 40 or less defectives when the expected number is 50 is quite small in this case.

What is the probability of getting 60 or more defectives? This is 1 minus the probability of getting 59 or less, i.e., $1 - B(59; 10,000; 0.005)$. When $r = 59$, t_+ is

$$t_+ = \frac{59 + 0.5 - 50}{7.02} = \frac{9.5}{7.02} = 1.35.$$

Thus by what we have obtained above $B(59; 10,000; 0.005) \doteq 0.9115$, and the probability of getting 60 or more is the same as 40 or less, i.e., 0.089. Hence the probability that the number of defects is less than 40 or greater than 60, that is, that the number of defects x does not satisfy $41 \leq x \leq 59$, is only 0.178.

5. Suppose that we want to approximate $P(10; 15)$, where $P(x; 15)$ is the cumulative Poisson distribution with mean 15. This can be done using the normal approximation and

$$P(r; \beta) \doteq \Phi \left(\frac{r + \frac{1}{2} - \beta}{\sqrt{\beta}} \right).$$

Recall that for a Poisson distribution with mean β, $\sigma = \sqrt{\beta}$. For the case under consideration,

$$\frac{r + \frac{1}{2} - \beta}{\sqrt{\beta}} = \frac{10 + 0.5 - 15}{3.86} = -\frac{4.5}{3.86} = -1.17.$$

Thus

$$P(10; 15) \doteq \Phi(-1.17) = 1 - \Phi(1.17) = 1 - 0.8790 = 0.121.$$

The correct answer is 0.1185, and the normal approximation does rather well in this case.

7-3   TREATMENT OF RANDOM VARIABLES WHICH CAN TAKE ON A VERY LARGE NUMBER OF VALUES

Often one encounters random variables which can take on a huge number of different values. It is frequently true that it is exceedingly clumsy to make probability computations involving such random variables if one proceeds directly using the techniques that we have discussed previously. For example, to compute the cumulative function for a given value of the random variable, it might be necessary to add up 100,000 different values of the probability function. This would be totally out of the question to carry out by hand and could become very burdensome even for a large scale digital computer. In this section we would like to suggest two ways in which one can avoid these complications. The remainder of the chapter will be devoted to a detailed study of one of these methods.

Before proceeding, let us give some examples of random variables which can take on a large number of different values. Consider once again the geologist and the structure he is examining for the possibility that it contains oil. For a structure of the type he is studying, the volume of oil in place might vary from 0 to 10 million barrels. We can think of the quantity of oil in place as being a random variable x. The quantity would never be measured in units smaller than a barrel. Nonetheless, however, x can take on about 10 million different values. As another example, the return on a project might vary from a loss of one million dollars to a profit of 10 million dollars. If we think of the return as being a random variable x and measure the return to the nearest cent, then x could take on more than one billion different values. To take a less extreme example, consider a process which turns out ball bearings. The diameter of any particular ball bearing can be thought of as a random variable. The diameter can be measured only to the nearest one hundred thousandth of an inch, but to this accuracy the variations in diameter make it possible for x to take on several thousand different values. As a final example, if we were concerned with the random variable x giving the number of gallons of gasoline sold per month at a particular station, x might vary from 50,000 to 80,000 gallons, and if x was measured to the nearest gallon, x could take on about 30,000 different values.

Given that we are studying some random variable x which takes on a large number of different values and for which it is difficult to make computations directly, there are basically two alternative approaches one can use to simplify the situation. These two approaches work in opposite directions. One decreases the number of alternatives. The other increases the number of alternatives unendingly. Both procedures are useful, and which is most appropriate depends on the situation. Frequently, either one can be used, and the choice then revolves about the question of which is most convenient.

Consider first the procedure which reduces the number of alternatives. Frequently, when we have a random variable which takes on a very large number of values, a little thought will indicate that the random variable provides us with too much detail about the outcome of the random experiment. We are not really interested in every possible value which x can take on. All we are really interested in is the probability that x will be in a relatively small number of intervals, that is, we can imagine that the total range of variation, $a \leq x \leq b$, of x is subdivided into a number of intervals by the points $\gamma_0 = a$, γ_1, γ_2, . . . , $\gamma_m = b$, and all we really care about is the probability that $\gamma_{j-1} \leq x < \gamma_j$ for $j = 1, \ldots, m$. Let e_j be the event that x lies in the interval $\gamma_{j-1} \leq x < \gamma_j$. Then the set of all e_j form a mutually exclusive and collectively exhaustive set of outcomes of the random experiment $\Re$ and can be used as a set of simple events. Given that there are a relatively small number of events e_j, we have now reduced the problem to one we can handle. This was done by modifying the model for $\Re$ from one whose event set contains at least as many elements as the different values which x can take on, to one whose event set is $E = \{e_1, \ldots, e_m\}$. Thus, for example, instead of being concerned about how many barrels of oil the structure might contain, to the nearest barrel, the geologist would probably find it quite satisfactory to be concerned instead only with a relatively small number of ranges of values. Thus he might want to estimate the probabilities that there are less than 100,000 barrels, between 100,000 and 200,000, between 200,000 and 500,000, between 500,000 and one million, and of one million barrel increments after this.

There is another way in which one can view the process of reducing the number of alternatives. This is simply to change the dimensions in which x is measured to some larger unit. Thus in the example given above dealing with the quantity of gasoline sold by a given station per month it might be quite satisfactory to measure sales only to the nearest thousand gallons, so that x would then be the number of thousands of gallons sold; now x would take on the values 50, 51, . . . , 80, so that instead of taking on about 30,000 different values x would now take only 31 values. With this interpretation one continues to use the same random variable, but changes the physical dimensions to a larger unit and measures x only to the nearest unit. This is also a technique that one often uses.

Let us now turn to the second procedure for handling random variables which can take on a large number of values. This one will occupy our attention for the remainder of this chapter. Consider some random variable x which takes on a large number of different values. Suppose initially that we do not know the probability function for x, but that we plan to determine approximately what it is by repeating the random experiment $\mathfrak{R}$ with which x is associated a large number of times. For example, x may be the diameter of a ball bearing. In this case we would proceed by measuring the diameters of a large number of ball bearings produced by the process. Let us begin by trying to estimate not the probability of each value of x, but instead the probability that x lies in various intervals. Thus we shall start out as if we were going to apply the procedure discussed above and use as events ranges of x rather than values of x. Imagine then that the range of variation of x is divided into m subintervals by the points γ_j. Assume that $\mathfrak{R}$ is performed a large number of times n, and let n_j be the number of times that the value of x was in the interval $\gamma_{j-1} \leq x < \gamma_j$. Then n_j/n can be used as our estimate of the probability that x will be the jth subinterval. Let us now observe what happens if we choose a new set of γ_j which are more closely spaced, so that we have a larger number of subintervals with the lengths of the subintervals being shortened. In particular, we shall imagine that each of the original subintervals has been divided in half, so that for each j there are now two subintervals I_j' and I_j'' corresponding to the original interval I_j. Thus n_j is now the sum of two numbers n_j' and n_j'', n_j' being the number of times the value of x lies in I_j' and n_j'' the number of times it lies in I_j''. In general then, both n_j'/n and n_j''/n will be less than n_j/n. What we are pointing out is that as the number of subintervals is increased and the lengths of the subintervals decreased, the probability that the value of x will lie in any one of the subintervals decreases. If we continue this process until finally we concern ourselves with the probabilities that x takes on the various possible values it can assume, we see that normally these will all be very small numbers, that is, when x can take on a very large number of values, it is frequently true that the probability that x takes on any particular one of these values is very small. This is an important feature to keep in mind.

Suppose next that we proceed as above by splitting the range of variation of x into m subintervals by the points γ_j and letting n_j be the number of times that the value of x lies in the jth subinterval, i.e., $\gamma_{j-1} \leq x < \gamma_j$. Let us now construct a histogram by erecting a rectangle over each subinterval such that the area of this rectangle is n_j/n. We shall take this area to be the probability that x lies in the jth subinterval. Since the base of the rectangle has length $\gamma_j - \gamma_{j-1}$, the altitude must be $n_j/n(\gamma_j - \gamma_{j-1})$. The histogram might look like that shown in Figure 7-14. The

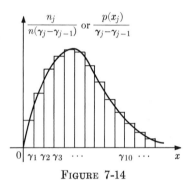

FIGURE 7-14

interesting thing about this histogram is that if we use a larger number of subintervals of shorter lengths, its shape does not change drastically. Instead the outline of the histogram gets closer and closer to a smooth curve. What we are saying is that although the probability that x will be in any given interval decreases as we decrease the length of the interval, the altitude of the histogram for any point in the interval does not change much. Why is this? If we split any subinterval into two subintervals of equal length, then if the original subinterval was small enough, we expect that the probability that x will be in either one of the new subintervals will be roughly half the probability that x lies in the original subinterval, that is, n'_j/n and n''_j/n are roughly half n_j/n. However, to determine the altitudes of the rectangles in the histogram for the new subintervals, we divide n'_j/n and n''_j/n by the length of the new subintervals which is half the length of the original subinterval. Thus each of the two new rectangles will have roughly the same altitude as the original rectangle. This explains why the change in shape of the histogram becomes less and less as we use finer and finer subdivisions.

Suppose now that we knew the probability function $p(x)$ for x, and imagine that x can take on the values in $X = \{x_1, \ldots, x_k\}$. It will be assumed that there are a very large number of such values. Let γ_j be the point halfway between x_j and x_{j+1} for each $j = 1, \ldots, k - 1$. Let us now obtain a histogram by constructing rectangles, the jth one having an area equal to $p(x_j)$. The base of this rectangle will extend from γ_{j-1} to γ_j for $j = 1, \ldots, k$, where we take γ_0 to be the same distance to the left of x_1 that γ_1 is to the right of x_1 and γ_k to be the same distance to the right of x_k that γ_{k-1} is to the left of x_k. If the area of the jth rectangle is to be $p(x_j)$, its altitude must be $p(x_j)/(\gamma_j - \gamma_{j-1})$. If x could take on thousands of different values in the interval illustrated, the histogram that we have just constructed would look much like the one illustrated in Figure 7-14, except that it would be much smoother and would look essentially like the smooth curve shown there.

We are at last ready to introduce the second procedure for treating random variables which can take on a very large number of values. Since if x is a random variable such that the outline of the histogram for x will look like a smooth curve, the corners being barely visible, why do we not simply approximate it by a smooth curve? This is precisely what we shall do. This smooth curve has the characteristic that for *every* value of x in the interval there is a number which is the height above the x-axis of the curve at this point. This curve is then the graph of a function which we can write symbolically $f(x)$. The probability that $x = x_j$ will now be approximated by the area between the smooth curve and the x-axis from γ_{j-1} to γ_j, and the probability that $x_i \leq x \leq x_j$ by the area between the smooth curve and the x-axis from γ_{i-1} to γ_j.

Let us now examine what has been gained by introducing the smooth curve which is the graph of $f(x)$ to approximate the histogram for x. The advantage gained is that the methods of the calculus can be conveniently used to determine the areas of interest and these procedures are often much easier to carry out than those required if one works directly with the probability function for x. In order to make use of the methods of the calculus, however, it is not sufficient merely to draw a smooth curve which approximates the histogram for x. One must have a specific formula for $f(x)$ which tells how to compute $f(x)$ for each x. The question then arises as to how one can determine explicitly the function $f(x)$. This is not always easy. If the probability function $p(x)$ for x is known, we can proceed using mathematics to try to determine a function which approximates $p(x_j)/(\gamma_j - \gamma_{j-1})$. Frequently, however, $p(x)$ is not known, and we must resort to experimental data to determine $f(x)$. In this case we can proceed in the manner discussed earlier to determine a histogram. Then we find some function whose graph approximates this histogram reasonably well and use it as $f(x)$.

7-4 INTUITIVE INTRODUCTION TO CONTINUOUS RANDOM VARIABLES

In several of the examples given in the last section it may have appeared to the reader that the random variables considered could really take on every possible value in some interval, and we used artifice assuming that measurements could be made only to limited accuracy in order to make the random variable take on a finite number of different values. This is not true, however, because both in the case where x represents the oil in place and that of the diameter of the ball bearing, even if we could make arbitrarily good measurements, x can take on only a finite number of different values. The reason for this is that oil and steel are made up of indivisible building blocks, atoms or molecules, and one of these is the smallest unit, that is, they are not infinitely divisible. In spite of the fact that all random variables dealt with in practice can actually take on only a finite number of different values, the notion of a random variable which can take on every possible real number in some interval is a very appealing one from an intuitive point of view, as we have just seen, even though it may be considered only an approximation to reality. Interestingly enough, it also happens to be a very useful one from a mathematical point of view. We would now like to investigate the possibility of building probability models having associated with them one or more random variables which can take on a continuum of values, that is, every value in some interval. The event sets in such cases must then have a continuum of simple events. We shall restrict our attention to cases where the values which the random variable can take on will serve as simple events.

Consider some random experiment $\mathfrak{R}$ which might be the manufacture of a ball bearing. To construct a model $\mathcal{E}$ for $\mathfrak{R}$, suppose that we decide to use as the event set E the set of all real numbers ξ in the interval $a \leq \xi \leq b$. Thus E contains an infinite number of elements which we shall refer to as a continuum of numbers. Now in the real world, only a finite set of the numbers in E will actually be events of $\mathfrak{R}$, but this does not prevent us, if it seems desirable to do so, allowing every number ξ, $a \leq \xi \leq b$, to be an element of E. $\mathcal{E}$ will then only be an approximation to the real world, but this is always true, and if it is a good approximation, this is all we can ask. We shall then imagine that in the model $\mathcal{E}$ every number in E is a possible outcome of $\mathfrak{R}$. The numbers (simple events) in E can be looked upon as the possible values which a random variable x can take on. We shall think of things in this way. The random variable x which can take on every value in the interval $a \leq x \leq b$ will be called a *continuous random variable*. The random variables which we have studied in previous chapters which can take on a finite number of values or all non-negative integers are referred to as *discrete random variables*.

To complete the model $\mathcal{E}$, let us suppose that in the actual real world experiment $\mathcal{R}$ where x can take on only a finite number of values, we have a situation like that considered in the previous section where $p(x_i)$, the probability that $x = x_i$, is very small for every value of x_i. We noted in the previous section that it could be convenient to introduce a function $f(x)$ whose graph is a smooth curve such that the probability that $x_i \leq x \leq x_j$ is the area between the graph of $f(x)$ and the x-axis from γ_i to γ_j. We shall now, for our model $\mathcal{E}$, imagine that for any two numbers α and β in X, not merely the values which x can actually take on in the real world, there is a probability $p(\alpha \leq x \leq \beta)$ that x will be in the interval $\alpha \leq x \leq \beta$. Furthermore, we shall assume that this probability can be determined by finding the area lying between the graph of a function $f(x)$ and the x-axis from α to β as shown in Figure 7-15. In other words, we shall intro-

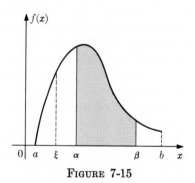

FIGURE 7-15

duce a function $f(x)$ whose domain is X, having the characteristic that if we wish to determine the probability that $\alpha \leq x \leq \beta$, we compute the area of the shaded set of points shown in Figure 7-15, that is, the area between the graph of $f(x)$ and the x-axis from α to β. The function $f(x)$ is called *a probability density function* or simply density function. Our mathematical model $\mathcal{E}$ for $\mathcal{R}$ will then consist of the event set X and the probability density function $f(x)$. We might at this point observe that what we were really suggesting in the previous section when recommending the approximation of the histogram for a random variable by a smooth curve was that we construct a mathematical model for the situation in which x is treated as a continuous random variable.

Let us now note some additional properties which $f(x)$ must possess if $\mathcal{E}$ is to be at all realistic. Since x must by assumption take on some value in the interval X, the probability that x lies in this interval should be 1, that is, the area between the graph of $f(x)$ and the x-axis from a to b should be 1. We shall require that $f(x)$ does have this property. Furthermore, we shall require that $f(x)$ be non-negative for every number in X. Although we could allow $f(x)$ to be negative and still interpret areas as probabilities, there are great mathematical conveniences to be gained by preventing $f(x)$ from being negative. There is no loss in generality by doing this because if $f(x)$ was negative in some interval, $-f(x)$ would be positive, and the areas between $f(x)$ and the x-axis and $-f(x)$ and the x-axis are the same. Thus we shall require that $f(\xi) \geq 0$ for each $\xi \in X$ and, in addition, the area between the graph of $f(x)$ and the x-axis over the entire interval X must be 1. These are the only restrictions that we shall place on $f(x)$ other than requiring that $f(x)$ have a graph for which we can compute areas.

For our model $\mathcal{E}$, what is the probability that x takes on a particular value ξ? This is the area between the graph of $f(x)$ and the x-axis at ξ, as illustrated in Figure 7-15. But this yields simply a straight line with no width. Thus the area is 0 and $p(\xi) = 0$. Our model $\mathcal{E}$ then says that $p(\xi) = 0$ for every $\xi \in X$. At first glance it seems ridiculous that the probability of every simple event should be zero. A little reflection shows, however, that this is reasonable and in fact it could not be any other way. Recall that we noted in the previous section that when a random variable can take on a large number of different values, it is often the case that all of these have a small probability. In constructing $\mathcal{E}$, we assumed that we were dealing with such situations and then considered an idealized situation where x could take on all values in some interval. As the number of different values x can take on increases, the probabilities of the individual values decrease, and when x can take on all values in the interval, the probability of each individual value must be 0. The reader may now agree that it is not implausible that our model should assign a 0 probability to every simple event. There remains, however, the question, "If every simple event has a probability of 0, how can the event that the value of x lies in the interval $\alpha \leq x \leq \beta$ have a positive probability?" It is at this point that we encounter a very important difference between the event set X that we are now considering and the event sets considered in the previous chapters. One encounters this same sort of situation in many different areas. For example, in physics one initially considers points which are imagined to have a mass associated with them. Then one later introduces the notion of a continuous fluid or solid (this being an idealization, of course). The mass at a given point in a continuous fluid is 0. Nonetheless, the mass of some finite volume of the fluid is not 0. Similarly, the distance that a car travels at a given instant of time is 0. Nonetheless, the car can travel a finite distance in a finite time. The density function $f(x)$ introduced above is the equivalent of the velocity of an automobile or the density of a fluid; $f(\xi)$ can be thought of as measuring the rate of change of probability at $x = \xi$. Although $p(\xi) = 0$, there is a rate of change of p at $x = \xi$, and when one moves a finite distance from ξ, the probability can change by a finite amount. To see a little more clearly why $f(\xi)$ can be interpreted as a rate of change of probability at x, recall from the previous section that when we construct a histogram for $p(x)$, the probability function for a random variable x which can take on a large number of values, the altitude of the rectangle associated with x_j is $p(x_j)/(\gamma_j - \gamma_{j-1}) = p(x_j)/h_j$, where $h_j = \gamma_j - \gamma_{j-1}$ is the length of the base of the rectangle. Now if we let the number of values which x can take on in the interval X increase unendingly, $p(x_j)$ will approach 0 as will h_j. The ratio $p(x_j)/h_j$, however, approaches a unique number which we denote by $f(x_j)$. Thus when x can take on all values, $p(x_j)$ can be looked upon as the probability that x lies in the interval $\gamma_{j-1} \le x \le \gamma_j$, and $f(x_j)$ is this probability divided by the length of the interval. As h_j gets smaller and smaller, $p(x_j)/h_j$ becomes the rate of change of the probability with respect to x at x_j, which is $f(x_j)$.

In the following sections we shall study continuous random variables in some detail and see how useful the notion really is. This will require the use of calculus, however. The reader not familiar with calculus might, after finishing this section and the next, turn to Section 7-15 which deals with the central limit theorem. We shall conclude this section by examining one particular density function which is of great usefulness and whose use can be understood without a knowledge of calculus. This density function is called the normal density function. We shall use the special symbolism $n(x; \mu,\sigma)$ rather than $f(x)$ to denote it. The function $n(x; \mu,\sigma)$ is

$$n(x; \mu,\sigma) = \frac{1}{\sigma\sqrt{2\pi}} e^{-(x-\mu)^2/2\sigma^2}, \tag{7-17}$$

and a random variable whose density function is (7-17) is said to be normally distributed or to have a normal distribution. We also refer to (7-17) as the normal distribution. In writing (7-17) we intend that the right-hand side as well as the left-hand side be interpreted as a symbolic representation for the entire function. To determine $n(\xi; \mu,\sigma)$, the value of the normal density function when $x = \xi$, we replace the symbol x on the right in (7-17) by ξ and evaluate the number so determined. The use of the normal density function requires the introduction of still another deviation from reality in addition to assuming that x can take on all values in some interval. When using the normal distribution, one assumes that x can take on any real value, however large or small, so that X the domain of the normal density function is the set of all real numbers. Once again this is a useful mathematical idealization which does not impair the practical usefulness of the probability model. The reason for this is that if α is larger than the maximum value which x can have, the probability that x will be in any interval $\alpha \leq x \leq \beta$ will generally be so small that it can be considered impossible from a practical point of view.

The function $n(x; \mu, \sigma)$ involves two parameters μ and σ. We shall show below with the use of calculus that μ is the expected value of x and σ is the standard deviation of x. The function $n(x; \mu, \sigma)$ takes on its maximum value at $x = \mu$. The value of σ determines how spread out the function is. In Figure 7-16 we have shown $n(x; \mu, \sigma)$ for a given μ and two different

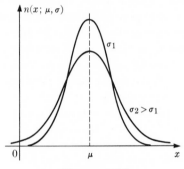

FIGURE 7-16

values of σ. We might note that $n(x; \mu, \sigma)$ is a legitimate density function for every real number μ and every positive number σ.

In the real world, if one constructs a histogram for some random variable using one of the methods discussed in the previous section, it often turns out that the histogram looks quite a bit like Figure 7-16, and the normal density function can then be used very conveniently in developing a mathematical model for the situation. For example, the histogram for the ball bearing diameters would very likely have this bell shape. The interesting thing about the normal distribution is that all computations involving it can be made using tables for the standardized normal density function $\varphi(t)$ and the cumulative function $\Phi(t)$ introduced in Section 7-1. On comparing (7-1) with (7-17), we see that $\varphi(t)$ is a normal density function having mean 0 and standard deviation 1. Suppose that we wish to compute (7-17) for a specific value of x, say ξ. If we compute $t_1 = (\xi - \mu)/\sigma$, we see from (7-1) that

$$n(\xi; \mu, \sigma) = \frac{1}{\sigma} \varphi(t_1),$$

that is,

$$n(\xi; \mu, \sigma) = \frac{1}{\sigma} \varphi \left(\frac{\xi - \mu}{\sigma} \right). \tag{7-18}$$

Thus from a table of $\varphi(t)$, such as Table D, we can easily evaluate $n(\xi;\mu,\sigma)$ for any ξ, μ, and σ.

Consider next the problem of evaluating the probability that $x \leq \xi$. We shall denote this probability by $N(\xi;\mu,\sigma)$. For each real number ξ we can determine a number $N(\xi;\mu,\sigma)$. This defines a function whose domain is the set of all real numbers. We shall represent this function symbolically as $N(x;\mu,\sigma)$. The function $N(x;\mu,\sigma)$ is called the *cumulative normal distribution*. We shall give an intuitive argument to show that there is a simple relation between $N(\xi;\mu,\sigma)$ and $\Phi(t)$. The rigorous proof requires calculus and is given below. To compute $N(\xi;\mu,\sigma)$ approximately we could find a value of α such that the area under the graph of $n(x;\mu,\sigma)$ to the left of α appeared negligible. Then we could divide the interval $\alpha \leq x \leq \xi$ into m subintervals by the equally spaced points $\gamma_0 = \alpha$, γ_1, ..., γ_{m-1}, $\gamma_m = \xi$. Let $h_j = \gamma_j - \gamma_{j-1}$. Denote by ρ_j the point halfway between γ_{j-1} and γ_j. Consider the rectangle whose base extends from γ_{j-1} to γ_j and whose altitude is $n(\rho_j;\mu,\sigma)$. The area of this rectangle is $n(\rho_j;\mu,\sigma)h_j$ and is approximately the area under $n(x;\mu,\sigma)$ from γ_{j-1} to γ_j, as we can see from Figure 7-17. Therefore, $N(\xi;\mu,\sigma)$ is approximately

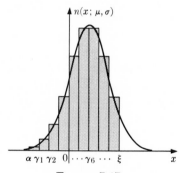

FIGURE 7-17

$\sum_{j=1}^{m} n(\rho_j;\mu,\sigma)h_j$. Now if we write $\tau_j = (\rho_j - \mu)/\sigma$, then $n(\rho_j;\mu,\sigma) = \varphi(\tau_j)/\sigma$. If $\delta_j = (\gamma_j - \mu)/\sigma$, $\gamma_j = \sigma\delta_j + \mu$ and

$$h_j = \gamma_j - \gamma_{j-1} = \sigma(\delta_j - \delta_{j-1}) = \sigma f_j$$

when we write $f_j = \delta_j - \delta_{j-1}$. Thus

$$\sum_{j=1}^{m} n(\rho_j;\mu,\sigma)h_j = \sum_{j=1}^{m} \varphi(\tau_j)f_j. \qquad (7\text{-}19)$$

But $\varphi(\tau_j)f_j$ is approximately the area under $\varphi(t)$ between δ_{j-1} and δ_j. Thus the sum $\sum_{j=1}^{m} \varphi(\tau_j)f_j$ is approximately $\Phi(\delta_m)$ which is $\Phi((\xi - \mu)/\sigma)$ since $\delta_m = (\gamma_m - \mu)/\sigma$ and $\gamma_m = \xi$. Now as the subdivisions get finer and finer, (7-19) always holds. Thus it would appear that

$$N(\xi; \mu,\sigma) = \Phi\left(\frac{\xi - \mu}{\sigma}\right) \qquad (7\text{-}20)$$

for every ξ. This is indeed correct, and we have provided a simple way to compute $N(\xi; \mu,\sigma)$ from a table of $\Phi(t)$. We might note incidentally that since the probability that $x = \xi$ is 0, $N(\xi; \mu,\sigma)$ is the probability that $x < \xi$ as well as the probability that $x \leq \xi$. We have now obtained the basic results (7-18) and (7-20), which allow us to make computations with the normal distribution using only the tables for $\varphi(t)$ and $\Phi(t)$.

7-5 EXAMPLES

Let us give some simple illustrations of the use of the normal distribution.

1. Let x be a random variable which is normally distributed with expected value $\mu = 3.5$ and standard deviation $\sigma = 2$. We shall evaluate the probability density at $x = 4.5$. This is $n(4.5; 3.5, 2)$. By (7-18) and Table D,

$$n(4.5; 3.5, 2) = \tfrac{1}{2}\varphi\left(\frac{4.5 - 3.5}{2}\right) = \tfrac{1}{2}\varphi(0.5) = \tfrac{1}{2}(0.3521) = 0.1760.$$

The probability that $x \leq 4.5$ is $N(4.5; 3.5, 2)$, or by (7-20) and Table E, $N(4.5; 3.5, 2) = \Phi(0.5) = 0.6915$, so that on performing the random experiment with which x is associated a large number of times, about 0.6915 percent of the time x would be less than or equal to 4.5.

2. Consider the production process which turns out ball bearings. Let us imagine that the process is in statistical control, and let x be the random variable representing the diameter of any given ball bearing. Assume that histogram data indicate that x is normally distributed with expected value 0.4020 inches with a standard deviation of 0.0020 inches. Suppose that to be considered acceptable the diameter of a ball bearing must be in the interval

$$0.3975 \leq x \leq 0.4070. \qquad (7\text{-}21)$$

We can now compute the probability that any given ball bearing produced will be defective. Let A_1 be the event that $x < 0.3975$ and A_2 the event that $x > 0.4070$. The ball bearing will be defective if either of these events occurs, i.e., if the event $A = A_1 \cup A_2$ occurs. Intuitively, we see that the events are exclusive, and if we denote by p the probability that a defective is produced, then $p = p(A_1) + p(A_2)$. However,

$$p(A_1) = N(0.3975; 0.4020, 0.0020) = \Phi\left(\frac{0.3975 - 0.4020}{0.0020}\right)$$

$$= \Phi(-2.25) = 1 - \Phi(2.25) = 1 - 0.9878 = 0.0122.$$

Consider next $p(A_2)$. This is the area under the normal density function to the right of $x = 0.4070$.   The area to the left of 0.4070 is $N(0.4070;$ $0.4020, 0.0020)$, and the area under the entire normal density curve is 1. Thus

$$p(A_2) = 1 - N(0.4070; 0.4020, 0.0020) = 1 - \Phi\left(\frac{0.4070 - 0.4020}{0.0020}\right)$$

$$= 1 - \Phi(2.5) = 1 - 0.9938 = 0.0062.$$

Hence $p = 0.0122 + 0.0062 = 0.0184$.   Now recall that when a process is in statistical control, the probability that any given unit will be defective is the long run fraction defective.   Thus for the process considered, the fraction defective of the ball bearings produced will be about 1.8 percent.   In this example we have shown that it is sometimes possible to compute the probability of a defective from a knowledge of the behavior of some more basic random variable, in this case, the diameter of the ball bearing.

3.   Let us return to the process for making ball bearings studied in Example 2.   By adjusting the settings on one or more machines, one can change μ, the expected diameter of a ball bearing.   Such adjustments may or may not simultaneously effect the standard deviation σ.   Frequently, they do not.   Let us then examine a situation where by setting the machines we are free to select the expected diameter of a ball bearing but that machine adjustments do not affect σ, that is, σ remains constant at the value 0.0020 independently of the value selected for μ.   We shall continue to suppose that if a ball bearing is to be acceptable, its diameter must satisfy (7-21).   Now the fraction defective will depend on the value of μ. From the results of Example 2 we see that the fraction defective for the process is related to μ by

$$p = 1 + \Phi\left(\frac{0.3975 - \mu}{0.0020}\right) - \Phi\left(\frac{0.4070 - \mu}{0.0020}\right) = p(A_1) + p(A_2). \quad (7\text{-}22)$$

For each μ there is determined a p.   Thus p is a function of μ.   We have illustrated how p varies with μ in Figure 7-18.   The minimum value of the fraction defective occurs, as one would expect intuitively, when μ is halfway between 0.3975 and 0.4070, i.e., for $\mu = 0.40225$, and the minimum fraction defective is $p = 0.0176$.   When μ is equal to 0.3975 or 0.4070, the fraction defective is 0.5 (why?).   To check one point on the graph, let us compute p when $\mu = 0.4080$.   The situation is illustrated in Figure 7-19; p is the area of the shaded set of points which is the area under the normal density curve lying to the right of 0.4070 and to the left of 0.3975.   In this case

$$\Phi\left(\frac{0.3975 - \mu}{0.0020}\right) = \Phi(-5.25) = 1 - \Phi(5.25) \doteq 0.$$

The value of $t = 5.25$ is not even tabulated in Table E because $\Phi(5.25)$ is

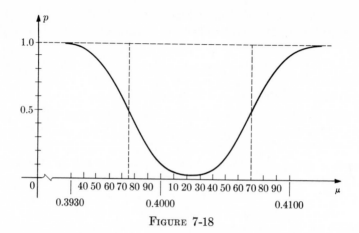

FIGURE 7-18

1 to four significant figures.   In other words the area to the left of 0.3975 is essentially 0.   Next

$$1 - \Phi\left(\frac{0.4070 - 0.4080}{0.0020}\right) = 1 - \Phi(-0.5) = \Phi(0.5) = 0.6915.$$

Thus by (7-22), $p = 0.6915$.

4.   We pointed out in Section 7-1 that if x has the binomial distribution $b(x; n,p)$, then for n sufficiently large, the outline of the histogram for the random variable $t = (x - \mu)/\sigma$ is very well approximated by the graph of $\varphi(t)$.   The reader will now, no doubt, suspect that under these conditions the outline of the histogram for x itself will be well approximated by $n(x; \mu,\sigma)$ where $\mu = np$ and $\sigma = \sqrt{npq}$.   This is indeed true as we shall now show.

The histogram for x will look something like that shown in Figure 7-3, and the probability that $x = r$ is the height of the rectangle at r since the

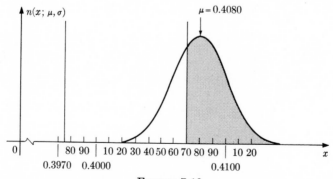

FIGURE 7-19

length of the base is 1. We would like to show that for large n this height is essentially $n(r;\ \mu,\sigma)$. To do this, let us compute the probability that $x = r$ from the histogram for t. This is the area of the histogram for t between $(r - \frac{1}{2} - \mu)/\sigma$ and $(r + \frac{1}{2} - \mu)/\sigma$, and the length of the base of this rectangle is $1/\sigma$. The altitude of the rectangle at $t = (r - \mu)/\sigma$ is for large n approximately $\varphi((r - \mu)/\sigma)$, as we noted in Section 7-1, and the area is approximately

$$\frac{1}{\sigma}\ \varphi\left(\frac{r - \mu}{\sigma}\right). \tag{7-23}$$

This then is approximately $b(r;\ n,p)$. However, from (7-18), (7-23) is $n(r;\ \mu,\sigma)$. Therefore, for large n

$$b(r; n,p) \doteq n(r; \mu,\sigma); \quad \mu = np, \quad \sigma = \sqrt{npq}, \tag{7-24}$$

and the outline of the histogram of x is well approximated by the graph of $n(x;\mu,\sigma)$. Thus, we see that it is possible to visualize the process of approximating $b(r;\ n,p)$ with the normal density function as one where we use instead of $b(r;\ n,p)$ the value of $n(r;\ np,\ \sqrt{npq})$. However, one usually uses (7-15) rather than (7-24). We ask the reader in the problems to compare these alternative approximation methods.

7-6° USE OF CALCULUS TO TREAT CONTINUOUS RANDOM VARIABLES

The great advantage of introducing the idealization of a continuous random variable is that the methods of the calculus can be introduced to aid us in solving problems. This is a very great advantage as we shall now see. In actuality, to develop rigorously and completely probability models for continuous random variables requires considerably more than an understanding of elementary calculus, and for this reason our development will occasionally have to omit certain points of rigor or leave unanswered some questions. These matters will be of little consequence as far as applications we shall study, however.

We shall here be considering event sets whose elements are numbers, and thus we shall denote the event set by X (or Y or Z) rather than E. The event set will contain an infinite number of elements and, in fact, a continuum of numbers. We shall restrict our attention to cases where X is the set of all numbers ξ satisfying

$$a \leq \xi \leq b, \tag{7-25}$$

or

$$\xi \geq a, \tag{7-26}$$

° Sections marked with an ° are intended for those familiar with calculus and may be omitted by readers not familiar with calculus.

or
$$\xi \leq b, \qquad\qquad (7\text{-}27)$$

or is the set of all real numbers ξ. We shall also allow X to be the union of two or more sets of the form (7-25), so that for example X might be the set of numbers ξ, where ξ lies in the interval $-5 \leq \xi \leq -1$ or the interval $2 \leq \xi \leq 15$. One could be much more general with respect to the event sets considered, but the types just discussed will be quite general enough for our purposes. The set X can be looked upon as the set of different values which a continuous random variable x can take on, and we shall in general think of things in this way.

With each number ξ of the event set, we shall associate a number $f(\xi)$, $f(\xi) \geq 0$, which we shall call the *probability density* for the random variable x at ξ. This association of a number $f(\xi)$ with each $\xi \in X$ defines a function whose domain is X. This function of a real variable which we shall denote symbolically by $f(x)$ will be called the *probability density function* or simply density function for x. We shall impose the additional restriction on $f(x)$ that

$$\int_X f(x)\, dx = 1, \qquad\qquad (7\text{-}28)$$

where by the symbolism $\int_X f(x)\, dx$ we mean the definite integral of $f(x)$, the density function for the random variable x, over X. If X is a set of the form (7-25), then

$$\int_X f(x)\, dx = \int_a^b f(x)\, dx; \qquad\qquad (7\text{-}29)$$

and if X is a set of the form (7-26), then

$$\int_X f(x)\, dx = \int_a^{\infty} f(x)\, dx; \qquad\qquad (7\text{-}30)$$

and if X is the set of all real numbers, then

$$\int_X f(x)\, dx = \int_{-\infty}^{\infty} f(x)\, dx. \qquad\qquad (7\text{-}31)$$

Note that (7-30) and (7-31) are improper integrals of the first kind. If $F(t) = \int_a^t f(x)\, dx$, then by definition

$$\int_a^{\infty} f(x)\, dx = \lim_{t \to \infty} F(t), \qquad\qquad (7\text{-}32)$$

when this limit exists. If the limit exists, then we say that the improper integral converges. In cases which will be of interest to us all improper integrals will converge.

For the probability models studied in the previous chapters, every subset of E was considered to be an event. We shall not try to decide whether every subset of X can be considered to be an event (this is not true in general) since one can think of very complicated subsets of X. However, any subset of X that we shall ever have need to consider will be an event. Consider then some event A which is a subset of X. We shall take as an axiom for our model that $p(A)$, the probability of A, is given by

$$p(A) = \int_A f(x)\, dx, \qquad (7\text{-}33)$$

that is, $p(A)$ is the integral of $f(x)$ over the subset A. Thus if A is the set of numbers ξ satisfying $\alpha \le \xi \le \beta$, then

$$p(A) = \int_\alpha^\beta f(x)\, dx.$$

The axiom (7-33) is the equivalent of (1-12) for probability models containing only a finite number of simple events.

We have already noted that not every subset of X will necessarily be an event. It is also true that not every event is such that (7-33) has meaning when the integral is interpreted to be the ordinary integral studied in elementary calculus. In order for (7-33) to have meaning for every event, one must use a more general definition of an integral. Such a generalization will be unnecessary for our purposes. For every event that will be of interest to us (7-33) will be meaningful in terms of the notions of integration studied in elementary calculus.

Equation (7-33) can be used to compute $p(x = \xi)$, the probability that $x = \xi$. In this case $A = \{\xi\}$ and contains just a single number. Then

$$p(x = \xi) = p(A) = \int_\xi^\xi f(x)\, dx = 0 \qquad (7\text{-}34)$$

by the way in which the definite integral is defined when the upper and lower limits are the same. Hence in $\mathcal{E}$, the probability that x takes on any particular value is 0. It is important to observe that $p(x = \xi) = 0$ does not here necessarily imply that the value ξ cannot occur. Every time $\mathcal{E}$ is performed some value of x will be observed. The long run relative frequency, if x did behave exactly as represented by $\mathcal{E}$, would be 0, however.

We might note that since we have assumed that $f(x) \ge 0$ over X, it follows that for any A for which the integral exists, $\int_A f(x)\, dx \ge 0$. Hence for any event A, $p(A) \ge 0$, as we desire it to be.

Let A and B be two events such that $A \cap B = \varnothing$, that is, A and B have no points of X in common. Then it follows from the definition of definite integrals that

$$\int_{A \cup B} f(x)\, dx = \int_A f(x)\, dx + \int_B f(x)\, dx, \qquad (7\text{-}35)$$

which becomes on using (7-33)

$$p(A \cup B) = p(A) + p(B), \quad A \cap B = \emptyset. \tag{7-36}$$

When $A \cap B = \emptyset$, A and B are called *exclusive or mutually exclusive events*. In particular, if $B = A^c$, where A^c is the complement of A, that is, the set of all points in X not in A, then $A \cup A^c = X$ and $A \cap A^c = \emptyset$, so that (7-36) becomes

$$1 = p(A) + p(A^c). \tag{7-37}$$

As an example of (7-36), suppose that A is the set of points ξ satisfying $-2 \le \xi \le -1$, and B is the set of points satisfying $0 \le \xi \le 3$; then

$$p(A \cup B) = \int_{A \cup B} f(x) \, dx = \int_{-2}^{-1} f(x) \, dx + \int_{0}^{3} f(x) \, dx. \tag{7-38}$$

Consider next two events A and B such that $A \cap B \ne \emptyset$. Write $C = A \cap B$. If D is the set of points from X which are in A but not in C, then $A = C \cup D$ and furthermore $C \cap D = \emptyset$. Thus

$$\int_{A} f(x) \, dx = \int_{C} f(x) \, dx + \int_{D} f(x) \, dx. \tag{7-39}$$

Similarly if E is the set of points in B which are not in C, then $B = C \cup E$ and $C \cap E = \emptyset$. Thus

$$\int_{B} f(x) \, dx = \int_{C} f(x) \, dx + \int_{E} f(x) \, dx. \tag{7-40}$$

Finally, $A \cup B = C \cup D \cup E$ and (why?)

$$\int_{A \cup B} f(x) \, dx = \int_{C} f(x) \, dx + \int_{D} f(x) \, dx + \int_{E} f(x) \, dx. \tag{7-41}$$

On adding (7-39) and (7-40), we see on using (7-41) that

$$\int_{A \cup B} f(x) \, dx = \int_{A} f(x) \, dx + \int_{B} f(x) \, dx - \int_{A \cap B} f(x) \, dx, \tag{7-42}$$

where we have replaced C by $A \cap B$. Thus on using the definition of the probability of an event we have

$$p(A \cup B) = p(A) + p(B) - p(A \cap B), \quad A \cap B \ne \emptyset. \tag{7-43}$$

Just as we did in the case where the event set had only a finite number of simple events, we shall consider $\emptyset$ to be an event and call it the impossible event. For obvious reasons, we define $p(\emptyset) = 0$. With this definition (7-43) can be imagined to hold in all cases, so that (7-36) is then simply a special case of (7-43). Equations (7-36), (7-37), and (7-43) are precisely the same as (1-13), (1-27), and (1-26), respectively.

Let us find an expression for the probability that $x \le \xi$. We shall denote this probability by $F(\xi)$. In this case $x \le \xi$ is the subset of A of X

containing all points of X whose value is not greater than ξ. We shall denote the integral of $f(x)$ over this set by $\int_{x \leq \xi} f(x)\, dx$ so that

$$F(\xi) = \int_{x \leq \xi} f(x)\, dx. \tag{7-44}$$

Thus if X is the form (7-25),

$$F(\xi) = \int_a^\xi f(x)\, dx, \tag{7-45}$$

and if X contains all real numbers or is of the form (7-27), then

$$F(\xi) = \int_{-\infty}^\xi f(x)\, dx, \tag{7-46}$$

this being an improper integral. For every $\xi \in X$ there is a number $F(\xi)$. This association defines a function, which we shall represent symbolically by $F(x)$, whose domain is X. $F(x)$ is called the *cumulative probability function, cumulative function,* or *cumulative distribution,* for the random variable x. $F(\xi)$ is the probability that $x \leq \xi$. Thus if $\xi_2 > \xi_1$, $F(\xi_2) \geq F(\xi_1)$ since the event A that $x \leq \xi_2$ is the union of B and C where B is the event $x \leq \xi_1$ and C is the event $\xi_1 < x \leq \xi_2$. Since B and C are exclusive events, we have by (7-36) $F(\xi_2) = F(\xi_1) + p(C)$ and $p(C) \geq 0$, thus implying that $F(\xi_2) \geq F(\xi_1)$.

Recall that the derivative of a function $F(x)$ at $x = \xi$ is by definition

$$\lim_{h \to 0} \frac{F(\xi + h) - F(\xi)}{h}$$

when this limit exists. Now for $h > 0$

$$F(\xi + h) = \int_{x \leq \xi + h} f(x)\, dx = \int_{x \leq \xi} f(x)\, dx + \int_\xi^{\xi + h} f(x)\, dx$$

when every point in the interval $\xi \leq x \leq \xi + h$ is in X. In this case

$$\frac{F(\xi + h) - F(\xi)}{h} = \frac{1}{h} \int_\xi^{\xi + h} f(x)\, dx. \tag{7-47}$$

As h gets closer and closer to 0, $\int_\xi^{\xi + h} f(x)\, dx$ becomes essentially $f(\xi)h$, and (7-47) approaches $f(\xi)$. Thus it would appear that $F'(\xi)$ exists and is equal to $f(\xi)$. The above is not a rigorous proof. However, one can prove that if $f(x)$ is continuous at each interior point in X, then $F(x)$ has a derivative at each interior point ξ in X and $F'(\xi) = f(\xi)$. This result is nothing but one form of the fundamental theorem of the calculus. The equation $F'(\xi) = f(\xi)$ can be interpreted intuitively as saying that the rate of change of the cumulative probability at ξ is the probability density $f(\xi)$. We shall deal only with functions $f(x)$ which are continuous over X (except for one problem). However, there is no reason why $f(x)$

cannot have a finite (or even an infinite) number of jump discontinuities. At such a discontinuity, $F(x)$ will be continuous, but will not have a derivative.

Either the density function $f(x)$ or the cumulative function $F(x)$ provides a complete description of the probabilistic behavior of x, and as we have noted above, one of these functions can be obtained from the other. Frequently, just as for discrete random variables, it is convenient to imagine that there is some chance mechanism which controls the behavior of x. We shall refer to this chance mechanism as the distribution of x. Since either function $f(x)$ or $F(x)$ provides a quantitative description of the distribution of x, we can use terminology such as the random variable x having the distribution $f(x)$ or the random variable x having the distribution $F(x)$.

7-7° EXAMPLES OF DENSITY FUNCTIONS

Any integrable function $\psi(x)$ of an ordinary variable x, which is defined for each point in X, is non-negative for each point in X, and also has the property that $\int_X \psi(x)\, dx > 0$, can be converted very simply into a function $f(x)$, which will serve as a density function for the model $\mathcal{E}$ whose event set is X, that is, as a density function for a random variable x defined over X. To see this, let

$$\alpha = \int_X \psi(x)\, dx.$$

By assumption $\alpha > 0$. Consider then the function $f(x) = \psi(x)/\alpha$. The function $f(x)$ is also integrable, defined for every point in X and non-negative for every such point. Furthermore,

$$\int_X f(x)\, dx = \frac{1}{\alpha} \int_X \psi(x)\, dx = 1.$$

Hence $f(x)$ will serve as a legitimate density function. Any function $f(x)$ with domain X which is non-negative over X and such that (7-28) holds can be used as a density function for the random variable x. Let us now provide some examples.

1.   Let X be the set of numbers ξ, $a \le \xi \le b$, $b > a$, and $\psi(x) = \lambda > 0$, so that $\psi(x)$ is equal to a positive constant over X. Then

$$\alpha = \int_X \psi(x)\, dx = \lambda \int_a^b dx = \lambda(b - a).$$

If $f(x) = \psi(x)/\alpha$, then

$$f(x) = \frac{1}{b - a} \qquad (7\text{-}48)$$

and $f(x)$ is a legitimate density function for the random variable x whose set of possible values is the event set X. The graph of $f(x)$ with domain X is illustrated in Figure 7-20. This density function is an important one and is given a special name. It is called the *uniform or rectangular density function*, and a random variable with this density function is said to have a *uniform or rectangular distribution*. When x has a uniform distribution, every point in X has the same probability density. This corresponds to the case of equally likely events for event sets containing only a finite number of simple events.

The cumulative uniform distribution may be easily determined. By (7-45),

$$F(\xi) = \int_a^\xi \frac{1}{b - a}\, dx = \frac{1}{b - a}\int_a^\xi dx = \frac{\xi - a}{b - a}, \quad a \le \xi \le b. \qquad (7\text{-}49)$$

Thus over X, $F(x) = (x - a)/(b - a)$ and is a straight line as shown in Figure 7-21. Note that $F(a) = 0$ and $F(b) = 1$.

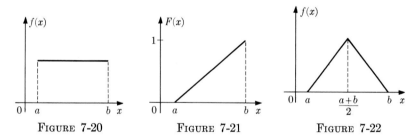

FIGURE 7-20   FIGURE 7-21   FIGURE 7-22

Situations frequently arise in the real world where it is convenient to imagine that a random variable is continuous and that this random variable has a uniform distribution. For example, a businessman may be expecting a telephone call between 9 and 12, and the precise time at which it arrives in this interval may be adequately represented as a random variable with a uniform distribution if no particular time interval is thought to have a higher probability than any other time interval. The same might be true of the arrival of a train or a plane.

An important characteristic of the uniform distribution is that for any interval A of length h which is in X, the probability that the value of x will be in A is $h/(b - a)$. To see this note that if A is the set $\alpha \le \xi \le \alpha + h$,

$$p(A) = \int_\alpha^{\alpha+h} \frac{dx}{b - a} = \frac{1}{b - a}[\alpha + h - \alpha] = \frac{h}{b - a}, \qquad (7\text{-}50)$$

and this is independent of α, that is, of where the initial point of the interval lies. Thus intervals of equal length all have the same probability, and the probability is proportional to the length of the interval. Hence the uniform distribution has, in the sense just referred to, the notion of equal probabilities implied in it.

2. It is not necessarily true that a density function $f(x)$ must be representable by a single formula over all of X. Let X again be the interval $a \leq \xi \leq b$, and consider the function

$$\psi(x) = \begin{cases} \beta(x - a), & \beta > 0, \ a \leq x \leq \dfrac{a + b}{2}, \\ \beta(b - x), & \dfrac{a + b}{2} < x \leq b. \end{cases} \tag{7-51}$$

Then $\psi(x) \geq 0$ over X and

$$\alpha = \int_X \psi(x) \, dx = \beta \int_a^{(a+b)/2} (x - a) \, dx + \beta \int_{(a+b)/2}^b (b - x) \, dx$$

$$= \frac{\beta}{8} [(b - a)^2 + (b - a)^2] = \frac{\beta(b - a)^2}{4}.$$

Then $f(x) = \psi(x)/\alpha$ is a legitimate density function with domain X, and

$$f(x) = \begin{cases} \dfrac{4(x - a)}{(b - a)^2}, & a \leq x \leq \dfrac{a + b}{2}, \\ \dfrac{4(b - x)}{(b - a)^2}, & \dfrac{a + b}{2} < x \leq b. \end{cases} \tag{7-52}$$

This density function is illustrated in Figure 7-22. At $x = (a + b)/2$, $f(x) = 2/(b - a)$.

3. Consider now a case where X consists of the set of all numbers ξ, $\xi \geq 0$. When the set X is unbounded, as in the case under consideration, one has much less freedom in selecting density functions than in cases where X is an interval of finite length. The reason for this is that in the unbounded case it is necessary that the integral (7-30) or (7-31) converge. In order for this to be true $f(x)$ must go to zero sufficiently rapidly as x becomes very large (and/or very small). The function $\psi(x) = e^{-\lambda x}$, $\lambda > 0$ is defined and is non-negative for every value of $x \geq 0$. Furthermore,

$$\alpha = \int_0^\infty e^{-\lambda x} \, dx = \lim_{t \to \infty} \int_0^t e^{-\lambda x} \, dx$$

$$= \lim_{t \to \infty} \left[\frac{1}{\lambda} (1 - e^{-\lambda t}) \right] = \frac{1}{\lambda}, \tag{7-53}$$

so that the integral converges and has the value $1/\lambda$. Consequently, we see that the function

$$f(x) = \lambda e^{-\lambda x}, \quad x \geq 0 \qquad (7\text{-}54)$$

is a legitimate density function for the event set X consisting of all non-negative numbers. The graph of $f(x)$ is shown in Figure 7-23. This

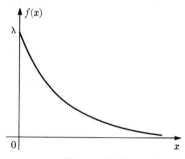

FIGURE 7-23

density function is one which arises frequently and is given a special name. It is called the *exponential density function or exponential distribution*.

4. Let $\mathcal{E}$ be a model with the event set X and density function $f(x)$. Let A be the event that $x \leq \alpha$ and B be the event that $x < \alpha$. We can easily prove that both of these events have the same probability, i.e., $p(A) = p(B)$. To do this, note that $A = B \cup C$ where C is the event $x = \alpha$. Now $B \cap C = \varnothing$, and therefore by (7-36) $p(A) = p(B) + p(C)$. However, by (7-34), $p(C) = 0$ since this is the event that $x = \alpha$. Thus the result follows.

5. In this chapter we have introduced the notion of a continuous random variable x having the characteristic that $p(x = \xi) = 0$ for every $\xi \in X$, but also having the characteristic that for every $\xi \in X$ there is given a probability density $f(\xi)$. In previous chapters we studied discrete random variables having the characteristic that for each value x_i which x can take on we have given a probability $p(x_i)$. On occasions one encounters situations where it is necessary to combine the notions of a discrete and continuous random variables into a single model. To be specific let us consider a model $\mathcal{E}$ having an event set X in which the simple events are numbers. Let us suppose that X is the union of two sets of numbers Y and Z where $Y \cap Z = \varnothing$. We shall assume that Y contains only a finite set of m numbers, while Z contains a continuum of a form such as (7-25), (7-26), or (7-27). Assume that for each number $\xi_i \in Y$, there is given a positive probability $p(\xi_i)$. Assume also that for each number ζ in Z, $p(\zeta) = 0$,

but there is specified a probability density $f(\zeta)$, $f(\zeta) \geq 0$. Instead of (1-7) or (7-28), we shall use as an axiom for this model the requirement that

$$\sum_{i=1}^{m} p(\xi_i) + \int_Z f(x)\, dx = 1. \tag{7-55}$$

Let A be some event, which will be a subset of X. We then take as an axiom for this model the requirement that the probability of A is

$$p(A) = \sum_{A \cap Y} p(\xi_i) + \int_{A \cap Z} f(x)\, dx, \tag{7-56}$$

where the symbolism on the summation sign indicates that we sum over those $\xi_i \in A \cap Y$. This model is a direct generalization of the two types of models which we have considered previously. We can look at the set X as being the set of possible values which a random variable x can take on. The random variable x will be called a mixed discrete-continuous random variable.

We have already studied an example where a model of the type just considered would be appropriate. Consider once again the structure that the geologist is studying. We can think of the amount of oil in place as a random variable x which perhaps can take on any value in the interval $0 \leq x \leq 100$ million. Now the value $x = 0$ is different from the other x values. It seems reasonable that the probability that $x = 0$ is positive and may be quite large, perhaps $p(0) = 0.8$. On the other hand, the probability that x takes on any other value, say $x = 100{,}101.5$ barrels, is essentially 0, and we can imagine that for our model, it is 0. However, associated with any positive value of x, say ξ, in the interval there is a probability density $f(\xi)$. Thus for this case the set Y contains the single number 0 and Z is the set of numbers ξ, $0 < \xi \leq 100$ million. In the future, we shall have very little occasion to use mixed discrete continuous random variables.

7-8°   RANDOM VARIABLES WHICH ARE FUNCTIONS OF x

Consider a probability model $\mathcal{E}$ having an event set X of the type discussed in Section 7-6 and having associated with each element ξ of X a probability density $f(\xi)$. We shall look at X as being the set of values which a continuous random variable x can take on. Let us now imagine that we associate with each number $\xi \in X$ another number $\zeta = \Theta(\xi)$. This rule of association then defines a function which we can represent symbolically as $y = \Theta(x)$. Let us imagine that this function whose domain is X has a range Y which is also a set of the type considered in Section 7-6.

We can then think of $\Theta(x)$ as defining a new continuous random variable y, and we shall say that y is a function of the random variable x.

Given the notion of a continuous random variable y which is a function of x, we can now proceed to introduce the notion of the expected value of y. To see how the expected value of y should be defined, we can imagine that $\mathcal{E}$ is our mathematical approximation of a situation where x can take on a large number m of values x_i with the probability of x_i being $p(x_i)$. In this case, from our previous work, we know that

$$\mu_y = \sum_{i=1}^{m} \Theta(x_i)p(x_i).$$

Now $p(x_i) \doteq f(x_i)h_i$, where h_i is the length of the base of the rectangle for x_i in the histogram for x. Thus

$$\mu_y \doteq \sum_{i=1}^{m} \Theta(x_i)f(x_i)h_i. \tag{7-57}$$

But this latter sum is essentially

$$\int_X \Theta(x)f(x)\ dx. \tag{7-58}$$

Hence for model $\mathcal{E}$ where x can take on a continuum of values we shall simply use (7-58) to be the definition of the expected value μ_y of y. Thus by definition

$$\mu_y = \int_X \Theta(x)f(x)\ dx. \tag{7-59}$$

Just as in the case of a discrete random variable, μ_y can be interpreted intuitively as the long run average value of y that would be obtained on making many independent trials of the relevant random experiment $\mathcal{R}$.

If in (7-59) we set $y = x$, so that $\Theta(x) = x$, then the expected value of x, μ_x, is

$$\mu_x = \int_X xf(x)\ dx. \tag{7-60}$$

The variance of x, $\sigma_x{}^2$, is defined to be the expected value of the variable $y = (x - \mu_x)^2$. Thus

$$\sigma_x{}^2 = \int_X (x - \mu_x)^2 f(x)\ dx. \tag{7-61}$$

As in the discrete case, we call $\sigma_x = \sqrt{\sigma_x{}^2}$ the standard deviation of x; σ_x is a rough measure of the sort of fluctuations about μ_x that can be expected to occur when $\mathcal{R}$ is repeated many times.

Suppose now that we have two random variables t and y defined in terms of x by the functions $t = \Theta_1(x)$, $y = \Theta_2(x)$. Then

$$z = at + by + cx + d \tag{7-62}$$

is also a random variable which is a function of x, say $z = \Theta(x)$, for any numbers a, b, c, and d, and

$$\Theta(x) = a\Theta_1(x) + b\Theta_2(x) + cx + d.$$

The expected value of z, μ_z, is

$$\mu_z = \int_X \Theta(x)f(x)\,dx = a\int_X \Theta_1(x)f(x)\,dx + b\int_X \Theta_2(x)f(x)\,dx$$

$$+ c\int_X xf(x)\,dx + d\int_X f(x)\,dx.$$

Thus

$$\mu_z = a\mu_t + b\mu_y + c\mu_x + d. \tag{7-63}$$

This result is precisely the same as (1-62) for discrete random variables, and (7-63) clearly holds when z is defined in terms of any finite number of other random variables.

We have defined σ_x^2 to be the expected value of $(x - \mu_x)^2$. However,

$$(x - \mu_x)^2 = x^2 - 2\mu_x x + \mu_x^2.$$

Hence from (7-63), σ_x^2 is the expected value of x^2 minus $2\mu_x$ times the expected value of x (which is μ_x) plus μ_x^2, thus

$$\sigma_x^2 = \int_X x^2 f(x)\,dx - \mu_x^2, \tag{7-64}$$

which is the analog of (1-71).

As another illustration of the use of (7-63), suppose that x is a continuous random variable with expected value μ_x and standard deviation σ_x. Consider the new random variable $t = (x - \mu)/\sigma_x$. Then by (7-63), μ_t, the expected value of t, is $1/\sigma_x$ times the expected value of x minus μ_x/σ_x, i.e., $\mu_t = 0$. The variance of t, σ_t^2 is then the expected value of t^2, i.e., $(x - \mu_x)^2/\sigma_x^2$. But the expected value of $(x - \mu_x)^2$ is σ_x^2. Hence $\sigma_t^2 = 1$. Thus t is a random variable with an expected value of 0 and standard deviation 1.

Equations (7-60) and (7-61) define the expected value and variance of the random variable x. We also refer to μ_x and σ_x^2 as the *mean and variance* of the density function $f(x)$ and of the distribution for x. This is the same terminology used for the discrete case.

Consider once again the random variable $y = \Theta(x)$. Just as we did for discrete random variables, we can construct a model in which the event set is the set Y of values which y can take on. The set Y is the range of the function $\Theta(x)$ when the domain is X. To complete the model, one must determine the density function $g(y)$ for y. This is not always an easy task. We shall show how it can be done in some simple and important cases, however. Generally, it is best to determine first $G(y)$, the cumulative distribution of y, and then obtain $g(y)$ by differentiation.

To be specific, let X be the set of all real numbers. First suppose that $y = ax + b$, $a > 0$. Then Y is also the set of all real numbers since, given any real number ζ, there is a value of ξ such that $\zeta = a\xi + b$. Consider now $G(\zeta)$, the probability that $y \leq \zeta$. Denote by A the subset of X for which $y \leq \zeta$. Then $G(\zeta) = p(A)$. To determine A, note that if y satisfies $y \leq \zeta$ and $y = ax + b$, then $ax + b \leq \zeta$ or $ax \leq \zeta - b$ or $x \leq (\zeta - b)/a$, since $a > 0$. Furthermore, any value of x satisfying this latter inequality yields a value of y satisfying $y \leq \zeta$. Hence A is the set $x \leq (\zeta - b)/a$, and $p(A) = F[(\zeta - b)/a]$ where $F(x)$ is the cumulative distribution for $f(x)$. Therefore

$$G(\zeta) = F\left(\frac{\zeta - b}{a}\right), \tag{7-65}$$

and

$$g(\zeta) = G'(\zeta) = F'\left(\frac{\zeta - b}{a}\right) = \frac{1}{a} f\left(\frac{\zeta - b}{a}\right) \tag{7-66}$$

on using the chain rule for differentiating a compound function. Thus

$$g(y) = \frac{1}{a} f\left(\frac{y - b}{a}\right); \quad y = ax + b, \quad a > 0, \tag{7-67}$$

and $g(y)$ has been expressed in terms of $f(x)$, the density function for x.

As a final example consider the case where $y = x^2$ and X is again the set of all real numbers. Now Y is the set $y \geq 0$, i.e., the set of all nonnegative numbers. Consider next the determination of $G(\zeta)$, the probability that $y \leq \zeta$. Let A be the subset of X for which $y \leq \zeta$. If a given value of y satisfies this relation and $y = x^2$, then $x^2 \leq \zeta$. This will be true if and only if $-\sqrt{\zeta} \leq x \leq \sqrt{\zeta}$. Hence this is the set A. To determine the probability of A, note that if C is the set $x \leq \sqrt{\zeta}$ and B is the set $x < -\sqrt{\zeta}$, then $C = A \cup B$ and $A \cap B = \varnothing$. Hence $p(C) = p(A) + p(B)$. But $p(C) = F(\sqrt{\zeta})$ and $p(B) = F(-\sqrt{\zeta})$. Consequently,

$$p(A) = G(\zeta) = F(\sqrt{\zeta}) - F(-\sqrt{\zeta}), \tag{7-68}$$

and on differentiating

$$g(\zeta) = \frac{1}{2\sqrt{\zeta}} [f(\sqrt{\zeta}) + f(-\sqrt{\zeta})], \quad \zeta > 0,$$

that is,

$$g(y) = \frac{1}{2\sqrt{y}} [f(\sqrt{y}) + f(-\sqrt{y})], \quad y > 0, \quad y = x^2. \tag{7-69}$$

In this case $g(y)$ is a more complicated function. Equation (7-69) holds only for $y > 0$. We can define $g(0)$ to be anything at all without influencing the model, since the value of a function at a single point has no influence on the values of definite integrals of this function. We shall later give some specific applications of the results just obtained.

7-9° EXAMPLES

1. We can easily compute the mean and variance of the uniform distribution (7-48). The mean μ is

$$\mu = \frac{1}{b-a} \int_a^b x\, dx = \frac{1}{2} \frac{b^2 - a^2}{b-a} = \frac{1}{2}(b+a) \qquad (7\text{-}70)$$

and is the midpoint of the interval X. The variance σ^2 is by (7-64)

$$\sigma^2 = \frac{1}{b-a} \int_a^b x^2\, dx - \frac{1}{4}(b+a)^2 = \frac{1}{3}\frac{b^3 - a^3}{b-a} - \frac{1}{4}(b+a)^2$$

$$= \frac{1}{3}(b^2 + ab + a^2) - \frac{1}{4}(b^2 + 2ab + a^2) = \frac{1}{12}(b-a)^2. \qquad (7\text{-}71)$$

2. Let us next compute the mean and variance of the exponential distribution (7-54). The mean μ is

$$\mu = \lambda \int_0^\infty x e^{-\lambda x}\, dx. \qquad (7\text{-}72)$$

This integral does converge, and to evaluate it we use the integration by parts formula

$$\int f_1(x) f_2'(x)\, dx = f_1(x) f_2(x) - \int f_2(x) f_1'(x)\, dx. \qquad (7\text{-}73)$$

Let $f_1(x) = \lambda x$ and $f_2'(x) = e^{-\lambda x}$. A primitive function for $f_2'(x)$ is $f_2(x) = -e^{-\lambda x}/\lambda$. Thus

$$\lambda \int_0^t x e^{-\lambda x}\, dx = -t e^{-\lambda t} + \int_0^t e^{-\lambda x}\, dx = -t e^{-\lambda t} - \frac{1}{\lambda} e^{-\lambda t} + \frac{1}{\lambda}. \quad (7\text{-}74)$$

Taking the limit as $t \to \infty$, we see that the terms involving t go to 0, and therefore

$$\mu = \frac{1}{\lambda}. \qquad (7\text{-}75)$$

Similarly the variance σ^2 is

$$\sigma^2 = \lambda \int_0^\infty x^2 e^{-\lambda x}\, dx - \frac{1}{\lambda^2}. \qquad (7\text{-}76)$$

The integral does converge, and to evaluate it we use integration by parts twice, first setting $f_1(x) = \lambda x^2$ and $f_2'(x) = e^{-\lambda x}$. Thus

$$\lambda \int_0^t x^2 e^{-\lambda x}\, dx = -t^2 e^{-\lambda t} + 2 \int_0^t x e^{-\lambda x}\, dx. \qquad (7\text{-}77)$$

The second integral is, except for the factor λ, just the integral evaluated above. Thus

$$\lambda \int_0^t x^2 e^{-\lambda x}\, dx = -t^2 e^{-\lambda t} - \frac{2t}{\lambda} e^{-\lambda t} - \frac{2}{\lambda^2} e^{-\lambda t} + \frac{2}{\lambda^2}. \qquad (7\text{-}78)$$

Taking the limit as $t \to \infty$, we see that all terms involving t go to 0 leaving $2/\lambda^2$. Hence from (7-76),

$$\sigma^2 = \frac{2}{\lambda^2} - \frac{1}{\lambda^2} = \frac{1}{\lambda^2}, \qquad (7\text{-}79)$$

and

$$\sigma = \frac{1}{\lambda}, \qquad (7\text{-}80)$$

so that μ and σ are numerically equal.

7-10° THE NORMAL DISTRIBUTION

In Section 7-4 we introduced the function

$$n(x; \mu, \sigma) = \frac{1}{\sigma\sqrt{2\pi}} e^{-(x-\mu)^2/2\sigma^2}, \qquad (7\text{-}81)$$

called the normal density function or normal distribution. It was suggested that this was a legitimate density function for a random variable which could take on any real value, and it was indicated that the mean and variance of the normal density function are μ and σ^2, respectively. Let us now prove these facts. From (7-81) we see that $n(\xi; \mu, \sigma) > 0$ for every real number ξ. To show that it is a density function over the set X of all real numbers, it remains to show that

$$\int_{-\infty}^{\infty} n(x; \mu, \sigma)\, dx = \frac{1}{\sigma\sqrt{2\pi}} \int_{-\infty}^{\infty} e^{-(x-\mu)^2/2\sigma^2}\, dx = 1. \qquad (7\text{-}82)$$

We shall now make a change of variable in the integral by introducing the new variable $t = h(x) = (x - \mu)/\sigma$. Then $h'(x) = 1/\sigma$ (i.e., $dt = dx/\sigma$, using differential notation), and when $x = \infty$, $t = \infty$; also when $x = -\infty$, $t = -\infty$. Thus

$$\int_{-\infty}^{\infty} n(x; \mu, \sigma)\, dx = \frac{1}{\sqrt{2\pi}} \int_{-\infty}^{\infty} e^{-t^2/2}\, dt = \int_{-\infty}^{\infty} \varphi(t)\, dt, \qquad (7\text{-}83)$$

where $\varphi(t)$ is the standardized normal density function (7-1). Thus we see that if the standardized normal density function integrates to 1 so will $n(x; \mu, \sigma)$ for any μ, and $\sigma > 0$.

To show that $\varphi(t)$ integrates to 1 is not straightforward. We shall use a method which involves a trick. Let

$$\alpha = \int_{-\infty}^{\infty} \varphi(t) \, dt. \qquad (7\text{-}84)$$

Then

$$\alpha^2 = \left[\int_{-\infty}^{\infty} \varphi(t) \, dt \right] \left[\int_{-\infty}^{\infty} \varphi(s) \, ds \right] = \frac{1}{2\pi} \int_{-\infty}^{\infty} \int_{-\infty}^{\infty} e^{-(t^2+s^2)/2} \, dt \, ds, \qquad (7\text{-}85)$$

and we have expressed α^2 as a double integral of the function

$$(1/2\pi)e^{-(t^2+s^2)/2}$$

over the entire ts-plane. The trick is to now convert to polar coordinates by writing $r^2 = t^2 + s^2$ and $dt \, ds = r \, d\Theta \, dr$. To integrate over the entire plane, r ranges from 0 to ∞ and Θ from 0 to 2π. Thus

$$\alpha^2 = \frac{1}{2\pi} \int_0^{\infty} \int_0^{2\pi} re^{-r^2/2} \, dr \, d\Theta = \int_0^{\infty} re^{-r^2/2} \, dr, \qquad (7\text{-}86)$$

since one can immediately integrate with respect to Θ. Now introduce the new variable $z = r^2/2$ (so that $dz = rdr$). When $r = 0$, $z = 0$; and when $r = \infty$, $z = \infty$. Hence

$$\alpha^2 = \int_0^{\infty} e^{-z} \, dz = \lim_{u \to \infty} [-e^{-u} + 1] = 1. \qquad (7\text{-}87)$$

Therefore $\alpha^2 = 1$ and $\alpha = 1$ or -1. However, α cannot be negative, so $\alpha = 1$, which is what we wished to show. Therefore, the normal density function is a legitimate density function.

To prove that μ is the expected value of $n(x; \mu, \sigma)$, it must be shown that

$$\mu = \int_{-\infty}^{\infty} x \, n(x; \mu, \sigma) \, dx. \qquad (7\text{-}88)$$

We ask the reader to do this in the problems.

To determine the variance of $n(x; \mu, \sigma)$, we must evaluate the integral

$$\frac{1}{\sigma\sqrt{2\pi}} \int_{-\infty}^{\infty} (x-\mu)^2 e^{-(x-\mu)^2/2\sigma^2} \, dx = \frac{\sigma^2}{\sqrt{2\pi}} \int_{-\infty}^{\infty} \left(\frac{x-\mu}{\sigma}\right)^2 e^{-(x-\mu)^2/2\sigma^2} \frac{dx}{\sigma}$$

$$= \frac{\sigma^2}{\sqrt{2\pi}} \int_{-\infty}^{\infty} t^2 e^{-t^2/2} \, dt. \qquad (7\text{-}89)$$

The change of variable $t = (x - \mu)/\sigma$ was used to obtain the above result. The latter integral can be integrated by parts if one writes $f_1(t) = t$ and $f_2'(t) = te^{-t^2/2}$ (so that a primitive function is $f_2(t) = -e^{-t^2/2}$). Thus

$$\frac{\sigma^2}{\sqrt{2\pi}} \int_{-\infty}^{\infty} t^2 e^{-t^2/2} \, dt = \frac{\sigma^2}{\sqrt{2\pi}} \int_{-\infty}^{\infty} e^{-t^2/2} \, dt = \sigma^2 \int_{-\infty}^{\infty} \varphi(t) \, dt = \sigma^2 \qquad (7\text{-}90)$$

since $f_1(t)f_2(t)$ becomes 0 at both limits. The integral does indeed have the value σ^2, and this is the variance of the normal distribution.

We shall use the symbol $N(x; \mu, \sigma)$ to denote the cumulative normal distribution. Inasmuch as $N(\xi; \mu, \sigma)$ is the probability that $x \leq \xi$, it follows on introducing the change of variable $t = (x - \mu)/\sigma$ that

$$N(\xi; \mu, \sigma) = \int_{-\infty}^{\xi} n(x; \mu, \sigma) \, dx = \int_{-\infty}^{(\xi-\mu)/\sigma} \varphi(t) \, dt = \Phi\left(\frac{\xi - \mu}{\sigma}\right). \quad (7\text{-}91)$$

Thus we have proved (7-20), a result which we obtained previously by a non-rigorous argument. As we have noted previously, it is not possible to express

$$\Phi(t) = \int_{-\infty}^{t} \varphi(\zeta) \, d\zeta \quad (7\text{-}92)$$

in terms of the elementary functions; $\Phi(t)$ is simply a new type of function, and to use $\Phi(t)$, it is necessary to construct tables of this function such as Table E at the end of the text.

Often it is of interest to know the probability that the value of a normally distributed random variable will be more than α standard deviations away from the mean, that is, the probability that $|x - \mu| > \alpha\sigma$. This is the probability that $x < \mu - \alpha\sigma$ or that $x > \mu + \alpha\sigma$. Hence $p(|x - \mu| > \alpha\sigma)$, the probability of the event $|x - \mu| > \alpha\sigma$, is

$$p(|x - \mu| > \alpha\sigma) = \Phi\left(\frac{-\alpha\sigma}{\sigma}\right) + 1 - \Phi\left(\frac{\alpha\sigma}{\sigma}\right) = 2[1 - \Phi(\alpha)]. \quad (7\text{-}93)$$

From Table E we see that

$$p(|x - \mu| > \sigma) = 0.3173; \quad (7\text{-}94)$$

$$p(|x - \mu| > 2\sigma) = 0.0455; \quad (7\text{-}95)$$

$$p(|x - \mu| > 3\sigma) = 0.0026. \quad (7\text{-}96)$$

What (7-96) says, for example, is that the long run relative frequency with which x lies more than three standard deviations from the mean is only 2.6 in a 1000. It is useful to remember roughly the three numbers given in (7-94) through (7-96).

We shall conclude this section by obtaining one more useful result. Let x have the normal distribution $n(x; \mu, \sigma)$. Consider now the random variable $y = x - \mu$. By (7-67) the density function for y is $n(y + \mu; \mu, \sigma)$ which is simply $n(y; 0, \sigma)$. Hence y has a normal distribution with mean 0 and standard deviation σ. Let us next introduce the random variable $z = y^2 = (x - \mu)^2$. By (7-69), the domain for z is the set of all non-negative numbers, and the density function $g(z)$ for z is

$$g(z) = \frac{1}{2\sqrt{z}}[n(\sqrt{z}; 0, \sigma) + n(-\sqrt{z}; 0, \sigma)] = \frac{1}{\sqrt{z}} n(\sqrt{z}; 0, \sigma)$$

$$= \frac{1}{\sigma\sqrt{2\pi z}} e^{-z/2\sigma^2} = \frac{z^{-1/2}}{\sigma\sqrt{2\pi}} e^{-z/2\sigma^2}. \quad (7\text{-}97)$$

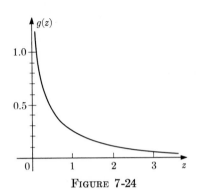

FIGURE 7-24

This density function is a special case of what we shall call a gamma density function in the next section. The graph of $g(z)$ for $\sigma = 1$ is shown in Figure 7-24. Note that $g(z)$ has a vertical asymptote at $z = 0$. We can define $g(0)$ to be anything we like, or leave it undefined. It does not make any difference.

We have given examples illustrating the use of the normal distribution in Section 7-5. We shall not give any more at this point.

7-11° THE GAMMA DISTRIBUTIONS

Consider the function

$$\psi_n(x) = \lambda(\lambda x)^n e^{-\lambda x}, \quad x \geq 0, \quad \lambda > 0, \tag{7-98}$$

where n is a non-negative integer. If $n = 0$, the reader will recognize that $\psi_n(x)$ reduces to the exponential distribution. We would like to show that any such function $\psi_n(x)$ can be converted into a legitimate density function for a random variable which can take on all non-negative values. To do this consider

$$\int_0^t \lambda(\lambda x)^n e^{-\lambda x} \, dx = \int_0^{\lambda t} y^n e^{-y} \, dy \tag{7-99}$$

for $n \geq 1$. Integration by parts with $f_1(y) = y^n$ and $f_2'(y) = e^{-y}$ yields

$$\int_0^t y^n e^{-y} \, dy = -y^n e^{-y} \big|_0^t + n \int_0^t y^{n-1} e^{-y} \, dy.$$

On taking the limit as $t \to \infty$, we see that

$$\int_0^\infty \psi_n(x) \, dx = n \int_0^\infty \psi_{n-1}(x) \, dx, \tag{7-100}$$

provided the integral on the right exists. But when $n \geq 2$,

$$\int_0^\infty \psi_{n-1}(x)\, dx = (n - 1) \int_0^\infty \psi_{n-2}(x)\, dx$$

if the integral on the right exists; thus

$$\int_0^\infty \psi_n(x)\, dx = n(n - 1) \int_0^\infty \psi_{n-2}(x)\, dx,$$

and on continuing this process, we conclude that

$$\int_0^\infty \psi_n(x)\, dx = n! \int_0^\infty \psi_0(x)\, dx \tag{7-101}$$

if the integral on the right exists. However, $\psi_0(x) = \lambda e^{-\lambda x}$ and we know since this is the exponential density function that the integral exists and has the value 1. Therefore, for every non-negative integer n

$$\int_0^\infty \psi_n(x)\, dx = n!. \tag{7-102}$$

Given (7-102), we see that each of the functions

$$g(x; n,\lambda) = \frac{\lambda(\lambda x)^n}{n!} e^{-\lambda x}, \quad \lambda > 0 \tag{7-103}$$

for n a non-negative integer is a legitimate density function for a random variable x when the domain X of the functions is taken to be the set of all non-negative real numbers, since $g(\xi; n,\lambda) \geq 0$ for each $\xi \geq 0$ and (7-103) integrates to unity. The density function $g(x; n,\lambda)$ is called a *gamma density function or gamma distribution of order n*, and the random variable x is said to have a gamma distribution of order n if its density function is $g(x; n,\lambda)$. The expression for $g(x; n,\lambda)$ looks a lot like the Poisson probability function. In fact

$$g(x; n,\lambda) = \lambda p(n; \lambda x). \tag{7-104}$$

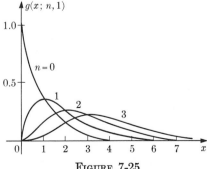

FIGURE 7-25

In Figure 7-25 we have illustrated the graphs of $g(x; n, \lambda)$ for several values of n and $\lambda = 1$.

It can be easily proved using the convergence test for improper integrals, which we shall not digress to consider (see [9]), that

$$\int_0^\infty \lambda(\lambda x)^\alpha e^{-\lambda x}\, dx, \quad \lambda > 0$$

converges for every real number $\alpha > -1$. Denote the value of this integral by $\Gamma(\alpha + 1)$. Then for every $\alpha > -1$ we can associate with α a number $\Gamma(\alpha + 1)$. This association defines a function which is called the *gamma function*. By definition

$$\Gamma(\alpha + 1) = \int_0^\infty \lambda(\lambda x)^\alpha e^{-\lambda x}\, dx = \int_0^\infty y^\alpha e^{-y}\, dy, \quad \lambda > 0. \quad (7\text{-}105)$$

We define (7-105) to be $\Gamma(\alpha + 1)$ rather than $\Gamma(\alpha)$ because by convention, for $\Gamma(\alpha)$, $\alpha - 1$ appears in the integral. We might note that from what we have proved above, $\Gamma(n + 1) = n!$ when n is a non-negative integer. Observe that the value of the integral in (7-105) is independent of λ, and $\Gamma(\alpha + 1) > 0$ for all $\alpha > -1$.

We can now see that any function

$$g(x; \alpha, \lambda) = \frac{\lambda(\lambda x)^\alpha}{\Gamma(\alpha + 1)}\, e^{-\lambda x}, \quad \lambda > 0, \quad \alpha > -1 \quad (7\text{-}106)$$

can serve as a legitimate density function for a random variable x which can take on any positive value. When $\alpha < 0$, $g(x; \alpha, \lambda)$ is not defined at $x = 0$ and $g(x; \alpha, \lambda)$ has a vertical asymptote at $x = 0$, so that the integral (7-105) is in this case also improper at $x = 0$. We shall not bother to define $g(x; \alpha, \lambda)$ at $x = 0$ when $\alpha < 0$ since it is irrelevant how the definition is made. The functions (7-103) are special cases of (7-106). Any function of the form (7-106) is called a *gamma density function or gamma distribution*, and the associated random variable x is said to have a gamma distribution.

It is very easy to compute the mean μ and variance σ^2 of any gamma distribution $g(x; \alpha, \lambda)$ since

$$\mu = \frac{\lambda}{\Gamma(\alpha + 1)} \int_0^\infty x(\lambda x)^\alpha e^{-\lambda x}\, dx = \frac{\lambda \Gamma(\alpha + 2)}{\lambda \Gamma(\alpha + 1)\Gamma(\alpha + 2)} \int_0^\infty (\lambda x)^{\alpha+1} e^{-\lambda x}\, dx$$

$$= \frac{1}{\lambda} \frac{\Gamma(\alpha + 2)}{\Gamma(\alpha + 1)} \int_0^\infty g(x; \alpha + 1, \lambda)\, dx = \frac{1}{\lambda} \frac{\Gamma(\alpha + 2)}{\Gamma(\alpha + 1)}. \quad (7\text{-}107)$$

If we integrate

$$\Gamma(\alpha + 2) = \int_0^\infty y^{\alpha+1} e^{-y}\, dy$$

by parts setting $f_1(y) = y^{\alpha+1}$ and $f_2'(y) = e^{-y}$, we obtain

$$\Gamma(\alpha + 2) = (\alpha + 1)\Gamma(\alpha + 1), \tag{7-108}$$

so that we see that for $g(x; \alpha,\lambda)$

$$\mu = \frac{\alpha + 1}{\lambda}. \tag{7-109}$$

In the same way we see that

$$\sigma^2 = \frac{\lambda}{\Gamma(\alpha + 1)} \int_0^\infty x^2(\lambda x)^\alpha e^{-\lambda x}\, dx - \mu^2$$

$$= \frac{1}{\lambda^2} \frac{\Gamma(\alpha + 3)}{\Gamma(\alpha + 1)} - \frac{(\alpha + 1)^2}{\lambda^2} = \frac{1}{\lambda^2}\left[(\alpha + 2)(\alpha + 1) - (\alpha + 1)^2\right],$$

so that

$$\sigma^2 = \frac{\alpha + 1}{\lambda^2}. \tag{7-110}$$

As α gets larger and larger, $g(x; \alpha,\lambda)$ gets closer and closer to the normal distribution having the same mean and variance as $g(x; \alpha,\lambda)$. That this is reasonable can be seen from Figure 7-25. Later we shall provide a justification for this behavior. More precisely

$$g(x; \alpha,\lambda) \doteq n\left(x; \frac{\alpha + 1}{\lambda}, \frac{\sqrt{\alpha + 1}}{\lambda}\right), \quad \alpha \text{ large.} \tag{7-111}$$

When α is large, probability computations involving the gamma distribution can be made using the normal distribution.

The gamma distributions form a very important class of distributions and they arise in a variety of ways as we shall see in somewhat greater detail later.

It happens to be the case that $\Gamma(\frac{1}{2}) = \sqrt{\pi}$, although we shall not attempt to prove this. However, if in (7-106) we set $\lambda = 1/2\sigma^2$ and $\alpha = -\frac{1}{2}$, we obtain on using $\Gamma(\frac{1}{2}) = \sqrt{\pi}$

$$g(x; -\tfrac{1}{2}, 1/2\sigma^2) = \frac{x^{-1/2}}{\sigma\sqrt{2\pi}} e^{-x/2\sigma^2}, \tag{7-112}$$

which on comparison with (7-97) shows that $g(z)$ of (7-97) is a gamma distribution with $\alpha = -\frac{1}{2}$ and $\lambda = 1/2\sigma^2$.

7-12° JOINT AND CONDITIONAL DENSITY FUNCTIONS

Consider a random experiment $\Re$ involving two random variables x and y, which it is convenient to treat as continuous random variables. We would now like to develop in a method analogous to Section 6-7 a model $\mathcal{E}$ which will allow us to make probability computations involving x and y. If y is a function of x or vice versa, we already know how to handle the problem. Thus in our present development we shall not make any such restriction.

Suppose that X is the set of values which x can take on and Y is the set of values which y can take on. We shall assume that X and Y are sets of the type discussed in Section 7-6. Consider now the set $W = X \times Y$. Each element of W will be an ordered pair of numbers of the form (ξ,ζ), where ξ is one of the possible values of x and ζ is one of the possible values of y. Then (ξ,ζ) can be looked upon as a point in the xy-plane, and W can be thought of as the collection of all such points. If X is the set $2 \leq \xi \leq 8$ and Y is the set $4 \leq \zeta \leq 8$, then W is the shaded rectangle shown in Figure 7-26. Every time $\mathfrak{R}$ is performed a value ξ of x and a

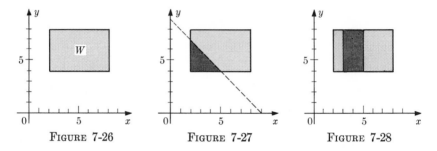

FIGURE 7-26   FIGURE 7-27   FIGURE 7-28

value ζ of y will be determined, i.e., an element $(\xi,\zeta) \in W$ is determined. To compute the probabilities of events involving both x and y, we need the equivalent of a joint probability function $p(x,y)$ for discrete random variables. To accomplish this we shall introduce a function $h(x,y)$, called the *joint probability density function* for x and y, having as its domain W. We shall require that $h(\xi,\zeta) \geq 0$ for every point $(\xi,\zeta) \in W$ and furthermore, the double integral of $h(\xi,\zeta)$ over W must be 1, so that

$$\iint_W h(x,y) \, dx \, dy = 1. \tag{7-113}$$

If D is any event involving x and y, i.e., is a subset of W, the probability of D will be taken to be

$$p(D) = \iint_D h(x,y) \, dx \, dy. \tag{7-114}$$

For example, if D is the event $x + y \leq 9$ when W is the set shown in Figure 7-26, then D is the darkly shaded set of points shown in Figure 7-27 and $p(D)$ is the integral of $h(x,y)$ over this triangular region. Suppose that D happens to be an event which makes a statement only about x, for example, say that $3 \leq x \leq 5$. For the event set of Figure 7-26, the event D is then the darkly shaded set of points shown in Figure 7-28. If A denotes the subset of X which corresponds to D, then $D = A \times Y$

and the double integral (7-114) can be represented as an iterated integral as follows:

$$p(D) = \int_A \left[\int_Y h(x,y) \, dy \right] dx, \qquad (7\text{-}115)$$

or for the particular example of Figure 7-28,

$$p(D) = \int_3^5 \left[\int_4^8 h(x,y) \, dy \right] dx.$$

Now since D involves only a statement about x, which says that x is in the subset A of X, then $p(D)$ should be capable of being determined from the density function $f(x)$ for x and should be

$$p(D) = \int_A f(x) \, dx. \qquad (7\text{-}116)$$

On comparing (7-115) and (7-116) we see it should be true that for every value ξ of x

$$f(\xi) = \int_Y h(\xi,y) \, dy, \qquad (7\text{-}117)$$

or symbolically the function $f(x)$ should be related to $h(x,y)$ by

$$f(x) = \int_Y h(x,y) \, dy. \qquad (7\text{-}118)$$

We shall require that this be the case. Similarly, we shall require that $g(y)$, the density function for y, is given by

$$g(y) = \int_X h(x,y) \, dx. \qquad (7\text{-}119)$$

Equations (7-118) and (7-119) are the analogs of (6-21) and (6-23) for discrete random variables. Our mathematical model $\mathcal{E}$ for dealing with the two random variables x and y will then be one for which the event set is W and for which we have defined a joint probability density $h(x,y)$ having the properties discussed above. When dealing with both a joint density function $h(x,y)$ for x and y as well as the density functions $f(x)$ and $g(y)$, it is convenient, in order to avoid confusion, to refer to $f(x)$ as the marginal density for x and $g(y)$ as the marginal density for y. This terminology is completely analogous to that used for discrete random variables.

Usually, but not always, when we are dealing with two continuous random variables, the random experiment $\mathcal{R}$ will either be one which is built up from two independent random experiments $\mathcal{R}_1$ and $\mathcal{R}_2$ with x referring to $\mathcal{R}_1$ and y to $\mathcal{R}_2$, or $\mathcal{R}$ will be a two stage random experiment in which x refers to the first stage and y to the second stage. Let us first consider the case where x is associated with $\mathcal{R}_1$ and y with $\mathcal{R}_2$ and $\mathcal{R}$ consists of performing independently $\mathcal{R}_1$ and $\mathcal{R}_2$. If the outcome of $\mathcal{R}_1$ can be satisfactorily described by the value of x and the outcome of $\mathcal{R}_2$ by the value of y, then $W = X \times Y$ will be a suitable event set for $\mathcal{R}$.   Let us now see that the joint probability function $h(x,y)$ for x and y can easily be obtained from the marginal density functions $f(x)$ and $g(y)$ for x and y, respectively. Suppose that A is a subset of X representing some event for $\mathcal{R}_1$, and B is a subset of Y representing an event for $\mathcal{R}_2$.   Consider the event D that the event A occurs on performing $\mathcal{R}_1$ and the event B occurs on performing $\mathcal{R}_2$, so that $D = A \cap B$ when A and B are thought of as subsets of W. When A is thought of as a subset of X and B as a subset of Y, then $D = A \times B$.   Since $\mathcal{R}_1$ and $\mathcal{R}_2$ are independent, we should have $p(D) = p(A)p(B)$.   However,

$$p(A) = \int_A f(x)\, dx; \quad p(B) = \int_B g(y)\, dy,$$

so

$$p(D) = \left[\int_A f(x)\, dx \right]\left[\int_B g(y)\, dy \right] = \int_B \left[\int_A f(x)g(y)\, dx \right] dy$$

$$= \iint_{A \times B} f(x)g(y)\, dx\, dy, \tag{7-120}$$

and we have expressed $p(D)$ as a double integral.   However, $p(D)$ should be given by (7-114).   Thus it appears that we should take the joint probability density function for x and y in this case to be $f(x)g(y)$, i.e.,

$$h(x,y) = f(x)g(y). \tag{7-121}$$

This is indeed what we shall do.   Equation (7-121) is the analog of (6-30) for discrete random variables.   Given this intuitive development, we shall now define what we mean by independent continuous random variables.

INDEPENDENT CONTINUOUS RANDOM VARIABLES.   *Two continuous random variables x and y are said to be independent if their joint probability density function $h(x,y)$ is equal to the product of the marginal density functions $f(x)$ and $g(y)$, that is, if (7-121) holds.*

Given a model $\mathcal{E}$ one can rigorously verify whether or not two random variables are independent.   Usually, however, one goes in the other direction using the intuitive notion of independent experiments to construct $\mathcal{E}$. When doing this, we see from what was obtained above that the random variables will be independent.

It is clear that if we are dealing with a random experiment involving several random variables we can introduce the notion of a joint density function for these random variables.   Furthermore, the random variables are said to be independent if the joint density function is the product of the marginal density functions for each of the random variables.

Let us now move on to studying cases where $\Re$ can be thought of as a two stage experiment in which $\Re_1$ will be the experiment for the first stage and $\Re_{\xi2}$ will be the experiment for the second stage. It will be imagined that the experiment for the second stage will depend on the value ξ of x observed as the result of the first stage. We shall imagine that the set of values which y takes on is Y independently of the outcome of $\Re_1$. However, the density function for y in $\Re_{\xi2}$ can in general depend on the value of x obtained when $\Re_1$ is performed. Denote by $f(x)$ the probability density function for x in $\Re_1$ and by $g(y|\xi)$ the probability density function for y in $\Re_{\xi2}$. It would now appear by analogy with (7-121) that $h(x,y)$, the joint probability density function for x and y, should be defined as

$$h(x,y) = g(y|x)f(x), \qquad (7\text{-}122)$$

and this is what we shall do.

Let us next introduce the notion of a conditional density function.

CONDITIONAL DENSITY FUNCTION. *Let $h(x,y)$ be the joint probability density function for x and y and suppose that the marginal density function $f(x)$ is not 0 at $x = \xi$. Then the function*

$$g(y|\xi) = \frac{h(\xi,y)}{f(\xi)} \qquad (7\text{-}123)$$

will be called the conditional probability density function for y given that $x = \xi$.

When in a two stage random experiment we define the joint density function by (7-122) it follows that $g(y|\xi)$ is the conditional density function for y given $x = \xi$, as we would expect intuitively that it should be. Conditional densities play the same role for continuous random variables that conditional probabilities do for discrete random variables. When $g(\zeta) \neq 0$ we define the conditional density function for x given that $y = \zeta$, which we shall denote by $f(x|\zeta)$ to be

$$f(x|\zeta) = \frac{h(x,\zeta)}{g(\zeta)}. \qquad (7\text{-}124)$$

When $f(\xi) \neq 0$ and $g(\zeta) \neq 0$, we see from (7-123) and (7-124) that

$$f(\xi|\zeta)g(\zeta) = g(\zeta|\xi)f(\xi),$$

or

$$f(\xi|\zeta) = \frac{g(\zeta|\xi)f(\xi)}{g(\zeta)}. \qquad (7\text{-}125)$$

Equation (7-125) is called Bayes' law for continuous random variables. As in the case of discrete random variables, Bayes' law is useful in situations where a two stage experiment is performed, the purpose of the second stage being to gain information about the first stage. We then look at the outcome of the second stage as serving to modify the density function for x at the first stage, that is, instead of using $f(x)$, we use

$$f(x|\zeta) = \frac{g(\zeta|x)f(x)}{g(\zeta)}.\tag{7-126}$$

The intuitive reasoning which indicates that (7-126) is what we should use for the density function for x, given that the second stage yields $y = \zeta$, is the following. In the real world both x and y are discrete and $p_1(\xi)$, the probability that $x = \xi$, is approximately $p_1(\xi) = f(\xi)h$, where h is the length of the base of the rectangle on the histogram for x at $x = \xi$. Similarly, $p_2(\zeta) = g(\zeta)u$ where u is the length of the base of the rectangle on the histogram for y at $y = \zeta$. Now if $p_2(\zeta|\xi)$ is the conditional probability that $y = \zeta$, given that $x = \xi$, then it must be equal to a conditional density, call it $g(\zeta|\xi)$, times u (since the lengths of the bases of the rectangles will be the same for the histogram for y given ξ as for y). Thus $p_2(\zeta|\xi) = g(\zeta|\xi)u$. Similarly, there is a function $f(x|\zeta)$ which approximates the histogram for x, given ζ, and hence $p_1(\xi|\zeta) = f(\xi|\zeta)h$. Bayes' law for the discrete case is

$$p_1(\xi|\zeta) = \frac{p_2(\zeta|\xi)p_1(\xi)}{p_2(\zeta)}.$$

Therefore, on substituting the approximations for these probabilities, we have

$$f(\xi|\zeta)h = \frac{g(\zeta|\xi)f(\xi)uh}{g(\zeta)u},$$

and on canceling u and h we obtain (7-125). Thus $f(x|\xi)$ given by (7-126) should be the function to approximate the histogram for x, given $y = \zeta$.

The next two sections will provide some illustrations of the uses of the material covered in this section. Before turning to these, however, let us discuss briefly one other type of situation which arises fairly frequently. For some random experiments where we deal with two random variables, it turns out to be convenient to treat one as continuous and the other as discrete. We shall discuss such cases here only with respect to two stage experiments. Let $\mathcal{R}$ be a random experiment for which the outcome first stage $\mathcal{R}_1$ is adequately described by a discrete random variable x with probability function $p_1(x)$, and imagine that the outcome of the second stage is described by a continuous random variable y whose density function is $g(y|x_i)$ when the outcome of $\mathcal{R}_1$ is x_i. We shall suppose that the set of values Y which y can take on does not depend on x_i. Let us now introduce a function $h(x,y)$, which we shall call the joint probability-density function for x and y and which is defined to be

$$h(x,y) = g(y|x)p(x).\tag{7-127}$$

It should be noted that $h(x,y)$ here cannot be interpreted in the same manner as when x and y are both continuous random variables. Thus if $g(y)$ is the density function for y, then

$$g(y) = \sum_{i=1}^{k} h(x_i,y) = \sum_{i=1}^{k} g(y|x_i)p(x_i). \qquad (7\text{-}128)$$

Furthermore, when $g(\zeta) \neq 0$, we can introduce a conditional probability function for x, given ζ, by writing

$$p(x|\zeta) = \frac{h(x,\zeta)}{g(\zeta)}. \qquad (7\text{-}129)$$

In addition,

$$p(x) = \int_Y h(x,y)\, dy = \int_Y p(x|y)g(y)\, dy. \qquad (7\text{-}130)$$

Let $p(x|\zeta)$ be defined by (7-129), so that it is the conditional probability function for x, given that at the second stage $y = \zeta$. Then Bayes' law becomes, on combining (7-127) and (7-129),

$$p(x|\zeta) = \frac{g(\zeta|x)p(x)}{g(\zeta)}. \qquad (7\text{-}131)$$

In precisely the same way, if the first stage variable x is to be considered continuous with density function $f(x)$ and the second stage variable y is to be considered discrete with the probability function for y being $p(y|\zeta)$ when $y = \zeta$ at the first stage, then if $p(y)$ is the probability function for y and $f(x|y_i)$ is the conditional density function for x, given at the second stage $y = y_i$, Bayes' law becomes

$$f(x|y_i) = \frac{p(y_i|x)f(x)}{p(y_i)}. \qquad (7\text{-}132)$$

We have not provided an intuitive justification for (7-128) through (7-132). We ask the reader to provide it in the problems.

7-13° GEOMETRIC PROBABILITY PROBLEMS

A number of interesting problems arise in which the random experiment $\mathcal{R}$ can be imagined to be composed of two independent random experiments $\mathcal{R}_1$ and $\mathcal{R}_2$, where the outcome of $\mathcal{R}_1$ is characterized by the value of a continuous random variable x having a uniform distribution, and the outcome of $\mathcal{R}_2$ is characterized by a continuous random variable y also having a uniform distribution. If X is the set of values x can take on and Y is the set of values y can take on, then $W = X \times Y$ provides a suitable event set for the model $\mathcal{E}$ of $\mathcal{R}$; and since $\mathcal{R}_1$ and $\mathcal{R}_2$ are independent, the joint density function is $h(x,y) = f(x)g(y)$, where $f(x)$ and $g(y)$ are the marginal density functions for x and y, respectively. Since each of these is a constant, $h(x,y) = \alpha$ is a constant also, and α must be $1/a$, where a is the area of the set of points W. If A is some event of $\mathcal{E}$, A is a subset of W and

$$p(A) = \iint_A h(x,y) \, dx \, dy = \frac{1}{a} \iint_A dx \, dy = \frac{b}{a}, \qquad (7\text{-}133)$$

where b is the area of the set of points A. Thus to find $p(A)$, the joint density function never needs to be considered. We simply divide the area of the set A by the area of the set W. Problems of this type are often referred to as geometric probability problems, since they reduce to problems of determining areas of regions. Let us now give two examples of such problems.

1. Consider a roulette wheel whose circumference is 100 inches. Imagine that the circumference is calibrated as a scale going from 0 to 100. Let us now suppose that the roulette wheel is spun, and after it stops we determine the reading ξ on scale opposite an indicator mark. Then we can think of ξ as a value of a continuous random variable x which can take on any value in the interval $0 \leq x \leq 100$. If the wheel is well balanced, it would seem to be true that x has a uniform density function $f(x) = 0.01$. We shall assume that this is the case. Suppose now that we spin the roulette wheel twice. Let x be the random variable representing the number where the wheel stopped on the first spin, and y the random variable representing the number on the second spin. The density function for y is the same as for x, i.e., $g(y) = 0.01$. Furthermore, the two spins represent independent random experiments, and therefore the joint density function for x and y is $h(x,y) = f(x)g(y) = 0.0001$ and the set $W = X \times Y$, which is the event set for the random experiment $\mathcal{R}$ representing the two spins is the square and its interior shown in Figure 7-29. The area of the square is $100(100) = 10^4$ square inches. Let ξ be the value of the number obtained on the first spin, that is, $x = \xi$, and ζ the number obtained on the second spin, $y = \zeta$. Imagine that we now draw a right triangle whose base has length ξ and whose altitude is ζ. We then ask the question: "What is the probability that the area of this triangle is less than or equal to 1000 square inches?" The area is $\xi\zeta/2$. What we are seeking then is the probability that $\xi\zeta \leq 2000$, or in other words, the probability of the event A that $xy \leq 2000$. The set of points in W having the property that $xy \leq 2000$ is the shaded region of Figure 7-29. The reason for this is that the set of points for which $xy = 2000$ is a hyperbola, and those in W with $xy \leq 2000$ are lying on or below this hyperbola. The probability of A is then the area of the shaded region in Figure 7-29 divided by 10^4, the area of the square. The area of the set A is the area of the rectangle lying to the left of $x = 20$ plus the area under the hyperbola for $x = 20$ to 100. Thus

$$b = 20(100) + 2000 \int_{20}^{100} \frac{dx}{x} = 2000 \, [1 + \log 5].$$

Hence
$$p(A) = 0.2[1 + \log 5] \doteq 0.52188,$$
and this is the probability that the area of the right triangle will be ≤ 1000 square inches.

2. Two friends, George and Harry, arrange to meet at a given place between 9 and 10 a.m. By agreement, the first to arrive will wait 15 minutes for the second, after which he will leave. What is the probability that the meeting will actually take place if the times of arrival of the individuals are independent random variables, each of which is uniformly distributed over the interval? Let x be the random variable giving the time of George's arrival and y the time of Harry's arrival. We can then think of the random experiment involved as one in which two spins of a roulette wheel are made. The number obtained on the first spin determines the time of George's arrival, and that obtained on the second spin the time of Harry's arrival. The event set of W for $\mathcal{R}$ is then the square shown in Figure 7-30 whose area is 3600 minutes squared.

We would like to compute the probability of the event A that the two individuals will meet. One way they will meet is if George arrives first and no more than 15 minutes ahead of Harry. Call this event B. The event B is described by a set of points in W which satisfy the inequalities $x \leq y$ and $y - x \leq 15$. The first of these simply requires that George arrives before (or at the same instant as) Harry. The set of points representing B is the lightly shaded region in Figure 7-30. The pair will also meet if Harry arrives first but not more than 15 minutes ahead of George. Call this event C. Then C is described by a set of points in W which satisfy the pair of inequalities $y \leq x$, $x - y \leq 15$. The set C is then the darkly shaded set of points in Figure 7-30. If the two individuals do meet, then either B or C will occur. Thus $A = B \cup C$, and A is represented by the lightly and darkly shaded regions in Figure 7-30. The probability of A is then the area of this set of points divided by 3600. Now the area of the

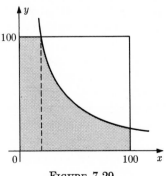

FIGURE 7-29

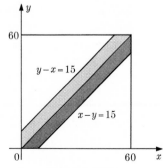

FIGURE 7-30

shaded set of points is 3600 minus the sum of the areas of the two unshaded triangular regions. Each of these has the area $45(45)/2$ or both together have the area $45(45) = 2025$ minutes squared; the area of the shaded set is then 1575, and the probability of A is

$$p(A) = \frac{1575}{3600} \doteq 0.4375.$$

7-14° LINEAR COMBINATIONS OF RANDOM VARIABLES

Let x be a continuous random variable which can take on values in the set X and let $f(x)$ be the density function for x over X. Similarly, let y be a continuous random variable which can take on values in the set Y, and let $g(y)$ be the density function for y over Y. Consider now a random experiment $\mathcal{R}$ for which we can use the mathematical model $\mathcal{E}$ having the event set $W = X \times Y$, with $h(x,y)$ being the joint density function for x and y over W. Next let $z = \Theta(x,y)$ be any function of x and y whose domain is W. This function serves to associate with each point in W a number δ. We can then think of the range of $\Theta(x,y)$ as being the set of possible values which a random variable z can take on, and we shall think of z as being a function of the two random variables x and y. We shall define μ_z, the expected value of z, to be

$$\mu_z = \iint_W \Theta(x,y)h(x,y) \, dx \, dy, \tag{7-134}$$

and μ_z has the intuitive interpretation of being a long run average value of z if $\mathcal{R}$ is repeated unendingly. The double integral can be evaluated as a repeated or iterated integral using one of the following two forms:

$$\mu_z = \int_X \left[\int_Y \Theta(x,y)h(x,y) \, dy \right] dx = \int_Y \left[\int_X \Theta(x,y)h(x,y) \, dx \right] dy. \tag{7-135}$$

An allowable function $\Theta(x,y)$ is simply $\Theta(x,y) = x$, i.e., $z = x$. In this case we would expect μ_z computed from (7-134) to be precisely the number μ_x that would be determined by computing the expected value of x using $f(x)$. Let us see that this is indeed the case. When $z = x$,

$$\mu_z = \int_X \left[\int_Y xh(x,y) \, dy \right] dx = \int_X x \left[\int_Y h(x,y) \, dy \right] dx$$

$$= \int_X xf(x) \, dx = \mu_x \tag{7-136}$$

as desired. This follows because of (7-118). Similarly if $z = y$, $\mu_z = \mu_y$ as would be expected, and if $z = (x - \mu_x)^2$, $\mu_z = \sigma_x^2$ as would be expected also.

Consider now any two random variables u and v associated with $\Re$, which are defined by the functions $u = \Theta(x,y)$ and $v = \Lambda(x,y)$. Denote by μ_u and μ_v, the expected values of u and v, respectively. We shall next introduce still another random variable z, by defining z as a linear combination of u and v, that is, $z = au + bv$, where a and b are given constants. Then according to (7-134), the expected value of z is

$$\mu_z = \iint_W \left[a\Theta(x,y) + b\Lambda(x,y)\right] h(x,y) \, dx \, dy$$

$$= a \iint_W \Theta(x,y)h(x,y) \, dx \, dy + b \iint_W \Lambda(x,y)h(x,y) \, dx \, dy$$

$$= a\mu_u + b\mu_v, \tag{7-137}$$

so that μ_z is the same linear combination of μ_u and μ_v as is z of u and v. This is, of course, precisely analogous to the result we had for the discrete random variables.

If we take $u = x$ and $v = y$ so that $z = ax + by$, then (7-137) yields

$$\mu_z = a\mu_x + b\mu_y. \tag{7-138}$$

Consider next the determination of the variance of z which is the expected value of $(z - \mu_z)^2$. By (7-138),

$$(z - \mu_z)^2 = \left[a(x - \mu_x) + b(y - \mu_y)\right]^2$$
$$= a^2(x - \mu_x)^2 + b^2(y - \mu_y)^2 + 2ab(x - \mu_x)(y - \mu_y). \tag{7-139}$$

Then using the same argument which led to (7-137) we see that σ_z^2, the variance of z, is related to σ_x^2, the variance of x; σ_y^2, the variance of y; and σ_{xy}, the expected value of $(x - \mu_x)(y - \mu_y)$, by

$$\sigma_z^2 = a^2\sigma_x^2 + b^2\sigma_y^2 + 2ab\sigma_{xy}. \tag{7-140}$$

The number σ_{xy} is called the covariance of x and y just as in the discrete case. When x and y are independent, so that $h(x,y) = f(x)g(y)$, $\sigma_{xy} = 0$ as in the discrete case. To see this observe that

$$\sigma_{xy} = \int_X \left[\int_Y (x - \mu_x)(y - \mu_y)f(x)g(y) \, dy\right] dx$$

$$= \left[\int_X (x - \mu_x)f(x) \, dx\right]\left[\int_Y (y - \mu_y)g(y) \, dy\right] = 0$$

because the expected values of $x - \mu_x$ and $y - \mu_y$ are both 0. Thus when x and y are independent,

$$\sigma_z^2 = a^2\sigma_x^2 + b^2\sigma_y^2, \quad x, y \text{ independent.} \tag{7-141}$$

Consider next the determination of the density function for z. As in Section 7-8, it is usually most convenient to first determine the cumulative function for z and then obtain the density function by differentiation.

If we denote by T the subset of points of W for which $z \leq \delta$, i.e., $ax + by \leq \delta$, then $Q(\delta)$ the probability that $z \leq \delta$ is

$$Q(\delta) = \iint_T h(x,y) \, dx \, dy. \qquad (7\text{-}142)$$

It is by no means easy to evaluate this integral in general. We shall study only two cases. First assume that x and y can take on all values so that W is the entire xy-plane. We shall also suppose that $b > 0$ in $z = ax + by$. This is no restriction for cases of practical interest. Now for specified values of δ and x, $ax + by \leq \delta$ when $y \leq b^{-1}(\delta - ax)$, $b > 0$. There exist such y for every real x. Therefore

$$Q(\delta) = \int_{-\infty}^{\infty} \left[\int_{-\infty}^{b^{-1}(\delta-ax)} h(x,y) \, dy \right] dx. \qquad (7\text{-}143)$$

On differentiating with respect to δ, we see that the density function $q(z)$ for z is

$$q(z) = b^{-1} \int_{-\infty}^{\infty} h[x, b^{-1}(z - ax)] dx, \qquad (7\text{-}144)$$

and if x and y are independent random variables

$$q(z) = b^{-1} \int_{-\infty}^{\infty} f(x) g[b^{-1}(z - ax)] dx. \qquad (7\text{-}145)$$

The random variable z in this case can take on all real values.

As an important example of this case suppose that x and y are independent random variables both of which have normal distributions, x having an expected value μ_x and standard deviation σ_x and y having an expected value μ_y and standard deviation σ_y. Let us determine the density function for $z = ax + by$. According to (7-145),

$$q(z) = \frac{1}{2\pi b \sigma_x \sigma_y} \int_{-\infty}^{\infty} e^{-(x-\mu_x)^2/2\sigma_x^2} \, e^{-(z-ax-b\mu_y)^2/2b^2\sigma_y^2} \, dx. \qquad (7\text{-}146)$$

The exponents in the integral can be combined, and after some algebraic manipulation, which we ask the reader to carry out in the problems, it can be shown that

$$\frac{(x-\mu_x)^2}{2\sigma_x^2} + \frac{(z-ax-b\mu_y)^2}{2b^2\sigma_y^2} = \frac{(x-\lambda)^2}{2\gamma^2} + \frac{(z-\mu)^2}{2\sigma^2}, \qquad (7\text{-}147)$$

where

$$\mu = a\mu_x + b\mu_y; \quad \sigma^2 = a^2\sigma_x^2 + b^2\sigma_y^2 \qquad (7\text{-}148)$$

$$\lambda = \mu_x + a \left(\frac{\sigma_x^2}{\sigma^2} \right)(z - \mu); \quad \gamma = \frac{b\sigma_x\sigma_y}{\sigma}. \qquad (7\text{-}149)$$

On using these results in (7-146), we obtain

$$q(z) = n(z; \mu,\sigma) \int_{-\infty}^{\infty} n(x; \lambda,\gamma)\, dx = n(z; \mu,\sigma) \qquad (7\text{-}150)$$

since the integral of the normal density is 1. Thus $q(z) = n(z; \mu,\sigma)$, and z also has a normal distribution, whose mean μ and variance σ^2 are given by (7-148). We have proved, therefore, that if x and y are independent random variables which are normally distributed, $z = ax + by$, $b > 0$, is also normally distributed. This is a very important result. It holds even if $a < 0$ and $b < 0$ as the reader is asked to show in the problems.

The other case we shall consider for determining $q(z)$ is that where both x and y can take on all non-negative values, so that W is the first quadrant of the xy-plane. We shall furthermore restrict our attention to the case where $z = x + y$, i.e., $a = 1$, $b = 1$. For any given values of δ and x, $x + y \le \delta$ if $0 \le y \le \delta - x$. For a given δ, x can take on only values in the interval $0 \le x \le \delta$. Hence

$$Q(\delta) = \int_0^\delta \left[\int_0^{\delta-x} h(x,y)\, dy \right] dx. \qquad (7\text{-}151)$$

Differentiating, we obtain

$$q(\delta) = \int_0^\delta h(x, \delta - x)\, dx, \qquad (7\text{-}152)$$

or

$$q(z) = \int_0^z h(x, z - x)\, dx. \qquad (7\text{-}153)$$

The procedure for differentiating (7-151) may not be familiar to the reader, and we ask him to derive the required result in the problems.

Suppose now that x and y are independent random variables, x having the gamma distribution $g(x; \alpha_1, \lambda)$ while y has the gamma distribution $g(y; \alpha_2, \lambda)$. Note that we are assuming that the same value of λ appears in both density functions. Let us now find the density function for $z = x + y$ in this case. Equation (7-153) is applicable in this case with $h(x,y) = f(x)g(y)$. Thus

$$
\begin{aligned}
q(z) &= \frac{\lambda^{\alpha_1+\alpha_2+2}\, e^{-\lambda z}}{\Gamma(\alpha_1 + 1)\Gamma(\alpha_2 + 1)} \int_0^z x^{\alpha_1}(z - x)^{\alpha_2}\, dx \\
&= \frac{\lambda(\lambda z)^{\alpha_1+\alpha_2+1}\, e^{-\lambda z}}{\Gamma(\alpha_1 + 1)\Gamma(\alpha_2 + 1)} \int_0^1 y^{\alpha_1}(1 - y)^{\alpha_2}\, dy, \qquad (7\text{-}154)
\end{aligned}
$$

the last integral following on using the change of variable $x = zy$. Now it can be proved, although we shall not attempt to give the proof, that

$$\int_0^1 y^{\alpha_1}(1 - y)^{\alpha_2}\, dy = \frac{\Gamma(\alpha_1 + 1)\Gamma(\alpha_2 + 1)}{\Gamma(\alpha_1 + \alpha_2 + 2)}. \qquad (7\text{-}155)$$

On using this result, we see that

$$q(z) = g(z; \alpha_1 + \alpha_2 + 1, \lambda), \tag{7-156}$$

so that z also has a gamma distribution. Note that the order of the distribution of z is $\alpha_1 + \alpha_2 + 1$, not $\alpha_1 + \alpha_2$. We have then proved another important result which is the following. If x and y are independent random variables with gamma distributions $g(x; \alpha_1, \lambda)$ and $g(y; \alpha_2, \lambda)$, respectively, then $z = x + y$ has the gamma distribution $g(z; \alpha_1 + \alpha_2 + 1, \lambda)$.

The results which we have obtained above can easily be generalized to the case where we have n continuous random variables $x\{1\}, \ldots, x\{n\}$. Let X_j be the set of values which $x\{j\}$ can take on, and let $W = X_1 \times \ldots \times X_n$. We can then construct a model $\mathcal{E}$ with W as the event set and having a joint density function for all n random variables defined over W. Then if we define a new random variable z as a linear combination of the $x\{j\}$ by writing

$$z = \sum_{j=1}^{n} a_j x\{j\}, \tag{7-157}$$

it follows that μ_z, the expected value of z, is

$$\mu_z = \sum_{j=1}^{n} a_j \mu_j, \tag{7-158}$$

where μ_j is the expected value of $x\{j\}$, and σ_z^2, the variance of z, is

$$\sigma_z^2 = \sum_{j=1}^{n} a_j^2 \sigma_j^2 + 2a_1 a_2 \sigma_{12} + 2a_1 a_3 \sigma_{13} + \cdots + 2a_{n-1} a_n \sigma_{n-1,n}, \tag{7-159}$$

where σ_j^2 is the variance of $x\{j\}$ and σ_{ij} is the covariance of $x\{i\}$ and $x\{j\}$. If the random variables are independent, then

$$\sigma_z^2 = \sum_{j=1}^{n} a_j^2 \sigma_j^2. \tag{7-160}$$

In particular, if the $x\{j\}$ are independent and each is normally distributed, then z is also normally distributed with expected value (7-158) and variance (7-160). This is proved by applying repeatedly the corresponding result for two random variables obtained above and noting that if $x\{1\}$, $x\{2\}$, and $x\{3\}$ are independent, then $a_1 x\{1\} + a_2 x\{2\}$, and $x\{3\}$ are independent. Similarly, if the $x\{j\}$ are independent, and $x\{j\}$ has the gamma distribution $g(x\{j\}; \alpha_j, \lambda)$, then $z = \sum_{j=1}^{n} x\{j\}$ has a gamma distribution $g(z; \alpha, \lambda)$ where

$$\alpha = \sum_{j=1}^{n} \alpha_j + n - 1. \tag{7-161}$$

We can now apply the material just considered to a situation which arises frequently. Consider a random experiment $\mathcal{R}$ which has associated with it a random variable x, which it is convenient to treat as being continuous. Let us imagine that we do not know the expected value of μ_x of x, and that we would like to estimate it experimentally. Since μ_x has the intuitive interpretation of being long run average value of x when $\Re$ is repeated unendingly, it would seem appropriate to estimate μ_x by making n independent trials of $\Re$ and computing the average of the values of x observed on each of these trials. Denote by $\Re_n$ the random experiment which consists of making n independent trials of $\Re$. Associated with $\Re_n$ there are now n random variables $x\{j\}$, where $x\{j\}$ refers to the outcome of the jth trial of $\Re$. If x has the expected value μ_x and variance σ_x^2, then each random variable $x\{j\}$ has the expected value μ_x and variance σ_x^2, since it is x for the jth trial. We can now associate with $\Re_n$ a new random variable $\bar{x}$ defined to be the following linear combination of the $x\{j\}$:

$$\bar{x} = \frac{1}{n}\sum_{j=1}^{n} x\{j\} = \frac{1}{n}x\{1\} + \cdots + \frac{1}{n}x\{n\}. \qquad (7\text{-}162)$$

The random variable $\bar{x}$ then represents the average of the $x\{j\}$. If on performing $\Re$, $x\{j\}$ takes on the value ξ_j, then $\bar{x}$ will take on the value $\bar{\xi} = \sum_{j=1}^{n} \xi_j/n$, and we shall use $\bar{\xi}$ as our estimate to μ_x. Since the value taken on by $\bar{x}$ will be used as our estimate of μ_x, it is interesting to know something about the behavior of the random variable $\bar{x}$. From what we have proved above, $\mu_{\bar{x}}$, the expected value of $\bar{x}$, is

$$\mu_{\bar{x}} = \frac{\mu_x}{n} + \cdots + \frac{\mu_x}{n} = \frac{n}{n}\mu_x = \mu_x, \qquad (7\text{-}163)$$

so that the expected value of $\bar{x}$ is precisely the same as the expected value of x. Furthermore $\sigma_{\bar{x}}^2$, the variance of $\bar{x}$, is

$$\sigma_{\bar{x}}^2 = \frac{\sigma_x^2}{n^2} + \cdots + \frac{\sigma_x^2}{n^2} = \frac{n}{n^2}\sigma_x^2 = \frac{\sigma_x^2}{n}, \qquad (7\text{-}164)$$

and the variance of $\bar{x}$ is the variance of x divided by n. Thus the spread of the values of $\bar{x}$ decreases with n and is less than the spread of the values of x about μ_x, so that when n is large the observed value $\bar{\xi}$ of $\bar{x}$ should be close to μ_x. This justifies our intuitive notion that if $\Re$ is repeated a large number of times and the values averaged, we should expect to obtain a rather good estimate of μ_x. If we repeat $\Re_n$ a large number of times (each $\Re_n$ involving n independent trials of $\Re$), the long run average value of $\bar{x}$ observed, that is, the average of the values of $\bar{x}$, will be μ_x and the variance of these will be σ_x^2/n. At the moment, there is only one case in which we can say something about the density function for $\bar{x}$. If x is normally distributed with expected value μ_x and variance σ_x^2, then $\bar{x}$ is also normally distributed with expected value μ_x and variance σ_x^2/n. This follows from what we have shown above. Now we shall point out in the next section that when n is large, $\bar{x}$ will be approximately normally distributed regardless of what the density function for x happens to be. This is a very important result which is made use of with great frequency in practice.

7-15 THE CENTRAL LIMIT THEOREM

One of the most remarkable results in probability theory is what is known as the central limit theorem. This theorem makes a statement about what happens in situations of the following sort. Suppose we consider a random experiment $\Re$ which has associated with it some random variable y having expected value μ_y and variance σ_y^2. The random variable y may be continuous or discrete. It does not matter which. Consider next the random experiment $\Re_n$, which consists of n independent trials of $\Re$. Now on each trial of $\Re$ some value of y will be observed. Denote by $y\{j\}$ the random variable representing y for the jth trial. Then each $y\{j\}$ has the expected value μ_y and variance σ_y^2. Furthermore each $y\{j\}$ has the same distribution, and the $y\{j\}$ are independent random variables. Consider now the random variable z associated with $\Re_n$ which is the sum of the $y\{j\}$, so that $z = \sum_{j=1}^{n} y\{j\}$. The central limit theorem then states that *as the number of trials of $\Re$ is increased unendingly, i.e., as n is increased unendingly, the distribution of z approaches a normal distribution with mean $n\mu_y$ and variance $n\sigma_y^2$.* A more precise statement says that the distribution of the random variable $t = (z - n\mu_y)/\sigma_y\sqrt{n}$ approaches $\varphi(t)$ as n increases unendingly. This is true even if y is discrete and can take on only two different values. Note, however, that it does not follow that z will take on only two different values if y does; z can take on $n + 1$ different values in this case, which will be a large number when n is large.

The proof of the central limit theorem requires the development of a number of concepts which we have not considered, and hence we shall not attempt to prove it. Furthermore, the mere fact that the distribution of z becomes normal for very large n is not necessarily of any practical interest. The question of practical interest is how rapidly does the distribution of z become normal. If n had to be 10^6 or greater, the central limit theorem would not be of much practical relevance. The surprising and very important thing, which does not follow directly from the central limit theorem, is that the distribution of z is often very well approximated by a normal distribution for very small values of n. This is of great practical value. For example, consider the problem studied at the end of the last section and let $y\{j\} = x\{j\}/n$. Then $z = \bar{x}$. The central limit theorem then states that the distribution of $\bar{x}$ approaches for large n a normal distribution with mean μ_x and variance σ_x^2/n regardless of what the distribution of the random variable x may be. When x is continuous,

$\bar{x}$ approaches a normal distribution very rapidly, even if the density function for x is far from normal. In fact, one can for many everyday computations which do not require great precision make probability computations involving $\bar{x}$ using the normal distribution when $n \geq 5$. This fact is made wide use of, especially in quality control work, as we shall point out in more detail later.

Let us next note how the central limit theorem can provide an understanding of why so many of the distributions which we have studied previously can be approximated by the normal distribution. Consider first the binomial distribution $b(x; n,p)$. Recall from Example 2 on p. 316 that x can be written as the sum of n independent variables $y\{j\}$, where $y\{j\} = 0$ or 1 and the $y\{j\}$ all have the same distribution. Thus as n gets larger and larger the distribution of x approaches the normal distribution. This shows that for sufficiently large n we should be able to approximate the binomial distribution with the normal, but it provides no indication of how large n must be. This information must come from other sources. Consider next the Pascal distribution, $b_P(y; r,p)$. We noted in Problem 18 for Sections 6-10 and 6-11 that y can be written as the sum of r independent variables $y\{j\}$, where $y\{j\}$ is the number of trials needed after the $(j-1)$st occurrence of e_1 to have another occurrence of e_1. The $y\{j\}$ all have the same distribution and as r gets larger and larger, the distribution of y approaches a normal distribution. The central limit theorem does not directly indicate that the hypergeometric distribution should be capable of being approximated by the normal distribution since the random variable involved cannot be written as the sum of independent, identically distributed random variables. Let us turn next to the Poisson distribution and recall that in Section 6-11 we showed that if we have n independent random variables $y\{j\}$, each of which has the Poisson distribution $p(y\{j\}; \beta)$, then $y = \sum_{j=1}^{n} y\{j\}$ has the Poisson distribution $p(y; n\beta)$. Thus as n becomes large $p(y; n\beta)$ should approach the normal distribution, and hence the normal distribution should be capable of being used to approximate the Poisson distribution when the mean is very large. Finally, consider the gamma distribution $g(x; n,\lambda)$ where n is a positive integer. Let $y\{j\}, j = 1, \ldots, n+1$ have an exponential distribution, that is, the gamma distribution $g(y\{j\}; 0, \lambda)$. Suppose that the $y\{j\}$ are independent. Then from (7-161) $x = \sum_{j=1}^{n+1} y\{j\}$ has the gamma distribution $g(x; n,\lambda)$. Thus for large n, the distribution of x approaches the normal distribution. This shows that for large n, $g(x; n,\lambda)$ should be capable of being approximated by the normal distribution.

Very frequently, sums of independent random variables will approach the normal distribution even if they are not identically distributed. This can occur even if they are not independent. In these cases it does not *necessarily* follow that the limiting distribution will be normal, however.

Given that sums of random variables often are essentially normally distributed under rather general conditions, we can see why many random variables occurring in practice are essentially normally distributed. For example, the variations in the diameters of ball bearings produced by a process can be thought of as due to the sum of a number of small chance effects such as variations in steel hardness, machine settings, etc. For this reason it would not be surprising to find that the distribution for the random variable representing the diameter of a ball bearing was essentially normal.

In this section we have seen that the central limit theorem and the general properties of sums of random variables can explain many of the properties of distributions we have observed previously and that are observed in nature. We have noted that the thing which makes the central limit theorem so important from a practical point of view is that convergence to a normal distribution is often very rapid. We shall make use of this on a number of occasions in the future.

7-16 RANDOM NUMBERS

Consider a random experiment $\mathfrak{R}$ which has associated with it some discrete or continuous random variable x. Let the distribution of x be characterized by the probability function $p(x)$ if x is discrete, or by the density function $f(x)$ if x is continuous. When $\mathfrak{R}$ is performed we observe some value of x, say ξ. We shall now introduce a new terminology which is very convenient. We shall say that the performance of $\mathfrak{R}$ *generates a random number from the distribution* $p(x)$ *or* $f(x)$. The random number is ξ, the value x takes on. If n independent trials of $\mathfrak{R}$ are made, the n values $\xi_1, \ldots, \xi_n$ of x observed on the n trials are said to be n random numbers from the distribution $p(x)$ or $f(x)$. One is frequently interested in obtaining a set of random numbers from a given distribution for a variety of reasons which will be explained below. One would like to be able to generate a sequence of random numbers from any given distribution without performing a number of independent trials of a complicated random experiment to do so. We shall see in this section how this can be done. It is important to note before going on, however, that the notion of a random number has no meaning without reference to some distribution from which it is imagined to be drawn. The reader should note this carefully because some works are not too precise on this point.

Let us first consider the problem of generating random numbers representing the values of a continuous random variable y which has a uniform distribution and which can take on numbers only in the interval $0 \leq y \leq$

1. These random numbers will be called *random numbers drawn from a uniform distribution on the unit interval.* One cannot really generate such random numbers in a rigorous sense because no physical process can represent exactly a continuous random variable. However, one can come arbitrarily close to doing this. Suppose then that we are content to generate random numbers of this sort that have only ten digits after the decimal point. Not every number in the interval $0 \leq y \leq 1$ can be written as a ten decimal number. There are, however, ten billion of them, and for most purposes, this can be considered to be a quite adequate approximation for all numbers in the interval. One can proceed to generate ten digit numbers which are essentially random numbers from the unit interval as follows. Suppose we have ten balls in an urn numbered 0, 1, 2, . . . , 9. We now mix the balls thoroughly and draw one. We write down the number on the ball drawn. We now replace the ball, mix the balls thoroughly again and draw another one. We write down the number on this ball after the number on that for the first ball, and then repeat the procedure. After ten repetitions we have generated ten digits which when written down one after the other might be 8003157821. If we place a decimal point in front of the number to yield 0.8003157821, this is a random number of the type desired. The probability of obtaining this number should be $1/10^{10}$, and any such ten digit number should have the same probability. If we continually repeat this experiment, every ten digits generated serve to define a random number from the uniform distribution on the unit interval. In this way a sequence of random numbers from the uniform distribution on the unit interval can be generated. It would be very clumsy to have to go through such a procedure every time one wanted random numbers of this form. Fortunately, this is not necessary. One reason for this is that tables of random numbers from the uniform distribution on the unit interval have been published. One well-known table is that prepared by the RAND Corporation [8]. Thus one could use this table instead of carrying out the above experiment repeatedly. There is another reason why it is unnecessary to carry out the above experimental procedure. Digital computers can be programmed to generate random numbers from the uniform distribution over the unit interval. We shall not attempt to discuss the procedures actually used. The most widely used one makes use of some results from the subject known as number theory. In actuality, the computer cannot perform any random experiments. Only deterministic operations can be carried out. For this reason the random numbers generated are not random in the strict sense of the word because they are generated by a deterministic process. They are referred to as pseudo-random numbers. They are close enough to being random numbers, however, that they can be used as such for almost all purposes. Thus we can, if we wish, have a computer

generate a sequence of random numbers from the uniform distribution over the unit interval for us.

Let us next turn to the problem of generating random numbers from an arbitrary distribution.   Interestingly enough, we shall show that if we can generate random numbers from the uniform distribution over the unit interval, we can generate random numbers from any distribution from them.   In other words, if we have a sequence of random numbers from the uniform distribution over the unit interval, we can convert them into a sequence of random numbers from any distribution.   To see how to do this, suppose first that we are interested in generating random numbers from the distribution $p(x)$ for a discrete random variable x.   Let $P(x)$ be the cumulative function for x, and suppose that the bar diagram for $P(x)$ looks like that shown in Figure 7-31.   We shall imagine that x can take on the values $x_1, \ldots, x_k$.   Now note that if y has the uniform distribution over the unit interval, the probability that the value of y will be in any interval of length d, $0 \le d \le 1$ is d.   Let us now generate a random number ζ from the uniform distribution over the unit interval.   In Figure 7-31, let us draw a horizontal line through the point ζ on the vertical axis and note the first bar this line intersects.   This is the bar for $x = x_5$ in Figure 7-31.   We then claim that x_5 is the random number generated from $p(x)$, and if we repeat this procedure first generating a random number from the uniform distribution and then determining in the manner just described a value of x, this generates a sequence of random numbers from $p(x)$.

To see that the process just described does generate a sequence of random numbers from $p(x)$, let us determine the probability that the value x_i of x will be selected.   Now x_i will be selected when the value ζ satisfies $P(x_{i-1}) < \zeta \le P(x_i)$ because then the bar corresponding to x_i will be the first one intersected by the line through ζ.   Note that $P(x_i) - P(x_{i-1}) = p(x_i)$, so that the length of the interval containing values of y which will yield x_i is $p(x_i)$.   The probability that the values of y will be in this interval is equal to the length of the interval, i.e., is $p(x_i)$.   But this is precisely what we want.   The probability of getting x_i is $p(x_i)$ and the value of x_i does not depend on any previous trials; thus the values of x so generated will be random numbers from the distribution $p(x)$.   Clearly, to determine the random number from $p(x)$ corresponding to ζ we do not need to use a diagram such as Figure 7-31.   All we need to do is subdivide the interval $0 \le \zeta \le 1$ into k subintervals, the ith of which I_i is the set of numbers $P(x_{i-1}) < \zeta \le P(x_i)$.   On generating ζ, we determine which interval I_i contains ζ.   If it is I_u, then the random number generated from $p(x)$ is x_u.

Consider now the case where we wish to generate random numbers from the density function $f(x)$ with domain X corresponding to a continuous random variable x.   Let $F(x)$ be the cumulative distribution function for

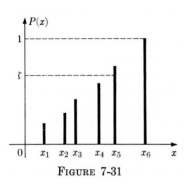

FIGURE 7-31

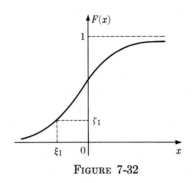

FIGURE 7-32

x, so that $F(\xi)$ is the probability that $x \leq \xi$. If we perform an experiment $\mathfrak{R}$ having associated with it the random variable x a number of times, we shall generate a sequence of values of x, which we can denote by ξ_1, ξ_2, ξ_3, ..., which are a set of random numbers from the distribution $f(x)$. These numbers will have the characteristic that if $\mathfrak{R}$ is repeated a very large number of times, the fraction of the numbers which are less than or equal to ξ will be $F(\xi)$. We are then looking for a process which corresponds to independent trials of $\mathfrak{R}$ which will generate a set of numbers with the characteristic just referred to. Suppose that the graph of $F(x)$ looks like that shown in Figure 7-32. Let us now select a particular value of x, say ξ, and let $\zeta = F(\xi)$. Every value ξ_1 of x which is less than ξ has the characteristic that if $\zeta_1 = F(\xi_1)$, then $\zeta_1 < \zeta$. Suppose now that we generate a random number ζ_1 from the uniform distribution over the unit interval. The probability that $\zeta_1 \leq \zeta$ is ζ. Consider the unique number ξ_1 having the property that $\zeta_1 = F(\xi_1)$. Now $\xi_1 \leq \xi$ if and only if $\zeta_1 \leq \zeta$. Thus the probability that $\xi_1 \leq \xi$ is $\zeta = F(\xi)$. This is true regardless of what value of ξ we select. Thus if we generate a sequence of random numbers ζ_1, ζ_2, ..., from the uniform distribution and determine the numbers ξ_1, ξ_2, ..., such that $\zeta_j = F(\xi_j)$, then the ξ_j form a sequence of random numbers from the distribution $f(x)$. This follows since the long run fraction of the numbers which are less than or equal to ξ is $F(\xi)$ for any ξ, which is precisely what we want, since the numbers do also have the property that they were generated by independent trials of an experiment. Thus if we generate a random number ζ_1 from the uniform distribution over the unit interval, we can find the corresponding random number ξ_1 from $f(x)$ by drawing a horizontal line through ζ_1 on the vertical axis in Figure 7-32 and determining where it crosses the graph of $F(x)$; the x-coordinate of this point is ξ_1. This is shown in Figure 7-32. If one wanted to generate random numbers from $f(x)$ using a computer, the computer would proceed in much the same way that we have just described. It would first generate a random number ζ_1 from the uniform distribution over the unit interval, and then it would determine the number ξ_1 such that $\zeta_1 = F(\xi_1)$.

If someone claims that he has a method for generating random numbers from a given distribution, but will only give us such numbers and not reveal how they are generated, it is not easy in general to determine whether or not they are really random numbers from the given distribution. If he gives us a lot of them, we can construct a histogram, and thus check whether the relative frequencies are what they should be. The difficult part is to check that they are random, that is, correspond to numbers that would be generated by independent trials of a random experiment. We shall not consider the various methods one can use to check on this aspect of the problem.

The notion of a random number helps us to unify the uses of the word random introduced on several occasions in prior chapters. For example, we referred to selecting a ball at random from an urn containing n balls. What is meant here is that if we imagine that the balls are numbered 1 to n we are performing an experiment which generates a random number from the uniform distribution whose domain is the set of positive integers $1, \ldots, n$. Later we spoke of selecting n balls at random from an urn containing N balls. There are $C_n{}^N$ simple events from this experiment, and if we imagine them to be numbered 1 through $C_n{}^N$, then we mean that on performing the experiment we generate a random number (which is the number assigned to the simple event observed) from the uniform distribution whose domain is the set of positive integers $1, \ldots, C_n{}^N$. Finally, we referred to a process generating defectives at random with the probability of a defective being p. What we mean here is that if the process does behave in this way, then if we examine any n units produced, the number of defectives in this sample will be a random number from the binomial distribution $b(x; n,p)$.

Frequently one encounters situations in practice where it is desired to generate random numbers from some uniform distribution. Usually, the problem corresponds to one where it is desired to select at random n balls from a set of N. Many opinion polls operate in this way. For example, suppose that we wished to select at random two students from a class of 50. This could easily be done using a random number table as follows. One first takes an alphabetic list of the students and assigns the first the number 00, the second the number 01, the fifteenth the number 14, and the last the number 49. Next one takes a table of random numbers and selects in an arbitrary way one of these numbers. The last two digits of this number, which might be 14, are used to select one of the students, i.e., student 15 is selected. If the last two digits yield a number greater than 49, one moves on to the next random number in sequence. This is continued until the last two digits yield a number less than 50. Once the first student is selected one simply continues in the table using the next number in sequence until another number is obtained whose last two digits yield a number less than 50 which is different from the first number obtained. This illustrates how random number tables can be usefully employed. In the next section we wish to study yet another important use for random numbers.

7-17 SIMULATION

One frequently encounters problems in probability theory and decision theory which cannot be solved by the methods we have considered thus far, either because the mathematics becomes too complicated or too time consuming to carry out. The advent of large scale digital computers has made possible the use of an alternative method, referred to as simulation, to determine a practical numerical solution (although not an analytical solution) to many very complicated problems. To see how the simulation procedure works, we shall begin by considering a very simple example. Assume that we have two independent random variables x and y with density functions $f(x)$ and $g(y)$, respectively. Suppose now that we introduce a new random variable z through the function $z = \Theta(x, y)$, and that we would like to determine the density function for z. As we have noted previously it may be an exceedingly difficult task to do this analytically, and indeed, it may be impossible to do in terms of functions that we are familiar with. Let us then consider an alternative procedure by which we can obtain a good numerical approximation to the density function for z. Let $\mathcal{R}$ be a random experiment in which we generate a random number ξ from $f(x)$ and a random number ζ from $g(y)$. Let $\Theta = \Theta(\xi, \zeta)$; Θ is then one of the values which z can take on. We can have a computer perform this experiment because, as we have seen in the previous section, the computer can generate random numbers from any distribution using the procedure for generating random numbers from the uniform distribution over the unit interval. Let us then have the computer perform this experiment thousands of times or perhaps even 100,000 times. We then generate a large number of values of z. These values can be used by the computer to construct a histogram. The outline of this histogram should be very close to the graph of the density function for z, and in this way one can determine numerically a good approximation to the density function for z. The process used here is referred to as simulation.

Simulation can be used to great advantage in solving single stage decision problems which are too complicated to solve in any other way. Frequently, the states of nature for a decision problem will be characterized by the values taken on by a sizable number n of different random variables (which are not in general independent) so that a state of nature is characterized by an ordered array of numbers $(\xi_1, \xi_2, \ldots, \xi_n)$ corresponding to the values taken on by the n random variables. There can easily be millions or billions of such states of nature, and frequently, it is convenient to imagine that some or all of the random variables are continuous. Often one can estimate at least roughly the distributions for each of the individual random variables, but it may be extremely cumbersome to obtain an analytical expression for the joint distribution. It may also be complicated to write down an expression for the utility as a function of the state of nature–action pairs. Even if all this could be done, it would be hopelessly complicated to try to compute the expected utility. In situations like this, simulation can be very effective.

The simulation procedure would proceed as follows. A set of random numbers corresponding to each random variable would be generated. This would determine the state of nature. Then the utility for each action would be determined. This would be repeated thousands of times. By this process thousands of utility values would be generated for each action. The average of these for each action would be determined, and this would be used for the expected utility. The action with the largest average utility would be selected. The procedure just suggested would be hopeless to carry out without a large computer, since it would require hundreds of man years to make the computations. It may even require several hours for the fastest computer to carry out. When, as is often the case, the random variables are dependent, then the random numbers must be generated in a particular sequence because the values obtained for some will influence the distributions from which others are to be generated.

We shall not provide a detailed example of the simulation procedure because it would take many pages to give the details. However, we shall explain the procedure a little more with the aid of an example. In Section 2-4 we considered an example involving the selection of one of two petroleum reservoirs to develop. The situation was assumed to be deterministic there. In the usual situation met in practice, however, there is a great deal of uncertainty. Let us illustrate how simulation could be used to estimate the expected value of the discounted profit from any particular reservoir. We shall again simplify the problem and not attempt to consider all relevant random variables. First one would want a random variable representing the quantity of oil in place (as we have noted previously this would be a mixed discrete-continuous random variable if nothing was known about whether oil was actually present). Then there would be another random variable (in actuality several random variables would be involved here) which describes how much of the oil present could be produced. It is by no means true that all the crude can be produced. The quantity varies from 10 to 70 percent, depending on a variety of factors. Next there would be a random variable describing the quality of the crude. Random variables might also be introduced for the thickness of the oil-bearing rock. This along with the volume would determine the areal extent and the number of wells to be drilled. Finally one would introduce several random variables for the price of the crude in different periods (these prices would depend on the quality of the crude). Given values of all these random variables and a development plan one can compute the discounted profit. Thus to find the expected discounted profit, the computer would go through the procedure of generating values for these random variables many times, and the expected discounted profit would then be determined by computing the average of the values obtained. In a case like this, it is often helpful also to have the computer construct a histogram for the profit so that management can see what sorts of variations could occur.

REFERENCES

The books by Fisz, Krickeberg, Parzen, and Wadsworth and Bryan are also appropriate for this chapter. In addition, the following are of interest.

1. Cramer, H., *Mathematical Methods in Statistics*. Princeton University Press, Princeton, N. J., 1946.

2. Gnedenko, B. V., and A. N. Kolmogorov, *Limit Distribution for Sums of Independent Random Variables*. Addison-Wesley, Reading, Mass., 1954.
A translation of a well-known Russian work. It gives an advanced discussion of the central and other limit theorems.

3. Hertz, D. B., "Risk Analysis in Capital Investment," *Harvard Business Review*, **42**, 95–106 (January 1964).
Illustrates how simulation can be used in certain types of decision problems.

4. Loéve, M., *Probability Theory*. Van Nostrand, Princeton, N. J., 1963.
An advanced treatment of continuous random variables is given.

5. McCord, J. R., and R. M. Moroney, *Introduction to Probability Theory*. Macmillan, New York, 1964.

6. Mood, A. M., and F. A. Graybill, *Introduction to the Theory of Statistics*, 2nd ed. McGraw-Hill, New York, 1963.
Gives a relatively elementary treatment of continuous random variables.

7. Neveu, J., *Mathematical Foundations of the Calculus of Probability*. Holden-Day, San Francisco, 1965.

8. RAND Corporation, *A Million Random Digits with 100,000 Normal Deviates*. Free Press, Glencoe, Ill., 1955.

9. Taylor, A. E., *Advanced Calculus*. Blaisdell, New York, 1955.
Beginning on p. 648 one finds a brief discussion of some of the most elementary properties of the gamma function.

PROBLEMS

Sections 7-1 and 7-2

1. Let x have the binomial distribution $b(x; 20, 0.5)$. Suppose that the random variable t is defined in terms of x by (7-2). What values does t take on? Construct carefully the histogram for t. On the same figure, draw the curve for $\varphi(t)$.

2. Let x have the binomial distribution $b(x; 10, 0.4)$. Suppose that the random variable t is defined in terms of x by (7-2). What values does t take on? Construct carefully the histogram for t. On the same figure, draw the curve for $\varphi(t)$.

3. Let x have the binomial distribution $b(x; 10, 0.2)$. Suppose that the random variable t is defined in terms of x by (7-2). What values does t take on? Construct carefully the histogram for t. On the same figure, draw the curve for $\varphi(t)$.

4. Let x have the binomial distribution $b(x; 10, 0.05)$. Suppose that the random variable t is defined in terms of x by (7-2). What values does t take on? Construct carefully the histogram for t. On the same figure, draw the curve for $\varphi(t)$.

5. Let x have the Poisson distribution $p(x; 5)$. Suppose that the random variable t is defined in terms of x by (7-2). What values does t take on? Construct carefully the histogram for t. On the same figure, draw the curve for $\varphi(t)$.

6. Let x have the Poisson distribution $p(x; 10)$. Suppose that the random variable t is defined in terms of x by (7-2). What values does t take on? Construct carefully the histogram for t. On the same figure, draw the curve for $\varphi(t)$.

7. Let y have the Pascal distribution $b_P(y; 8, 0.5)$. Suppose that $t = (y - \mu_y)/\sigma_y$. What values can t take on? Construct carefully the histogram for t. On the same figure, draw the curve for $\varphi(t)$.

8. Use the normal approximation to estimate

$$b(2; 20, 0.5), \quad b(10; 20, 0.5), \quad b(15; 20, 0.5), \quad b(20; 20, 0.5)$$

and compare the approximate values so obtained with the correct values.

9. Use the normal approximation to estimate

$$B(4; 20, 0.5), \quad B(10; 20, 0.5), \quad B(16; 20, 0.5)$$

and compare the approximate results with the correct values.

10. Use the normal approximation to estimate

$$b(2; 9, 0.2), \quad b(4; 9, 0.2), \quad b(8; 9, 0.2)$$

and compare the approximate values with the correct values.

11. Use the normal approximation to estimate the probability that $|x - 60| < 5$ when x has the distribution $b(x; 200, 0.3)$.

12. Use the normal approximation to estimate the probability that in a production run of 1000 units, the number of defectives will exceed 50 if the process is in statistical control and the probability that any given unit will be defective is 0.04.

13. Use the normal approximation to estimate the probability that if 100 students are selected at random from a group of 1000 students containing 300 girls and 700 boys, that at least 40 girls will be in the 100 students selected.

14. Use the normal approximation to estimate

$$p(4; 30), \quad p(10; 30), \quad p(50; 30).$$

15. Use the normal approximation to estimate

$$P(6; 30), \quad P(10; 30), \quad P(40; 30), \quad P(60; 30).$$

16. Use the normal approximation to estimate the probability that more than 100 tosses of a fair coin will be required to obtain 50 heads.

Sections 7-3 through 7-5

1. Take a box of 50 or more matches and measure carefully the length of each one. Does the length appear to have the characteristics of a random variable? Construct a histogram for the lengths. Is there some smooth curve which might approximate well the outline of this histogram?

2. A sample of 1000 ball bearings was selected from the output of a process for making ball bearings, and the diameter of each was measured. The numbers having diameters lying in given intervals are indicated in Table 7-1. The interval $(2, 3)$

TABLE 7-1

DATA ON BALL BEARINGS

Interval	Number	Interval	Number
$(-10, -5)$	9	$(0, 1)$	225
$(-5, -4)$	20	$(1, 2)$	115
$(-4, -3)$	50	$(2, 3)$	100
$(-3, -2)$	100	$(3, 4)$	25
$(-2, -1)$	150	$(4, 5)$	4
$(-1, 0)$	200	$(5, 10)$	2

means that the ball bearing diameter ξ lay in the interval $0.2502 \le \xi < 0.2503$ in., and the interval $(-3, -2)$ means that the ball bearing diameter ξ lay in the interval $0.2497 \le \xi < 0.2498$ in. Construct a histogram for the random variable representing the ball bearing diameter, and estimate the probability that the diameter ξ of a given ball bearing will be in the interval $0.2502 \le \xi \le 0.2505$.

3. In many practical situations, such as the one considered in the previous problem, one will be dealing with some random variable x whose distribution is unknown, and to find out something about this distribution, the relevant random experiment will be performed a number of times, say n, thus generating n values of x, call them $\xi_1, \ldots, \xi_n$. If n is large, our discussion from Chapter 1 shows that $\bar{\xi} = \sum_{i=1}^{n} \xi_i/n$ should be close to the expected value μ_x of x and $\bar{\xi}$ will be used as our estimate of μ_x. In this case then, it also follows from the discussion of Chapter 1 that if $s_x^2 = \sum_{i=1}^{n} (\xi_i - \bar{\xi})^2/n$, this should be a good approximation to σ_x^2, the variance of x, that is, s_x^2 will be our estimate of σ_x^2. If for some reason we are not given the individual values ξ_i, but are given instead data such as that in Table 7-1 which indicates the number of times that the value of x lay in a certain interval, we can still estimate μ_x and $\sigma_x{}^2$ as follows. Let

$$\bar{\xi}_g = \sum_{i=1}^{m} x_i \left(\frac{n_i}{n}\right); \quad s_{x_g}^2 = \sum_{i=1}^{m} (x_i - \bar{\xi}_g)^2 \left(\frac{n_i}{n}\right),$$

where x_i is the midpoint of the ith interval and n_i is the number of times that the value of x lay in the ith interval. We then use $\bar{\xi}_g$ and $s_{x_g}^2$ as our estimates of μ_x and $\sigma_x{}^2$. Indicate why this is reasonable if m and n are large. Use these results to estimate the mean and variance of the random variable x in Problem 2. Can any simplifications be introduced in computing these quantities?

4. If, on investigating some random variable x, one finds that the histogram looks like it might be approximated by the normal distribution, one must then decide which normal distribution is appropriate, that is, one must specify μ and σ in $n(x; \mu, \sigma)$. To do this the procedure normally used is to compute $\bar{\xi}$ or $\bar{\xi}_g$ and s_x or s_{x_g} for x as indicated in Problem 3 and use $\mu = \bar{\xi}$ or $\bar{\xi}_g$ and $\sigma = s_x$ or s_{x_g} so that one uses a normal distribution with the same mean and variance as x. Use this procedure and the results of Problem 3 to determine the normal distribution which might hopefully be used as a density function for the random variable x of Problem 2. Plot the graph of this normal distribution on the same figure that was used in Problem 2 to construct the histogram for x. Does the normal distribution appear to fit well?

5. Often the quality of parts that a manufacturer receives from a supplier can be characterized by the behavior of some random variable which can be conveniently thought of as being continuous. The variable may be a length, diameter, weight, resistance, etc. The manufacturer can gain a great deal of information about what his supplier is doing without ever asking the supplier, by occasionally taking a sizable sample of the parts and measuring the value of the basic random variable for each unit in the sample. Then a histogram for the random variable is constructed and studied. As an example, suppose that a manufacturer purchases brass bushings from a supplier. The nominal inside diameter of the bushing is 1 inch, and the manufacturer cannot use it if the diameter deviates by more than 0.006 in. on the large side or 0.003 in. on the small side. He has indicated this to the supplier. From a given lot the manufacturer selects at random 1100 bushings and measures carefully the inside diameter. The results are given in Table 7-2 where the numbers of bushings whose diameters lie in various intervals

TABLE 7-2

DATA FOR BUSHING DIAMETERS

Interval	Number	Interval	Number
$(-4, -3)$	1	$(2, 3)$	100
$(-3, -2)$	142	$(3, 4)$	50
$(-2, -1)$	200	$(4, 5)$	25
$(-1, 0)$	275	$(5, 6)$	12
$(0, 1)$	160	$(6, 7)$	7
$(1, 2)$	125	$(7, 10)$	3

are listed. The interval (2, 3) means that the diameter ξ was in the interval $1.002 \leq \xi < 1.003$. Construct a histogram for the bushing diameters. What can you conclude about the supplier's manufacturing process and the action he is taking? What would you estimate the density function representing the diameters of bushings coming off the supplier's production line would look like? Hint: Not all the supplier's customers will necessarily have precisely the same limitations on the inside diameter of the bushing.

6. A manufacturer produces shafts for electric motors. The diameter of the shaft can be conveniently imagined to be a continuous random variable, and when the process is in control, it behaves as if each shaft produced is the result of an independent trial of a random experiment in which the diameter x has the normal distribution $n(x; 0.75, 0.002)$. Suppose that to be classified as satisfactory, the diameter of the shaft cannot be less than 0.746 or greater than 0.753. What is the long run fraction defective produced by the process?

7. For the situation described in Problem 6, suppose that the manufacturer can select the expected value of the diameter of the shaft by suitably adjusting the lathes and that this has no influence on the standard deviation. Construct a graph showing the fraction defective produced by the process as a function of μ, the expected diameter of the shaft. What value of μ gives the minimum fraction defective?

8. Consider the binomial distribution $b(x; 10, 0.5)$. Draw a histogram for this distribution, and on the same figure plot the graph of the normal distribution whose mean and standard deviation are the same as $b(x; 10, 0.5)$.

9. Consider the Poisson distribution $p(x; 10)$. Draw a histogram for this distribution, and on the same figure plot the graph of the normal distribution with the same mean and standard deviation.

10. Let x have the normal distribution $n(x; 10, 2)$. Compute the probability that in performing the associated random experiment, the value ξ of x will be either in the interval $-5 \leq \xi \leq 1$ or the interval $8 \leq \xi \leq 10$.

11. Let x have the normal distribution $n(x; \mu, \sigma)$. Determine the probability that on performing the associated random experiment, the value ξ of x will not be more than one standard deviation away from the mean. Show that this probability is independent of μ and σ.

12. Let x have the normal distribution $n(x; \mu, \sigma)$. Show that the probability that $x > \mu + 2\sigma$ is the same as the probability that $x < \mu - 2\sigma$. Illustrate this geometrically.

13. Suppose that x has a normal distribution with mean 3 and standard deviation σ. Plot the graphs of the density function for x when $\sigma = 0.2, 0.8, 1$, and 3.

14. Suppose that x has a normal distribution. What must the standard deviation of this distribution be if the probability that the value of x is more than two units away from the mean (on either side) is 0.40?

15. We have noted that $b(r; n, p)$ can be approximated by the normal distribution either through the use of (7-24) or (7-15). Compare the results obtained using these two alternative methods to approximate:

   (a) $b(4; 10, 0.5)$;   (b) $b(1; 10, 0.5)$;   (c) $b(2; 10, 0.1)$.

16.   Re-solve Problem 15 for the following cases:

   (a) $b(6; 10, 0.1)$;   (b) $b(10; 30, 0.5)$;   (c) $b(6; 7, 0.4)$.

Sections 7-6 and 7-7

1. Suppose that the set X of values which a random variable x can take on is $X = X_1 \cup X_2$, where X_1 is the set of numbers $-6 \leq \xi \leq 2$ and X_2 is the set of numbers $5 \leq \xi \leq 10$. What does the integral (7-28) become in this case?

2. In the text we considered only events A for which (7-33) has a clear meaning. However, it is not hard to think of rather complicated events to which the discussion in the text does not seem to be immediately applicable. Suppose, for example, that x can take on all values in the interval $0 \leq \xi \leq 1$ and has a uniform distribution there. Let A be the event that x is a rational number and B be the event that x is an irrational number. Can you compute the probability of A and the possibility of B? What is the probability of $A \cup B$?

3. Suppose that we wish to convert $\psi(x) = \alpha x^2$ to a density function over the set X of numbers $0 \leq \xi \leq 1$. What value should be assigned to α? Sketch the graph of this density function. Determine the cumulative function for x, and sketch the graph of the cumulative function.

4. Re-solve Problem 3 when the domain for the density function is the interval $-1 \leq \xi \leq 1$.

5. Suppose that x can take on values in the interval $0 \leq \xi \leq 2$ and that we wish to use as a density function for x the function $f(x) = -0.1(x - 1)^2 + \beta$. What value should be assigned to β? Sketch the graph of $f(x)$. Also determine the cumulative function for x and sketch its graph.

6. For the situation outlined in Problem 3, what is the probability that the value x will be in the interval $0.2 \leq \xi \leq 0.3$ when the associated random experiment is performed?

7. For the situation outlined in Problem 4, what is the probability that $x \geq 0.1$?

8. For the situation outlined in Problem 4, what is the probability that $x \geq 0.1$ or $x \leq -0.9$?

9. For the situation outlined in Problem 5, what is the probability that the value will be in the interval $0.8 \leq \xi \leq 1.2$ when the associated random experiment is performed?

10. Suppose that x has an exponential distribution (7-54). What is the probability that the value of x observed on performing the associated random experiment will be in the interval $2/\lambda \leq \xi \leq 4/\lambda$?

11. Suppose that the random variable x can take on any value in the interval $0 \leq \xi \leq 5$. Show that the following function is a legitimate density function: $f(\xi) = 0.05, 0 \leq \xi \leq 2; f(\xi) = 0.3, 2 < \xi \leq 5$. Sketch the graph of $f(x)$. Determine the cumulative function for x. Does this function have a derivative at $\xi = 2$? What is the probability that when the associated random experiment is performed, the observed value of x will be in the interval $1 \leq \xi \leq 3$?

12. Let x be a continuous random variable with density function $f(x)$. Show that $f(x)$ can be arbitrarily redefined at any finite number of values in its domain without changing the probability of any event A, when the probability of A is computed using (7-33).

13. Show that $f(x) = [\pi(1 + x^2)]^{-1}$ is a legitimate density function for a random variable which can take on all real numbers. This is referred to as the Cauchy distribution.

14. Consider a random experiment $\Re$ for which we are using a model $\mathcal{E}$ involving the continuous random variable x. Suppose that as $\Re$ is being performed or after it is completed, we are told that the event A has occurred, $p(A) > 0$, but we are not told what value x has taken on. Show how to construct a new conditional probability model $\mathcal{E}_c$ which would be appropriate for making any additional computations. In particular show that for $\mathcal{E}_c$, A is the event set, and the density function for x is $f(x)/p(A)$, where $f(x)$ is the density function for x in $\mathcal{E}$.

15. Suppose that x has an exponential distribution with $\lambda = 0.2$, and on performing $\Re$ we are told that the event $x \leq 3$ has occurred. Determine, using the results of Problem 14, the conditional model $\mathcal{E}_c$ and compute the probability that the value of x lies in the interval $0 \leq \xi \leq 1$.

16. Determine the cumulative probability function for the exponential distribution, and sketch the graph of this function.

17. Determine the cumulative probability function for the second example of Section 7-7, and sketch the graph of this function.

18. Consider a model $\mathcal{E}$ with the event set X and with the density function $f(x)$ defined over X. Show that if X is not the set of all real numbers, we can use the model $\mathcal{E}^+$ whose event set is all real numbers and for which there is defined the density function,

$$g(\xi) = \begin{cases} f(\xi), & \xi \in X \\ 0, & \xi \notin X \end{cases}$$

and for any event A, $p(A)$ will be the same using either model, that is, $\mathcal{E}^+$ is a suitable model if $\mathcal{E}$ is and vice-versa. This result is equivalent to the situation in the discrete case where we noted that we can include impossible events in the event set if we assign them a zero probability, and the new model will be equivalent to the original one.

19. Consider the function whose domain is the interval $0 \leq x \leq 4$, and whose value is $x/2$, $0 \leq x \leq 1$; $(2 - x)/2$, $1 \leq x \leq 2$; $(x - 2)/2$, $2 \leq x \leq 3$; $(4 - x)/2$, $3 \leq x \leq 4$. Plot the graph of this function and show that it can be used as a legitimate density function $f(x)$ for a random variable x which can take on values in the interval $0 \leq x \leq 4$. Determine the cumulative distribution for x, and plot the graph of this function.

20. Let x be a random variable which can take on values in the interval $x \geq 1$.

For what value of α will $f(x) = \alpha/x^2$ serve as a density function for x? Determine the cumulative function for x in this case. Sketch the graphs of $f(x)$ and $F(x)$.

21. Let x be a random variable which can take on any real value. For what value of α will

$$f(x) = \alpha|x|/(1 + x^2)^2$$

yield a legitimate density function for x? Determine the cumulative function for x in this case. Sketch the graphs of $f(x)$ and $F(x)$.

22. Suppose that we consider a random variable x which can take on values in any one of the intervals

$$n \leq x \leq n + (1/n), \quad n = 1, 2, 3, \ldots.$$

There is an infinite number of such intervals. What is X in this case? Illustrate graphically. What does (7-28) become in this case? Is it possible to introduce a density function $f(x)$ which is a constant over X?

23. Suppose that we consider a random variable x which can take on values in any one of the intervals

$$n \leq x \leq n + r^n, \quad 0 < r < 1, \quad n = 1, 2, 3, \ldots.$$

What is X in this case? What does (7-28) reduce to here? Is it possible to introduce a density function $f(x)$ which is a constant over X?

24. Let x be a random variable which can take on all real values. For what value of α is $f(x) = \alpha e^{-|x|}$ a legitimate density function for x? Sketch the graph of this density function, and determine the cumulative function.

Sections 7-8 and 7-9

1. Determine the mean and variance of the density function introduced in Problem 3 for Sections 7-6 and 7-7.

2. Determine the mean and variance of the density function introduced in Problem 4 for Sections 7-6 and 7-7.

3. Determine the mean and variance of the density function introduced in Problem 5 for Sections 7-6 and 7-7.

4. Determine the mean and variance for the density function introduced in Problem 11 for Sections 7-6 and 7-7.

5. What problems are encountered in attempting to compute the mean and variance for the density function introduced in Problem 13 for Sections 7-6 and 7-7?

6. Let x be a random variable which can take on all non-negative values, and let x have an exponential distribution. Determine the density function for $y = x^2$.

7. Let x be a random variable having a uniform distribution over the interval $a \leq \xi \leq b$. Determine the density function for $y = x^2$.

8. Let x be a random variable with density function $f(x)$, defined for all real numbers x, and let $y = ax + b$, $a < 0$. Show that $g(y)$, the density function for y, is

$$g(y) = \frac{1}{|a|} f\left(\frac{y - b}{a}\right).$$

What is the domain for $g(y)$?

9. Let the random variable x have the density function $f(x)$. Denote by $M(\theta)$ the expected value of the random variable $y = e^{\theta x}$. For every θ for which the integral (7-59) exists there is a number $M(\theta)$. Thus we can think of $M(\theta)$ as a function of θ whose domain is the set of values for which (7-59) exists. Note that $\theta = 0$ is always in the domain of $M(\theta)$. Why? The function $M(\theta)$ is called the *moment generating function* for the distribution $f(x)$. The reason for this is that $M'(\theta)$, the derivative of $M(\theta)$ evaluated at $\theta = 0$, is μ_x; and more generally $M^{(j)}(0)$, which is the jth derivative of $M(\theta)$ evaluated at $\theta = 0$, is the expected value of x^j. Prove this. Hint: $e^{\theta x} = \sum_{j=0}^{\infty} \theta^j x^j / j!$. Multiply by $f(x)$ and integrate over X. Integrate the series term by term without being concerned about rigorously showing that this is valid. This yields $M(\theta) = \sum_{j=0}^{\infty} \mu_j \theta^j / j!$, where μ_j is the expected value of x^j. Now differentiate with respect to θ and set $\theta = 0$. Provide an alternative proof by differentiating $M(\theta) = \int_X e^{\theta x} f(x)\, dx$.

10. Determine the moment generating function for the uniform distribution (7-48), and in this way determine the mean and variance of this distribution. The definition of the moment generating function is given in Problem 9.

11. Determine the moment generating function for the exponential distribution, and in this way determine the mean and variance of this distribution. The definition of the moment generating function is given in Problem 9.

12. In dealing with single stage inventory problems of the type discussed in Section 4-3, it is often convenient to treat the random variable x representing the demand as a continuous random variable and also to allow the quantity stocked to be any non-negative number. Suppose that x has the density function $f(x)$, and let the costs be defined as in Section 4-3, so that, for example, if x is the demand and h the number of units stocked, the gain from sales on units left over is $R(h - \xi)$ when $x = \xi$. Develop the model under these assumptions, and show that h^*, the optimal quantity to stock, is the number such that

$$F(h^*) = \frac{S + T - C}{S + T - R},$$

where $F(x)$ is the cumulative function for x.

13. A buyer for a department store is trying to decide how many of a high fashion dress to purchase for the coming season. The entire stock must be purchased in advance, and there is no opportunity to reorder later in the season. Each dress costs the store \$25 and retails for \$55. Any dresses left over at the end of the season can be sold for cost. However, for each dollar invested in a dress sold at cost at the end of the season, the buyer feels that he loses \$0.12 in lost profits that he could have obtained by investing the funds in other merchandise. He also believes that for each dress demanded which cannot be supplied from stock there is a goodwill loss of \$50. The buyer believes that the demand will be between 200 and 400 dresses, and any number in this interval is as likely as any other number. Treating the demand as a continuous random variable and using the results of Problem 12, determine how many dresses the buyer should stock. Compute his optimal expected profit assuming that discounting is not required.

14. Re-solve Problem 13 treating the demand as an exponential distribution with the same mean as the distribution in Problem 13. How do you explain the results obtained?

15. Re-solve Problems 4, 7, and 8 for Section 4-3, treating the random variable as continuous.

16. Re-solve Problem 11 for Section 4-3, treating the random variable as continuous.

17. A business man is expecting a call between 9:00 and 11:00 a.m. The time of arrival of the call can be assumed to be a random variable with a uniform distribution. What is the expected length of time that he will have to wait after 9:00 a.m. for the call to arrive?

18. Let x be a random variable defined over X having a density function $f(x)$. The function $F_c(x)$ having the characteristic that $F_c(\xi)$ is the probability that $x \geq \xi$ is called the complementary cumulative function. How are $F(x)$, the cumulative function, and $F_c(x)$ related? Determine the complementary cumulative function for the uniform and exponential distributions, and sketch the graph of each of these functions. What is the derivative of $F_c(x)$ at $x = \xi$?

19. Determine μ_x and $\sigma_x{}^2$ for the random variable x introduced in Problem 19 for Sections 7-6 and 7-7.

20. Determine μ_x and $\sigma_x{}^2$ for the random variable x introduced in Problem 20 for Sections 7-6 and 7-7.

21. Determine μ_x and $\sigma_x{}^2$ for the random variable x introduced in Problem 21 for Sections 7-6 and 7-7.

22. Determine μ_x and $\sigma_x{}^2$ for the random variable x introduced in Problem 24 for Sections 7-6 and 7-7.

23. Prove that if x is a random variable which can take on all real values, then when α is a point of symmetry of $f(x)$, it follows that $\mu_x = \alpha$, provided μ_x exists.

24. Let x be a random variable which can take on any non-negative value, and let $f(x)$ be the density function for x. Determine the density function for $y = \sqrt{x}$.

25. Let $F_c(x)$ be the complementary cumulative function defined in Problem 18. Prove that if X is the set of values ξ, $0 \leq \xi \leq a$ or $0 \leq \xi \leq \infty$, then

$$\mu_x = \int_X F_c(x)\, dx;$$

and show by actually evaluating the integral that this holds true when x has an exponential distribution.

Section 7-10

1. Show directly that

$$\mu = \int_{-\infty}^{\infty} x\, n(x; \mu, \sigma)\, dx.$$

Hint: Break up the integral into two parts, one from $-\infty$ to 0 and the other from 0 to ∞.

2. Express the integral

$$\int_{\xi}^{\infty} (x - \mu)n(x; \mu, \sigma)\, dx$$

in terms of the functions $\varphi(t)$ and $\Phi(t)$ so that the integral can be easily evaluated for a given ξ, using tables for these functions.

3. Show that

$$\int_{u}^{\infty} t\varphi(t)\, dt = \varphi(u).$$

4. Sales of bread on a given day in a supermarket can be well approximated by a normal distribution with mean 200 loaves and standard deviation 30 loaves. Each loaf costs the market $0.22, and it is sold for $0.25. Any loaves not sold at the end of the day will be sold the next day when they are placed on a stale bread counter and priced at $0.15 per loaf. What is the optimal number of loaves to stock if no other costs are involved? Compute the expected profit per day when the optimal number of loaves is stocked. Also compute the expected profit per day when the expected demand is stocked.

5. Re-solve Problem 4 if there is a goodwill loss of $0.25 for each loaf demanded which cannot be supplied.

6. Compute the moment generating function for the normal distribution $n(x; \mu, \sigma)$, and in this way determine the mean and variance of this distribution. The moment generating function is defined in Problem 9 for Sections 7-8 and 7-9.

7. A manufacturer produces resistors. Consider a particular resistor he produces whose nominal resistance is 1000 ohm. The actual resistance of any unit produced can be thought of as a random variable which has the normal distribution $n(x; 1000, 45)$. The manufacturer sells both one percent and ten percent resistors, one percent meaning that the resistance should be within one percent of the nominal value. To obtain these two classifications, he proceeds as follows. He inspects all resistors coming off the line, and those whose resistance does not differ by more than 10 ohms from 1000 ohms, he selects as one percent resistors. The rest he sells as ten percent resistors. Thus, someone buying a ten percent resistor will never get one having the nominal resistance. Determine the density function for ten percent resistors, and sketch the graph of this function. If a ten percent resistor is considered defective when the resistance lies outside the ten percent limits, what is the fraction defective produced of ten percent resistors?

8. Re-solve Problem 7 if the resistance x has the normal distribution $n(x: 990, 45)$.

9. Let x have the normal distribution $n(x; \mu, \sigma)$. Determine the density function for $y = |x|$.

10. A large manufacturer of household detergents is about to make a run on a particular product. The filling of the boxes is done automatically by machines. For a given setting, the machine does not always put the same amount in each box. The amount going into any given box can be looked upon as a random variable x. Experiments have indicated that x is normally distributed with a standard deviation of 0.2 ounces. The expected value of x can be chosen arbitrarily within the range of interest by suitably adjusting the machine. The boxes of the detergent are labeled as containing 32 ounces. It is desired to select the expected value of x so that no more than one box in one thousand has less than 32 ounces. What value should be selected for μ? If the detergent costs \$0.005 per ounce to produce, how much could be saved on a run of ten million boxes, if the mean was selected so that no more than one box in one hundred has less than 32 ounces?

11. Consider a machined part which is produced on a particular lathe in a machine shop. The diameters of the parts turned out will not always be precisely the same, but will vary somewhat from one piece to another due to a variety of causes. The diameter x of any particular piece can then be looked upon as a random variable. The expected value μ of x can be selected by proper setting of the lathe. The standard deviation is a constant σ independent of the lathe setting. Experience indicates that x is essentially normally distributed. In order to pass inspection, the diameter x of any piece must be in the interval $\alpha \leq x \leq \beta$. If $x < \alpha$, the piece must be scrapped. If $x > \beta$, the piece can be reworked. The shop under consideration does not rework pieces. Instead, it sells pieces with $x > \beta$ to another shop at a price p_1. Each piece which passes inspection is sold at a price $p > p_1$. The cost of raw materials, labor, and machine time for each piece which enters production is k. Express that μ which maximizes the expected weekly profit in terms of the other parameters introduced above.

Section 7-11

1. Show that

$$\int_y^\infty g(x; n, \lambda) \, dx = P(n; \lambda y),$$

where $P(n; \beta)$ is the cumulative Poisson probability.

2. Let $G(x; n, \lambda)$ be the cumulative function for $g(x; n, \lambda)$. Express $G(x; n, \lambda)$ in a form which can be computed with the aid of tables for the Poisson distribution.

3. Determine the moment generating function for $g(x; \alpha, \lambda)$, and in this way compute the mean and variance of this distribution. The moment generating function is defined in Problem 9 for Sections 7-8 and 7-9.

Section 7-12

1. In Section 6-7 we studied joint probability functions for two or more random variables. Let $p(x, y)$ be such a function for the two random variables x and y. We illustrated in Figure 6-3 how such a function could be represented geometrically. Suppose now that instead of representing $p(x, y)$ by a bar diagram, we represent it by a histogram in which probabilities are represented by volumes. About the point (x_u, y_v) in the xy-plane, we construct a rectangle and use this rectangle as the base of a parallelepiped whose volume is $p(x_u, y_v)$. What is the height of the parallelepiped? By analogy with the procedure used in obtaining a histogram for $p(x)$, how should the rectangles in the xy-plane be determined? Illustrate in the xy-plane these rectangles in the case where x can take on the values $0, 1, \ldots, 5$ and y the values $0, 1, \ldots, 8$. When x and y can take on a large number of values, the outline of the histogram (which is now a surface) will appear rather smooth and we can imagine it as being approximated by a smooth surface which is the graph of some function $h(x, y)$. Then $h(x, y)$ is what we have called the joint probability density function for x and y in the text. Use this approach to explain the logic behind (7-113) and (7-114).

2. Use the approach suggested in Problem 1 to provide an intuitive justification for (7-118), (7-119), and (7-121).

3. Use the approach suggested in Problem 1 to provide an intuitive interpretation of $g(\zeta|\xi)$ and $f(\xi|\zeta)$.

4. What is the geometric equivalent of the histogram introduced in Problem 1 for the case where we find it convenient to treat one of the variables as discrete and the other as continuous? Use this to explain (7-129) through (7-132).

5. Suppose that $W = X \times Y$ is the rectangle with corners at $(-5, 2)$, $(6, 2)$, $(-5, 7)$, and $(6, 7)$ and that $h(x, y)$ is a constant over W. What value must $h(x, y)$ have for each point in W in this case? When $h(x, y)$ is a constant, we say that x and y are jointly uniformly distributed. Determine the marginal density functions for x and y and the conditional density functions. Prove that in this case x and y are independent random variables.

6. For the situation described in Problem 5, compute the probability of the event $x \leq 0$, $y \leq 3$ and of the event $x^2 + (y - 2)^2 \leq 4$.

7. Let W be the rectangle with corners at $(0, 0)$, $(0, 2)$, $(3, 0)$, $(3, 2)$. For what value of α is

$$h(x, y) = \alpha[100 - (x - 1)^2 - (y - 1)^2]$$

a legitimate density function over W? Sketch the graph of this density function.

8. For the situation described in Problem 7, compute $f(x)$ and $g(y)$, and sketch the graphs of these functions.

9. For the situation described in Problem 7, compute the conditional density functions $f(x|\zeta)$ and $g(y|\xi)$, and sketch the graphs of these functions for $\zeta = 1$ and $\xi = 1$.

10. For the situation outlined in Problem 7, what is the probability that $x \leq 1$ and $y \leq 1$?

11. For the situation outlined in Problem 7, what is the probability that $x + y \leq 1$?

12. For the situation outlined in Problem 7, what is the probability that

$$(x - 1)^2 + (y - 1)^2 \leq 1?$$

13. Determine the value of α for which $h(x, y) = \alpha e^{-(x+y)}$ becomes a possible joint density function for the random variables x and y when both random variables can take on any non-negative values. Are x and y independent random variables in this case? Determine the probability that $x + y \leq 7$.

14. Determine the value of α for which $h(x, y) = \alpha xy$ becomes a possible joint density function for the random variables x and y, when x and y must be in the intervals $0 \leq x \leq 1$, $0 \leq y \leq 2$. Are x and y independent random variables in this case? Determine the probability that $xy \leq 1$.

15. The cumulative function for a joint density function $h(x, y)$ for two random variables x and y is defined to be

$$H(\xi, \zeta) = \int_{x \leq \xi} \int_{y \leq \zeta} h(x, y) \, dx \, dy.$$

How can $h(x, y)$ be obtained from $H(x, y)$? How can $f(x)$ and $g(y)$, the marginal density functions, be obtained from $H(x, y)$? Determine $H(x, y)$ for the density functions introduced in Problems 5 and 13.

16. Suppose that x and y are two random variables with the joint density function $h(x, y)$. Let z be a new random variable defined by $z = \Theta(x, y)$. Show how to determine the density function for z. Illustrate the determination using the density function introduced in Problem 13 when $z = x + y$.

17. Let x and y be two independent random variables, y being one that can take on all positive real values. Assume that $f(x)$ and $g(y)$ are the density functions for x and y. Consider the random variable $z = x/y$. Show that $H(\Theta)$, the probability that $z \leq \Theta$, is given by

$$H(\Theta) = \int_0^\infty F(\Theta y) g(y) \, dy.$$

Obtain an expression for $h(z)$, the density function for z.

18. Suppose that x has the standardized normal distribution and the variable y^2 has the distribution $g(y^2; -\frac{1}{2}, \frac{1}{2})$. Determine the density function for $z = x/y$.

Section 7-13

1. One roulette wheel whose circumference is calibrated as a scale going from 0 to 100 is spun and stops on the number ξ. Another roulette wheel whose circumference is calibrated on a scale going from 0 to 50 is spun and stops on the number ζ. A right triangle is constructed having a base of length ξ and altitude of length ζ. What is the probability that the area of this triangle is less than or equal to 75?

2. Two individuals plan to meet between 9 and 11 a.m. The times of arrival of each are independent random variables having a uniform distribution. The individuals agree that the one arriving first will wait 20 minutes for the second, and then go on if the second individual does not arrive. What is the probability that a meeting actually takes place?

3. A roulette wheel whose circumference is calibrated as a scale going from 0 to 100 is spun and stops at the number ξ. It is spun again and stops at the number ζ. On a rod of length 100 we mark the points ξ and ζ (measuring from the left end of the rod). The rod is then broken at these two points to yield three pieces. What is the probability that a triangle can be formed from the three pieces?

4. A roulette wheel whose circumference is calibrated as a scale going from 0 to 100 is spun and stops on the number ξ. On a rod of length 100 we mark the number ξ and then break the rod at this point. What is the probability that the length of the shorter of the two pieces will be greater than 20?

5. A coin of diameter d is tossed on a tiled floor. The tiles are square and have length r, $r > d$. What is the probability that the coin when it comes to rest does not lie across any side of a tile, that is, it lies entirely within a tile? What assumption did you make here?

6. A rod of length r is tossed onto a flat table ruled with parallel lines whose spacing is $2r$. What is the probability that when the rod comes to rest it intersects one of the ruled lines? What assumptions are needed here?

Section 7-14

1. For the situation described in Problem 7 of Section 7-12, compute the expected value of x. Compute also the expected value of x using the marginal density function determined in Problem 8 for the same section. Similarly, compute the expected value of y.

2. For the situation described in Problem 7 of Section 7-12, let $z = x^2 + y^2$. Compute the expected value z.

3. If σ_{xy} is the covariance of x and y, show that

$$\sigma_{xy} = \iint_W xyh(x, y) \, dx \, dy - \mu_x\mu_y.$$

4. Use the results of Problems 1 and 3 to compute the covariance of x and y for the situation outlined in Problem 7 of Section 7-12.

5. Compute the variance of x and the variance of y for the situation described in Problem 7 of Section 7-12.

6. For the situation outlined in Problem 7 of Section 7-12, let $z = 3x - 4y$. Compute directly the expected value and variance of z. Also, using the results of Problems 1, 5, and 6 compute these using (7-138) and (7-140).

7. Let x have the normal distribution $n(x; \mu_x, \sigma_x)$ and y the normal distribution $n(y; \mu_y, \sigma_y)$. Assume that x and y are independent. Let $z = ax + by$, $b < 0$. Show that z has a normal distribution with expected value and variance (7-148).

8. Go through the algebra which leads to (7-147). Hint: Add and subtract an appropriate quantity in one expression, and then complete the square.

9. Suppose that x and y are independent random variables with distributions $n(x; \mu_x, \sigma_x)$ and $n(y; \mu_y, \sigma_y)$. Show that $z = y - x$ has a normal distribution $n(z; \mu, \sigma)$ where

$$\mu = \mu_x - \mu_y; \quad \sigma^2 = \sigma_y{}^2 + \sigma_x{}^2.$$

This is a useful result. As one illustration of its usefulness, suppose that one manufacturer makes shafts for electric motors, the diameter x being a normally distributed random variable with expected value 1 in. and standard deviation 0.0010 in. Another manufacturer makes the bushings which the shaft passes through. The diameter of the hole in the bushing is a normally distributed random variable y with mean 1.002 in. and standard deviation 0.0010 in. If we select a shaft and a bushing, $z = y - x$ is the clearance when the shaft is put in the bushing, a negative value of z meaning that the diameter of the shaft is greater than the diameter of the bushing. What is the probability that for a shaft and bushing selected at random, the shaft will not fit into the bushing? To operate properly the clearance should be between 0.001 and 0.003 in. What is the probability that the clearance will be in this interval?

10. For the situation described in Problem 9, suppose that nothing can be done about the variances. What should be the expected diameter of the hole in the bushing to maximize the probability that the clearance will be in the desired interval? Assume that the expected shaft diameter remains unchanged.

11. Let x have a normal distribution $n(x; 10,1)$. Let us make ten independent trials of the associated random experiment $\mathfrak{R}$, thus generating ten values of x. Denote by $\bar{\xi}$ the average of these ten values. What is the probability that $\bar{\xi}$ is more than 0.2 units away from $\mu_x = 10$?

12. For the situation described in Problem 11, what is the minimum number of independent trials of $\mathfrak{R}$ that must be made in order that $\bar{\xi}$, the average of the x values so obtained, will have the property that the probability that $\bar{\xi}$ is more than 0.01 units from $\mu_x = 10$ is 0.01 or less?

13. We have shown previously that if x has the normal distribution $n(x; \mu, \sigma)$, then $z = (x - \mu)^2$ has the gamma distribution $g(z; -1/2, 1/2\sigma^2)$. What is the distribution of z/n, where n is a natural number? Suppose that we make n independent trials of $\mathfrak{R}$, and let $x\{j\}$ be the random variable representing x on the jth trial. Let $y = \sum_{j=1}^{n} (x\{j\} - \mu)^2/n$. What is the distribution for y? This distribution, although a gamma distribution, is given a special name, the chi squared distribution.

14. Use the definition of a derivative and the properties of integrals to show that the derivative of (7-151) is (7-152).

15. Consider a random experiment $\mathfrak{R}$ involving n random variables $x\{j\}$. Suppose that we introduce n new random variables $y\{j\}$ by letting each $y\{j\}$ be some function of the n variables $x\{j\}$. Finally, suppose that we define a random variable z to be a linear combination of the $y\{j\}$. Obtain a formula for computing μ_z, and use this formula to prove (7-158) and (7-159).

16. Prove that if $x\{1\}$, $x\{2\}$, and $x\{3\}$ are independent random variables, then $y = a_1x\{1\} + a_2x\{2\}$ and $x\{3\}$ are independent random variables. Generalize this result to n independent random variables, and use it to obtain (7-161).

17. Consider three independent random variables $x\{1\}$, $x\{2\}$, and $x\{3\}$, each of which has a uniform distribution over the interval $0 \le \xi \le 1$. Determine the density function for $y = x\{1\} + x\{2\}$ and $z = y + x\{3\}$. Sketch the graphs of these density functions.

Section 7-15

1. Let x have the exponential distribution $\lambda e^{-\lambda x}$, $x \ge 0$. Suppose that $\mathfrak{R}_n$ is the random experiment which consists in performing n independent trials of the experiment $\mathfrak{R}$ which generates a value of x. Let $\bar{x}\{n\}$ be the random variable representing the average of the values of x observed on each independent trial of $\mathfrak{R}$. What is the density function for $\bar{x}\{n\}$? On the same graph, sketch the density functions for x, $\bar{x}\{1\}$, $\bar{x}\{2\}$, $\bar{x}\{3\}$, $\bar{x}\{4\}$, and $\bar{x}\{5\}$. Does $\bar{x}\{n\}$ appear to be approaching a normal distribution reasonably rapidly? Note that the distribution of x is far from normal.

2. Number ten pennies from 0 to 9. Place these in a container, and repeat 100 times the experiment in which the pennies are thoroughly mixed, and a penny is drawn and the number on it noted. Construct a histogram for x, the number appearing on the penny selected. Let the base of the rectangle for $x = r$ extend from $r - \frac{1}{2}$ to $r + \frac{1}{2}$. Now pair successive numbers obtained so that there are 50 pairs. Determine the average of each pair of numbers, and construct a histogram for $\bar{x}\{2\}$, the random variable giving the average of the pairs. Next subdivide the original outcome into sets of four numbers, so that there are 25 sets of four numbers. Compute the average of each set of four numbers, and construct a histogram for $\bar{x}\{4\}$, the random variable representing the average of these four numbers.

Section 7-16

1. Use numbered pennies to generate ten two-digit random numbers from the uniform distribution over the unit interval.

2. Use the results of Problem 1 and the table for $\varphi(t)$ to generate ten random numbers from the standardized normal distribution.

CHAPTER 8

USE OF EXPERIMENTS IN DECISION PROBLEMS

*Knowledge is of two kinds. We know a subject our-
selves, or we know where we can find information upon it.*

Dr. Samuel Johnson

8-1 INTRODUCTION

After a rather long digression to develop a variety of topics in probability
theory, we now wish to return to studying single stage decision problems.
The model introduced in Chapter 3 and considered in some detail in
Chapter 4 is completely general. In this chapter we wish to study a
particular class of single stage decision problems which have the characteristic that in determining the probabilities of the states of nature we
make use of historical data or personal feelings and, in addition, make use
of the results of a random experiment. Let us now describe in more
detail the type of problem that we have in mind.

In Chapter 3 we thought of a single stage decision problem as one in
which first the decision maker selects an action and then later nature
selects a state of nature. Now there is nothing in the formulation of the
problem which requires that the state of nature actually be determined
after the decision maker selects an action. All that is implied is that at
the time the decision maker selects the action he does not know what the
state of nature is. It is irrelevant whether nature selected the state of
nature millions of years before the decision maker selects an action or
whether the state of nature is determined after the action is chosen, so
long as in either case the decision maker does not know what the state
of nature is, but can think of the state of nature as being the outcome of
the random experiment.

Now many interesting decision problems have the characteristic that
the state of nature is determined prior to the time the decision maker

selects an action. There is one very important distinction between problems of this sort and those where the state of nature is determined after an action is selected. When the state of nature has been determined before the decision maker selects an action, then there exists the possibility that the decision maker can gain additional information about what the state of nature is or, for a sufficiently high cost, even ascertain precisely what the state of nature is. This chapter will be concerned with problems where the state of nature has been determined before the decision maker selects an action and where there exists the possibility of getting more information about the state of nature before making a decision. We shall be assuming that the way in which the decision maker can obtain additional information is to perform a random experiment. The experiment will yield some information about the state of nature, although in general it will not be able to determine precisely what the state of nature is. We shall begin by showing how the experimental results can be combined with other information to determine the probabilities of the states of nature. Later we shall consider the problem of whether it is worthwhile to perform an experiment to obtain additional information, and if so, which of a variety of possible experiments is the one that should actually be performed.

8-2 USE OF BAYES' LAW TO DETERMINE POSTERIOR PROBABILITIES

Consider a single stage decision problem for which there are m states of nature, which will be represented symbolically by $e_1, \ldots, e_m$, and r possible actions, symbolized by $a_1, \ldots, a_r$, one of which will be selected by the decision maker. Let U_{ij} be the utility for the decision maker if he selects action a_i and the state of nature turns out to be e_j. We shall assume that the state of nature has been determined before the decision maker selects the action to take, but that he does not know what the state of nature is. We shall suppose, however, that he has assigned a probability p_j that the state of nature is e_j. If the situation is one that is repeated, then p_j is the long run fraction of the time that nature selects the state e_j. If the situation is not one that can be given a frequency interpretation, then the p_j are personal probabilities, i.e., weights, which are assigned by the decision maker to reflect his feelings about the situation, and which if desired can be visualized as ensemble relative frequencies. Since we are assuming that the state of nature is already determined when the action is selected, it is clear that the probabilities assigned to the states of nature must be independent of the action selected. We shall be making this assumption throughout this chapter. The problem could then be represented by a decision tree of the type suggested in Chapter 3 as shown in Figure 8-1. However, it is very convenient here to indicate the proper time phasing, and thus draw the tree so that nature makes the first decision. This is done in Figure 8-2. When things are done in this way, it is important to have a way of indicating that the decision maker does not know what state nature selected. A convenient way to do this is to indicate in one way or another the sets of nodes having the characteristic that the decision maker does not know at which node in a given set he is. Thus in Figure 8-2 we have indicated that the decision maker does not know at which of the m nodes he is by enclosing them all inside a dashed curve. Figure 8-2 then represents the situation in the case where nothing is done to gain more information about the state of nature.

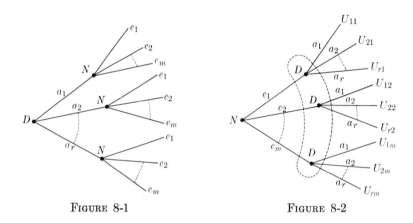

FIGURE 8-1   FIGURE 8-2

Let us now imagine that before selecting an action, the decision maker decides to perform a random experiment $\mathcal{R}$ to try to learn something more about the state of nature. We shall suppose that the event set for $\mathcal{R}$ is $F = \{f_1, \ldots, f_s\}$, and that this is independent of what the state of nature happens to be. However, the probability of any particular simple event f_u will in general depend on the state of nature and the probability of f_u when the state of nature is e_j will be denoted by w_{ju}. Thus $w_{ju} \geq 0$ and $\sum_{u=1}^{s} w_{ju} = 1$ for each j. We see that the actual random experiment performed will then depend on what the state of nature is, since the probabilities will depend on the state of nature. In other words, the appropriate mathematical model to use for $\mathcal{R}$ will depend on the state of nature. If the state of nature is e_j, then the appropriate model to use is one having the event set F with the probability of f_u being w_{ju}.

When the decision maker performs the random experiment $\mathcal{R}$ before selecting an action, the decision tree now becomes a little more complicated

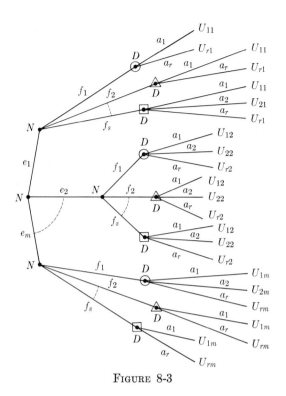

FIGURE 8-3

and can be represented as shown in Figure 8-3. To indicate the sets of nodes having the characteristic that the decision maker does not know at which node of the set he is, we have inscribed circles, triangles, and squares about the nodes. The only thing the decision maker knows at the time the decision is made is the outcome of $\Re$, and hence the decision maker is

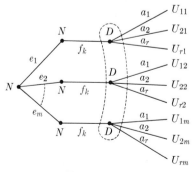

FIGURE 8-4

unable to distinguish between any two nodes both of which correspond to the same outcome of $\mathfrak{R}$. Once $\mathfrak{R}$ is performed and it is observed that the outcome of $\mathfrak{R}$ is f_k, then the decision tree reduces to Figure 8-4 which is of precisely the same form as Figure 8-2.

After observing the outcome f_k of $\mathfrak{R}$, what the decision maker wishes to do is construct a probability model which is the appropriate one given f_k. The probabilities to be used in this model will be written $p(e_j|f_k)$. For problems in which the decision situation can be repeated, $p(e_j|f_k)$ should represent the long run relative frequency of e_j for those cases where $\mathfrak{R}$ yields the outcome f_k. Now $\mathfrak{R}$ can be thought of as the second stage of a two stage experiment. In the first stage nature selects the state of nature, and at the second stage nature selects the outcome of $\mathfrak{R}$. The purpose of performing $\mathfrak{R}$ is to gain information as to what the outcome of the first stage was. In Section 6-5 we studied experiments of this type and showed how to compute $p(e_j|f_k)$ by use of Bayes' law. For the two stage experiment $p(e_j|f_k)$ is the conditional probability of e_j given that the outcome of the second stage is f_k. In terms of the probabilities introduced above, Bayes' law (6-18) becomes

$$p(e_j|f_k) = \frac{p_j w_{jk}}{\displaystyle\sum_{v=1}^{m} p_v w_{vk}}, \tag{8-1}$$

or if we write $p(f_k|e_j) = w_{jk}$, we have

$$p(e_j|f_k) = \frac{p(f_k|e_j)p_j}{\displaystyle\sum_{v=1}^{m} p(f_k|e_v)p_v} = \frac{p(f_k|e_j)p_j}{p(f_k)}. \tag{8-2}$$

The reader will note that we have modified slightly the notation employed in Chapter 6.

We shall, using the terminology introduced in Chapter 6, refer to the probabilities p_j as the prior probabilities for the states of nature (before $\mathfrak{R}$ is performed) and the conditional probabilities $p(e_j|f_k)$ as the posterior probabilities of the states of nature (the probabilities to use after the experiment $\mathfrak{R}$ is performed). Bayes' law (8-1) tells us how to compute the posterior probabilities. Once the posterior probabilities have been determined, these are the probabilities that are used for the states of nature, and the solution of the problem is determined as in Chapter 4 by finding the action which maximizes the expected utility:

$$\sum_{j=1}^{m} U_{ij} p(e_j|f_k). \tag{8-3}$$

We have now shown in general terms how to handle single stage decision problems in which a random experiment is performed before an action is selected. The only difference between the procedure in this case and that used in Chapter 4 is that one additional step is inserted to combine the experimental results with the prior probabilities to obtain the posterior probabilities, which are the ones actually used in the decision theory model. The procedure is thus very simple conceptually. In practice, of course, just as for the cases where no experiment was performed, the situation can become very complex with respect to actually carrying out the details of determining the posterior probabilities and determining the action which yields the largest expected utility, and a variety of special techniques are often used in carrying out the details. For example, it is frequently convenient to imagine that the states of nature can be described by the values of a continuous random variable and/or that the outcomes of $\Re$ can be described by the values of a continuous random variable. This does not involve any conceptual changes, but merely requires that one modify appropriately Bayes' law and the technique used for computing the expected utilities in (8-3).

As a result of performing the experiment $\Re$ the decision maker revises his estimate of the probability that e_j will occur from p_j to $p(e_j|f_k)$. The value of $p(e_j|f_k)$ depends on both all the p_j and on the experiment $\Re$. We indicated in Chapter 4 that a decision maker is in bad shape if he knows absolutely nothing about the probabilities of the states of nature. Now in the event that there exists the possibility of performing an experiment to gain information about the state of nature, we feel that if the experiment is a very discriminating one and gives a considerable amount of information about the state of nature, then it may not be very important whether the decision maker knows much about the prior probabilities p_j for the states of nature. This intuitive notion is, generally speaking, correct. Let us prove, in particular, that if $\Re$ actually determines what the state of nature is then, provided that the decision maker did not assign a prior probability of 0 to this state of nature, call it e_q, the posterior probability of e_q computed from Bayes' law is 1. Imagine that f_k is the event which says that e_q is the state of nature when e_q is actually the state of nature. If $\Re$ does indeed indicate what the state of nature is, we must have $w_{qk} = 1$, $w_{jk} = 0$, $j \neq q$. Then when e_q is the state of nature, $\Re$ yields the outcome f_k and (8-1) becomes

$$p(e_q|f_k) = p_q/p_q = 1, \quad \text{if } p_q \neq 0. \tag{8-4}$$

One can see from examples what the situation is when the experiment is very discriminating but not perfect. Let us illustrate this.

EXAMPLE. Suppose that there are three states of nature e_1, e_2, and e_3 to which the prior probabilities $p_1 = 0.2$, $p_2 = 0.5$, $p_3 = 0.3$ are assigned. Suppose that we perform an experiment $\Re$ which has three outcomes

f_1, f_2, f_3, where f_u says that the state of nature is e_u. Imagine that this experiment is quite discriminating, and $w_{11} = 0.90$, $w_{12} = 0.04$, $w_{13} = 0.06$, $w_{21} = 0.07$, $w_{22} = 0.92$, $w_{23} = 0.01$, $w_{31} = 0.02$, $w_{32} = 0.04$, $w_{33} = 0.94$. Consider the case where $\Re$ yields the outcome f_1. Then the posterior probabilities are

$$p(e_1|f_1) = \frac{0.90(0.2)}{0.90(0.2) + 0.07(0.5) + 0.02(0.3)} = \frac{0.18}{0.221} = 0.815;$$

$$p(e_2|f_1) = \frac{0.07(0.5)}{0.221} = \frac{0.035}{0.221} = 0.158;$$

$$p(e_3|f_1) = \frac{0.02(0.3)}{0.221} = \frac{0.006}{0.221} = 0.027.$$

Thus the prior probability $p_1 = 0.2$ is changed to a posterior probability of 0.815 as a result of the experiment.

Suppose that instead of the above prior probability assignment, the assignment $p_1 = 0.7$, $p_2 = 0.2$, $p_3 = 0.1$ is used. Let us again compute the posterior probabilities, given that f_1 is the outcome of $\Re$. Now

$$p(e_1|f_1) = \frac{0.90(0.7)}{0.90(0.7) + 0.07(0.2) + 0.02(0.1)} = \frac{0.63}{0.646} = 0.975;$$

$$p(e_2|f_1) = \frac{0.07(0.2)}{0.646} = 0.022; \quad p(e_3|f_1) = \frac{0.02(0.1)}{0.646} = 0.003.$$

Thus, although the prior probabilities are quite different in the two cases just considered, there is a relatively small difference in the posterior probabilities.

In general, one cannot determine the posterior probabilities of the states of nature without having some assignment for the prior probabilities. However, as we have just seen, the importance of the prior probabilities becomes less and less as the random experiment performed becomes more and more discriminating. When the experiment is not extremely discriminating, then the prior probabilities, as might be expected, have an important influence on the posterior probabilities.

Having given a general discussion of the way in which the results of a random experiment can be incorporated into our model of a single stage decision problem, we shall now illustrate the procedure with several specific examples. These will serve also to develop some additional theory.

8-3 THE INDEPENDENT OIL PRODUCER EXAMPLE

We shall begin with a grossly over-simplified version of a type of decision problem which is faced with great frequency by so-called independent operators in the oil business. An independent operator is trying to decide whether or not to buy a tract of land for the possibility that a reservoir of crude petroleum lies beneath the surface. The individual concerned is a trained geologist and has decided that so far as making the right decision is concerned it is sufficient to imagine that there are only three states of nature. These are e_1, there is no oil; e_2, there are 500,000 barrels that can be produced; and e_3, there are two million barrels that can be produced. Based on intuition and prior experience, he assigns the following prior probabilities to these states of nature:

$$p_1 = 0.6, \quad p_2 = 0.3, \quad p_3 = 0.1. \tag{8-5}$$

Before deciding whether to purchase the tract, the independent operator decides to perform a seismic experiment. The seismic experiment will not tell him what the state of nature is, but will give him additional information on the matter. Imagine that the seismic experiment has four outcomes f_1, f_2, f_3, and f_4, which we might think of as low, medium, high, and very high readings. (This is far from realistic, but a realistic description would be quite complicated and extended.) The conditional probabilities $w_{jk} = p(f_k|e_j)$ are shown in Table 8-1. Note that the numbers in each

TABLE 8-1

CONDITIONAL PROBABILITIES FOR
SEISMIC EXPERIMENT

	e_1	e_2	e_3
f_1	0.50	0.40	0.10
f_2	0.30	0.40	0.30
f_3	0.15	0.15	0.35
f_4	0.05	0.05	0.25

column (not each row) must sum to 1. The numbers in Table 8-1 might in practice be obtained from the physics of the problem.

For the problem under consideration the operator believes that discounted monetary values accurately reflect his utility. He feels that if he buys the tract and no oil is present, he will incur a loss of $800,000. If 500,000 barrels are present, he will make a discounted profit of $400,000, and if two million barrels are present, the discounted profit will be $2 million. If no seismic experiment is performed, his expected discounted profit on buying the tract is

$$0.6(-800,000) + 0.3(400,000) + 0.1(2,000,000) = -\$160,000;$$

and therefore he would not buy the tract, since on not buying it his expected discounted profit is 0.

Suppose now that the seismic experiment is performed and the outcome is f_3, a high reading. Let us determine the best action for the operator to take. First we compute the posterior probabilities of the states of nature using Bayes' law (8-1). From (8-5) and Table 8-1 we see that

$$p(e_1|f_3) = \frac{0.15(0.6)}{0.15(0.6) + 0.15(0.3) + 0.35(0.1)} = \frac{0.09}{0.09 + 0.045 + 0.035}$$

$$= \frac{0.09}{0.170} = 0.530;$$

$$p(e_2|f_3) = \frac{0.045}{0.170} = 0.264; \quad p(e_3|f_3) = \frac{0.035}{0.170} = 0.206.$$

Note that in computing the posterior probabilities, we needed only the third row in Table 8-1. Note also that the denominator in Bayes' formula is the same for each case, i.e., is $p(f_3)$.

Using the posterior probabilities, let us next compute the expected discounted profit if he buys the tract. This gives

$$0.530(-800,000) + 0.264(400,000) + 0.206(2,000,000) = \$93,600.$$

With f_3 being the outcome of the experiment, it becomes desirable to purchase the tract since the expected profit if he does not purchase it remains 0. In the computations we did not include the cost of making the seismic experiment because it is unnecessary to do so. If the cost is α and we included this cost, then the expected discounted profit if he purchases the tract is $93,600 - \alpha$ and is $-\alpha$ if he does not. Thus the same action is chosen. Recall that changing the utility function by a constant does not change the action selected. Through this simple example we see that when an experiment is performed, the optimal action to choose in the light of the experimental evidence may be quite different from the one which would be selected if there was no opportunity to perform an experiment before selecting an action.

8-4 THE RADIO MANUFACTURER EXAMPLE

A small manufacturer of private brand radios has purchased a lot of 200,000 resistors from a foreign producer for use in an upcoming production run of a particular model. Let us suppose that the manufacturer is concerned about the fraction of defective resistors in the lot. Prior experience with the supplier indicates that the fraction defective will either be 0.001, 0.005, or 0.03; and he believes that the probability that the fraction defective is 0.001 is 0.70, that it is 0.005 is 0.25, and that it is 0.03 is 0.05. To check on the quality, he selects at random from the lot a sample of 1000 resistors and determines the number of defectives in the sample. Given the outcome of the sample, the manufacturer must decide among three alternative courses of action. These are a_1, use the lot in the production run without further inspection; a_2, inspect the entire lot and replace defective resistors with good ones purchased locally; a_3, return the lot and use only resistors purchased locally. The manufacturer does have the freedom to return the lot, but if he does so, he must use locally procured resistors in making the production run because there will not be sufficient time available for getting a new lot from the foreign supplier.

Before going on to discuss the costs involved, let us summarize what has been said thus far in the terminology of a decision problem. We imagine that at the supplier's plant a random experiment is performed which leads to one of three outcomes e_1, e_2, and e_3, e_1 being that the lot fraction defective $p = 0.001$, e_2 that $p = 0.005$, and e_3 that $p = 0.03$. The probabilities assigned to these three events are $p_1 = 0.70$, $p_2 = 0.25$, and $p_3 = 0.05$. There are three actions a_1, a_2, and a_3 open to the decision maker. Before actually selecting an action he performs the random experiment which involves the selection of a sample of 1000 resistors from the lot and determining the number of defectives in the lot.

Let us now turn to the costs involved. For simplicity we shall imagine that included in the manufacturing process for locally produced resistors there is an automatic checking device, so that all locally produced resistors purchased will be good. However, each locally purchased resistor costs $0.06, which is $0.01 more than the foreign produced one. Each defective resistor used in the production process will be caught at a particular quality control check point which checks the partially completed chassis. However, to replace a defective part with a good one (purchased locally) costs $0.50. To inspect the entire lot remaining after the sample is taken costs $1600. If the manufacturer returns the lot, he incurs shipping charges of $150. In this case, of course, he does not pay for the lot.

The manufacturer feels that monetary values adequately represent his feelings in the situation, and therefore the action to take is the one which minimizes his expected cost. Given the above data, we can construct the payoff table shown in Table 8-2. In this table we have given only those costs incurred over and above the cost of purchasing the lot from the foreign supplier and the cost of making the experiment. These are the only costs needed, since to obtain the total cost it is only necessary to add some number δ to every entry in Table 8-2. The same action will be

TABLE 8-2

PAYOFF TABLE FOR RADIO MANUFACTURER EXAMPLE

	e_1	e_2	e_3
a_1	$100 - 0.44\,r$	$500 - 0.44\,r$	$3000 - 0.44\,r$
a_2	1612	1660	1960
a_3	2150	2150	2150

selected either way.   Consider then the determination of the entry when
a_1 is the action selected and e_1 turns out to be the state of nature.   We
recall that a_1 means that the lot is sent into production after the sample
is taken, and e_1 means that $p = 0.001$, that is, there are 200 defective
resistors.   Each defective going into production costs \$0.50.   We shall
assume that before going into production any defectives in the sample
are replaced by good ones procured locally.   Thus if r defectives are found
in the sample, the cost will be

$$0.5(200 - r) + 0.06r = 100 - 0.44r.$$

The other entries in the first row are determined in the same manner.   For
the second row consider the entry in the column corresponding to e_1.   In
this case the entire lot is inspected at a cost of \$1600 (over the cost of
the experiment), and the 200 defectives are replaced by good units at a
cost of \$12.   The other two entries in the second row are obtained in the
same manner.   Finally, for a_3 the lot is returned to the supplier at a cost
of \$150 and 200,000 resistors are procured locally at a cost of \$2000 above
the cost of the lot received from the foreign supplier.   On examining
Table 8-2, we note immediately that regardless of what the state of nature
turns out to be, the cost on taking action a_2 is less than that on taking a_3.
Hence a_3 will never be the action selected and we can ignore it when
computing the expected costs.   In other words, it would never pay to
ship back the lot and use only locally produced resistors.

Suppose now that on taking the sample of 1000 resistors the manufacturer finds that 25 are defective.   Let us determine whether he should
take action a_1 or a_2 in this case.   To do so we first determine the posterior
probabilities using Bayes' law.   To use Bayes' law we must determine the
conditional probabilities $p(25|0.001)$, $p(25|0.005)$, and $p(25|0.03)$, where
for example, by $p(25|0.001)$ we mean the probability of obtaining 25 defec-
tives in a sample of 1000 when the lot fraction defective is 0.001.   The
precise computation of these probabilities would require the use of the
hypergeometric distribution.   However, since the sample size is small with
respect to the lot size and the lot fraction defective is small in every case,
the hypergeometric distribution can be approximated by the Poisson distribution with mean $1000p$, where p is the lot fraction defective.   Thus

$$p(25|0.001) = p(25; 1) \doteq 0.0000; \quad p(25|0.005) = p(25; 5) \doteq 0.0000;$$

$$p(25|0.03) = p(25; 30) \doteq \Phi\left(\frac{25.5 - 30}{5.47}\right) - \Phi\left(\frac{24.5 - 30}{5.47}\right)$$

$$= \Phi(-0.824) - \Phi(-1.01) = 0.0488.$$

To compute $p(25; 30)$ we used the normal approximation.

The probabilities $p(25|0.001)$ and $p(25|0.005)$ are 0 to four decimals.

Hence we see immediately from Bayes' law that to four decimal places, the posterior probabilities are

$$p(e_1|25) = 0; \quad p(e_2|25) = 0; \quad p(e_3|25) = 1,$$

and after making the experiment, the manufacturer concludes that it is almost certain that the lot fraction defective is 0.03. Note that he would reach this same conclusion regardless of what the prior probabilities of the states of nature were, provided that p_3 was not so small that more than four decimal places would be needed to reach a conclusion.

Given the above posterior probabilities we see at once that the expected cost if action a_1 is taken is $3000 - 0.44(25)$ and is 1960 if action a_2 is taken. The minimum expected cost occurs when action a_2 is selected. Thus the entire lot should be inspected and defective resistors replaced with good ones purchased locally.

8-5° THE RADIO MANUFACTURER EXAMPLE CONTINUED

The reader no doubt felt that in the above example (and in the first example) it was very artificial to assume that there were only three states of nature possible. In the previous example the fraction defective could in principle take on 200,001 values corresponding to having 0, 1, . . . , 200,000 defective resistors in the lot. Thus it would appear that the lot fraction defective could, in any event, take on a rather large number of different values. This suggests that instead of merely assuming that it takes on only a very small number of values, it might be desirable to go to the other extreme and imagine that the lot fraction defective can be represented by a continuous random variable.

Let us then consider what is involved if the manufacturer in the previous example decides to treat the lot fraction defective as a continuous random variable. In this case there will be an infinite number of states of nature corresponding to the continuum of values which the lot fraction defective can take on. To develop a mathematically sound model of a single stage decision problem where the states of nature can take on a continuum of values, we not only need a probability model for this case (which was developed in Chapter 7), but we also need to generalize the model of the decision maker. Recall in Chapter 2 we assumed that the decision maker was considering only a finite number of alternatives. This is always the situation in the real world, but for a model with an infinite number of states of nature, to be rigorous, we would have to modify our model of a decision maker to allow for such cases. We shall not attempt to make such a modification. We shall simply look at the continuous case as an

_____

° Recall that the sign ° on a section heading indicates that calculus is required.

approximation, and we shall suppose that the decision maker can determine a utility function such that he should select the action which maximizes his expected utility. In most cases that will be of interest to us we
shall, as before, use the profit as a measure of utility. One could develop
a more general model of a decision maker, but we shall not do so.

Given that the lot fraction defective p is going to be treated as a continuous random variable, the next question that arises is how one determines the prior density function $f(p)$ for p. Generally speaking, when
a decision maker is faced with a problem of this sort, he will not have
sufficient historical data to construct an accurate histogram for p. About
the best he will be able to do is estimate roughly the expected value and
standard deviation of p. He will not have any strong feelings as to precisely what the shape of $f(p)$ will be, although from the nature of the
problem and intuitive feelings, he will have a rough idea of what $f(p)$
should look like. Under these circumstances, the problem then reduces
to finding a density function that can be handled mathematically, which
has the desired mean and standard deviation and which has roughly the
desired shape. This is about the best one can do. Fortunately, the
precise shape is generally not very important, and if the experiment is
quite discriminating, even the grosser details such as the mean and variance
will not be critical either.

Let us now apply this approach to the problem at hand. Suppose that
in one way or another the manufacturer decides that the expected value
of p is μ_0 and that the standard deviation is σ_0. Furthermore, he feels that
it will always be true that $0 \leq p \leq 0.1$, and thus he would like a density
function with this domain, and whose graph looks something like that
shown in Figure 8-5. He is not sure, however, whether it should be like

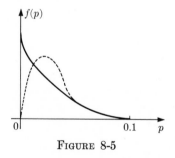

FIGURE 8-5

the solid curve or the dashed one. Note that both curves in Figure 8-5
look roughly like they could be the graph of a gamma distribution. The
domain for the gamma functions contains all non-negative real numbers,

however, and one might feel this rules out the use of a gamma density function here. We can note though that if μ_0 and σ_0 are small enough, the probability that $p > 0.1$ when p has a gamma distribution is negligible. Thus, inasmuch as the gamma distribution is relatively easy to work with, it would seem reasonable to use a gamma density for the prior distribution of p. To determine the parameters α and λ in the gamma distribution, the values μ_0 and σ_0 specified by the manufacturer are used along with (7-109) and (7-110). On dividing (7-109) by (7-110), we see that $\lambda = \mu_0/\sigma_0^2$ and then substituting this into (7-109) it follows that $\alpha = (\mu_0/\sigma_0)^2 - 1$. This shows that once μ_0 and σ_0 are specified, a unique gamma density is determined. We need not directly concern ourselves with the question of the shape it should have. This is determined by μ_0 and σ_0. In particular, if $\sigma_0 \geq \mu_0$, then $\alpha \leq 0$, and the gamma density will have a shape roughly like the solid curve in Figure 8-1 (in actuality the $f(p)$ axis is a vertical asymptote when $\alpha < 0$). When $\mu_0 > \sigma_0$, so that $\alpha > 0$, it will look roughly like the dashed curve in Figure 8-1. Let us suppose then that the prior distribution for p is $f(p) = g(p; \alpha,\lambda)$ with α and λ being determined as indicated above.

Imagine next that the manufacturer performs the same random experiment referred to in the previous example, that is, he selects 1000 resistors at random and determines the number of defective ones. Let us determine the posterior density function for p when there are r defectives in the sample. To be a little more general, we shall find the posterior distribution for any sample size n, provided that it is small in comparison to the lot size. As in the previous section, we shall use the Poisson approximation to the hypergeometric distribution, so that $p(r|\rho)$, the conditional probability of getting r defectives when the lot fraction defective $p = \rho$, will be $p(r; n\rho)$, where $p(r; n\rho)$ is the Poisson probability that $x = r$ when the expected value of x is $n\rho$. The two stage experiment we are considering here is one where the outcome of the first stage is described by a continuous random variable and the outcome of the second stage by a discrete random variable. Thus the over-all experiment consisting of the two stages involves both a discrete and a continuous random variable, and (7-132) is the appropriate form of Bayes' law to use in this case. Hence if the posterior density function for p, given that r defectives are found in the sample, is denoted by $f(p|r)$, then

$$f(p|r) = \frac{p(r; np)g(p; \alpha,\lambda)}{\displaystyle\int_0^\infty p(r; np)g(p; \alpha,\lambda)\, dp}, \qquad (8\text{-}6)$$

since the denominator in (8-6) is by (7-130) the probability that there will be r defectives in the sample.

Now

$p(r; np)g(p; \alpha, \lambda)$

$$= \left[\frac{(np)^r}{r!}e^{-np}\right]\left[\lambda\frac{(\lambda p)^\alpha}{\Gamma(\alpha+1)}e^{-\lambda p}\right] = \left[\frac{\lambda^{\alpha+1}n^r}{r!\Gamma(\alpha+1)}\right]p^{\alpha+r}e^{-(n+\lambda)p}$$

$$= \left[\frac{\lambda^{\alpha+1}n^r}{(\lambda+n)^{\alpha+r+1}}\right]\left[\frac{\Gamma(\alpha+r+1)}{r!\Gamma(\alpha+1)}\right]g(p; n+\lambda, \alpha+r). \qquad (8\text{-}7)$$

Then

$$\int_0^\infty p(r; np)g(p; \alpha, \lambda)\,dp$$

$$= \left[\frac{\Gamma(\alpha+r+1)}{r!\Gamma(\alpha+1)}\right]\left[\frac{\lambda^{\alpha+1}n^r}{(\lambda+n)^{\alpha+r+1}}\right]\int_0^\infty g(p; n+\lambda, \alpha+r)\,dp$$

$$= \left[\frac{\Gamma(\alpha+r+1)}{r!\Gamma(\alpha+1)}\right]\left[\frac{\lambda^{\alpha+1}n^r}{(\lambda+n)^{\alpha+r+1}}\right]. \qquad (8\text{-}8)$$

On taking the ratio of (8-7) and (8-8), we see from (8-6) that

$$f(p|r) = g(p; \alpha+r, \lambda+n). \qquad (8\text{-}9)$$

Hence the posterior density function for p is also a gamma distribution. It is a gamma distribution with a different mean and variance than the prior distribution, however. If μ_1 and σ_1^2 are the mean and variance of $f(p|r)$, then from (7-109) and (7-110),

$$\mu_1 = \frac{\alpha+r+1}{\lambda+n}; \quad \sigma_1^2 = \frac{\alpha+r+1}{(\lambda+n)^2}. \qquad (8\text{-}10)$$

Having determined the posterior density function for p, all that remains is to compute the expected cost for each of the actions using this density function and then to choose the action with the smallest expected cost. Let us now express the three random variables representing the cost incurred on taking each of the three possible actions as functions of the random variable p. For a_1, the lot is sent directly into production, except that defectives found in the sample are replaced by good units. Thus if $K_1(p)$ is the cost when action a_1 is taken and the lot fraction defective is p, we see from the previous section that

$$K_1(p) = 100{,}000p - 0.44r.$$

When action a_2 is taken, the lot is inspected completely at a cost of $1600 and defectives are replaced by good units procured locally. Thus $K_2(p)$, the cost when action a_2 is selected and the lot fraction defective turns out to be p, is

$$K_2(p) = 1600 + 12{,}000p.$$

The cost for taking action a_3 is independent of p and is

$$K_3(p) = 2150.$$

The expected cost on taking action a_1 is

$$\bar{K}_1 = \int_0^\infty K_1(p)g(p; \alpha + r, \lambda + n)\, dp$$

$$= 100,000 \int_0^\infty pg(p; \alpha + r, \lambda + n)\, dp - 0.44r \int_0^\infty g(p; \alpha + r, \lambda + n)\, dp$$

or

$$\bar{K}_1 = 100,000\mu_1 - 0.44r, \qquad (8\text{-}11)$$

where μ_1 is the mean of the posterior distribution $g(p; \alpha + r, \lambda + n)$ for p. By (7-109)

$$\mu_1 = \frac{\alpha + r + 1}{\lambda + n}. \qquad (8\text{-}12)$$

Similarly, the expected costs on taking actions a_2 and a_3 are

$$\bar{K}_2 = 1600 + 12,000\mu_1 \qquad (8\text{-}13)$$

and

$$\bar{K}_3 = 2150. \qquad (8\text{-}14)$$

In (8-12), we can eliminate α and λ, replacing them with the values expressed in terms of μ_0 and σ_0. Recall that

$$\alpha = (\mu_0/\sigma_0)^2 - 1; \quad \lambda = \mu_0/\sigma_0^2.$$

Thus

$$\mu_1 = \frac{\mu_0^2 + r\sigma_0^2}{\mu_0 + n\sigma_0^2}. \qquad (8\text{-}15)$$

Having gone through a great deal of manipulation above, we have now reached an interesting conclusion. One only needs to go through the manipulation once. All the manufacturer has to do to make a decision is to compute μ_1 from (8-15) and then $\bar{K}_1$ from (8-11), $\bar{K}_2$ from (8-13) and $\bar{K}_3$ from (8-14). The optimal action is the one which yields the smallest expected cost. The procedure can be simplified even more if we note that in (8-11) the term $0.44r$ is almost always negligible. Then each $\bar{K}_i$ is a linear function of μ_1. We have plotted the graphs of these three lines in Figure 8-6. It will be noted that for $\mu_1 < \gamma_1$ action a_1 is the one to be used; if $\gamma_1 < \mu_1 < \gamma_2$, then action a_2 is the one to be used; and if $\mu_1 > \gamma_2$, then action a_3 is the one to use. When $\mu_1 = \gamma_1$, the manufacturer is indifferent between a_1 and a_2; and when $\mu_1 = \gamma_2$ he is indifferent between a_2 and a_3. Now γ_1 is that value of μ_1 for which $\bar{K}_1 = \bar{K}_2$. On setting $\bar{K}_1 = \bar{K}_2$ and solving for μ_1 we obtain the value $\gamma_1 = 0.0182$. Similarly γ_2 is the value of μ_1 for which $\bar{K}_2 = \bar{K}_3$. This value is $\gamma_2 = 0.0458$. Observe that unlike the model for the previous section, action a_3 cannot be omitted. Action a_3 is the action to choose when $\mu_1 > \gamma_2$.

We have now shown that for the manufacturer to determine the action

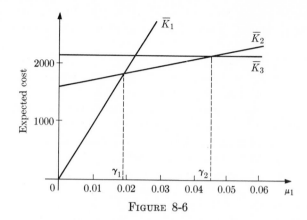

FIGURE 8-6

to take it is only necessary to compute μ_1 from (8-15) and compare the value with γ_1 and γ_2. For example, suppose that the manufacturer decides that $\mu_0 = 0.003$ and $\sigma_0 = 0.006$. Suppose furthermore that he takes a sample of 1000 resistors from the lot and finds 25 defectives. Then

$$\mu_1 = \frac{9 \times 10^{-6} + 900 \times 10^{-6}}{3 \times 10^{-3} + 36 \times 10^{-3}} = \frac{909}{39} \times 10^{-3} = 0.0233.$$

Thus action a_2 should be selected. This is the same conclusion that was reached in the previous section using a different type of model.

8-6 THE TEXTILE MANUFACTURING EXAMPLE

A textile manufacturer has just purchased enough continuous filament rayon yarn to weave 100,000 yards of a particular synthetic fabric. This yarn formed part of a single production run at the chemical plant which makes the yarn. The textile manufacturer must decide whether to weave the fabric under consideration on new high speed looms or on the older and slower looms. The proper choice depends on the mean breaking strength of the synthetic fiber. If this mean breaking strength is exceptionally low, it will cause troubles with frequent breaks on either type of loom, but will be worse with the high speed looms. In an intermediate range of breaking strengths there will be essentially no trouble with the slow looms, but there will be a considerable amount of trouble with the high speed looms. However, if the quality of the fiber is especially good, no trouble whatever will be encountered on using the high speed looms.

Let us begin our study of this problem by explaining in a little bit more detail what we mean by breaking strength. The filament yarn is received on spools, and there will be thousands of such spools. Suppose that we cut the yarn on each spool into pieces one inch in length. We take each such piece and clamp one end of it. A stretching force is applied to the other end and is increased until the filament breaks. The pounds force ξ needed to break the filament is noted. The breaking force will vary from one piece to another, and this force can be conveniently imagined to be a continuous random variable. Associated with every one inch piece of filament we can imagine that there is a number ξ, which is the breaking strength of this piece. Each such ξ is then a possible value of the random variable x. It has been the manufacturer's experience that the standard deviation σ of x never changes perceptibly and always has the value 3 pounds. Thus we shall assume that the standard deviation of x is known and $\sigma = 3$. The expected value of x, unlike the variance, has not been found to be always constant. One can imagine that at the time the yarn is produced a random experiment is performed which determines the expected value of x for that batch. The textile manufacturer in cooperation with the producer has studied the behavior of the expected value of x and feels that it is adequate for his purposes to suppose that the expected value of x takes on only three different values μ_1, μ_2, and μ_3. These values are $\mu_1 = 50$ pounds force, $\mu_2 = 47$ pounds force, and $\mu_3 = 45$ pounds force. If p_j is the probability that the expected value of x is μ_j, then the textile manufacturer believes that $p_1 = 0.30$, $p_2 = 0.50$, and $p_3 = 0.20$. In other words, if he purchased a large number of batches from the producer, essentially 0.30 of them would have an expected value of x equal to μ_1, 0.50 an expected value μ_2, and 0.20 an expected value μ_3.

We can now think of the expected value of x as being the state of nature. There are then three possible states of nature, and we shall simply label these μ_1, μ_2, and μ_3. There are two actions that the textile producer is considering: one, call it a_1, is to weave the cloth on the high speed looms, and the other, call it a_2, is to weave the cloth on the old slower looms. The industrial engineering department has done a cost study, and the results are presented as a payoff table in Table 8-3. In measuring the

TABLE 8-3

PAYOFF TABLE FOR TEXTILE MANUFACTURER

	μ_1	μ_2	μ_3
a_1	0	800	1500
a_2	400	600	800

costs the norm was taken to be the cost on the high speed looms for good quality yarn. The costs given are then incremental costs over and above this cost, so that if the state of nature is μ_2 and the high speed looms are used, the cost is $800 more than if the state of nature is μ_1. We shall not concern ourselves with the technical details of precisely how these costs were obtained. Suffice it to say that the manufacturer believes that they are sufficiently accurate that he is quite willing to use them in reaching a decision.

Before deciding which action to take, the manufacturer chooses at random 25 spools, and then selects at random 25 numbers $\Theta_1, \ldots, \Theta_{25}$ from a uniform distribution whose domain is the length of the yarn on the spools. A length Θ_i is then unwound from spool i, and a one inch piece of filament is cut out. This gives 25 one inch pieces of the filament. The spools are then rewound after splicing the filaments together. The breaking strength of each of the 25 one inch pieces of filament is determined accurately. Let ξ_i be the breaking strength of the ith piece, and $\bar{\xi} = \sum_{i=1}^{25} \xi_i/n$, so that $\bar{\xi}$ is the average breaking strength for the 25 pieces. Now the random experiment $\mathcal{R}$ which consists of measuring the breaking strength of the 25 pieces of filament can be looked upon as the performance of 25 independent trials of a random experiment $\mathcal{R}^*$, which consists in observing a value of x. Associated with the ith trial is a random variable $x\{i\}$, which denotes x for the ith trial. Thus if the state of nature is μ_j, each $x\{i\}$ has an expected value of μ_j, and a standard deviation $\sigma = 3$. Then associated with $\mathcal{R}$ is the random variable $\bar{x} = \sum_{i=1}^{25} x\{i\}/n$; $\bar{\xi}$ is the value of $\bar{x}$ observed on performing $\mathcal{R}$. From Section 7-14, we know that the expected value $\mu_{\bar{x}}$ of $\bar{x}$ is μ_j and $\sigma_{\bar{x}}^2$ the variance of $\bar{x}$ is $\sigma^2/25$, since 25 trials of $\mathcal{R}^*$ are involved in $\mathcal{R}$. Thus

$$\mu_{\bar{x}} = \mu_j; \quad \sigma_{\bar{x}} = \tfrac{3}{5} = 0.6. \tag{8-16}$$

The manufacturer is not certain precisely what the density function for x looks like. However, he believes that roughly speaking it would have a graph of the same shape as the normal distribution. Now recall that if a random variable y is the sum of n independent identically distributed random variables, then the central limit theorem says that as n becomes larger and larger, the distribution of y gets closer and closer to the normal distribution, and practical experience indicates that the distribution of y may be very close to normal for rather small n even if the distribution of x is not too close to being normal. From this we could reasonably conclude that the distribution of $\bar{x}$ is quite close to being normal. However, given that there is good reason to believe that the distribution of x does not deviate radically from normality, then there should be no question at all about assuming that for the accuracy required here the distribution of $\bar{x}$ can be considered to be normal with mean and standard deviation (8-16). This is what we shall do.

Suppose now that on performing the experiment $\mathcal{R}$, it is found that $\bar{x} = \bar{\xi} = 48.0$. We shall assume that there are no errors in measuring the breaking strengths, so that $\bar{\xi}$ is indeed the value of $\bar{x}$. We then wish to determine which action the textile manufacturer should take. To do this we first compute the posterior probabilities of the states of nature by applying Bayes' law. For the two stage experiment under consideration, we can look at the outcome of the first stage, that is, the state of nature, as being the value taken on by a discrete random variable, and the outcome of the second stage being the value of a continuous random variable $\bar{x}$. The appropriate form of Bayes' law to use in this case is then (7-131), so that

$$p(\mu_j|48) = \frac{n(48; \mu_j, 0.6)p_j}{n(48; \mu_1, 0.6)p_1 + n(48; \mu_2, 0.6)p_2 + n(48; \mu_3, 0.6)p_3}. \quad (8\text{-}17)$$

Now

$$0.6n(48; \mu_1, 0.6) = \varphi\left(\frac{48 - 50}{0.6}\right) = \varphi(-3.33) = 0.002165$$

$$0.6n(48; \mu_2, 0.6) = \varphi\left(\frac{48 - 47}{0.6}\right) = \varphi(1.67) = 0.09893$$

$$0.6n(48; \mu_3, 0.6) = \varphi\left(\frac{48 - 45}{0.6}\right) = \varphi(5) \doteq 0.$$

Thus

$$p(\mu_1|48) = \frac{0.002165(0.30)}{0.002165(0.30) + 0.09893(0.50)} = \frac{0.0006495}{0.05010} = 0.0129$$

$$p(\mu_2|48) = \frac{0.04946}{0.05010} = 0.9871; \quad p(\mu_3|48) = 0.$$

Note that roughly the same posterior probabilities would be obtained for a wide range of prior probabilities.

Once we have obtained the posterior probabilities, it is simple to decide which action to take. We compute the expected cost for each action and select the smallest expected cost. Thus the expected costs for a_1 and a_2 are respectively

$$0 + 800(0.9871) = \$790; \quad 400(0.0129) + 600(0.9871) = \$596.$$

Hence action a_2 yields the lowest expected cost, and the cloth should be woven on the slow looms.

8-7° THE TOMATO SOUP COMPANY'S PROBLEM

A large producer of tomato soup owns several farms in the San Joaquin valley in California, on which it grows tomatoes. In good years, these farms yield a sufficient quantity for the company's production requirements. When the yield is low, however, it is necessary to purchase tomatoes on the outside. If tomatoes are purchased on the outside, it is possible to contract for part or all of a farmer's crop before the tomatoes are fully ripe, that is, before the season begins, or it is possible to purchase tomatoes at a higher price at the height of the season. About a month before the crop begins to ripen is the time when the production manager of the plant must decide whether to contract for tomatoes on the outside, or to take a chance that the company farms will produce a sufficient quantity for production needs. If he does not contract for any, he can still meet production requirements by purchasing his needs at a considerably higher price at the time production is being carried out. The time has now arrived for him to make this decision.

Let us now see how decision theory can be used to aid the manager in deciding what quantity (weight) of tomatoes should be contracted for. The yield of the company farms can be looked upon as a random variable y which it is very convenient to treat as a continuous random variable that can take on any non-negative value. The yield from the farms will be measured in tons. Suppose that $f(y)$ is the production manager's estimate of what the density function for y is for the current year. Denote by Q the production requirement in tons and by h, $h \geq 0$, the number of tons of tomatoes to be contracted for before the season begins. We shall assume that tomatoes will cost C_1 dollars per ton if contracted for before the season starts, and C_2 dollars per ton after the season starts, $C_2 > C_1$. If $y + h > Q$, so that more tomatoes are available than are required for production, there is nothing that can be done except to dump them. The extra tomatoes are a total loss. Let us now determine $K(h)$, the expected cost, when h tons are contracted for before the season begins. The h tons will cost $C_1 h$ dollars. If it turns out that $y + h < Q$, an additional quantity $Q - y - h$ tons must be purchased at a cost of $C_2(Q - y - h)$. The total cost of tomatoes purchased is then a random variable z, which is

$$ z = \begin{cases} C_1 h + C_2(Q - y - h), & y < Q - h \\ C_1 h, & y \geq Q - h. \end{cases} \tag{8-18} $$

The expected cost $K(h)$ is then the expected value of z and is

$$ K(h) = \int_0^\infty z f(y)\, dy = \int_0^\infty C_1 h f(y)\, dy + \int_0^{Q-h} C_2(Q - y - h) f(y)\, dy $$

$$ = C_1 h + C_2 \int_0^{Q-h} (Q - h - y) f(y)\, dy, $$

or

$$ K(h) = C_1 h + C_2(Q - h)F(Q - h) - C_2 \int_0^{Q-h} y f(y)\, dy, \tag{8-19} $$

where $F(y)$ is the cumulative distribution function for y.

The optimal h will either be an h which satisfies $K'(h) = 0$, $K'(h)$ being the derivative of $K(h)$, or will be $h = 0$. Now

$$K'(h) = C_1 - C_2 F(Q - h) - C_2(Q - h)f(Q - h) + C_2(Q - h)f(Q - h)$$
$$= C_1 - C_2 F(Q - h). \tag{8-20}$$

On setting $K'(h) = 0$, we obtain

$$F(Q - h) = C_1/C_2. \tag{8-21}$$

Inasmuch as $F(y)$ normally increases with increasing y, there will usually be either one $h \geq 0$ for which (8-21) holds or no $h \geq 0$ for which (8-21) holds. If $F(Q) < C_1/C_2$, then there is no $h \geq 0$ for which (8-21) holds and $K'(h) > 0$ for all $h \geq 0$. Thus in this case $K(h)$ increases with h, and the optimal h is $h = 0$, so that no tomatoes should be contracted for before the start of the season. If $F(Q) > C_1/C_2$, there will in general be a unique h, call it h^*, such that (8-21) holds for h^*. Then $K'(h) < 0$, $h < h^*$, and $K'(h) > 0$, $h > h^*$ so that $K(h)$ decreases up to h^* and then increases with h. Thus in this case, h^* is the optimal quantity to contract for before the beginning of the season. We have thus shown how the production manager can determine the optimal quantity to contract for before the beginning of the season when he knows the density function for y. The reader should note the similarity between this problem and the single stage inventory problem. Here the state of nature represents the yield of the company farms, and the actions are the quantities to contract for before the season begins. We have assumed, of course, that monetary values correctly represent the production manager's utility. The action to take is then selected so as to minimize the expected cost.

Let us now turn to the question of how the density function $f(y)$ can be estimated. The company has 10,000 acres planted in tomatoes. Imagine that in any arbitrary way this land is divided into 10,000 plots of one acre each. Land and growing conditions in the San Joaquin valley are rather uniform in the area where these farms are located, and therefore any one acre plot is to all outward appearances like any other one. The yield of tomatoes on any given acre plot, say plot j, can be conveniently imagined to be a continuous random variable $x\{j\}$. We shall now construct the following probability model to represent the situation. The random experiment $\Re$ which consists of growing the tomatoes and observing the yield y, will be looked upon as composed of 10,000 independent trials of a random experiment $\Re^*$ which consists of growing tomatoes on one acre and observing the yield. The jth trial represents the growing of tomatoes on the jth acre, and the random variable representing the yield on this trial is $x\{j\}$. Thus, by assumption, each $x\{j\}$ has the same mean μ and variance σ^2. In other words, $x\{j\}$ is the symbol used on the jth trial of $\Re^*$ for a random variable x which is the yield per acre, that is, the yield on performing $\Re^*$. In any given year then, the yields from each of the 10,000 acres can be looked upon as giving 10,000 values ξ_j for x. An average of these 10,000 values gives a number $\bar{\xi}$ which is the average yield per acre for that year, and $\bar{\xi}$ is a number which should be close to μ if μ was estimated correctly. Similarly, $s_x{}^2 = \sum_{j=1}^{10,000} (\xi_j - \bar{\xi})^2/n$ should be close to σ^2, if σ^2 was estimated correctly. Under the assumptions made, $y = \sum_{j=1}^{10,000} x\{j\}$ and $\mu_y = 10{,}000\mu$. Furthermore, since the $x\{j\}$ are assumed to be independent, $\sigma_y{}^2 = 10{,}000\sigma^2$. This explains the model that we are going to use. It seems like a reasonable one to use when growing conditions are rather uniform. There will always be differences in land, quality, etc., and a better model could be developed to take these into account, but this would require a rather detailed study which the production manager is quite sure would not pay for itself.

We shall now forget about y for the moment, but will instead study the random variable x representing the yield per acre in a little more detail. The expected value of x changes from year to year depending on growing conditions. Sometimes the yield per acre will be high and sometimes low. Experiments performed by the company have indicated, however, that the standard deviation σ of x is essentially a constant and has the value 2 tons of tomatoes per acre. Furthermore x is quite close to being normally distributed. On studying a histogram of the mean yield per acre over the past 15 years, the production manager, although realizing that the data are not sufficient to indicate clearly what the prior distribution for μ is, feels that it is quite reasonable to assume that μ has a normal prior distribution with a mean of 60 tons per acre and a standard deviation of 4 tons per acre. Thus he assumes that μ has the distribution $n(\mu; 60,4)$.

Since a number of random variables and distributions have been introduced thus far, it may be helpful to pause and tie things together. What we are interested in obtaining is the density function $f(y)$ for y. We are thinking of the random experiment $\Re$ which generates a value of y as a two stage experiment. In the first stage a random experiment $\Re_1$ is performed which determines μ, the mean yield per acre, that is, the expected value of x. Intuitively, the first stage determines growing conditions for the year. At the second stage the experiment $\Re$ is performed, which consists of 10,000 independent trials of $\Re^*$, each trial yielding a value of x. We have denoted the random variable x for the jth trial by $x\{j\}$. Finally, $y = \sum_{j=1}^{10,000} x\{j\}$. Now associated with $\hat{\Re}$, the two stage experiment, we can imagine that there is a joint density function $h(y, \mu)$. Furthermore, $h(y, \mu) = f(y|\mu)g(\mu)$, where $g(\mu)$ is the marginal density for μ and $f(y|\mu)$ is the conditional density for y given μ. Then by (7-119) and (7-122), $f(y)$, the marginal density for y, which is what we wish to compute is

$$f(y) = \int h(y, \mu)\, d\mu = \int f(y|\mu)g(\mu)\, d\mu, \qquad (8\text{-}22)$$

the integrals being taken over the set of values which μ can take on. It is easy to see what $f(y|\mu)$ is. Recall that y has mean $10{,}000\mu$ and variance

$10,000\sigma^2$. Since y is the sum of 10,000 independent random variables all of which have the same distribution, which is close to normal, we know from the central limit theorem that for a given μ, y will be, to the accuracy required, normally distributed with mean $10,000\mu$ and standard deviation $\sqrt{10,000}\ \sigma$. Hence

$$f(y|\mu) = n(y; 10,000\mu,200), \qquad (8\text{-}23)$$

since $\sqrt{10,000}\ \sigma = 200$. Now the prior distribution for μ is assumed to be $n(\mu; 60,4)$. Thus, without any additional information we would set $g(\mu) = n(\mu; 60,4)$, use (8-23) and determine $f(y)$ from (8-22). Then, knowing $f(y)$, h^* could be determined from (8-21).

Before making a decision, however, the production manager can obtain information about the value of μ for the current season by performing an experiment. At the time he must make a decision, which is about a month before the crop ripens, it is possible to get rather accurate estimates of what the yield will be on any given piece of land which is studied. It is out of the question, however, to make such a study for the entire farm system. Instead, three different one acre plots are selected at random from the 10,000 one acre plots, and each is studied to estimate the yield. The estimated yields are 55, 57, and 59 tons, respectively, and the average of these is 57 tons. We shall treat these numbers as if they are the correct yields. This is not quite true, but is quite close to being correct. If they are the correct yields, then the average 57 is the value of a random variable $\bar{x}$ representing the average of the values of x obtained on three independent trials of $\mathcal{R}^*$. Thus $\bar{x}$ has the expected value μ and standard deviation

$$\sigma_{\bar{x}} = \sigma/\sqrt{3} = 2/\sqrt{3} = 1.155.$$

We shall assume that the distribution of x is sufficiently close to being normal that the distribution of $\bar{x}$ can be treated as normal. In other words, the distribution of $\bar{x}$ is $n(\bar{x}; \mu,1.155)$.

Given the outcome of this experiment, we would next like to estimate the posterior distribution for μ. This can be done using Bayes' law for the case where the random variables at both stages are continuous random variables. The appropriate form is (7-126), so that if $g(\mu|57)$ denotes the posterior distribution for μ when $\bar{x} = 57$, we have

$$g(\mu|57) = \frac{n(57; \mu,1.155)n(\mu; 60,4)}{\displaystyle\int_{-\infty}^{\infty} n(57; \mu,1.155)n(\mu; 60,4)\ d\mu}. \qquad (8\text{-}24)$$

It is useful to determine a general expression for the posterior density function for a random variable μ when the prior distribution is normal with mean μ_0 and standard deviation σ_0 and the conditional distribution for the random variable for the second stage, call it z, also has a normal distribution with a mean equal to the value of μ and standard deviation σ_c. The case we are particularly interested in is a special case of this. If the value γ of z is observed, then $g(\mu|\gamma)$, the posterior density function for μ, is given by

$$g(\mu|\gamma) = \frac{n(\gamma;\mu,\sigma_c)n(\mu;\mu_0,\sigma_0)}{\displaystyle\int_{-\infty}^{\infty} n(\gamma;\mu,\sigma_c)n(\mu;\mu_0,\sigma_0)\,d\mu}. \tag{8-25}$$

To determine $g(\mu|\gamma)$, note first that

$$n(\gamma;\mu,\sigma_c)n(\mu;\mu_0,\sigma_0) = \frac{1}{2\pi\sigma_c\sigma_0}\, e^{-[(\gamma-\mu)^2/2\sigma_c^2]-[(\mu-\mu_0)^2/2\sigma_0^2]}. \tag{8-26}$$

Now if we define $\sigma_1{}^2$, μ_1, and $\sigma_z{}^2$ by

$$\frac{1}{\sigma_1{}^2} = \frac{1}{\sigma_c{}^2} + \frac{1}{\sigma_0{}^2}, \tag{8-27}$$

$$\mu_1 = \left(\frac{\sigma_1}{\sigma_c}\right)^2 \gamma + \left(\frac{\sigma_1}{\sigma_0}\right)^2 \mu_0, \tag{8-28}$$

and

$$\sigma_z{}^2 = \sigma_c{}^2 + \sigma_0{}^2, \tag{8-29}$$

then

$$\left(\frac{\gamma-\mu}{\sigma_c}\right)^2 + \left(\frac{\mu-\mu_0}{\sigma_0}\right)^2 = \left(\frac{\mu-\mu_1}{\sigma_1}\right)^2 + \left(\frac{\gamma-\mu_0}{\sigma_z}\right)^2. \tag{8-30}$$

Furthermore,

$$\frac{1}{\sigma_c\sigma_0} = \frac{\sqrt{\sigma_c{}^2+\sigma_0{}^2}}{\sigma_c\sigma_0}\, \frac{1}{\sqrt{\sigma_c{}^2+\sigma_0{}^2}} = \frac{1}{\sigma_1\sigma_z}. \tag{8-31}$$

Consequently,

$$n(\gamma;\mu,\sigma_c)n(\mu;\mu_0,\sigma_0) = n(\gamma;\mu_0,\sigma_z)n(\mu;\mu_1,\sigma_1). \tag{8-32}$$

Therefore, on using (8-32)

$$\int_{-\infty}^{\infty} n(\gamma;\mu,\sigma_c)n(\mu;\mu_0,\sigma_0)\,d\mu = n(\gamma;\mu_0,\sigma_z) \int_{-\infty}^{\infty} n(\mu;\mu_1,\sigma_1)\,d\mu$$

$$= n(\gamma;\mu_0,\sigma_z). \tag{8-33}$$

Hence on dividing (8-32) by (8-33), we have

$$g(\mu|\gamma) = n(\mu;\mu_1,\sigma_1). \tag{8-34}$$

Equations (8-33) and (8-34) are important ones and are generally useful. In words, (8-33) says that if we have a two stage random experiment having associated with it two random variables μ and z, μ referring to the first stage and z to the second stage, and if the marginal distribution for μ is normal with mean μ_0 and standard deviation σ_0, and if the conditional distribution for z given the value of μ is normal with a mean equal to the value of μ and standard deviation σ_c, then the marginal distribution for z is normal with mean μ_0 and standard deviation $\sigma_z = \sqrt{\sigma_c^2 + \sigma_0^2}$. Equation (8-34) says that under these circumstances, the conditional density for μ given the value of z is also normal with mean μ_1 and standard deviation σ_1. Note that μ_1 is a linear combination of the observed value of z and μ_0, the expected value of μ for the prior distribution. The weight given to γ is $(\sigma_1/\sigma_c)^2$ and that to μ_0 is $(\sigma_1/\sigma_0)^2$. Note also that

$$\left(\frac{\sigma_1}{\sigma_c}\right)^2 + \left(\frac{\sigma_1}{\sigma_0}\right)^2 = 1.$$

If σ_0 is much greater than σ_c, then from (8-27), $\sigma_1 \doteq \sigma_c$ and $\mu_1 \doteq \gamma$; while if σ_c is much greater than σ_0, $\mu_1 \doteq \mu_0$.

We can now apply the general results just obtained to the specific case of interest (8-24). For (8-24), $\gamma = 57$, $\mu_0 = 60$, $\sigma_c = 1.155$, $\sigma_0 = 4$. Then

$$\frac{1}{\sigma_1^2} = \frac{1}{(1.155)^2} + \frac{1}{4^2} = 0.745 + 0.0625 = 0.8075,$$

and

$$\sigma_1^2 = 1.235 \quad \text{or} \quad \sigma_1 = 1.11.$$

Thus

$$\mu_1 = \frac{1.235}{1.34}(57) + \frac{1.235}{16}(60) = 0.922(57) + 0.078(60) = 57.2.$$

Therefore, the posterior distribution for μ is normal with mean 57.2 and standard deviation 1.11, that is, is $n(\mu; 57.2, 1.11)$. Given the posterior distribution for μ, we can determine the posterior density function for y. We apply (8-22) using for $g(\mu)$ the posterior distribution for μ and for $f(y|\mu)$, (8-23). Thus

$$f(y) = \int_{-\infty}^{\infty} n(y; 10{,}000\mu, 200) n(\mu; 57.2, 1.11) \, d\mu. \qquad (8\text{-}35)$$

Let us introduce the new variable $\mu_c = 10{,}000\mu$. Then

$$n(\mu; 57.2, 1.11) = n(\mu_c; 57.2 \times 10^4, 1.11 \times 10^4) \times 10^4,$$

and $d\mu = d\mu_c/10^4$. Thus

$$f(y) = \int_{-\infty}^{\infty} n(y; \mu_c, 200) n(\mu_c; 57.2 \times 10^4, 1.11 \times 10^4) \, d\mu_c. \qquad (8\text{-}36)$$

The integral in (8-36) now has the same form as (8-33), and hence

$$f(y) = n(y; 57.2 \times 10^4, 1.11 \times 10^4) \qquad (8\text{-}37)$$

since σ_y the standard deviation of $f(y)$ is

$$\sigma_y^2 = (200)^2 + (1.11)^2 \times 10^8 = (1.11)^2 \times 10^8.$$

Having at last determined $f(y)$, the optimal quantity of tomatoes to contract for on the outside can be determined from (8-21). Suppose that production requirements are for 60×10^4 tons. Assume that the price per ton if contracted for ahead of time is \$20 and is \$27 if purchased at the peak of the season. Then on using (8-37), (8-21) becomes

$$\Phi\left[\frac{60 \times 10^4 - h - 57.2 \times 10^4}{1.11 \times 10^4}\right] = \frac{20}{27} = 0.741.$$

The value of t for which $\Phi(t) = 0.741$ is 0.647, and therefore

$$2.8 \times 10^4 - h = 0.647(1.11) \times 10^4 = 0.718 \times 10^4,$$

or

$$h \doteq 2.08 \times 10^4 = 20{,}800.$$

Therefore the production manager should contract for about 21,000 tons on the outside, which would be about 375 acres of tomatoes.

8-8 SUMMARY OF EXAMPLES

In the last five sections, examples have been presented to illustrate how the information provided by a random experiment can, through the use of Bayes' law, be used to modify the prior distribution for the states of nature to yield a posterior distribution. Once the posterior distribution is obtained, then the problem is solved in precisely the same manner as in Chapter 4. The examples point out that not infrequently it is very convenient to describe both the state of nature and the outcome of the experiment by numbers, so that one random variable can be introduced to represent the state of nature and another for the outcome of the experiment. Each of these random variables may be treated as being either discrete or continuous. The examples have illustrated all possible combinations which can occur. These are (1) the states of nature and outcomes of the experiment are discrete; (2) the states of nature are described by a discrete random variable, while the outcomes of the experiment are described by a continuous random variable; (3) the states of nature are described by a continuous random variable, while the outcomes of the states of nature are described by a discrete random variable; and finally, (4) both the states of nature and the outcomes of the experiment are described by continuous random variables. The general procedure followed is precisely the same in each case although the mathematical techniques used vary with the situation. When the states of nature are described by a continuous random variable, then in general, calculus must be used to solve the decision problem regardless of whether the outcomes of the experiment are imagined to be described by a discrete or a continuous random variable. In the other cases, calculus is not needed even though the outcomes of the random experiment are described by a continuous random variable x, unless calculus must be employed to determine the distribution of x.

8-9　STATES OF NATURE DESCRIBED BY TWO RANDOM VARIABLES

In all of the examples studied previously the states of nature could be described by a single number which could be looked upon as the value of some random variable. We now wish to study cases where each state of nature requires two numbers for its description. Thus we are now supposing that the state of nature e_j is described by a pair of numbers, say $\langle x_u, y_v \rangle$. The prior probability p_j of e_j we shall write as $p_j = p(x_u, y_v)$. The numbers x_u and y_v can be looked upon as the values taken on by two random variables x and y. In other words, the random experiment $\Re_s$ which generates the state of nature can be imagined to have associated with it two random variables x and y, and the values taken on by these two random variables can be used to characterize the state of nature. Let X and Y be the set of values which x and y can take on when $\Re_s$ is performed, and let $W = X \times Y$. Then W can be used as an event set for $\Re_s$ in a model $\mathcal{E}_s$. The joint probability function for x and y in $\mathcal{E}_s$ we shall denote by $p(x, y)$. This function will be assumed to have the property that when evaluated at $x = x_u$ and $y = y_v$, the value of the function is p_j, the prior probability of e_j. Denote the marginal probability functions for x and y by $p_1(x)$ and $p_2(y)$, respectively, and the conditional density function for y given that $x = x_u$ by $p_2(y|x_u)$.

Every state of nature will be represented by some element of W, and we can think of every element of W as being a state of nature if we allow some states of nature to have a 0 probability, thus implying that we believe them to be physically impossible. Hence we can think of W as being the set of states of nature, and $p(x, y)$ as the prior probability function for the states of nature. The utility, if action a_j is selected and the state of nature turns out to be e_j, will be denoted by $U_{ij} = U_i(x_u, y_v)$. Thus if no additional information could be obtained by performing a random experiment, the action to select would be the one which yields the largest value of

$$\sum_{u=1}^{l} \sum_{v=1}^{h} U_i(x_u, y_v) p(x_u, y_v), \tag{8-38}$$

where x can take on l different values and y a total of h different values.

Let us now suppose that a random experiment $\Re$ can be performed to obtain information about the state of nature. We wish to study the case where $\mathfrak{R}$ has the peculiar feature that it gives us information only about the value of x and no information whatever about the value of y. To be more precise about what we mean by this statement, suppose that $\mathfrak{R}$ yields one of the outcomes $f_1, \ldots, f_s$ (which may or may not be thought of as numbers), and denote the conditional probability of f_k given that the state of nature is $\langle x_u, y_v \rangle$ by $p(f_k | x_u, y_v)$. When we say that $\mathfrak{R}$ gives information only about the value of x, we mean that $p(f_k | x_u, y_v)$ has the same value for every v, i.e., is independent of y. We can indicate this by writing

$$p(f_k | x_u, y_v) = p(f_k | x_u), \quad \text{all } v. \tag{8-39}$$

We wish to show that in cases of this sort one can effectively reduce the decision problem to one in which only a single number is needed to characterize the state of nature. This is an extremely useful result as we shall point out in more detail later. Let us now consider how the problem can be simplified.

Suppose then that $\mathfrak{R}$ is performed and yields the outcome f_k. The posterior probability, that the state of nature is $\langle x_u, y_v \rangle$, is then

$$p(x_u, y_v | f_k) = \frac{p(f_k | x_u) p(x_u, y_v)}{p(f_k)}, \tag{8-40}$$

where

$$p(f_k) = \sum_{u=1}^{l} \sum_{v=1}^{h} p(f_k | x_u) p(x_u, y_v)$$

$$= \sum_{u=1}^{l} p(f_k | x_u) \left[\sum_{v=1}^{h} p(x_u, y_v) \right] = \sum_{u=1}^{l} p(f_k | x_u) p_1(x_u). \tag{8-41}$$

Note that we have just shown that $p(f_k)$ can be computed using the marginal distribution for x rather than $p(x, y)$.

Once the posterior probabilities of the states of nature have been determined, one selects the action to take by finding that i for which $\bar{U}_i$ is as large as possible, where

$$\bar{U}_i = \sum_{u=1}^{l} \sum_{v=1}^{h} U_i(x_u, y_v) p(x_u, y_v | f_k). \tag{8-42}$$

However, on using (8-40) in (8-42)

$$\bar{U}_i = \frac{1}{p(f_k)} \sum_{u=1}^{l} \sum_{v=1}^{h} U_i(x_u, y_v) p(f_k | x_u) p(x_u, y_v). \tag{8-43}$$

Now $p(x_u, y_v)$ can be written

$$p(x_u, y_v) = p_2(y_v | x_u) p_1(x_u). \tag{8-44}$$

If this is used in (8-43) we obtain

$$\bar{U}_i = \sum_{u=1}^{l} \frac{p(f_k | x_u) p_1(x_u)}{p(f_k)} \left[\sum_{v=1}^{h} U_i(x_u, y_v) p_2(y_v | x_u) \right]. \tag{8-45}$$

Next write

$$\overline{U}_{iu} = \sum_{v=1}^{h} U_i(x_u, y_v) p_2(y_v | x_u), \tag{8-46}$$

and

$$\overline{U}_i = \sum_{u=1}^{l} \overline{U}_{iu} p(x_u | f_k), \tag{8-47}$$

where

$$p(x_u | f_k) = \frac{p(f_k | x_u) p_1(x_u)}{p(f_k)}. \tag{8-48}$$

We have just obtained a very interesting and important result because we have effectively reduced the problem to one in which the states of nature are described by the values of a single random variable x, and the experiment $\Re$ is performed to give information about x. Let us then explain in detail what we have shown and after this illustrate how useful the result is. We have been studying a decision problem in which the states of nature are described by the values of two random variables x and y. It is possible to perform an experiment $\Re$ to obtain information about the state of nature. However, $\Re$ provides information only about the value of x. For such a problem we have proved above that the problem can be solved as follows. First compute the numbers $\overline{U}_{iu}$ given by (8-46); $\overline{U}_{iu}$ is the expected utility given that the state of nature has $x = x_u$, that is, it is the expected value of the utility with respect to y, given that $x = x_u$. Consider then a new problem in which the states of nature are characterized by the values taken on by x, so that x_u can denote a state of nature, and suppose that the utility when action a_i is selected and the state of nature turns out to be x_u is $\overline{U}_{iu}$. Let $p_1(x_u)$ be the prior probability for x_u in the new problem, where $p_1(x)$ is the marginal probability function for x in the original problem. Now perform $\Re$ and determine the posterior probability for each state of nature x_u in the new problem using Bayes' law in the usual way. Note that (8-48) is nothing but Bayes' law for the new problem. This yields the posterior probabilities $p(x_u | f_k)$. Use these probabilities to select the action which maximizes the expected utility, that is, which maximizes $\overline{U}_i$ in (8-47). This action and the maximum expected utility are precisely the same as would be obtained by solving the original problem having the states of nature described by the values of two random variables.

Let us now point out how useful these results are. We have in reality already used them without explicitly saying so at least once. This was done in Section 8-6 in the textile manufacturing example. In that example, we assumed that the cost was determined when the expected value of the breaking strength was known. This is not true in actuality. For any given expected breaking strength, the cost of producing the fabric on any particular type of loom will be a random variable. Thus the states of nature are not characterized by the expected breaking strength alone, but are characterized by two random variables, the expected breaking strength and the production costs. The experiment performed told us nothing about the costs. It only gave us information about the expected breaking strength. Thus the problem is really one of the type we have been discussing in this section. What we did in Section 8-6 was apply the theory developed here. We first computed the expected cost of production on a given loom for a given expected breaking strength, and we then solved the problem as if these expected costs were the actual costs that would be incurred if the expected breaking strength had the value specified. In Section 8-6 we did not mention that the costs for a given breaking strength were really expected costs. This procedure reduced the problem to one in which the state of nature was completely characterized by the expected breaking strength. The justification for using this procedure follows from what we have proved in this section. It is very frequently convenient to carry out an averaging of the costs over one random variable and reduce the problem to one in which the states of nature are characterized by the value of just a single random variable.

The theory developed above can be modified slightly to handle another type of problem which sometimes occurs. We have assumed in the examples studied previously that the outcome f_k of the random experiment $\Re$, designed to gather information about the state of nature, depended only on the random variable whose value we were attempting to measure. This is not always the case, however. The outcome of the experiment may depend not only on the value of the random variable x of interest but on the value of another extraneous random variable y as well. The random variable y must then be taken into account when making the computations. To be specific, consider a decision problem having the characteristic that if no experiment was to be performed, the states of nature could be described by the values taken on by a single random variable x. Let $p_1(x)$ be the prior probability function for x and $U_i(x_u)$ be the utility if action a_i is selected and the state of nature turns out to be x_u. Suppose now that we perform a random experiment $\Re$, having $f_1, \ldots, f_s$ as its possible outcomes, to gain information about the value of x. Imagine, however, that the outcome of $\Re$ depends not only on x but on another random variable y.

To handle this situation, it is convenient to consider a new decision problem in which the state of nature is described by a pair of values $\langle x_u, y_v \rangle$ for the two random variables x and y. Denote by $p(x, y)$ the prior joint probability function for x and y. The utility for $\langle x_u, y_v \rangle$ will be taken to be $U_i(x_u)$ and is independent of y_v. The set of actions will be the same for the new problem and the original problem. Let $p(f_k|x_u, y_v)$ be the conditional probability that $\Re$ will have the outcome f_k when $x = x_u$ and $y = y_v$. Then, since the outcome of $\Re$ is assumed to depend only on the values of x and y, $p(x_u, y_v | f_k)$, the posterior probability of $\langle x_u, y_v \rangle$, given f_k is found from Bayes' law

$$p(x_u, y_v | f_k) = \frac{p(f_k | x_u, y_v)p(x_u, y_v)}{\sum\limits_{u=1}^{l} \sum\limits_{v=1}^{h} p(f_k | x_u, y_v)p(x_u, y_v)}, \qquad (8\text{-}49)$$

and the action to select is the one which maximizes

$$\sum_{u=1}^{l} \sum_{v=1}^{h} U_i(x_u)p(x_u, y_v | f_k) = \sum_{u=1}^{q} U_i(x_u)p_1(x_u | f_k), \qquad (8\text{-}50)$$

where

$$p_1(x_u | f_k) = \sum_{v=1}^{h} p(x_u, y_v | f_k). \qquad (8\text{-}51)$$

Note that $p(x, y | f_k)$ is the posterior joint distribution of x and y, and $p_1(x | f_k)$ is the posterior marginal distribution for x.

We have now shown how the extraneous random variable y can be taken into account. We enlarge the problem to one where the states of nature are described by the values of both x and y. This problem is then solved in the usual way. As one example of how such a situation could arise, the reading from the seismic experiment referred to in Section 8-3 depends not only on the petroleum contained in the structure under consideration, but also on the water that is present. If one wished to take this into account, one could let x refer to the oil in place and y to the water in the structure. One would then have to determine $p(x, y)$, the prior distribution of x and y. Depending on circumstances, it might be reasonable to assume that x and y were independent random variables, so that $p(x, y) = p_1(x)p_2(y)$. Then a prior probability function for the water in place would need to be estimated. After this was done, the conditional probabilities $p(f_k | x_u, y_v)$ would need to be determined. For example, it might be reasonable to construct a model in which the reading from the seismic experiment depended on $x_u + y_v$, the sum of the oil and water in place. Having made the estimates of the necessary probability functions, one could then solve the problem in the manner described above.

In this section we have discussed two types of situations involving decision problems where the state of nature is characterized by the values taken on by two random variables. In one of these cases we started out with such a problem and showed that if the random experiment yielded information about only one of the random variables, the problem could be converted to a simpler form in which the state of nature was characterized by the value of just a single random variable. For the other class of problems, the situation was that in the absence of an experiment, only a single number was needed to characterize the state of nature, but because the random experiment involved another extraneous random variable, it was necessary to convert the problem to a form where the state of nature is described by the values taken on by two random variables.

8-10   TWO ACTION PROBLEMS WITH LINEAR UTILITIES

A type of problem that is encountered fairly frequently, is one where just two alternative actions are being considered, and which, in addition, has the feature that each state of nature e_j can be characterized by a single number x_j. The x_j can be imagined to be the values that a random variable x takes on. It is also frequently the case that the utility U_{1j} received on taking action a_1 when the state of nature turns out to be x_j is related to x_j by a linear equation, and similarly for U_{2j}. Let us write these linear equations as

$$U_{1j} = ax_j + b; \quad U_{2j} = cx_j + d, \quad a \neq c. \tag{8-52}$$

Consider then the linear equations

$$U_1 = ax + b; \quad U_2 = cx + d, \tag{8-53}$$

where in (8-53) we imagine that x can take on all real values. The graphs of these two equations will then look something like the two straight lines

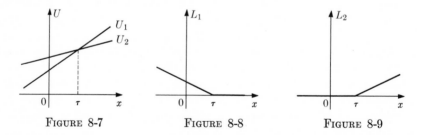

FIGURE 8-7   FIGURE 8-8   FIGURE 8-9

shown in Figure 8-7. Let τ be the point of intersection of these two lines, so that

$$\tau = \frac{d - b}{a - c}. \tag{8-54}$$

We can now note that if x_j is the state of nature and $x_j > \tau$, then action a_1 is the appropriate one to take since $U_1 > U_2$; whereas if $x_j < \tau$, action a_2 is the appropriate one to take since $U_2 > U_1$. When $x_j = \tau$, the decision maker is indifferent between the two actions. Given these observations, we see that the regrets L_{1j} and L_{2j} on taking actions a_1 and a_2 when the state of nature is x_j are

$$L_{1j} = \begin{cases} 0, & x_j \geq \tau \\ (c-a)x_j + (d-b), & x_j < \tau; \end{cases} \qquad L_{2j} = \begin{cases} (a-c)x_j + (b-d), & x_j > \tau \\ 0, & x_j \leq \tau. \end{cases}$$

$$(8\text{-}55)$$

Consider then the functions

$$L_1(x) = \begin{cases} 0, & x \geq \tau \\ (c-a)x + (d-b), & x < \tau; \end{cases} \qquad L_2(x) = \begin{cases} (a-c)x + (b-d), & x > \tau \\ 0, & x \leq \tau. \end{cases}$$

$$(8\text{-}56)$$

The graphs of these two functions are shown in Figures 8-8 and 8-9. Note that whereas (8-53) represents a pair of linear functions, the functions (8-56) are nonlinear. From what we proved in Chapter 4, we know that the same action will be chosen by minimizing the expected regret as by maximizing the expected utility.

Let us next examine in a little more detail the procedure for solving a problem of the type being considered. Because of (8-52), the expected utilities $\overline{U}_1$ and $\overline{U}_2$ for actions a_1 and a_2 are simply

$$\overline{U}_1 = a\mu_x + b; \qquad \overline{U}_2 = c\mu_x + d, \qquad (8\text{-}57)$$

where μ_x is the expected value of x. This holds both for the case where x is treated as discrete and where x is treated as continuous. It also holds regardless of whether an experiment is performed to obtain information about the state of nature. If no experiment is performed, then μ_x is the mean of the prior distribution for x, and if an experiment is performed, then μ_x is the mean of the posterior distribution of x. Now observe that $\overline{U}_1$ and $\overline{U}_2$ are related to μ_x by the same linear equations which relate U_1 and U_2 to x. Therefore we see that $\overline{U}_1 > \overline{U}_2$ if $\mu_x > \tau$; and $\overline{U}_2 > \overline{U}_1$ if $\mu_x < \tau$. It follows then that we really do not need to compute $\overline{U}_1$ and $\overline{U}_2$ to determine what action to select. We merely compute μ_x; and if $\mu_x > \tau$, action a_1 is selected; whereas if $\mu_x < \tau$, action a_2 is selected. The whole problem then reduces to one of evaluating μ_x for either the prior or posterior distribution, whichever is appropriate. This procedure is not valid in general, of course. It depends critically on the assumption that the utilities are related to x by linear equations.

It is worthwhile to examine in just a little more detail the case where an experiment is performed and the assumptions are made that x is normally distributed, and the outcome of the experiment is also normally distributed with mean ξ, if ξ is the state of nature. To be specific, suppose that the prior distribution for x is assumed to be $n(x; \mu_0, \sigma_0)$ and that we perform an experiment to estimate the value ξ of x. Imagine that the outcome of the experiment is characterized by a random variable y, and y has the normal distribution $n(y; \xi, \sigma_c)$. Suppose that the experiment is now performed and yields the value $y = \gamma$. In Section 8-7 we showed that the posterior distribution of x is normal and that its mean is

$$\mu_1 = \left(\frac{\sigma_1}{\sigma_c}\right)^2 \gamma + \left(\frac{\sigma_1}{\sigma_0}\right)^2 \mu_0; \quad \frac{1}{\sigma_1{}^2} = \frac{1}{\sigma_c{}^2} + \frac{1}{\sigma_0{}^2}. \tag{8-58}$$

From what we have shown above, action a_1 should be selected if $\mu_1 > \tau$, and action a_2 if $\mu_1 < \tau$. However, $\mu_1 > \tau$ if and only if

$$\gamma > \left(\frac{\sigma_c}{\sigma_1}\right)^2 \tau - \left(\frac{\sigma_c}{\sigma_0}\right)^2 \mu_0 = \rho. \tag{8-59}$$

Similarly, $\mu_1 < \tau$ if and only if $\gamma < \rho$. We have thus reached an interesting conclusion. To determine what action to take, we only need to compute the number ρ, and if γ the outcome of the experiment satisfies $\gamma > \rho$, then action a_1 should be taken; whereas if $\gamma < \rho$, the action to select is a_2. This provides a very simple decision rule for solving a problem of this type. It should be noted, of course, that a_1 is selected when $\gamma > \rho$ only because $U_1 > U_2$ when $x > \tau$. If the actions were labeled so that $U_2 > U_1$, when $x > \tau$, then action a_2 should be selected when $\gamma > \rho$. Let us provide an example of its usefulness.

EXAMPLE. A manufacturer of a variety of petrochemicals is about to make a batch of a particular, very expensive product. One of the raw materials for this chemical is manufactured in a petroleum company's refinery. The yield of the petrochemical is critically dependent on the sulfur content in the raw material. The sulfur content is always very low, but nonetheless even small quantities reduce significantly the yield below the maximum possible yield. Experiments have shown that the yield is related to the sulfur content by a linear equation. The profit received from a batch is directly proportional to the yield. Thus the profit received is related to the sulfur content by a linear equation. This equation is

$$U_1 = 25,000 - 100,000x, \tag{8-60}$$

where U_1 is the profit in dollars and x is the percent by weight of sulfur in the raw material.

The sulfur content in the raw material depends on a variety of factors such as the mix of crudes run through the refinery and the operating temperatures of the units at the refinery. The chemical producer estimates on the basis of his previous experience that the sulfur content can be viewed as a random variable x having a normal distribution with mean 0.05 and standard deviation 0.02.

Now the chemical producer is able to further treat the raw material before using it. He can put the raw material through a desulfurization process. If he does this, the sulfur content will be reduced to 0.04 percent. This desulfurization operation costs $2000, however. His profit from the batch if he uses the desulfurization process will then be, on using (8-60)

$$U_2 = 25{,}000 - 100{,}000(0.04) - 2000 = 19{,}000, \qquad (8\text{-}61)$$

and this is independent of what the sulfur content was originally in the raw material.

The chemical producer then has two courses of action open to him. He can use the raw material directly, call this a_1, or he can first put it through the desulfurization process, call this a_2. Consider first what he should do if he is going to base his decision on the prior distribution for x, this prior distribution having mean 0.05. If $\bar{U}_1$ and $\bar{U}_2$ are the expected utilities corresponding to a_1 and a_2, then by (8-57)

$$\bar{U}_1 = 25{,}000 - 100{,}000(0.05) = 20{,}000; \quad \bar{U}_2 = 19{,}000, \quad (8\text{-}62)$$

and he should not use the desulfurization process.

Before actually making a decision on whether or not to use the desulfurization process, the petrochemical producer performs a chemical analysis to determine the sulfur content in the raw material. Inasmuch as the sulfur content is very small, it is difficult to perform the analysis with great accuracy. Furthermore, the analysis is fairly time consuming and costly. Previous experience has shown, however, that if ξ is the actual sulfur content, the estimate of the sulfur content given by the experiment is a random variable y having a normal distribution with mean ξ and standard deviation 0.03. To try to improve the accuracy of the experiment, the manufacturer takes three different samples from the raw material, analyzes each, and averages the results. We shall assume that the sulfur content is absolutely uniform throughout the raw material. Then the three analyses represent three independent trials of the same random experiment. Hence the average of the values on these three trials is a random variable having a normal distribution with mean ξ and standard deviation $\sigma_c = 0.03/\sqrt{3} = 0.01732$.

Suppose now that the three analyses are performed. When the results are averaged, the number 0.058 is obtained as the estimate of the sulfur content. We wish to decide, given this result, whether the desulfurization process should be used. All we need to do is apply (8-59) with $\gamma = 0.058$, noting that when $\gamma > \rho$ desulfurization should be used. To do so, we must compute ρ, however. The value τ for which $U_1 = U_2$ is $\tau = 0.06$, since when $x = 0.06$, $U_1 = 19{,}000$. Furthermore, $\mu_0 = 0.05$, $\sigma_0 = 0.02$, $\sigma_c = 0.01732$, and by (8-58)

$$\frac{1}{\sigma_1{}^2} = \frac{1}{(0.01732)^2} + \frac{1}{(0.02)^2} = 10{,}000[0.333 + 0.250] = 5830.$$

Then

$$(\sigma_c/\sigma_1)^2 = 0.5830(3) = 1.749; \quad (\sigma_c/\sigma_0)^2 = \tfrac{3}{4} = 0.75.$$

Therefore
$$\rho = 1.749(0.06) - 0.75(0.05) = 0.0674.$$

Now $0.058 < \rho$; therefore the desulfurization process should not be used.

8-11* TECHNIQUES NOT INVOLVING PRIOR PROBABILITIES

In Sections 4-9 and 4-10 we discussed some procedures which could be used for selecting an action in cases where the probabilities of the states of nature were not known. We would now like to generalize those rules to problems in which an experiment is performed to gain information about the state of nature before an action is selected. The procedures introduced in Sections 4-9 and 4-10 will be generalized in such a way that they do not make any use of prior probabilities for the states of nature, but do make use of the experimental results. In particular, they make use not only of the outcome f_k of the experiment $\Re$, but also of the conditional probabilities $p(f_k|e_j)$ that the outcome is f_k when the state of nature is e_j.

To proceed we shall introduce once again the notion of a strategy. The experiment $\Re$ will yield one of the outcomes $f_1, \ldots, f_s$. A strategy will here be defined as a rule which tells the decision maker what action to take for each of the s possible outcomes of the experiment. A strategy S is then characterized by an ordered array of s symbols $\langle \alpha_1, \ldots, \alpha_s \rangle$, where each α_k denotes one of the actions a_i, and the ordered s-tuple of numbers is to be interpreted to mean that if f_k is the outcome of $\Re$, then the action symbolized by α_k should be used. Thus one possible strategy would be $S = \langle a_1, a_1, a_2, \ldots, a_5 \rangle$, and it means that if $\Re$ yields f_1 or f_2 take action a_1, if it yields f_3 take action a_2, etc., if it yields f_s take action a_5. Suppose that there are r different actions. Then α_1 can represent any one of these r actions and similarly for $\alpha_2, \ldots, \alpha_s$. Thus there are $h = r^s$ different strategies of the type which we have just introduced. What we now wish to do is select one of these strategies for the decision maker to use. Any strategy tells the decision maker what to do under every possible circumstance, since it tells him what action to take for every possible outcome of the experiment.

Suppose now that we have written down each of the h possible strategies and have numbered them from 1 to h. We shall denote the vth one by S_v. Let us imagine that the decision maker decides to use S_v and that S_v says to use action a_{i_k} when the experiment $\Re$ yields the outcome f_k. As usual, U_{ij} will denote the utility received if the decision maker selects action a_i and the state of nature turns out to be e_j. If the decision maker selects strategy S_v and the state of nature turns out to be e_j, the utility for the

---

* Recall that sections marked with an asterisk contain material which may be omitted without loss of continuity.

decision maker is not determined because the action selected will depend upon the outcome of $\Re$. In other words, once S_v is selected, and it is the case that the state of nature is e_j, the utility becomes a random variable defined with respect to $\Re$. Denote by $\overline{U}_{vj}$ the expected utility when strategy S_v is selected and the state of nature is e_j. Then

$$\overline{U}_{vj} = \sum_{k=1}^{s} U_{tkj} p(f_k|e_j), \qquad (8\text{-}63)$$

where $p(f_k|e_j)$ is the probability that $\Re$ will yield f_k when the state of nature is e_j.

At this point we can construct a table similar to a payoff table in which the columns refer to the states of nature, but the rows refer to strategies rather than actions. The entries $\overline{U}_{vj}$ in the table are the expected utilities when the strategy selected is S_v and the state of nature turns out to be e_j. The format for this table is shown in Table 8-4. We shall call this the

TABLE 8-4

STRATEGY PAYOFF TABLE

	e_1	e_2				e_m
S_1	$\overline{U}_{11}$	$\overline{U}_{12}$		. . .		$\overline{U}_{1m}$
S_2	$\overline{U}_{21}$	$\overline{U}_{22}$				$\overline{U}_{2m}$
. . .	. . .	. . .				
S_h	$\overline{U}_{h1}$	$\overline{U}_{h2}$				$\overline{U}_{hm}$

strategy payoff table. It should be noted that it can be a staggering undertaking to construct a strategy payoff table even for decision problems of very modest size. The reason for this is that the number of strategies r^s can be very large even though r and s are not very large. Furthermore, each entry in the table requires the computation of an expected value.

Once one has the strategy payoff table, it is fairly obvious how the rules introduced in Section 4-9 should be generalized to the type of situation under consideration. One applies the rules to the strategy payoff table in precisely the same way that they were applied to the payoff table in Section 4-9. Before explaining the way in which these rules are applied here, it will be instructive to show the connection between the strategy payoff table and the payoff table in the case where the prior probabilities of the states of nature are known. Suppose that p_j is the prior probability for e_j. Recall that if $\Re$ yields the outcome f_k, the way the decision maker determines the action to select is by computing the posterior probabilities of the states of nature

$$p(e_j|f_k) = \frac{p(f_k|e_j)p_j}{p(f_k)}, \tag{8-64}$$

and then determining the action which maximizes

$$\sum_{j=1}^{m} U_{ij}p(e_j|f_k) = \frac{1}{p(f_k)} \sum_{j=1}^{m} U_{ij}p(f_k|e_j)p_j. \tag{8-65}$$

Note, however, that since $p(f_k)$ does not depend on i, the value of i which maximizes (8-65) also maximizes

$$\sum_{j=1}^{m} U_{ij}p(f_k|e_j)p_j. \tag{8-66}$$

Conversely, the i which maximizes (8-66) maximizes (8-65). Thus the action to take is the one which maximizes (8-66). Suppose that we denote by β_k the action which maximizes (8-66) for f_k. There is then an optimal action to take for each value of k. Let $S^* = \langle \beta_1, \beta_2, \ldots, \beta_s \rangle$. Then S^* is a strategy and it is what we shall call an optimal strategy for the given prior probabilities, since regardless of what the outcome of $\Re$ is, it tells the decision maker to use the best action for that outcome. Note that S^* is one of the strategies listed in the strategy payoff table.

Suppose now that in the strategy payoff table we select the strategy which maximizes

$$\sum_{j=1}^{m} \overline{U}_{vj}p_j. \tag{8-67}$$

We then claim that S^* is such a strategy. To prove this, we use (8-63) and note that

$$\sum_{j=1}^{m} \overline{U}_{vj}p_j = \sum_{j=1}^{m} \left[\sum_{k=1}^{s} U_{ikj}p(f_k|e_j) \right] p_j = \sum_{k=1}^{s} \left[\sum_{j=1}^{m} U_{ikj}p(f_k|e_j)p_j \right], \tag{8-68}$$

where a_{i_k} is the action which S_v says to select when $\Re$ yields the outcome f_k. We wish to determine $i_1, \ldots, i_s$ so that (8-68) is as large as possible. Now (8-68) will be maximized if and only if for each k, i_k is chosen so as to maximize

$$\sum_{j=1}^{m} U_{i_kj}p(f_k|e_j)p_j.$$

But this is precisely (8-66) and we know that it is maximized when the action is β_k. This is true for every k. Thus S^* maximizes (8-67), and this is what we wished to prove.

We have shown that there are two ways in which we can determine an optimal strategy S^* for a given set of prior probabilities. One way is to proceed in the manner discussed in Section 8-1.   We compute for a given outcome of $\mathcal{R}$ the posterior probabilities and then determine the action which maximizes the expected utility.   This is done for each outcome of $\mathcal{R}$, and the set of actions obtained (which may not be unique) yields S^* or an S^*.   This procedure makes use of the payoff table.   The alternative procedure is to construct a strategy payoff table.   We then look at the numbers in this table as being utilities and, using the prior probabilities to compute the expected utility, select the strategy which maximizes the expected utility.   The S^* obtained above will also be the strategy or one of the strategies obtained by this latter procedure.

Let us now return to showing how the rules of Section 4-9 can be applied here.   To apply the Laplace criterion, one simply finds the strategy which maximizes (8-67) when $p_j = 1/m$.   As before, this corresponds to assuming that a priori the states of nature are equally likely.   A strategy determined in this way will be called a Laplace strategy.   To apply the max-min criterion, let

$$U_v{}^+ = \min_j \overline{U}_{vj}. \tag{8-69}$$

Then the strategy to use is the one which maximizes $U_v{}^+$.   Such a strategy will be called a max-min strategy.   It is the strategy for which the smallest entry in any row of the strategy payoff table is made as large as possible.   To apply the max-max criterion, let

$$U_v{}^* = \max_j \overline{U}_{vj}. \tag{8-70}$$

Then the strategy is selected for which $U_v{}^*$ is as large as possible.   Such a strategy will be called a max-max strategy.   The optimism index is applied as follows.   A number α, $0 \le \alpha \le 1$ is selected, and the numbers

$$\hat{U}_v(\alpha) = \alpha U_v{}^* + (1 - \alpha)U_v{}^+ \tag{8-71}$$

are computed, and the strategy chosen is the one which yields the largest value of $\hat{U}_v(\alpha)$.   Such a strategy will be called an optimism index strategy. Finally, to use the min-max regret criterion, one computes

$$M_j = \max_v \overline{U}_{vj}, \tag{8-72}$$

and then the regrets

$$L_{vj} = M_j - \overline{U}_{vj}. \tag{8-73}$$

Next one computes

$$L_v{}^+ = \max_j L_{vj}, \tag{8-74}$$

and the strategy selected is the one yielding the smallest $L_v{}^+$.   Such a strategy will be called a min-max regret strategy.   Thus each of the criteria is used on the strategy payoff table in precisely the same way as on the payoff table in Section 4-9.

We shall now illustrate several of these rules by applying them to the independent oil producer example studied in Section 8-3. The reader should review that example at this point. There are two actions and four outcomes of the experiment, and therefore there are $2^4 = 16$ strategies. In Table 8-5 we have listed these strategies and have constructed the

TABLE 8-5

STRATEGY PAYOFF AND REGRET TABLE FOR OIL PRODUCER

	Payoff			Regret		
	e_1	e_2	e_3	e_1	e_2	e_3
$S_1 = \langle a_1, a_1, a_1, a_1 \rangle$	−800,000	400,000	2,000,000	800,000	0	0
$S_2 = \langle a_1, a_1, a_1, a_2 \rangle$	−760,000	380,000	1,500,000	760,000	20,000	500,000
$S_3 = \langle a_1, a_1, a_2, a_1 \rangle$	−680,000	340,000	1,300,000	680,000	60,000	700,000
$S_4 = \langle a_1, a_1, a_2, a_2 \rangle$	−640,000	320,000	800,000	640,000	80,000	1,200,000
$S_5 = \langle a_1, a_2, a_1, a_1 \rangle$	−560,000	240,000	1,400,000	560,000	160,000	600,000
$S_6 = \langle a_1, a_2, a_2, a_1 \rangle$	−440,000	180,000	700,000	440,000	220,000	1,300,000
$S_7 = \langle a_1, a_2, a_2, a_2 \rangle$	−400,000	160,000	200,000	400,000	240,000	1,800,000
$S_8 = \langle a_1, a_2, a_1, a_2 \rangle$	−520,000	220,000	900,000	520,000	180,000	1,100,000
$S_9 = \langle a_2, a_1, a_1, a_1 \rangle$	−400,000	240,000	1,800,000	400,000	160,000	200,000
$S_{10} = \langle a_2, a_2, a_1, a_1 \rangle$	−160,000	80,000	1,200,000	160,000	320,000	800,000
$S_{11} = \langle a_2, a_2, a_2, a_1 \rangle$	−40,000	20,000	500,000	40,000	380,000	1,500,000
$S_{12} = \langle a_2, a_2, a_2, a_2 \rangle$	0	0	0	0	400,000	2,000,000
$S_{13} = \langle a_2, a_2, a_1, a_2 \rangle$	−120,000	60,000	700,000	120,000	340,000	1,300,000
$S_{14} = \langle a_2, a_1, a_2, a_2 \rangle$	−240,000	160,000	600,000	240,000	240,000	1,400,000
$S_{15} = \langle a_2, a_1, a_1, a_2 \rangle$	−360,000	220,000	1,300,000	360,000	180,000	700,000
$S_{16} = \langle a_2, a_1, a_2, a_1 \rangle$	−280,000	180,000	1,100,000	280,000	220,000	900,000

strategy payoff table. In the table a_1 stands for the action which involves purchasing the property, while a_2 stands for the action of not purchasing it. The minimum $\bar{U}_{vj}$ always occurs in the first column. The largest number in the first column is 0, which occurs for S_{12}. Thus the max-min strategy is S_{12}. This strategy says that he should not buy the property regardless of what the outcome of the experiment is. Clearly, the max-min strategy is too conservative here and is not of much value to the oil producer, since in applying it he would essentially always get the same result and would be forced out of business. To find the max-max strategy, we look for the largest entry in the table. This is 2,000,000 and occurs for S_1. Thus S_1 is the max-max strategy. It says he should always buy the property regardless of what the outcome of the experiment is. This is not a very sound strategy either. In Table 8-5 we have also presented a regret table. The reader can easily check that the minimum value of the maximum regret is taken on at S_9, so that S_9 is the min-max regret strategy. This strategy borders on being a reasonable one. It says that he should not buy the property if the outcome of $\mathfrak{R}$ is the lowest reading, while he should buy it for every other outcome.   We leave to the problems the task of obtaining the Laplace strategy and the determination of the optimism index strategy for every possible value of α, $0 \le \alpha \le 1$.   We also ask the reader to show that when the prior probabilities are given by (8-5), then $S^* = S_{10}$ is the optimal strategy.

It is possible to introduce mixed strategies for problems of the type being considered here, just as one did in Section 4-10.   The decision maker is using a mixed strategy if instead of selecting one of the strategies S_v considered above, which will now be referred to as pure strategies, he allows a game of chance to select the strategy he will use.   A mixed strategy is then characterized by a set of probabilities $q_1, \ldots, q_h$, where q_v is the probability that the game of chance will select pure strategy S_v. The rules discussed above can be generalized to deal with mixed strategies in precisely the same way as in Section 4-10.   When a mixed strategy is used, a two stage experiment is performed before the decision maker selects an action.   The first stage is the game of chance which selects the strategy, and the second stage is the random experiment $\mathcal{R}$ whose outcome determines which action will be taken once the strategy is selected.   The expected utility, computed with respect to this two stage experiment given that the state of nature is e_j, is

$$\sum_{v=1}^{h} q_v \overline{U}_{vj}. \tag{8-75}$$

A max-min mixed strategy is one where the q_v are selected so that the minimum over j of (8-75) is made as large as possible.   The max-min mixed strategy can be found by solving the linear programming problem

$$\sum_{v=1}^{h} q_v \overline{U}_{vj} - \rho \ge 0, \quad v = 1, \ldots, h,$$

$$\sum_{v=1}^{h} q_v = 1; \quad q_v \ge 0, \text{ all } v, \tag{8-76}$$

and the variable ρ is to be maximized.

When there are only two states of nature, the situation can be represented geometrically in precisely the same manner described in Section 4-11, the only difference being that the corners in Figure 4-10 will now refer to pure strategies rather than actions.   The max-min strategy for the present case can be found in precisely the same manner that was discussed in Section 4-11.

If the prior probabilities of the states of nature are specified to be p_j, $j = 1, \ldots, m$, a Bayes' mixed strategy is one in which the q_v are determined so as to maximize

$$z = \sum_{j=1}^{m} \left[\sum_{v=1}^{h} q_v \overline{U}_{vj} \right] p_j = \sum_{v=1}^{h} \left[\sum_{j=1}^{m} \overline{U}_{vj} p_j \right] q_v. \qquad (8\text{-}77)$$

Precisely the same proof as that given in Section 4-12 shows that at least one pure strategy will be a Bayes' mixed strategy, and in fact, S^* is a Bayes' mixed strategy.

8-12 SELECTION AMONG ALTERNATIVE EXPERIMENTS

We have been concerned in this chapter with showing how the results of a random experiment performed with the purpose of gaining information about the state of nature could be incorporated into the single stage decision model. We always made the assumption in analyzing such situations that a specific experiment was going to be performed. We did not attempt to consider whether it was desirable to perform the experiment or whether the experiment being used was the best of a number of possible alternative experiments. We now wish to generalize the analysis to the point where it is possible to decide whether an experiment should be performed, and if so, which of a number of alternative experiments is the most appropriate one.

Consider then the following type of situation. At some time in the past a random experiment was performed which determined the state of nature. A decision maker must select one of the actions a_i, $i = 1, \ldots, r$. He does not know what the state of nature is, but he knows that it will be one of the m states symbolized by e_j, $j = 1, \ldots, m$. Either on the basis of historical information or his personal feelings, he assigns the prior probability p_j to e_j. Before actually selecting the action to be taken, the decision maker can, if he wishes, perform *one* of d random experiments $\mathfrak{R}_h$, $h = 1, \ldots, d$. The random experiment $\mathfrak{R}_h$ has s_h possible outcomes, which will be represented symbolically by f_{hk}, $k = 1, \ldots, s_h$. The conditional probability of f_{hk}, given that the state of nature is e_j, will be denoted by $p_h(f_{hk}|e_j)$ or w_{hjk}. The decision maker does not need to perform any of the experiments if it does not seem advisable to do so. To simplify the discussion, it will be very convenient to think of the alternative of not performing any experiment as a random experiment $\mathfrak{R}_0$ which has only one outcome f_0 and $p(f_0|e_j) = 1$; $\mathfrak{R}_0$ thus gives no information and is equivalent to not performing any experiment. With this convention precisely one of $d + 1$ random experiments is to be performed. If experiment $\mathfrak{R}_h$ is used, then action a_i is selected and, ultimately the state of nature turns out to be e_j, the decision maker's utility will be denoted by U_{hij}. In our previous work we did not concern ourselves with the cost of the experiment because it was assumed that the experiment was to be performed, and its cost did not influence the action to be selected. In the present situation, however, different experiments will in general cost different amounts to perform, and this must be taken account of. We shall assume that the utilities U_{hij} reflect the cost of the experiment involved.

The decision maker must first select a random experiment, and then after the random experiment is performed, he must select an action. The structure of the decision tree for this situation is shown in Figure 8-10.

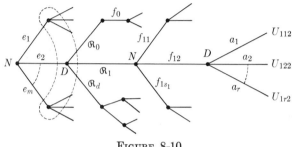

FIGURE 8-10

The entire tree is not shown because it would take up too much space. We can now note that the problem under consideration is a special case of what we referred to in Chapter 3 as a two stage decision problem. At the first stage the experiment is chosen. At the second stage, after the experiment selected at the first stage is performed, the decision maker selects the action to be taken, this decision being based on the outcome of the experiment.

In Chapter 3 we presented the general theory for solving the two stage problem under consideration. It would probably be helpful for the reader to review Sections 3-3 and 3-4 at this point. A strategy for this two stage decision problem is characterized by specifying the experiment to be performed at the first stage, and then giving a decision rule which tells what action should be selected for each possible outcome of the experiment. Thus a strategy S can be described by writing

$$S = \{\mathcal{R}_h, \langle \alpha_1, \ldots, \alpha_{s_h} \rangle\}, \tag{8-78}$$

and this means that experiment $\mathcal{R}_h$ should be performed; and if the outcome of $\mathcal{R}_h$ is f_k, then action α_k should be taken. Selection of a strategy places the decision maker in a two stage lottery. The first stage is the random experiment which selects the state of nature, and the second stage is the random experiment performed to gain information about the state of nature. Let us examine this two stage experiment in a little more detail. Recall from Chapter 2 that to rank the various two stage lotteries corresponding to the different strategies it is only necessary to compute the expected utility for each and arrange them in order of decreasing expected utility. We then wish to see what is involved in determining the expected utility. Before considering the general case, let us consider a very simple example illustrated in Figure 8-11, where there are just two

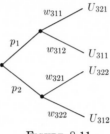

FIGURE 8-11

states of nature, and the experiment $\Re_3$ has just two possible outcomes. The strategy we are considering is one which selects action a_2 if the experiment yields the outcome f_1 and action a_1 if the experiment yields the outcome f_2. The probability that the utility will be U_{322} is $p_2 w_{321}$. Thus the expected utility for this two stage lottery is

$$p_1 w_{311} U_{321} + p_1 w_{312} U_{311} + p_2 w_{321} U_{322} + p_2 w_{322} U_{312}. \qquad (8\text{-}79)$$

We can think of this as being the expected utility associated with the strategy which yields this two stage lottery.

Consider now the general case. Suppose we select a strategy S which uses the experiment $\Re_h$ and for which $\alpha_k = a_{i_k}$. The expected utility of this strategy, which is the expected utility of the resulting two stage lottery if S is adopted, is

$$\bar{U}_S = \sum_{k=1}^{s_h} \sum_{j=1}^{m} p_j w_{hjk} U_{hikj}. \qquad (8\text{-}80)$$

An optimal strategy is one which yields the largest value of $\bar{U}_S$. Thus to solve the problem one could evaluate $\bar{U}_S$ for each strategy S and then select the strategy or one of the strategies which yields the largest $\bar{U}_S$. Generally speaking, there are a very large number of strategies, and it can be extremely laborious to determine an optimal strategy even for problems which, if the experiment was specified, would be relatively easy to solve. For example, if there were four experiments, each of which had three possible outcomes and five actions, there would be $4(5)^3 = 500$ strategies, and (8-80) would have to be evaluated for each of these. By examining (8-80) in a little more detail, we can see that it is possible to reduce the computational effort considerably, although the effort required is still very burdensome.   However, we shall also make an interesting connection with what we have studied earlier in this chapter.   We shall show that the problem of selecting an experiment can be determined by solving a series of problems where the experiment is specified and then combining the results suitably.

To determine an optimal strategy S^*, which is the strategy that gives the maximum value of (8-80), we can proceed as follows.   Consider first all strategies which say to use experiment $\mathfrak{R}_h$.   Let $S^*(h)$ be the strategy or one of the strategies which maximizes (8-80) for the given h.   This strategy is optimal if experiment h must be used.   Let $\overline{U}_h$ be the value of (8-80) for $S^*(h)$.   Then the maximum value of $\overline{U}_S$ must be the maximum with respect to h of the $\overline{U}_h$ because all we have done is partition all strategies into different categories according to the experiment used.   Then (8-80) was evaluated for each strategy, and we selected the largest value so obtained for each category.   The largest value of (8-80) over all strategies must then be the maximum of the $\overline{U}_h$.

Let us now consider the determination of $S^*(h)$.   When h is fixed, the only thing that we are free to select in (8-80) are the indices i_k on U_{hikj}, that is, we are free to choose, for each k, the action a_{i_k} which will be α_k.   This will be done in such a way that (8-80) is maximized.   Note that (8-80) can be written

$$\overline{U}_S = \sum_{j=1}^{m} p_j w_{hj1} U_{hi_1j} + \sum_{j=1}^{m} p_j w_{hj2} U_{hi_2j} + \cdots + \sum_{j=1}^{m} p_j w_{hjs_h} U_{hi_{s_h}j} \quad (8\text{-}81)$$

and that the selection of the action a_{i_1} to be used when $\mathfrak{R}_h$ yields f_{h1} influences only the first sum in (8-81), while a_{i_2} influences only the second, etc.   Consequently, if for each k we select α_k to be the action which maximizes

$$\sum_{j=1}^{m} p_j w_{hjk} U_{hij}, \quad (8\text{-}82)$$

then the resulting set $\langle \alpha_1, \ldots, \alpha_{s_h} \rangle$ yields a strategy $S^*(h)$, since when these actions are used, $\overline{U}_S$ in (8-81) is maximized for the given h.

The expression in (8-82) looks familiar.   To see this more clearly, let us write $w_{hjk} = p_h(f_{hk}|e_j)$ and multiply and divide (8-82) by $p_h(f_{hk})$, where $p_h(f_{hk})$ is the marginal probability of f_{hk} when $\mathfrak{R}_h$ is the experiment.   Thus (8-82) becomes

$$p_h(f_{hk}) \sum_{j=1}^{m} U_{hij} \frac{p_h(f_{hk}|e_j)p_j}{p_h(f_{hk})} = p_h(f_{hk}) \sum_{j=1}^{m} U_{hij} p_h(e_j|f_{hk}), \quad (8\text{-}83)$$

where we have applied Bayes' law to introduce the posterior probabilities of states of nature.   Inasmuch as $p_h(f_{hk})$ is independent of i, (8-83) and hence (8-82) will be maximized for the a_i which maximizes

$$\sum_{j=1}^{m} U_{hij} p_h(e_j | f_{hk}). \tag{8-84}$$

We can now make the interesting observation that the maximization of (8-84) is what we have been carrying out all through this chapter, since in (8-84), we are finding the action which maximizes the expected utility computed using posterior probabilities obtained as a result of performing the experiment $\mathfrak{R}_h$. This is, of course, what we would expect intuitively. The optimal action to take, if $\mathfrak{R}_h$ is performed and yields the outcome f_{hk}, should be precisely the one we would determine by the methods of Section 8-1. Denote this action by β_{hk}. Furthermore, let $\bar{U}_{hk}$ be the expected utility (8-84) when β_{hk} is the action used. Thus $\bar{U}_{hk}$ is the maximum of (8-84) over i. Then the maximum of (8-81) for a given h, which we have denoted by $\bar{U}_h$, is from (8-82) and (8-83)

$$\bar{U}_h = \sum_{k=1}^{s_h} \bar{U}_{hk} p_h(f_{hk}). \tag{8-85}$$

We can interpret $\bar{U}_h$ as being the maximum value of the expected utility, given that the experiment to be performed is $\mathfrak{R}_h$. It is the maximum expected utility in the sense that regardless of what the outcome of $\mathfrak{R}_h$ is, the decision maker selects the best action in the light of that outcome. To determine the experiment which should be performed, we simply select the one which yields the largest value of $\bar{U}_h$.

Let us now summarize the computational technique we have developed for solving the two stage decision problem. The solution to this problem determines the experiment which should be performed, and in addition, determines the action to be taken for each possible outcome of this experiment. To solve the problem we first select an experiment $\mathfrak{R}_h$ and a particular outcome of this experiment f_{hk}. For this experiment and this outcome we determine using the procedure developed in Section 8-1 the optimal action β_{hk} to be taken and the corresponding expected utility $\bar{U}_{hk}$. Observe that $\bar{U}_{hk}$ is the maximum expected utility after $\mathfrak{R}_h$ is performed, given that the outcome was f_{hk}. We repeat this for every possible outcome of $\mathfrak{R}_h$. Then we compute $\bar{U}_h$ from (8-85) which is the maximum expected utility given that $\mathfrak{R}_h$ will be performed, but prior to actually performing $\mathfrak{R}_h$. Finally, the experiment to be performed is the one which yields the largest number $\bar{U}_h$. To solve the problem we see that a whole series of single stage decision problems must be solved, one for each outcome of each of the experiments. This can be a very laborious undertaking if the computations are to be made by hand. However, it is somewhat less laborious than simply computing (8-80) for every strategy and picking the strategy which yields the largest value of (8-80). The reason is that in order to determine the action to take when $\mathfrak{R}_h$ yields the outcome f_{hk}, it is unnecessary to evaluate the whole sum (8-80) each time; it is only necessary to evaluate (8-82), that part of the sum which involves the outcome f_{hk}. This observation reduces very considerably the effort needed to solve the problem.

The procedure we have suggested for solving the two stage problem under consideration can be looked upon as one in which we progressively work our way back from the terminal branches of the decision tree to the node where the decision maker selects the experiment to perform. This is illustrated in Figure 8-12. The clarity of the representation is improved

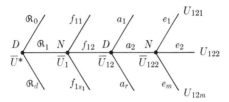

FIGURE 8-12

here if one moves the random experiment representing the determination of the state of nature from the beginning of the tree to the end. The sequence of computations is the following

$$\overline{U}_{hki} = \sum_{j=1}^{m} U_{hij} p_h(e_j | f_{hk}) \quad \text{for each } h, k, \text{ and } i; \tag{8-86}$$

$$\overline{U}_{hk} = \max_{i} \overline{U}_{hki}; \tag{8-87}$$

$$\overline{U}_{h} = \sum_{k=1}^{s_h} \overline{U}_{hk} p_h(f_{hk}); \tag{8-88}$$

$$\overline{U}^{*} = \max_{h} \overline{U}_{h}. \tag{8-89}$$

Very frequently, one will be working with problems in which costs are used rather than profits or utilities. While one could interpret the negatives of the costs as utilities, it is inconvenient to introduce many minus signs. This is unnecessary because if we replace the U's in (8-86) through (8-89) by K's, where the K's are costs or expected costs (the subscripts remaining unchanged), the procedure for solving the problem is once again given by (8-86) through (8-89), except that the max in (8-87) and (8-89) is replaced by a min.

8-13 EXAMPLES

We shall now give some examples illustrating the theory developed in the previous section. Because of the length of the numerical computations involved, the examples will be restricted to very simple ones.

1. A firm which designs and builds automatic electronic control devices markets one device which controls high temperature and pressure reactors for the chemical process industry.   Part of the manufacturing process involves alignment of these devices under simulated operating conditions. The systems are then shipped to field offices where installation in the customer's plant is handled.   For one reason or another, the systems occasionally get out of alignment in transportation.   In the field a simple piece of checkout equipment is used to determine whether the system seems to be in alignment.   Unfortunately, the checkout equipment cannot simulate actual operating conditions too well, and thus it does not always indicate correctly whether the system is indeed in alignment.   The checkout test can then be looked at as a random experiment performed to obtain information on the state of nature.   Let us suppose that there are just two states of nature: e_1, the system is in alignment, and e_2, the system is not in alignment.   The checkout equipment gives one of two readings: f_1, which says that the system is in alignment, and f_2, which says that the system is not in alignment.   The conditional probabilities of these readings given the state of nature are

$$p(f_1|e_1) = 0.95; \quad p(f_2|e_1) = 0.05; \tag{8-90}$$

$$p(f_1|e_2) = 0.1; \quad p(f_2|e_2) = 0.9. \tag{8-91}$$

At a particular field office, past experience has shown that ten percent of the time the systems get out of alignment during transportation from the plant.   Each system is tested using the checkout equipment.   Based on the outcome of the test, the system is either installed as is at the customer's plant, call this action a_1, or some engineers are sent out from the plant to align the system, call this action a_2.   The cost of bringing engineers out from the plant to align the system is $500.   If a system which is out of alignment is installed in the customer's plant, the cost of correcting things varies somewhat, but the expected value of this cost is estimated to be $20,000.   The cost of performing the test with the checkout equipment amounts to $50.

Let us show that it is definitely worthwhile to use the checkout equipment, and also determine the expected cost reduction per installation on using it.   To do this, it is only necessary to determine the expected cost associated with alignment on installing a system when the checkout equipment is not used, and that when it is.   The difference will be the expected savings per system installed as a result of using the checkout equipment.

In Table 8-6 we have shown the payoff table using costs for the case where no checkout is made.   When the checkout equipment is used, one adds the $50 cost of the checkout to each entry in the table.

TABLE 8-6

PAYOFF TABLE FOR EXAMPLE

	e_1	e_2
a_1	0	20,000
a_2	500	500

The prior probabilities of e_1 and e_2 are $p_1 = 0.90$ and $p_2 = 0.10$. Given that $\mathcal{R}_0$ is performed, that is, no checkout is made, the expected cost if action a_1 is taken is $0.10(20,000) = \$2000$, and if action a_2 is taken is $\$500$. Thus the optimal action when no checkout is made is a_2, that is, engineers from the plant should come out to align the system and the expected cost associated with this action is $\$500$. Thus in the terminology of the previous section $S^*(0) = \{\mathcal{R}_0, a_2\}$ and $\bar{K}_0 = \bar{K}_{00} = \$500$ (since there is only one outcome of $\mathcal{R}_0$, call it f_0, which can be imagined to say "no information").

Consider now the case where the checkout equipment is used. We first determine the optimal action to take and the corresponding expected cost for each of the two possible readings on the checkout equipment. Suppose that the reading is f_1, which says that the system is in alignment. The posterior probabilities of the states of nature are then

$$p(e_1|f_1) = \frac{p(f_1|e_1)p_1}{p(f_1)}; \quad p(e_2|f_1) = \frac{p(f_1|e_2)p_2}{p(f_1)}, \tag{8-92}$$

and from (8-90) and (8-91)

$$p(f_1) = p(f_1|e_1)p_1 + p(f_1|e_2)p_2 = 0.95(0.9) + 0.1(0.1) = 0.865, \tag{8-93}$$

so that

$$p(e_1|f_1) = \frac{0.855}{0.865} = 0.989; \quad p(e_2|f_1) = \frac{0.1(0.1)}{0.865} = 0.011. \tag{8-94}$$

The expected cost, exclusive of the cost of using the checkout equipment, when action a_1 is taken is $0.011(20,000) = \$220$ and is $\$500$ if action a_2 is taken. The expected costs including the cost of making the checkout are then $\$270$ and $\$550$, respectively. The appropriate action to take when the reading is f_1 is then a_1, that is, install without alignment and the expected cost is $\$270$, so that $\bar{K}_{11} = \$270$ when we denote by $\mathcal{R}_1$ the experiment in which the checkout equipment is used.

Consider next the case where the checkout equipment gives the reading f_2. Then the posterior probabilities of the states of nature are

$$p(e_1|f_2) = \frac{p(f_2|e_1)p_1}{p(f_2)}; \quad p(e_2|f_2) = \frac{p(f_2|e_2)p_2}{p(f_2)}, \tag{8-95}$$

and

$$p(f_2) = p(f_2|e_1)p_1 + p(f_2|e_2)p_2 = 0.05(0.9) + 0.9(0.1) = 0.135.$$

Thus

$$p(e_1|f_2) = \frac{0.045}{0.135} = 0.333; \quad p(e_2|f_2) = \frac{0.09}{0.135} = 0.667. \qquad (8\text{-}96)$$

The expected cost if action a_1 is taken (exclusive of the cost of the check-out) is $0.667(20,000) = \$13,340$ or $\$13,390$ including the cost of the check-out. If action a_2 is taken, the cost including the checkout cost is \$550. The smallest of these is \$550, so that $\bar{K}_{12} = \$550$, and the optimal action to take is a_2. Thus $S^*(1) = \{\mathscr{R}_1, \langle a_1, a_2 \rangle\}$, and the expected cost before the checkout is performed, given that the optimal action is taken for either reading after the checkout is performed, is

$$\bar{K}_1 = p(f_1)\bar{K}_{11} + p(f_2)\bar{K}_{12} = 0.865(270) + 0.135(550),$$

so that $\bar{K}_1 = \$308$. Now $\bar{K}_0 = \$500$; hence the expected savings per system installed resulting from using the checkout equipment is \$192. The decision tree for the above problem, which also illustrates the steps in performing the computations, is shown in Figure 8-13.

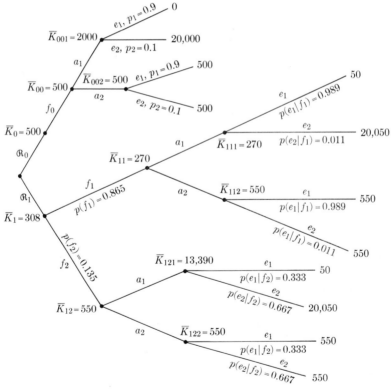

FIGURE 8-13

It is of interest to compute the cost of uncertainty for this example. If it was possible to determine ahead of time what the state of nature was, then the system would be installed directly at no cost if it was e_1, and engineers would be sent from the plant to align it at a cost of \$500 if it was e_2. The expected cost under certainty is then

$$0.9(0) + 0.1(500) = \$50.$$

We have seen above the best one can do using the checkout equipment is to reduce the expected cost to \$308. The expected cost of uncertainty is thus \$258 per system installed.

2. A television producer buys a certain resistor from a supplier in lots of 10,000 units. Previous experience has suggested that the lot fraction defective will, to an adequate degree of approximation, take on only two values 0.005 or 0.03 with the prior probability of the smaller value being 0.90. The producer checks on the supplier's quality by taking a sample from each lot and determining the number of defectives r in the sample. Based on the value of r, the lot is either accepted or is rejected. Every resistor in a rejected lot is inspected, and defectives are replaced by good units. It does not cost the producer anything to replace a defective by a good unit because the supplier replaces every defective returned to him with a good resistor (and also pays the cost of returning the defectives). However, on the average, it costs \$0.015 to inspect each resistor, so that the cost of inspecting an entire lot is \$150. When a lot is inspected 100 percent, we shall assume that the lot sent to production has no defectives in it. This implies that we are assuming that the inspectors do not make any mistakes allowing some defectives to slip through. Any defective resistor which goes into production will be caught, but costs \$1.00 to be replaced.

The producer is considering two alternative sampling plans, call them $\mathcal{R}_1$ and $\mathcal{R}_2$. In $\mathcal{R}_1$ a sample of 100 resistors is selected at random and the number of defectives in the sample is determined. In $\mathcal{R}_2$ a sample of 200 resistors is selected at random and the number of defectives in the sample is determined. The producer would like to determine an optimal strategy for each of these experiments and then determine which of the two experiments he should perform.

Consider first the case where $\mathcal{R}_1$ is performed. The cost of performing this experiment is $0.015(100) = \$1.50$. There may be an additional cost of setting up the experiment which is independent of the size of the sample. We need not concern ourselves with this cost here because it will be incurred regardless of whether $\mathcal{R}_1$ or $\mathcal{R}_2$ is performed and will thus have no influence on the comparisons. The number of defectives r in the sample can be $0, 1, 2, \ldots, 100$. The conditional probabilities $p(r|0.005)$ and $p(r|0.03)$ of obtaining r defectives when the lot fraction defective is 0.005 and 0.03, respectively, are hypergeometric probabilities, but they can be approximated by the Poisson distribution because the sample size is small as is the lot fraction defective.   Thus

$$p(r|0.005) \doteq p(r; 0.5); \quad p(r|0.03) \doteq p(r; 3).$$

Let us now proceed to determine the optimal action to take for each possible value of r.   Denote by a_1 the action that the lot is accepted and by a_2 the action that the lot is rejected and inspected 100 percent.   The costs including the cost of performing the experiment are shown in the payoff table in Table 8-7.   We have assumed that any defectives found

TABLE 8-7

PAYOFF TABLE FOR EXAMPLE

	e_1	e_2
a_1	$51.5 - r$	$301.5 - r$
a_2	150	150

in the sample are replaced by good units.   We have denoted by e_1 the state of nature that the lot fraction defective is 0.005, while e_2 refers to a lot fraction defective of 0.03.

The posterior probabilities of the states of nature, given that r defectives are found in the sample, are

$$p(e_1|r) = \frac{p(r; 0.5)p_1}{p(r)}; \quad p(e_2|r) = \frac{p(r; 3)p_2}{p(r)}, \tag{8-97}$$

and

$$p(r) = p(r; 0.5)p_1 + p(r; 3)p_2. \tag{8-98}$$

Consider first the case where $r = 0$.   From Table C at the rear of the text

$$p(0) = 0.6065(0.9) + 0.0498(0.1) = 0.5508. \tag{8-99}$$

Then

$$p(e_1|0) = \frac{0.5458}{0.5508} = 0.991; \quad p(e_2|0) = \frac{0.00498}{0.5508} = 0.009.$$

The expected cost, if action a_1 is taken, is

$$51.5(0.991) + 301.5(0.009) = \$53.75,$$

whereas if action a_2 is taken, the cost is \$150.   Thus the lot should be accepted when no defectives are found in the sample and $\bar{K}_{10} = 53.75$.

Consider next the case where $r = 1$.   Then

$$p(1) = 0.3033(0.9) + 0.1494(0.1) = 0.2879, \tag{8-100}$$

and

$$p(e_1|1) = \frac{0.2730}{0.2879} = 0.948; \quad p(e_2|1) = \frac{0.01494}{0.2879} = 0.052.$$

The expected cost on taking action a_1 is

$$50.5(0.948) + 300.5(0.052) = \$63.7,$$

while it is \$150 if action a_2 is taken. Therefore the lot should also be accepted if one defective is found in the sample and $\bar{K}_{11} = 63.7$.

Suppose now that two defectives are found in the sample. In this case

$$p(2) = 0.0758(0.9) + 0.2240(0.1) = 0.0906, \qquad (8\text{-}101)$$

and

$$p(e_1|2) = \frac{0.0682}{0.0906} = 0.753; \quad p(e_2|2) = \frac{0.0224}{0.0906} = 0.247.$$

If action a_1 is taken, the expected cost is

$$49.5(0.753) + 299.5(0.247) = \$111.5,$$

whereas if a_2 is taken, the cost is \$150. Thus the lot should be accepted when two defectives are found in the sample and $\bar{K}_{12} = 111.5$.

If three defectives are found in the sample, we have

$$p(3) = 0.0126(0.9) + 0.2240(0.1) = 0.0337, \qquad (8\text{-}102)$$

and

$$p(e_1|3) = \frac{0.0113}{0.0337} = 0.336; \quad p(e_2|3) = \frac{0.0224}{0.0337} = 0.664.$$

If action a_1 is taken in this case, the expected cost is

$$48.5(0.336) + 298.5(0.664) = \$214,$$

whereas if a_2 is taken, the cost is \$150. Thus when three defectives are found the action to take is a_2 and, consequently, $\bar{K}_{13} = 150$.

At this point we can observe that if action a_2 should be taken when $r = 3$, then action a_2 should be taken for any $r > 3$ also, since if $r > 3$, $p(e_2|r) > p(e_2|3)$ and the expected cost on taking action a_1 will be even greater than for $r = 3$, and hence $\bar{K}_{1r} = 150$ for $r > 3$. Therefore, we have determined an optimal strategy for $\mathfrak{R}_1$: It is the acceptance of the lot when the number of defectives in the sample is less than or equal to 2 and the rejection of the lot otherwise. Here we have a very simple decision rule that can be used when $\mathfrak{R}_1$ is performed. The number 2 is frequently referred to in quality control as the *acceptance number c.* In general, if c is the acceptance number, the lot is accepted if $r \leq c$ and rejected if $r > c$.

Let us now determine $\bar{K}_1$, the expected cost associated with putting a lot through the sampling plan. This is the expected cost before $\mathfrak{R}_1$ is performed, given that the best action is always taken in the light of the outcome of $\mathfrak{R}_1$. Thus

$$\bar{K}_1 = \bar{K}_{10}p(0) + \bar{K}_{11}p(1) + \bar{K}_{12}p(2) + \bar{K}_{13}p(3)$$
$$+ \cdots + \bar{K}_{1,100}p(100). \qquad (8\text{-}103)$$

Then on using the $\bar{K}_{1r}$ values obtained above and the $p(r)$ from (8-99) through (8-101),

$$\bar{K}_1 = 53.8(0.5508) + 63.7(0.2879) + 111.5(0.0906) + 150 \sum_{r=3}^{100} p(r).$$

Inasmuch as $\sum_{r=0}^{100} p(r) = 1$ if the exact hypergeometric probabilities were used, this will be very close to being true when the Poisson approximation is used, and therefore

$$\sum_{r=3}^{100} p(r) = 1 - p(0) - p(1) - p(2) = 1 - 0.9293 = 0.0707.$$

Consequently,

$$\bar{K}_1 = 29.6 + 18.4 + 10.1 + 10.6 = \$68.7. \tag{8-104}$$

We can easily compute the expected cost of uncertainty when $\mathcal{R}_1$ is used. If the state of nature could be determined ahead of time, action a_1 would be best if the state of nature was e_1, and a_2 if the state of nature was e_2. Thus the expected cost under certainty is

$$0.9(50) + 0.1(150) = \$60,$$

since 50 defectives go into production when e_1 is the state of nature. To determine the expected cost of uncertainty, we must know the fixed cost involved in setting up the experiment. We have not specified this; call it λ. Then the expected cost on performing $\mathcal{R}_1$ is $\lambda + 68.7$, so that the expected cost of uncertainty is $\lambda + 8.7$. We might note that if no experiment was performed, it would always be best to take action a_1 with the expected cost per lot being

$$0.9(50) + 0.1(300) = \$75.$$

Thus it is worthwhile to perform $\mathcal{R}_1$ if $\lambda < \$6.30$, but it cannot yield an expected cost reduction of more than $\$6.30$ per lot. The expected cost of uncertainty if no experiment is performed is only $\$15$ per lot. Of course, when many lots are used per year, the savings on using $\mathcal{R}_1$ may amount to several thousand dollars per year.

Let us now turn to $\mathcal{R}_2$ where the sample size is 200. In this case

$$p(r|0.005) \doteq p(r; 1); \quad p(r|0.03) \doteq p(r; 6).$$

We shall not trouble the reader with all of the details in this case. In Table 8-8, we have summarized the results, giving $p(r)$, the action to take, and $\bar{K}_{2r}$. Since it is optimal to take action a_2 when $r = 4$, it is optimal to take a_2 for every $r > 4$. Hence the optimal strategy when $\mathcal{R}_2$ is performed is to accept the lot if three or less defectives are found and to reject the lot otherwise. The acceptance number is then $c = 3$. The expected cost per lot when $\mathcal{R}_2$ is performed is

TABLE 8-8

RESULTS OF COMPUTATIONS FOR $\mathcal{R}_2$

r	0	1	2	3	4
$p(r)$	0.331	0.332	0.170	0.064	0.027
Action	a_1	a_1	a_1	a_1	a_2
K_{2r}	53.2	53.5	57.2	85.0	150

$$\bar{K}_2 = 53.2(0.331) + 53.5(0.332) + 57.2(0.170)$$
$$+ 85.0(0.064) + 150 \sum_{r=4}^{200} p(r).$$

Now

$$\sum_{r=4}^{200} p(r) = 1 - 0.331 - 0.332 - 0.170 - 0.064 = 1 - 0.897 = 0.103,$$

so

$$\bar{K}_2 = 17.6 + 17.8 + 9.7 + 5.4 + 15.5 = \$66.0.$$

Since $K_1 = \$68.7$, we see that it is preferable to perform $\mathcal{R}_2$ rather than $\mathcal{R}_1$, the expected cost reduction per lot on using $\mathcal{R}_2$ being about \$3.00. This expected cost reduction per lot on using $\mathcal{R}_2$ rather than $\mathcal{R}_1$ is not large in absolute value, but it is large compared to the possible cost reduction which could be obtained using $\mathcal{R}_1$ rather than not using any experiment. In this sense then, $\mathcal{R}_2$ is much better than $\mathcal{R}_1$. The reader should note that the variable costs of performing $\mathcal{R}_1$ and $\mathcal{R}_2$ have been included in $\bar{K}_1$ and $\bar{K}_2$, and hence the additional cost of performing $\mathcal{R}_2$ has been accounted for.

The procedure which we have introduced in this example could be used to determine the optimal sample size rather than merely for comparing two or more experiments with specified sample sizes. This would be done by computing for every sample size n, the optimal acceptance number c for the given n, and $\bar{K}_n$, the expected cost per lot before the experiment is performed. The optimal n would be the one which yielded the smallest $\bar{K}_n$. This would yield the best of all possible experiments of the type where one selects a sample from the lot and determines the number of defectives in the sample. The specification of a sample size n and an acceptance number c defines what we referred to on p. 267 as a single sampling plan. We have seen here how to determine the best sampling plan for the situation under consideration. It is exceedingly tedious to find the best plan making the computations by hand (although a number of shortcuts can be introduced). However, the computations could easily be carried out on a computer. The determination of sampling plans is an important problem in practice. The traditional procedure for determining sampling plans is different from the procedure suggested here. The traditional approach will be considered in the next chapter.

REFERENCES

The books by Schlaifer, and Blackwell and Girshick referred to in Chapter 4 are also useful references for this chapter. In addition, the following two works are of interest.

1. Chernoff, H., and L. E. Moses, *Elementary Decision Theory*. Wiley, New York, 1959.

    This book, written at an elementary level, discusses exclusively cases where experiments are performed to gain information about the state of nature. Considerable attention is devoted to procedures which do not make use of prior probabilities.

2. Raiffa, H., and R. Schlaifer, *Applied Statistical Decision Theory*. Harvard University, Boston, 1961.

    This is a fairly advanced treatment and extension of some of the material introduced in Schlaifer's book. The "applied" in the title is perhaps a little misleading because the prospective reader who is expecting a lot of practical examples and discussion of applications will be disappointed.

PROBLEMS

Section 8-2

1. A decision maker is considering what action to take in a decision situation which is repeated frequently and for which there are three states of nature e_1, e_2, and e_3. From historical data he has observed that e_1 occurred 15 percent of the time; e_2, 30 percent of the time; and e_3, 55 percent of the time. The state of nature is determined before he makes a decision, and an experiment $\mathcal{R}$, which has two outcomes f_1 and f_2, is performed to gain additional information. On performing $\mathcal{R}$, the outcome f_2 is obtained. If $p(f_2|e_1) = 0.30$, $p(f_2|e_2) = 0.50$, and $p(f_2|e_3) = 0.10$, what probabilities should be used for the states of nature in deciding what action to select? Give an intuitive explanation as to why these are the appropriate probabilities. Does the result depend in any way on how many outcomes $\mathcal{R}$ has?

2. A decision maker is considering a decision problem in which there are four states of nature to which he has assigned the following prior probabilities $p_1 = 0.20$, $p_2 = 0.25$, $p_3 = 0.35$, $p_4 = 0.20$. To obtain more information about the state of nature, he performs an experiment $\mathcal{R}$ which yields the outcome f_1, the conditional probabilities for which are

$$p(f_1|e_1) = 0.10, \quad p(f_1|e_2) = 0.80, \quad p(f_1|e_3) = 0.10, \quad p(f_1|e_4) = 0.05.$$

What are the probabilities of the states of nature which the decision maker should use in selecting the action to take?

3. A decision maker is considering a decision problem with three states of nature to which he has assigned the prior probabilities $p_1 = 0.30$, $p_2 = 0.50$, and $p_3 = 0.20$. He performs an experiment $\mathcal{R}$ to obtain more information about the state of nature. $\mathcal{R}$ yields the outcome f_1 for which the conditional probabilities are $p(f_1|e_1) = 0.4$, $p(f_1|e_2) = 0.4$, $p(f_1|e_3) = 0.4$. What are the posterior probabilities for the states of nature? What is the intuitive explanation for this? Can it be the case that some outcomes of $\mathcal{R}$ will not give any information about the state of nature while others will? Construct a numerical example to illustrate this.

4. Consider a decision problem in which the prior probabilities of the states of nature are denoted by p_j. Suppose now that a random experiment $\mathcal{R}_1$ is performed to gain information on the state of nature and it yields the outcome f_{1k}. Assume that Bayes' law is used to compute posterior probabilities $p(e_j|f_{1k})$. Imagine that another random experiment $\mathcal{R}_2$ is then performed to gain still more information about the state of nature and yields the outcome f_{2h} (the probability of which may depend on the outcome of $\mathcal{R}_1$ as well as on the state of nature). Bayes' law is then applied to compute posterior probabilities $p(e_j|f_{1k}, f_{2h})$, using the $p(e_j|f_{1k})$ as prior probabilities. Alternatively, one could consider $\mathcal{R}_1$ and $\mathcal{R}_2$ to represent a single random experiment $\mathcal{R}$. Then Bayes' law could be applied to compute posterior probabilities $p_1(e_j|f_{1k}, f_{2h})$, using the p_j as prior probabilities. Prove that it is always true that

$$p(e_j|f_{1k}, f_{2h}) = p_1(e_j|f_{1k}, f_{2h}).$$

In other words, prove that if $\mathcal{R}$ can be decomposed into two or more random experiments, the results of these experiments can all be used at once or can be digested sequentially one after the other and the results obtained will be the same in either case. Hint: The experiment which determines the state of nature, $\mathcal{R}_1$ and $\mathcal{R}_2$, can be looked at collectively as a three stage experiment.

5. For a single stage decision problem having four states of nature, an experiment $\mathcal{R}$ is performed to obtain more information and yields the outcome f_1, the conditional probabilities for which are

$$p(f_1|e_1) = 0.1, \quad p(f_1|e_2) = 0.8, \quad p(f_1|e_3) = 0.1, \quad p(f_1|e_4) = 0.05.$$

Determine the posterior probabilities for the states of nature when the prior probabilities are

(a) $p_1 = 0.3$, $p_2 = 0.1$, $p_3 = 0.4$, $p_4 = 0.2$;
(b) $p_1 = 0.2$, $p_2 = 0.6$, $p_3 = 0.1$, $p_4 = 0.1$.

6. For a single stage decision problem having four states of nature, an experiment $\mathcal{R}$ is performed to obtain more information and yields the outcome f_1, the conditional probabilities for which are

$$p(f_1|e_1) = 0.3, \quad p(f_1|e_2) = 0.6, \quad p(f_1|e_3) = 0.4, \quad p(f_1|e_4) = 0.2.$$

Determine the posterior probabilities for the states of nature when the prior probabilities are

(a) $p_1 = 0.2$, $p_2 = 0.4$, $p_3 = 0.3$, $p_4 = 0.1$;
(b) $p_1 = 0.5$, $p_2 = 0.2$, $p_3 = 0.1$, $p_4 = 0.2$.

Section 8-3

1. Determine the expected cost of uncertainty for the example worked out in this section if the seismic experiment costs $1000 to perform.

2. What action should the independent operator take if the seismic experiment yields the outcome f_2? What is his expected profit in this case? What is the expected cost of uncertainty in this case if the seismic experiment costs $1000 to perform?

3. What action should the independent take if the seismic experiment yields the outcome f_1? What is his expected profit in this case? What is the expected cost of uncertainty in this case if the seismic experiment costs $1000 to perform?

4. What action should the independent take if the seismic experiment yields the outcome f_3 and the conditional probabilities are not those shown in Table 8-1, but are instead: $p(f_3|e_1) = 0.10$, $p(f_3|e_2) = 0.30$, and $p(f_3|e_3) = 0.20$?

5. Suppose that the independent oil operator decides that in addition to performing a seismic study, he will do a magnetic study of the region. This employs a magnetometer, which gives an indication of the earth's magnetic field. For simplicity, suppose that the magnetometer gives only three readings g_1 (high), g_2 (medium), and g_3 (low) and the conditional probabilities of these readings, given the state of nature are those in Table 8-9. The outcome of the magnetic study does not depend in any way on the outcome of the seismic experiment. What should the operator do when the seismic experiment yields the outcome f_2 and the magnetometer gives the reading g_3? What is his expected profit in this case? What is the

TABLE 8-9

	e_1	e_2	e_3
g_1	0.60	0.30	0.20
g_2	0.30	0.60	0.50
g_3	0.10	0.10	0.30

expected cost of uncertainty if the magnetometer experiment costs $2000 to perform?

6. For the situation described in Problem 5, what action should the operator take if the seismic experiment yields the outcome f_3 and the magnetometer gives the reading g_1? What is the expected profit in this case, and what is the expected cost of uncertainty?

7. Solve the example in this section, using regrets and minimizing the expected regret. Is the minimum expected regret, the expected cost of uncertainty in this case? How does the cost of the experiment enter in?

8. A pharmaceutical manufacturer is trying to decide whether to undertake a widespread marketing and sales campaign for a new drug. The decision hinges on the question of how many people may be adversely affected by the drug. The state of nature can be imagined to be described by p the probability that the drug will adversely affect any particular individual, that is, the long run fraction of individuals that will be adversely affected. It is felt that for purposes of making a decision, it can be imagined p can take on any three values 0.0005, 0.002, or 0.01. Let us refer to the three states of nature as e_1, e_2, and e_3, respectively. If the drug is marketed, the regrets are 0, \$500,000, \$2,000,000 when the state of nature turns out to be e_1, e_2, or e_3, respectively. If the drug is not marketed, the corresponding regrets are \$5,000,000, \$1,000,000, and 0. Based on the extensive animal experiments, the firm estimates the prior probabilities of the states of nature to be 0.60, 0.35, and 0.05, respectively. To gain more information about the reaction on humans, clinical tests on 500 human patients were carried out, and it was found that 3 showed adverse reaction to the drug. Should the firm market the drug?

9. A publisher is trying to decide whether to publish a manuscript he has received. In making a decision he feels that it is sufficient to imagine that there are just four states of nature which are e_1, the book will sell an average of 500 copies per year; e_2, the average annual sales will be 1500 copies; e_3, the average annual sales will be 3000 copies; e_4, the average annual sales will be 10,000 copies. The prior probabilities which he assigns to these states of nature are respectively 0.30, 0.40, 0.25, and 0.05. The discounted profits if he publishes the book are for each of the states of nature $-\$30,000$, \$4000, \$12,000, and \$100,000. The discounted profit is 0 if he does not publish it. To gain additional information, he sends the book to a reviewer who says that he likes the manuscript. From previous experience with the reviewer, the publisher feels that the conditional probabilities of the states of nature given this response from the reviewer are respectively 0.10, 0.30, 0.50, 0.10. Should he publish the book? What is the expected cost of uncertainty?

Section 8-4

1. What is the expected cost of uncertainty in the example studied in this section if the cost of performing the experiment is \$15?

2. What action should the producer take if he finds ten defectives in the sample rather than 25? What is the expected cost? What is the expected cost of uncertainty if the cost of performing the experiment is \$15?

3. Suppose that the producer takes a sample of 2000 resistors instead of 1000. What action should he take if 35 defectives are found in the sample?

4. Solve the example in this section using regrets.

5. Suppose that on reviewing his records, the producer finds that he made an error in his original assessment and decides that the prior probabilities should be $p_1 = 0.70$, $p_2 = 0.2995$, and $p_3 = 0.0005$. Under these conditions what action should be taken when he finds 25 defectives in the sample?

6. Suppose that the producer decided that a lot fraction defective of 0.02 was also a possible state of nature. He now assigns prior probabilities of 0.70, 0.25, 0.025, and 0.025 to the lot fraction defectives 0.001, 0.005, 0.02, and 0.03, respectively. What action should he take in this case if 25 defectives are found in the sample?

Section 8-5

1. If one uses the model developed in this section, what action should be taken if ten defectives are found in the sample?

2. Suppose that the mean and standard deviation of the prior distribution are $\mu_0 = 0.002$ and $\sigma_0 = 0.008$. Obtain the form of the prior distribution and sketch its graph. What action should the decision maker take if ten defectives are found in the sample?

3. Can you determine the posterior density function for the situation being considered in this section if the prior distribution is assumed to be normal? What are the difficulties involved? Would the normal distribution be a reasonable one to use for the prior distribution? Why or why not?

4. Re-solve Problem 8 for Section 8-3 under the assumption that the prior distribution for p is a gamma density with mean 0.004 and standard deviation 0.003. Imagine that the discounted profit U, if the drug is sold, is related to p by $U = 10^7 - 0.5 \times 10^9 p$, and that a loss of one million dollars is involved if the drug is not marketed.

Section 8-6

1. Compute the expected cost of uncertainty for the example of this section if the cost of performing the experiment is $25.

2. What action should be taken if the experiment yields an average breaking strength of $\bar{\xi} = 49$ lb?

3. What is the smallest value of $\bar{x}$ that would result in action a_1 being taken?

4. Suppose that the manufacturer tested 50 pieces of yarn rather than 25. What is the smallest value of $\bar{x}$ that would result in action a_1 being taken in this case?

Section 8-7

1. Derive (8-30) in detail.

2. How many acres of tomatoes should the production manager contract for ahead of the season if he has no opportunity to determine what is taking place in the current year, but must base his decision strictly on historical data?

3. Develop a model which generalizes the one developed in the text to the case where surplus tomatoes can be disposed of at a price of C_3 dollars per ton, $C_3 < C_1$.

4. Apply the model developed in Problem 3 to the situation studied in the text for the case where $C_3 = 15 per ton.

5. How many acres should the production manager contract for ahead of the season if the estimated yields on the three acres are 54, 55, and 59?

6. Re-solve the problem studied in Section 8-6 under the assumption that the prior distribution for the mean breaking strength is normal with mean 47 lb and standard deviation 2 lb.

7. A Florida orange grower must decide each year whether to sell his oranges to a local processor of frozen orange juice or to sell them to a dealer who will market them as fresh fruit. The best action to take depends on the mean diameter of the oranges. This varies from season to season depending on growing conditions. If he sells them for frozen juice processing, his profit as a function of the mean diameter μ (measured in inches) is $15,000 + 200\mu$ dollars and is $5000 + 4000\mu$ if he sells them for fresh fruit. The diameter x of any orange can be looked upon as a random variable with mean μ and standard deviation 0.75 in. He feels that for the current year the prior distribution for μ is normal with mean 2.8 in. and standard deviation 0.6 in. One thousand oranges are selected at random after the oranges are picked, and the diameters are measured. The resulting average diameter is 2.2 in. What action should the grower take?

Section 8-9

1. Consider once again the example in Section 8-3. The producer in estimating the discounted profits assumed that the price per barrel of oil was going to be $4. Suppose that on reflection he decides, however, it may turn out to be $3 per barrel, with the probability that it will be $4 being 0.7. If the price turns out to be $3 per barrel, his discounted profits will be $-\$1,100,000$, $250,000$, and 1.2 million for the states of nature e_1, e_2, and e_3, respectively. Re-solve the problem under this new set of assumptions in two different ways, first treating the states of nature as being described by the values of two random variables, and then by averaging the profits corresponding to the different prices per barrel. Show that the same results are obtained either way.

2. Consider again the problem studied in Section 8-6. Suppose that the standard deviation of x is not always the same from batch to batch, but that it must be treated as a random variable in the same manner as the expected value of x. For simplicity, suppose that σ takes on only two values, 3 and 5, with probabilities 0.7 and 0.3, respectively. Assume that the value taken on by σ does not in any way depend on the expected value of x. Re-solve the example studied in Section 8-6 under this new set of assumptions.

3. Re-solve Problem 3 for Section 8-6 under the assumptions concerning the behavior of σ made in Problem 2 above.

Section 8-10

1. What is the expected cost of uncertainty for the example considered in this section if the experiment costs $200 to perform?

2. Determine the value of ρ in (8-59) if the prior distribution for the sulfur content has a mean of 0.04 and a standard deviation of 0.015.

3. Solve Problem 6 for Section 8-7 using the simplifications introduced in this section.

4. A manufacturer has the opportunity to purchase a lot of one million ball bearings that another manufacturer purchased from a foreign manufacturer and then due to a change in production plans could not use after they were delivered. The manufacturer who is considering purchasing the ball bearings is concerned about the surface hardness of the bearings. This hardness is measured using a special piece of equipment and is expressed as a hardness number. The hardness number x for any particular ball bearing can be imagined to be a random variable. The nature of the production process is such that σ_x is always essentially 20. However, μ_x can vary considerably from batch to batch, and thus must be considered to be a random variable. The manufacturer knows a little about the foreign manufacturer and on the basis of this assumes that the prior distribution for μ_x is normal with mean 80 and standard deviation 10. To gain more information, the manufacturer measures the hardness of 20 ball bearings. The average of the hardness numbers so obtained is 71. The manufacturer on the basis of this information must decide whether to buy the lot or to purchase a lot of the same quantity from a local manufacturer. The cost if he purchases the ball bearings from the local manufacturer will be $200,000. The local manufacturer controls the hardness very closely and thus there is essentially no uncertainty about μ_x for the ball bearings he produces. The cost if he purchases the foreign produced lot will be a random variable K, which is a function of μ_x and is $K = \$100,000 + 15,000 (80 - \mu_x)$. What action should the manufacturer take?

Section 8-11

1. Consider a single stage decision problem for which the payoff table is that shown in Table 8-10. The state of nature is determined before an action is selected, and a random experiment $\mathcal{R}$ is performed to gain more information about the state of nature. The conditional probabilities for the outcomes of $\mathcal{R}$ are given in Table 8-11. If the prior probabilities for the states of nature are $p_1 = 0.8$ and $p_2 = 0.2$, determine an optimal pure strategy S^* for the decision maker to use.

<table>
<tr><td colspan="3" align="center">TABLE 8-10</td></tr>
<tr><td></td><td>e_1</td><td>e_2</td></tr>
<tr><td>a_1</td><td>-5</td><td>20</td></tr>
<tr><td>a_2</td><td>-3</td><td>15</td></tr>
<tr><td>a_3</td><td>0</td><td>10</td></tr>
</table>

<table>
<tr><td colspan="3" align="center">TABLE 8-11</td></tr>
<tr><td></td><td>e_1</td><td>e_2</td></tr>
<tr><td>f_1</td><td>0.6</td><td>0.3</td></tr>
<tr><td>f_2</td><td>0.3</td><td>0.4</td></tr>
<tr><td>f_3</td><td>0.1</td><td>0.3</td></tr>
</table>

2. For the situation outlined in Problem 1, construct a strategy payoff table and determine the max-min, max-max, and Laplace strategies; the min-max regret strategy; and the optimism index strategy for every α, $0 \leq \alpha \leq 1$.

3. Use a graphical procedure to determine the max-min mixed strategy for the situation outlined in Problem 1, using the strategy payoff table constructed in Problem 2.

4. Use a graphical procedure to determine the mix-max regret mixed strategy for the situation outlined in Problem 1.

5. Determine the optimal strategy for the situation described in Problem 1, using the strategy payoff table constructed in Problem 2. Also, show that the same strategy is obtained as in Problem 1.

6. Use a graphical method and the strategy payoff table constructed in Problem 2 to determine the Bayes' mixed strategy. Show that this strategy is the same as that obtained in Problem 1.

7. Utilize the results of Problem 4 to determine a Bayes' mixed stragegy using regrets. Call this a Bayes' regret mixed strategy. Show that this strategy is the same as that obtained in Problem 1.

8. In Table 8-5 determine the Laplace strategy and the optimism index strategy for each α, $0 \le \alpha \le 1$.

9. When the prior probabilities are given by (8-5), show that S_{10} is the optimal strategy in Table 8-5.

Sections 8-12 and 8-13

1. Consider the problem studied in Section 8-3. If a seismic experiment costs $3000 to perform, is it worthwhile to perform it in the case under consideration?

2. Consider both the problem studied in Section 8-3 and the magnetometer experiment described in Problem 5 for that section. If the seismic experiment costs $3000 and the magnetic study $4000, which experiment is preferable if one and only one of them is to be performed?

3. For the situation outlined in Problem 2, is it worthwhile to perform both the seismic and magnetometer experiments?

4.° Generalize the theory developed in Section 8-12 to the case where the outcome of each experiment $\mathcal{R}_i$ is the value of a continuous random variable. Show how to determine the value of the experiment $\mathcal{R}_i$ before it is performed and then how to select the most suitable experiment.

5. If it cost $30,000 to perform the clinical test involving human beings referred to in Problem 8 of Section 8-3, would you have recommended that the test be made?

6. If it cost $2000 to test the ball bearings referred to in Problem 4 of Section 8-10, would it have appeared worthwhile a priori to perform the experiment?

° Problems marked with ° require a knowledge of calculus.

CHAPTER 9

CONNECTIONS WITH CLASSICAL STATISTICS

For my thoughts are not your thoughts,
neither are your ways my ways, . . .

Isaiah, 55:8

9-1 CLASSICAL STATISTICS

Problems of the type we discussed in the first part of the previous chapter
have received a great deal of attention from statisticians, and at least one
chapter of almost any statistics book is devoted to a study of them.
Interestingly enough, however, if we gave the reader several statistics
texts and pointed out the chapters which we claimed were dealing with the
same problems as studied in the previous chapter, he after examining these
texts might quite possibly see no connection whatever between the material
discussed in them and the material discussed in the previous chapter.
The reader would find no mention of costs or prior probabilities or posterior probabilities, or even actions.   Instead he would be reading material
dealing with what would be referred to as testing hypotheses.   The approach we introduced in Chapter 8 for making use of experimental results
in decision problems by means of Bayes' law is often referred to as the
Bayesian approach to statistics.   The alternative approach which one finds
in all standard statistics texts is now referred to as *the classical or objectivist
approach.*   We wish to devote a large part of this chapter to a discussion
of the classical approach and to pointing out some of the basic differences
between it and the Bayesian treatment.   No attempt will be made to
present a thorough study of hypothesis testing.   Only sufficient detail will
be given to make possible a comparison with Bayesian methods.

In addition to hypothesis testing, another but not independent area of
great interest in classical statistics is that of *estimation.*   Estimation, as
the name suggests, is concerned with the problem of trying to estimate

one or more parameters of some distribution by experimentation. We have already given attention to problems of this type, and we shall investigate them in somewhat more detail in this chapter.

To begin our discussion of classical statistics and its relation to the Bayesian approach, some of the simplest aspects of the subject known as hypothesis testing will be studied.

9-2 HYPOTHESES

Very frequently, one must deal with random variables whose distribution is not known in complete detail. For example, suppose that a coin is tossed ten times and the number of heads is noted. If x is the random variable representing the number of heads obtained, then x should have the binomial distribution $b(x; 10, p)$, where p is the probability of a head. However, we can never really know what p is, and therefore the distribution of x is not completely known. As another example, consider a process which turns out shafts for electric motors. Let x be the random variable representing the diameter of any shaft produced. It is never possible to know the distribution of x. The best one can do is determine approximately what it is. Thus one might assume that to an adequate approximation x has a normal distribution with a given mean and variance. Any conjecture about the distribution of a random variable x is referred to in classical statistics as a *hypothesis*. For example, one might make the hypothesis that x has a normal distribution, or the hypothesis that the value of p in $b(x; n,p)$ is 0.15.

Is there any way one can prove that a hypothesis about some distribution is correct or is false? It is important to note that in general there is no way in which this can be done. By performing random experiments which in one way or another involve the distribution, one can gather data which may strongly indicate that the hypothesis is false or true, but normally no procedure exists by which one could ever demonstrate incontrovertibly that the hypothesis is true or false. There are exceptions to this statement, however. For example, let x be the random variable representing the number of defective capacitors in a sample of size n selected at random from a lot of size N. Then we expect that x has the hypergeometric distribution $h(x; n,p,N)$. A hypothesis concerning the distribution of x might be that the lot fraction defective p has some specified value. This hypothesis could be proved or disproved simply by checking every capacitor in the lot and determining the fraction defective. This situation is unusual, however. There exists no way, for example, that one could prove that the mean of the distribution for the diameter of motor shafts turned out by some production process was indeed one inch.

Let us now illustrate by a simple example how a random experiment can be used to "test" a hypothesis. This example will point up an asymmetry in the testing procedure which is very frequently encountered. The experiment will have the characteristic that it may very well convince us that the hypothesis is false, but it cannot convince us that the hypothesis is true. What we have in mind here will become clear as the example is studied.

Suppose we make the hypothesis that a given coin is fair. We can think of this as making a hypothesis about the distribution of a random variable, since the number of heads x obtained on n tosses is a random variable having the binomial distribution $b(x; n,p)$, and we are making the hypothesis that $p = \frac{1}{2}$. Assume that this coin is tossed 100 times, and 98 heads are obtained. Although this could happen with a fair coin (this event has a positive probability of occurring), most individuals would feel that the outcome of this experiment provided sufficient evidence to abandon the hypothesis that the coin is fair. What is the justification for reaching this conclusion? It is not based on the fact that the probability of obtaining 98 heads is very small if the coin is fair, since the probability of obtaining 50 heads is also small. Rather it is based on the following type of reasoning. The expected value of x when $n = 100$ and $p = \frac{1}{2}$ is $\mu = 50$, and the standard deviation of x is $\sigma = \sqrt{25} = 5$. For a μ of 50, $b(x; n,p)$ can be approximated reasonably well by the normal distribution, and we know that the probability that $|x - \mu| > \sigma$ is about 0.3173 and that $|x - \mu| > 2\sigma$ is about 0.0455 and that $|x - \mu| > 3\sigma$ is about 0.003. Now $3\sigma = 15$. Hence, only about 3 times in 1000 would x be greater than 65 or less than 35. On the other hand, if $p = 0.80$, for example, the probability that $x > 65$ is very large. This type of reasoning leads one to suspect very strongly that $p > \frac{1}{2}$. The above discussion has thus illustrated how the outcome of an experiment could well lead an individual to abandon some hypothesis.

We might now ask, could the outcome of an experiment of the type considered above ever convince us that the hypothesis was correct? The answer here is generally no. If we obtained 50 heads on 100 tosses, does this convince us that $p = \frac{1}{2}$? There is no reason why it should, since obtaining 50 heads is quite consistent with having $p = 0.49$ or $p = 0.51$ or $p = 0.5052$ or $p = 0.47823$, etc. By performing more and more trials, we could progressively narrow down the range of p values which we felt were consistent with the outcome of the experiment, but it would never be possible to decide with reasonable assurance that one particular p value was indeed the probability of a head. This points up the asymmetrical nature of the experiment in giving information about or *testing* the hypothesis $p = \frac{1}{2}$. The outcome of the experiment may well convince us that the hypothesis is not true, but it cannot convince us that it is true. This is the sort of situation normally encountered. The reader may then wonder at this point what is to be gained by formulating a hypothesis and then testing it by performing an experiment. We shall return to this question shortly, after discussing the procedure for testing hypotheses in a little more detail.

9-3 TESTING HYPOTHESES

It is convenient to subdivide hypotheses into several different categories. A hypothesis concerning some parameter of a distribution such as the mean or variance is called a *parametric hypothesis*. A parametric hypothesis which states that the parameter has a specific value, say $\mu = 2$, is called a *simple hypothesis*. A parametric hypothesis which states that the parameter may have one of several possible specified values, or lies in some given interval, say $2 \leq \mu \leq 4$, is called a *composite hypothesis*. A hypothesis which makes a statement about the form of the distribution rather than about a parameter is called a *nonparametric hypothesis*. Thus the hypothesis that x is normally distributed would be what is called a nonparametric hypothesis.

A procedure, whereby a random experiment is performed and on the basis of the outcome of this experiment we decide whether or not to reject some given hypothesis, is referred to as a *statistical test* of the hypothesis. The hypothesis being tested is frequently referred to as the *null hypothesis*. The reason for this is that, frequently, one is trying to decide which of two or more hypotheses seems the most reasonable, and the one being tested is given a special name to distinguish it from the others. We noted in the previous section that an experiment may allow us to reject a hypothesis, but it will seldom be of such a nature that it will convince us that the hypothesis is true. In spite of this observation, it is usually the case in practice that if we do not reject a hypothesis as a result of a statistical test, then we proceed as if we accepted the hypothesis as true, even though we may suspect or even know that it is not true. The rationale behind this will appear below. Thus one frequently finds in statistics books the statement that as a result of testing a hypothesis we either accept or reject the null hypothesis. This is not true at all. As a result of the experiment, we may reject the hypothesis, or we may decide that the outcome of the experiment does not contradict the hypothesis. In the latter case we may then take the same action as if the hypothesis were true. This is not the same as accepting the hypothesis to be true.

Let us now formalize the procedure of testing a hypothesis, call it H_0. The procedure is basically the same regardless of the type of hypothesis being tested. To test H_0 we perform a random experiment $\Re$, which yields a value ζ of some random variable y. Based on the value ζ we either reject H_0 or we do not reject H_0 (and this is frequently referred to as accepting H_0). The random variable y is referred to as the *statistic* being used to test the hypothesis. Generally speaking, y is selected so that as the value of y gets larger and larger (or smaller and smaller), the truth of the hypothesis becomes more and more unlikely. The basic decision to be made is how large must ζ, the observed value of y, be if it is to be considered to be large enough to reject the hypothesis. This decision is usually made as follows. It will be assumed that if H_0 is true the distribution for y is determined. The problem then reduces to one of deciding whether or not ζ, the observed value of y, is consistent with the distribution for y determined by H_0. If ζ is too large, it will be rather unlikely that y does have the distribution determined by H_0, and in this case H_0 is rejected. Let $Q(y)$ be the complementary cumulative function for y when H_0 is true. The probability that $y \geq \zeta$ when H_0 is true is $Q(\zeta)$. The procedure for determining whether ζ is large enough to reject H_0 is then to select a number α, and to reject H_0 if $Q(\zeta) \leq \alpha$. In other words, if the probability that $y \geq \zeta$ is less than or equal to α, then the hypothesis is rejected. Otherwise the hypothesis is not rejected. The critical probability α is called the *significance level* of the test. How is α to be selected? The classical theory provides no rules for doing this. Generally, and arbitrarily, α is often selected either to have the value 0.01 or 0.05. If it turns out that ζ, the observed value of y, is such that $Q(\zeta) \leq \alpha$, then the test is said to be *significant*. When the test is significant, the null hypothesis is rejected.

The situation just described is illustrated geometrically in Figure 9-1,

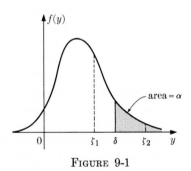

FIGURE 9-1

where the graph of the density function for y when H_0 is true is shown. The shaded region will be imagined to have area α. If the value of y observed is ζ_1, the area to the right of ζ_1 is greater than α, and in this case the hypothesis would not be rejected. However, if $y = \zeta_2$, the area to the right of ζ_2 is less than α. In this case the test is significant, and the null hypothesis is rejected. We can now note that when y is a continuous random variable, there is a unique value of y, call it δ, such that $Q(\delta) = \alpha$. Given α, the value of δ is determined. However, once δ is known, it is very simple to decide whether the test is significant or not. If $\zeta \geq \delta$, the test is significant, and H_0 is rejected. If $\zeta < \delta$, H_0 is not rejected. If the distribution of y is discrete, there may not be any value δ of y such that $Q(\delta) = \alpha$. There will, however, always be a smallest value of y, call it δ_1, such that $Q(\delta_1) \leq \alpha$. Thus if $\zeta \geq \delta_1$, H_0 is rejected and if $\zeta < \delta_1$, H_0 is not rejected. The number δ or δ_1 is frequently referred to as the *critical value* of the statistic y. This explains how one proceeds to test a hypothesis using some specified experiment $\Re$. Whether or not the test yields a significant result depends, of course, on the arbitrarily chosen value for α. As we have indicated above, α is generally chosen to have the value 0.01 or 0.05. We might also observe that when y is a continuous random variable, then α is the probability that H_0 will be rejected if, in fact, H_0 is true. If y is discrete, $Q(\delta_1)$ is the probability that H_0 will be rejected if H_0 is true. Normally, this will be very close to α, so that in either case α can usually be looked upon as the probability of rejecting H_0 when H_0 is true.

9-4 EXAMPLES OF HYPOTHESIS TESTING

We shall now give some very simple examples illustrating the concept of testing hypotheses.

1. Extensive life tests on the standard 150 watt electric bulb made by a particular manufacturer have indicated that the life of a bulb can be considered to be a random variable having a normal distribution with mean $\mu_0 = 1000$ hours and a standard deviation $\sigma = 100$ hours. An engineer claims to have devised a new filament which will increase the expected life of a bulb without changing the normality of the distribution or σ. In other words, he claims that with the new filament the life x will be a random variable having a normal distribution $n(x; \mu_1, \sigma)$ where $\mu_1 > 1000$. The company would like to decide whether or not his claim is justified. To the classical statistician, the problem here would be viewed as one of testing a hypothesis. What is the hypothesis to be tested? There exists a whole array of hypotheses which one might test. For example, one might try to test the hypothesis that $\mu_1 = 1100$ or $\mu_1 = 1200$, etc. This is not what would normally be done, however. The procedure that a classical statistician would probably suggest is to take as the null hypothesis the one which says that no change has been made, that is, $\mu_1 = \mu_0$ and x has the distribution $n(x; 1000,100)$. Then on performing an experiment, if the result is significant, the null hypothesis is rejected and it is agreed that the new filament is better. Otherwise, it would be assumed that there is no reason to discard the null hypothesis, and the engineer's claim might either be rejected or the matter set aside for further study.

Since our interest lies in the mean life of a bulb, the logical statistic to use in testing the null hypothesis is $\bar{x}$, the average life of the bulbs tested. Suppose then that 1000 light bulbs using the new filament are tested, and it is found that the average of the life of these bulbs is 1020 hours. Let us determine whether or not this is significant at the one percent level, that is, for $\alpha = 0.01$. If the null hypothesis is true, $\bar{x}$, the average life of 1000 bulbs, will have a normal distribution with mean 1000 and standard deviation $\sigma = 100/\sqrt{1000} = 3.13$. The critical value δ of $\bar{x}$ is the one for which $Q(\delta) = 0.01$ when H_0 is true, that is,

$$1 - \Phi\left(\frac{\delta - 1000}{3.13}\right) = 0.01 \quad \text{or} \quad \Phi\left(\frac{\delta - 1000}{3.13}\right) = 0.99.$$

Hence from Table E,

$$\frac{\delta - 1000}{3.13} = 2.326 \quad \text{or} \quad \delta = 1007.$$

Since the observed value 1020 of $\bar{x}$ is greater than $\delta = 1007$, the test is significant at the one percent level, and the null hypothesis would be rejected.

To reject the null hypothesis means that we do not believe that x has the normal distribution $n(x; 1000,100)$. Does it mean, however, that we agree with the engineer that x has the distribution $n(x; \mu_1, 100)$, $\mu_1 > 1000$? Although we would probably believe that $\mu_1 > 1000$, there is no reason whatever from the information given to believe that x is normally distributed with $\sigma = 100$. Information on this latter question could easily be obtained, however, by constructing a histogram for x using the 1000 values of x observed in the experiment.

2.   Suppose that we make the null hypothesis H_0 that a given coin is fair, and that we decide to test this hypothesis at the five percent level of significance by tossing the coin 100 times and observing the number of heads obtained. Denote the random variable representing the number of heads obtained by x. In this case, we wish to reject the hypothesis if the number of heads is especially large or especially small, that is, if $y = |x - 50|$ is too large, 50 being the expected number of heads if H_0 is true. Thus we shall reject the hypothesis if the probability that y is greater than $|r - 50|$ is less than or equal to 0.05 where r is the value of x observed. The random variable y is then the statistic being used to test the hypothesis. The probability of obtaining r heads when H_0 is true is $b(r; 100, 0.5)$. Inasmuch as the mean in this case is 50, let us use the normal approximation in making the computations. It is accurate enough for our purposes. Now let us see how to find a number γ such that the probability that $y \geq \gamma$ is 0.05.

Note that $y \geq \gamma$ if $x - 50 \geq \gamma$ or if $x - 50 \leq -\gamma$. Since the normal distribution is symmetric about its mean, the probability of $x - 50 \geq \gamma$ is the same as $x - 50 \leq -\gamma$, and we want

$$p(y \geq \gamma) = p(x - 50 \geq \gamma) + p(x - 50 \leq -\gamma) = 2p(x - 50 \geq \gamma) = 0.05$$

or $p(x - 50 \geq \gamma) = 0.025$. Now

$$p(x - 50 \geq \gamma) = 1 - \Phi(\gamma/5),$$

since $\sigma = 5$, so we must have $\Phi(\gamma/5) = 0.975$. From Table E, $\gamma/5 = 1.96$, or $\gamma = 9.8$. Therefore if $x \geq 59.8$ (i.e., ≥ 60) or less than $50 - 9.8 = 40.2$ (i.e., $x \leq 40$), H_0 will be rejected. Thus if on performing the experiment 57 heads were obtained, H_0 would not be rejected. Does this mean that we accept H_0 as being true? There is no basis for concluding that H_0 is true if 57 heads are obtained. The obtaining of 57 heads would be quite consistent with a whole array of other hypotheses.

3.   Suppose that a fertilizer manufacturer has brought out a new fertilizer which he claims gives an increased yield of corn as compared to that of his standard fertilizer. A farmer wishes to perform an experiment to see if this claim appears to be valid. One way to look at the farmer's problem is as one of testing a hypothesis. The null hypothesis is made that there is no difference between the new and standard fertilizers. As a result of the experiment, the farmer either rejects the null hypothesis (and hence presumably concludes that the new fertilizer is better) or he does not reject the null hypothesis (and in this case presumably concludes that there is no substantial evidence indicating that the new fertilizer is better). Let us imagine then that the farmer does proceed in this manner and decides to test the null hypothesis at the five percent significance level.

Let us now examine the situation in more detail. Imagine that based on his previous experience the farmer believes that the yield per acre for the standard fertilizer can be looked upon as a random variable x with a normal distribution having mean μ and standard deviation σ. The mean μ varies from year to year depending on weather conditions, but σ seems to remain essentially constant at 111 bushels per acre. According to the null hypothesis then, the random variable y representing the yield per acre when the new fertilizer is used will have the normal distribution $n(y: \mu, 111)$. The important thing to note at this point is that the farmer cannot proceed as in Example 1 and simply raise some corn on several acres using the new fertilizer, compute $\bar{\zeta}$ the average yield per acre and reject the hypothesis if $\bar{\zeta}$ is too large. This could be done if μ was known and never changed from year to year. However, it has been assumed that μ does change. The farmer runs into a certain difficulty here which is typical of problems which involve comparison of two treatments. He would like to test the fertilizers under identical conditions, which among other things would imply using the same piece of land in each case and the same growing conditions. Essentially the same growing conditions can be obtained if he makes a comparison of the regular and new fertilizer in the same growing season. This automatically rules out using the same piece of land for both, however. Since land is more uniform from one acre to another than are growing conditions from one year to the next, he decides to conduct the test by trying out both fertilizers in the same year. He would like, however, to avoid insofar as possible introducing any bias due to the quality of the land. There will always be slight differences from one acre to another. One of many possible ways to average out possible differences would be to use a scheme such as that shown in Figure 9-2. In the shaded areas he would use the new fertilizer and in the unshaded areas the regular fertilizer.

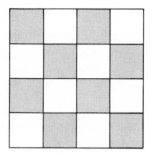

FIGURE 9-2

Let us then suppose that the farmer selects 16 acres of land and employs the scheme shown in Figure 9-2, using the new fertilizer on eight acres and the regular one on eight acres. He determines $\bar{\zeta}$, the average yield per acre, using the new fertilizer and this turns out to be 1450 bushels (on the cob). The average yield per acre ξ using the regular fertilizer is 1320 bushels. Let $\bar{x}$ be the random variable representing the average yield per acre from the eight acres using the regular fertilizer and $\bar{y}$ the random variable representing the average yield per acre for the eight acres where the new fertilizer is used. Since x has a normal distribution with $\sigma = 111$, it follows that if we assume that the yields from each of the eight acres are identically distributed independent random variables, then $\bar{x}$ has a normal distribution with the same mean and with standard deviation $\sigma_{\bar{x}} = 111/\sqrt{8} = 39.3$ (see p. 389). According to the null hypothesis, y has the same distribution as x and therefore $\bar{y}$ has the same distribution as $\bar{x}$.

The value of $\Theta = \bar{\zeta} - \xi$ will determine whether or not the farmer rejects the null hypothesis. Now Θ is a value of the random variable $z = \bar{y} - \bar{x}$, and z will then be the statistic used to test the hypothesis. When H_0 is true, $\bar{y}$ has the same normal distribution as $\bar{x}$. From Section 7-14 we know that then z also has a normal distribution with mean 0 and variance $\sigma_z^2 = \sigma_{\bar{x}}^2 + \sigma_{\bar{y}}^2$. Thus $\sigma_z = 39.3\sqrt{2} = 55.5$. The null hypothesis that there is no change thus reduces to the assumption that z has the distribution $n(z; 0, 55.5)$. To test the null hypothesis, we determine if the observed value of z is consistent with z having the distribution $n(z; 0, 55.5)$. This is done using a significance level of 0.05. The critical value δ of z is then that value such that $Q(\delta)$, the probability that $z \geq \delta$, is $\alpha = 0.05$. Consequently,

$$Q(\delta) = 1 - \Phi(\delta/55.5) = 0.05 \quad \text{or} \quad \Phi(\delta/55.5) = 0.95.$$

From Table E, $\delta/55.5 = 1.645$ or $\delta = 91.2$. Therefore, if Θ, the observed value of z, satisfies $\Theta \geq 91.2$, the null hypothesis is rejected. Otherwise it is not rejected. For the case under consideration

$$\Theta = \bar{\zeta} - \bar{\xi} = 1450 - 1320 = 130.$$

Thus $\Theta > 91.2$ and the test is significant, so that the null hypothesis is rejected. In this case then, the farmer would presumably conclude that the new fertilizer is indeed superior to the regular one.

4. In Chapter 5 we introduced the notion of a control chart for monitoring the behavior of a production process. A control chart such as that shown in Figure 5-4 can be looked upon as a device for testing a null hypothesis concerning the production process. The null hypothesis is that defectives are generated at random and the probability of a defective is p. Each time a sample is taken the hypothesis is tested. If the number of defectives obtained lies outside the control limits, the hypothesis is rejected and some action is taken to see what is wrong, if anything. If the number of defectives obtained lies inside the control limits, no action is taken and in this sense one proceeds as if the null hypothesis was accepted as being true. The significance level for this test is the probability α that the number of defectives will be outside the control limits. This varies a little depending on p and n, but α is approximately 0.003.

9-5 HYPOTHESIS TESTING AND SELECTION OF ACTIONS

What are the reasons that one might be interested in testing some hypothesis? These could vary from one situation to another, and may reflect scientific curiosity, for example. In the great majority of cases, however, the hypothesis is tested for the purpose of selecting one of two alternative courses of action. The control chart referred to in the fourth example of the previous section serves to select one of two courses of action after every sample is taken. Either one does nothing, or one decides to see if something is wrong with the production process. The farmer referred to in the third example is probably not testing the new fertilizer merely out of scientific curiosity. He wants to decide whether to use the new fertilizer or to continue using the regular one.

We see therefore that the problem facing an individual who is about to test a hypothesis is very frequently a problem in statistical decision theory. The individual is trying to decide which of two actions to select, and before making the decision, he has the opportunity to perform a random experiment to gain more information about the state of nature, each state of nature in this case being characterized by a single number. This then is just a special case of the general type of problem which we discussed in the previous chapter. The classical and decision theory approaches are quite different, as the reader will readily appreciate, since the classical approach makes no use of prior probabilities or of costs. Let us compare the two approaches to solving the same problem by illustrating the decision theory approach to solving the farmer's problem concerning the new fertilizer which was studied in Example 3 of the previous section.

The farmer would like to know whether he should use the new fertilizer in the future, call this action a_1, or continue to use the regular fertilizer, call this action a_2. The classical approach to solving the problem was given in the previous section. Let us summarize the classical approach in the language of decision theory. The basis of the classical procedure is to perform a random experiment, and depending on the outcome of this experiment either action a_1 or action a_2 is selected. The way the decision is made is as follows. The null hypothesis is set up that there is no difference between the new fertilizer and the old one. This implies that the statistic z has the distribution $n(z; 0, 55.5)$. Next a significance level α is chosen, and in the classical approach it is usually taken to be 0.01 or 0.05, or occasionally as large as 0.10. Next if Θ, the observed value of z, is such that $Q(\Theta)$, the probability that $z \geq \Theta$ when H_0 is true, is less than α, then H_0 is rejected. Rejection of H_0 presumably implies that the farmer believes the new fertilizer is an improvement and will take action a_1 and use the new fertilizer. If the test is not significant, he then takes action a_2 and continues to use the regular fertilizer. Let δ_1 be the value of z such that $Q(\delta_1) = \alpha$. Then the entire hypothesis testing procedure reduces to a simple rule for deciding what action to take. If $\Theta \geq \delta_1$, action a_1 is taken; and if $\Theta < \delta_1$, action a_2 is taken.

Let us now outline the decision theory approach to the same problem. The two possible actions are those described above. The thing that determines which action is the appropriate one to take is μ, the expected value of the increase in the yield per acre on using the new fertilizer over using the regular one. Thus μ describes the state of nature, and each different value of μ represents a different state of nature. Associated with each state of nature μ there is an expected profit $U_1(\mu)$ if the new fertilizer is used, and an expected profit $U_2(\mu)$, which is a constant independent of μ, if the regular fertilizer is used. Presumably, the new fertilizer will cost more than the old fertilizer, and this is reflected in the profit. Note that $U_1(\mu)$ and $U_2(\mu)$ are expected profits, since the actual profit will depend on the actual crop yield and the market price, both of which may be imagined to be random variables. What we are saying is that more than just one number is needed to describe the state of nature. However, the experiment to be performed gives information about μ only, and hence we have utilized the results of Section 8-9 and averaged over the random variables about which no information is obtained.

The next step in the decision theory approach is for the farmer to estimate a prior distribution for μ, μ now being treated as a random variable. He might do this on the basis of his experiences with the fertilizer company in the past. The prior distribution could be one which allowed for μ to be negative, so that the new fertilizer could actually be worse than the regular one, or it might be one which considered only non-negative values for μ. In the first case, it would seem quite reasonable to assume that the prior distribution for μ is normal, and in the second case, one of the gamma density functions might be used.

Before making a decision the farmer performs an experiment to gain information about the state of nature. There is no difference whatever in the experiments to be performed in using the classical approach or the decision theory approach. In other words, the experiment described in the previous section would be quite satisfactory from the decision theory point of view, although it may not be the best experiment. To use Bayes' law, however, some additional assumptions not made in the previous section are needed. It will be assumed that if y is the random variable representing the yield per acre using the new fertilizer, then y is normally distributed. Furthermore, it will be assumed that the standard deviation of y is independent of how much the new fertilizer improves the expected yield and is, in fact, the same as for the regular fertilizer. This is reasonable if both fertilizers react in more or less the same way to soil differences. It might not be reasonable if the new fertilizer did especially well in comparison to the regular one in some circumstances but not in others. One next needs to consider the meaning of μ in a little more detail; μ is the expected increase in the yield per acre when using the new fertilizer as compared to using the standard one. Now conceivably μ could vary with the type of land and with the type of weather encountered during the growing season. We shall then assume that the farmer's soil is sufficiently uniform that the effects of the soil differences are not critical. We need not necessarily assume that μ is totally independent of weather conditions, but we shall assume that if it is desirable to use the new fertilizer under one type of weather condition, it will be desirable to use it under essentially all other conditions. Thus the experiment which the farmer performs has relevance not only for the weather conditions encountered during the growing season, but for essentially all weather conditions. Given the above assumptions, if μ has the value λ, then the conditional density for $z = \bar{y} - \bar{x}$, given the value of μ, is $n(z; \lambda, 55.5)$. When we suppose that the prior distribution for μ is that appropriate to the weather conditions actually encountered during the season, the results of the experiment can then be used to determine the posterior distribution for μ, and hence the expected profit for each action. The action giving the largest expected profit is then the action the farmer should select. As we noted in Section 8-10 for a special case, the decision theory approach implicitly determines a number δ_2, which can be determined explicitly if desired, such that if $\Theta \geq \delta_2$, action a_1 should be taken, while if $\Theta < \delta_2$, action a_2 should be taken, Θ being the observed value of z.

After summarizing the classical and decision theory approach to the same problem, we see that in quite different ways they both ultimately lead to a decision rule of the type which says take action a_1 if $\Theta \geq \delta$ and a_2 otherwise. The value of δ will, however, normally be different in the two cases. It is really then the determination of the appropriate value of δ which is the crucial thing. The value of δ used determines whether one will make a good decision or a poor one. It is instructive to study this point in a little more detail. If the new fertilizer is significantly more profitable than the regular one, this will show up clearly in the experiment if the experiment is at all discriminating, and one does not need an intricate decision model to decide what to do. One should use the new fertilizer, and both the classical approach and the decision theory approach will indicate that this is the appropriate action to take. Equally well, if the new fertilizer is bad enough, this will be evident at once from the experiment if the experiment is at all discriminating, and no intricate decision model is needed to decide what action should be taken. Clearly one should continue to use the regular fertilizer. Where a good model is really useful is in situations where things are not quite as clear cut as the two alternatives just referred to, and it is here that the classical approach seems to fall down rather badly. It is difficult to make a sound decision in economic problems without considering the costs and revenues involved, and these are not considered at all in the classical approach. Furthermore, except when the experiment performed is very discriminating, the prior probabilities also play an important role. These are not used in the classical approach either, one reason being that many classical statisticians would deny that prior probabilities have any meaning unless they were obtained from a considerable quantity of frequency data.

There is one more peculiar characteristic of the classical approach that should be noted before going on.   When α is as small as 0.01 or 0.05, which are the usually recommended values of α, the random experiment performed must yield a result very unfavorable to the null hypothesis before this is rejected, since α is the probability of rejecting H_0 when it is true. This means that the decision maker definitely wants to avoid taking the action appropriate to rejecting H_0 unless he is quite sure H_0 is false.   In other words, the classical procedure implies that it is much more desirable to take the action associated with H_0 even if H_0 is not true than it is to take the action associated with rejecting H_0 when H_0 is true.   There are situations where this is realistic.   It would be much more serious, for example, to approve for use a drug that caused cancer than it would be to reject a safe and useful drug.   However, it is by no means true that the majority of business problems are of this form.   What we are saying is that the value of α chosen by classical statisticians is often too small.   It weights things too much in favor of one of the actions in comparison to the other one.

In the previous section we presented an actual numerical example involving the two fertilizers.   Let us conclude this section by continuing the example and illustrating the decision theory approach.   Assume that the prior distribution for μ is normal with mean 10 and standard deviation 20. Thus a priori the farmer believes that the new fertilizer is probably a little better than the regular one.   Assume that the expected profit per acre per year if the regular fertilizer is used is $60, and when the new fertilizer is used is $59 + 0.5\mu$, μ being the expected increase in the yield per acre (μ may be negative, of course).   We then have a problem which is precisely of the type discussed in Section 8-10, where the utilities are linear.   We know that the posterior distribution of μ is normal, and its mean and variance are given by (8-58).   Furthermore, (8-59) tells us how to determine the value of δ_2.   For the case under consideration, $U_1 = U_2$ when

$$60 = 59 + 0.5\mu \quad \text{or} \quad \mu = 2.$$

Thus $\tau = 2$.   Furthermore, $\mu_0 = 10$, $\sigma_0 = 20$, since these are the parameters of the prior distribution for μ, and $\sigma_c = \sigma_z = 55.5$ from the results of the previous section.   Then from (8-58)

$$\frac{1}{\sigma_1^2} = \frac{1}{(55.5)^2} + \frac{1}{(20)^2} = 0.000323 + 0.00250 = 0.00283,$$

and

$$\sigma_1^2 = 353 \quad \text{or} \quad \sigma_1 = 18.8.$$

Therefore, from (8-59)

$$\delta_2 = \left(\frac{3100}{353}\right)(2) - \left(\frac{3100}{400}\right)(10) = 17.5 - 77.5 = -60,$$

and one reaches the astonishing conclusion that δ_2 is negative, and that even if the new fertilizer yielded an average of 60 bushels per acre less than the regular one, the farmer should still use the new fertilizer. Why is this true? The reason is that the experiment performed is not very discriminating in the sense that σ_c is considerably larger than σ_0, and from (8-58), the expected value of the posterior distribution of μ depends much more on μ_0 than on the observed value Θ of z. This is therefore a case where the prior distribution has a very important influence on what decision should be made, and it would appear that if the farmer used the classical approach there is a good chance that he would reject the new fertilizer when in actuality he should use it.

9-6 SELECTION OF EXPERIMENT

The reader will no doubt have from the previous section the impression that the classical approach to handling two action decision problems leaves a great deal to be desired. This would certainly seem to be a correct impression for economic type decision problems. However, the classical theory was presented in an especially bad light in the previous section because it was assumed that the experiment was specified. It is normally the case that when applying the classical approach one will also determine the experiment to use. By the experiment we shall mean the sample size. Thus, for example, instead of arbitrarily assuming that the farmer tests the new and regular fertilizers each on eight acres, the number of acres to be used would be determined also. We now wish to show how the sample size is determined in the classical approach. It will be recalled that the determination of the optimal experiment by means of the Bayesian theory can involve a great deal of computation. Very frequently, the classical approach involves relatively little computation.

When the experiment is specified in advance, the classical theory proceeds to select an action by testing some null hypothesis at a specified level of significance. The selection of H_0 and α determines the critical number δ. This procedure makes no provision for selecting the sample size, i.e., the experiment. To make such a selection possible something new must be introduced. This is done as follows. Note that in testing a null hypothesis, we merely attempt to decide whether or not to reject H_0. We do not attempt to select between two or more alternative hypotheses. Suppose that instead of merely considering H_0, we consider two alternative hypotheses H_0 and H_1, and we look upon the experiment to be performed as serving to reject one of these two hypotheses, thus implying that we shall act as if the one not rejected is true. For example, in the fertilizer problem discussed in the previous two sections, H_0 might be the hypothesis that the new fertilizer is the same as the regular one, while H_1 is the hypothesis that the new fertilizer improves the average yield per acre by 50 bushels, everything else remaining unchanged.   One of the hypotheses is referred to as the null hypothesis and is denoted by H_0, while the other is called the alternative hypothesis.   Either one can be considered to be the null hypothesis.

It is important to understand one thing at this point.   When H_0 and H_1 are selected, there is no real implication that these are the only two possible hypotheses, or even that they are much more likely than other possible hypotheses.   The procedure being followed here is similar to one we have often used in solving decision problems.   Even though we knew that there could be a large number of different states of nature for some problem, we often made the approximation that only a very small number of different states were possible.   The justification for this was that being more accurate in our representation would not significantly improve our decision making ability.   The same idea is involved in the classical approach. However, here it is carried all the way, and it is assumed that in order to determine both the experiment and the decision rule it is sufficient to imagine there are only two different states of nature corresponding to the hypotheses H_0 and H_1.   For example, the classical approach would say that to decide how much experimentation is needed in order to select which fertilizer to use, it would be satisfactory to proceed as if only two values of μ were possible, even though one is quite sure this is not true.

Let us now see how the introduction of two hypotheses makes it possible to select an experiment.   Consider first the case where the experiment is specified.   To be specific, let us use the fertilizer example again.   Suppose that H_0 is $\mu = 0$, and H_1 is $\mu = 50$.   If H_0 is true, the probability density for the statistic z is $n(z; 0, 55.5)$, and if H_1 is true, z has the normal distribution $n(z; 50, 55.5)$, provided the assumptions made in the previous section are valid.   Both of these density functions are shown in Figure 9-3.   Sup-

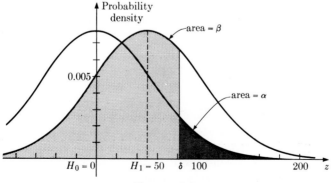

FIGURE 9-3

pose now that one proceeds to test H_0 at the five percent significance level. Then the critical value is determined, and if $z \geq \delta$, the hypothesis H_0 is rejected.   The probability of rejecting H_0 when H_0 is true is the significance level α.   The rejection of H_0 when it is true is frequently referred to as *an error of type 1* or of the first kind.   However, when two hypotheses are involved, there is another type of error one can commit.   This is the error of rejecting H_1 when H_1 is true. H_1 will be rejected if $z < \delta$.   The probability of rejecting H_1 when H_1 is true is denoted by β, and this error is called *an error of type 2* or an error of the second kind.   When we look upon H_0 and H_1 as being the only two alternatives, then α is the probability of accepting H_1 when H_0 is true, and β is the probability of accepting H_0 when H_1 is true, that is, α is the probability of accepting H_1 when H_1 is false, and β is the probability of accepting H_0 when H_0 is false.   The probability of accepting H_0 when H_1 is true is the probability that $z < \delta$ when H_1 is true.   This is the area of the lightly shaded region shown in Figure 9-3, and the area of this region is β.   It is clear at once, for the situation being considered, that there is a very high probability of accepting H_0 if H_1 is in fact true.   The important thing to note here is that once the experiment is specified and the significance level at which H_0 is to be tested is selected, the value of β is also determined.   In other words, the probability of accepting H_0 when H_1 is in fact true is determined, and this value may be very large.

Now we would like to have some control over type 2 errors, and in fact, we might like to make β just as small as α.   How can this be done?   It can be done by selecting the sample size, which is to say, the experiment. For the example under consideration, the sample size refers to the number of acres of corn that are going to be planted to test out the two fertilizers. Let us agree that the same number of acres will be treated with the new fertilizer as are treated with the regular fertilizer.   If n is the number of acres treated with the new fertilizer, then since x and y are assumed to have the same standard deviation of 111, $\bar{x}$ and $\bar{y}$ have standard deviations $111/\sqrt{n}$ and z has the standard deviation $111\sqrt{2/n}$.   Thus as the sample size increases the standard deviation of z decreases.   In Figure 9-4, we have shown the density functions for z under the alternative assumptions that H_0 and H_1 are true when a sample size of 72 acres is treated with the new fertilizer.

If one now proceeds to test H_0 using the same five percent significance level and the increased sample size, it is seen that the value of δ is here much smaller than in Figure 9-3 and, in addition, β has been reduced considerably.   It would appear then that by suitably selecting the sample size one can reduce β as much as one desires while keeping α at some specified value.   This is indeed true.   Suppose next that the decision maker specifies H_0 and H_1 as well as α and β, the probabilities of making errors of

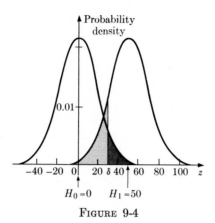

FIGURE 9-4

type 1 and type 2. We shall then show that it is possible to determine the sample size n and the critical value δ of z so that the probability of rejecting H_0 when it is true is precisely α, and the probability of rejecting H_1 when it is true is not greater than β. It may not be possible to make the probability of rejecting H_1 when it is true precisely equal to β because n must be an integer. If n did not have to be an integer, the probability could be made precisely β.

Suppose that H_0 is the hypothesis that $\mu = 0$ and H_1 is the hypothesis that $\mu = \lambda$, $\lambda > 0$. For generality, let us denote the standard deviation of x by σ. By assumption, this is also the standard deviation of y. The standard deviations of $\bar{x}$ and $\bar{y}$ are then $\sigma/\sqrt{n}$, and $\sigma_z = \sigma\sqrt{2/n}$. When H_0 is true, z then has the normal distribution $n(z; 0, \sigma_z)$. We want the probability of rejecting H_0 when it is true to be α so that

$$1 - \Phi(\delta/\sigma_z) = \alpha \quad \text{or} \quad \Phi(\delta/\sigma_z) = 1 - \alpha. \tag{9-1}$$

From Table E we can then determine a number γ_1 such that if

$$\delta/\sigma_z = \gamma_1, \tag{9-2}$$

then (9-1) holds. When H_1 holds, z has the normal distribution $n(z; \lambda, \sigma_z)$, and we would like to have the probability of rejecting H_1, when it is true, be β, so that

$$\Phi\left(\frac{\delta - \lambda}{\sigma_z}\right) = \beta. \tag{9-3}$$

From Table E we can then determine a number γ_2 such that if

$$(\delta - \lambda)/\sigma_z = \gamma_2, \tag{9-4}$$

then (9-3) holds. Now from (9-2), $\delta = \gamma_1\sigma_z$. If we use this in (9-4), we obtain

$$\gamma_1\sigma_z - \lambda = \gamma_2\sigma_z \quad \text{or} \quad (\gamma_1 - \gamma_2)\sigma_z = \lambda,$$

and since $\sigma_z = \sigma\sqrt{2/n}$, we have

$$\sqrt{n} = \sqrt{2}\,\sigma(\gamma_1 - \gamma_2)/\lambda,$$

so

$$n = 2\sigma^2(\gamma_1 - \gamma_2)^2/\lambda^2. \tag{9-5}$$

The value of n determined from (9-5) may not be an integer. Let us then use for n the smallest integer greater than or equal to the value of n determined from (9-5). Finally, we determine δ from (9-2), so that

$$\delta = \gamma_1\sigma\sqrt{2/n}. \tag{9-6}$$

Then a sample size n and a critical number δ have been determined, so that the probability of rejecting H_0 when it is true is α and the probability of rejecting H_1 when H_1 is true is not greater than β.

Let us now apply these results to the specific example we have been studying where $\sigma = 111$, $\lambda = 50$, and $\alpha = 0.05$. We have never specified β. We shall work out the example using $\beta = 0.10$. Then from Table E $\gamma_1 = 1.645$ and $\gamma_2 = -1.28$, and hence from (9-5),

$$n = 2(111)^2(1.645 + 1.28)^2/(50)^2 = 84.$$

To the accuracy with which the calculations were made, n is an integer, and $n = 84$, so that 84 acres should be tested with the new fertilizer (with an equal number of acres being tested with the regular fertilizer). Thus we see that by increasing the sample size from 8 to 84 acres, one can reduce tremendously the probability of a type 2 error, while maintaining the same probability of a type 1 error. We can now use (9-6) to obtain the critical number. It is

$$\delta = 1.645(111)(1.414)/\sqrt{84} = 28.3,$$

which is a much smaller value than was obtained when only eight acres was used as the sample size.

9-7   DETERMINATION OF SINGLE SAMPLING PLANS

The classical approach discussed in the last section has been used extensively in quality control to determine sampling plans for incoming inspection. We would like to show in this section how this is done. We shall consider the following sort of situation. Periodically, a firm or the government purchases lots of some item from a supplier. To check on the supplier's quality, a sample of size n is selected at random from each lot. The items in the sample are classified as either good or defective, and the total number r of defectives in the sample is determined. The purchaser must then select one of two actions. He either accepts or rejects the lot.

The decision will be based on the magnitude of r, that is, there is a number c, called the acceptance number, such that if $r \leq c$ the lot is accepted and is rejected if $r > c$. The problem then reduces to that of determining the sample size n and the acceptance number c. Once these are determined the sampling plan is completely specified. The decision theory approach for solving this problem was presented in Section 8-13, and we noted there that this method involves quite a bit of computation to carry out by hand, although it could be done quite easily on a computer. The classical approach which we shall now study requires considerably less numerical computation.

The thing which determines the quality of the lot is the lot fraction defective p. In the classical approach one particular lot fraction defective, call it p_1, is selected such that if the fraction defective in the lot was p_1, it would be desirable to accept the lot. Clearly, there exists a whole range of lot fraction defectives p having this characteristic. The number p_1 is one of these. The classical approach provides no rules for selecting p_1. In quality control terminology p_1 is called the *acceptable quality level*, abbreviated AQL. Next, another value p_2 of p is selected having the characteristic that if the lot fraction defective is p_2 then it would be desirable to reject the lot. Once again there is no unique such value for p_2, and the classical theory provides no rules for selecting p_2. In quality control terminology p_2 is called the *lot tolerance fraction defective* and is abbreviated LTFD. The classical theory then proceeds as if the state of nature (which is the lot fraction defective) will be either p_1 or p_2. Denote by H_0 the hypothesis that $p = p_1$ and by H_1 the hypothesis that $p = p_2$. The random experiment which involves taking the sample and determining the number of defectives in it can be looked upon as one where one is testing the null hypothesis H_0. If $r \leq c$, we act as if H_0 were accepted as true, and if $r > c$, we act as if H_1 were accepted as true. Suppose then the probability of rejecting H_0 when H_0 is true is specified to be α, and the probability of rejecting H_1 when H_1 is true is specified to be β. This specification of H_0, H_1, α, and β then serves to determine the sample size n and the acceptance number c, as we have indicated in the previous section. The details are slightly different here, however, from the example considered in the previous section. Let us then examine the procedure for determining n and c.

Essentially the only cases of practical interest are those where n is small with respect to the lot size, and the lot fraction defective is small even for $p = p_2$. Then the probability of finding r defectives in the sample when the lot fraction defective is p is given to an adequate approximation by the Poisson probability $p(r; np)$, so that the probability of finding r defectives when H_0 is true is $p(r; np_1)$, and is $p(r; np_2)$ when H_1 is true. The probability of rejecting H_0 when H_0 is true is $1 - P(c; np_1)$, where $P(x; np)$ is the cumulative Poisson distribution. Similarly $P(c; np_2)$ is the probability of rejecting H_1 when H_1 is true. Therefore, it is desired to determine an n and c such that

$$1 - P(c; np_1) = \alpha; \quad P(c; np_2) = \beta. \tag{9-7}$$

Inasmuch as n and c must both be integers we cannot guarantee that it will be possible to have either one or both of the equations in (9-7) hold as strict equalities. However, it is possible to find an n and c such that

$$1 - P(c; np_1) \leq \alpha; \quad P(c; np_2) \leq \beta. \tag{9-8}$$

One can then attempt to find the smallest n and the corresponding c such that

$$P(c; np_1) \geq 1 - \alpha; \quad P(c; np_2) \leq \beta. \tag{9-9}$$

The procedure is the following. Imagine that we select any value of c. Let us then determine the value of the mean of the Poisson distribution, call it ψ_1, such that $P(c; \psi_1) = 1 - \alpha$. In addition, let us find the value of the mean of the Poisson distribution, call it ψ_2, such that $P(c; \psi_2) = \beta$. Figure 9-5 shows what the graph of $P(c; \psi)$ as a function of ψ is like. Now

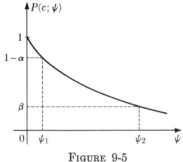

FIGURE 9-5

determine the ratio ψ_1/ψ_2. We want this to be p_1/p_2. In general, it will not be p_1/p_2, however. If c is too small, ψ_1/ψ_2 will be less than p_1/p_2, whereas if c is too large, ψ_1/ψ_2 will be greater than p_1/p_2. We then construct a table starting perhaps at $c = 0$ and increase c one unit at a time until ψ_1/ψ_2 changes from being less than p_1/p_2 to being greater than or equal to p_1/p_2. Let δ be the smallest value of c for which $\psi_1/\psi_2 \geq p_1/p_2$. For $c = \delta$, compute ψ_1/p_1 and let n_1 be the largest integer less than or equal to ψ_1/p_1. Then if we use $c = \delta$ and $n = n_1$, the first inequality in (9-9) will be satisfied, since $n_1p_1 \leq \psi_1$. Furthermore, since $\psi_1/p_1 \geq \psi_2/p_2$, it will usually be the case that $n_1 \geq \psi_2/p_2$ or $n_1p_2 \geq \psi_2$, so that the second inequality in (9-9) will also be satisfied. It is conceivable that $n_1p_2 < \psi_2$, so that the second inequality in (9-9) may not quite be satisfied, but if it is not quite satisfied, it is nothing to worry about. Thus the procedure will accomplish to a satisfactory degree of accuracy the desired result. The reader should provide the explanation for why it leads to essentially the smallest value of n.

Although the above description of the determination of c and n may sound a little complicated, it is quite simple, as we shall now illustrate by an example.

EXAMPLE: Suppose that we wish to construct a sampling plan for a situation where the AQL is 0.005 and the LTFD is 0.03, so that $p_1 = 0.005$ and $p_2 = 0.03$. Suppose furthermore that $\alpha = 0.10$ and $\beta = 0.10$. To make the computations we can use Table C. This is a poor table for these computations because one really needs a table of cumulative Poisson probabilities and one needs a table giving more values for the mean. However, Table C can be used to convey the general idea. From Table C it is not possible to determine ψ_1 and ψ_2 as described above because so few values of the mean are tabulated. We have therefore used for ψ_1 the largest tabulated mean such that $P(c; \psi_1) \geq 0.90$, and for ψ_2, the smallest tabulated mean such that $P(c; \psi_2) \leq 0.10$. The details are given in Table 9-1. We begin with $c = 0$. The largest value of the mean ψ_1 in Table C such that $P(0; \psi_1) \geq 0.90$ is $\psi_1 = 0.10$. Similarly, the smallest value of the mean ψ_2 such that $P(0; \psi_2) \leq 0.10$ is $\psi_2 = 3$. Then $\psi_1/\psi_2 = 0.033$, which is less than $p_1/p_2 = 0.167$. We next consider $c = 1$ and repeat the procedure, obtaining the results shown in Table 9-1. We continue and

TABLE 9-1

DETERMINATION OF SAMPLING PLAN

c	ψ_1	ψ_2	ψ_1/ψ_2
0	0.10	3	0.033
1	0.50	4	0.125
2	1.0	6	0.167

make the computations for $c = 2$. We then see that in going from 1 to 2 the value of ψ_1/ψ_2 changes from being less than p_1/p_2 to being equal to p_1/p_2. Thus $\delta = 2$. Now $\psi_1 = 1$ and $p_1 = 0.005$, so that $\psi_1/p_1 = 200$ and hence $n_1 = 200$. Therefore the sampling plan to be used is the one which takes a sample of size 200 and accepts the lot if 2 or less defectives are found, otherwise rejecting it. Note that when $n = 200$, $np_2 = 6$ and $P(2; 6) = 0.0620 < \beta$ as desired.

It is now of interest to compare in a little more detail the classical and decision theory approaches to the determination of single sampling plans. Both methods ultimately lead to the specification of a sample size n and an acceptance number c. To use decision theory, one needs a prior distribution for the lot fraction defective p. This is not always easy to obtain in practice, although one frequently has some relevant information. Furthermore, one must know the costs involved. To obtain these one must take into account what happens when a lot is rejected and what happens when a defective unit goes into the production process. These costs are often difficult to determine also, but once again this can be done if sufficient effort is devoted to it. The basic question then reduces to whether the expense and effort needed to obtain the prior distribution and costs are justified. The classical approach does not require a knowledge of either one of these. This is not always a simple question to answer. By appropriately choosing H_0, H_1, α, and β the classical approach can always be made to yield precisely the same sampling plan as would be obtained from the decision theory model. Thus if these quantities are chosen correctly, the classical theory will yield a good sampling plan. The question is then whether it is possible to make an appropriate selection of H_0, H_1, α, and β without having some knowledge of the prior distribution of p and the costs. In general, of course, this would not be possible. One feature which frequently serves to simplify the problem here is that the cost of inspection is often sufficiently small that one can take a sample which is large enough to make a good decision without knowing too much about the prior distribution of p. Thus if one has an intuitive feeling for the approximate p value at which lots should start to be rejected, then the classical approach can yield a quite satisfactory plan. As has been noted above, the classical approach is the one normally used to determine sampling plans and has been used quite successfully. It is hard to say what sorts of additional savings might be obtained by government and industry if the more detailed decision theory analysis was adopted. It seems clear that in some areas it would definitely be worthwhile to use decision theory, while in other areas it would not.

A convenient way to characterize the behavior of a single sampling plan is through the use of the operating characteristic curve for the sampling plan, which was introduced in Example 3 of Section 5-13 and illustrated in Figure 5-5. The operating characteristic curve is the graph of the function $P_a(p)$, where $P_a(p)$ is the probability that the lot will be accepted if the lot fraction defective is p. If one knows what sort of an operating characteristic curve he would like for a sampling plan, then if two points on this curve are selected, as shown in Figure 9-6, these will serve to determine a sampling plan having an operating characteristic curve which passes

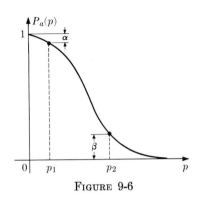

FIGURE 9-6

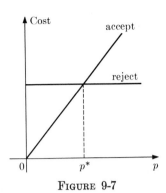

FIGURE 9-7

through these two points (or comes close to passing through them). The reason for this is that if we set AQL $= p_1$, LTFD $= p_2$, with α and β having their usual meaning, the classical approach determines an n and c, so that (9-7) is approximately satisfied, that is, the operating characteristic curve for the plan n and c essentially passes through the points $(p_1, 1 - \alpha)$, (p_2, β). Thus the classical procedure can be looked upon as a procedure for finding the sampling plan whose operating characteristic curve passes through two specified points.

Suppose that the costs of accepting and rejecting the lot as a function of the fraction defective p look like those shown in Figure 9-7, so that if $p < p^*$, the appropriate action is to accept the lot, and if $p > p^*$, the lot

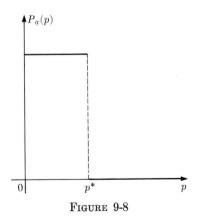

FIGURE 9-8

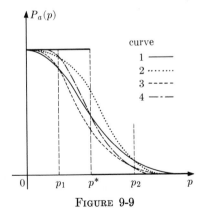

FIGURE 9-9

should be rejected. The ideal sampling plan would then have an operating characteristic curve which is that shown in Figure 9-8. This is in fact the operating characteristic curve for the sampling plan which has $n = N$, N being the lot size, and c being the largest integer less than or equal to p^*N. If in using the classical approach, one selects $p_1 < p^*$ and $p_2 > p^*$, then for specified values of α and β, the operating characteristic curve for the resulting sampling plan will look like that of curve 1 in Figure 9-9. If α is decreased without changing β, the new sampling plan will yield a larger value of n and will have an operating characteristic curve which looks like that of curve 2 in Figure 9-9. If β is decreased rather than α, one will obtain an operating characteristic curve which looks like curve 3 in Figure 9-9. If both α and β are decreased, this will yield a sampling plan having the largest n of the four we have just considered, and its operating characteristic curve will look like that of curve 4 in Figure 9-9.

9-8 ESTIMATION

Thus far in this chapter we have been discussing hypothesis testing and its relation to decision theory. We would now like to study very briefly another major area of interest of classical statistics, which is that of estimation. The problem of estimation is of great importance in decision theory as well as in classical statistics. In decision theory, however, one is not interested in estimation for its own sake. Instead, estimation problems arise indirectly in the process of solving decision problems.

Estimation, as the name implies, is concerned with estimating some parameter or parameters associated with a given random variable. In the overwhelming majority of cases the only parameters one is concerned with estimating are the expected value and variance of the random variable, and these are the estimation problems we shall consider. There exists a variety of other parameters that one could conceivably be interested in estimating, such as the mode of some distribution, for example, but these arise relatively rarely, and we shall not spend time studying such problems.

Suppose then that we are considering a random experiment $\mathfrak{R}$, which has associated with it some random variable x. Let us imagine that our model of $\mathfrak{R}$ is incomplete and that we are unable to compute the expected value of x from the model. To complete the model we must estimate μ_x from experimental data. We have already considered problems of this type many times in our previous work. In the past, the procedure used to estimate μ_x was to make n independent trials of $\mathfrak{R}$ and then to compute $\bar{\xi}$ the average of the n values of x observed. The value $\bar{\xi}$ was then our estimate of μ_x. The justification for using this approach lies in the intuitive observation made in Chapter 1 that μ_x is the long run average value of x. Further justification was obtained in Chapter 7. We showed there that if $\mathfrak{R}_n$ is the random experiment which consists of making n independent trials of $\mathfrak{R}$, we can associate with $\mathfrak{R}_n$ the random variables $x\{1\}, \ldots, x\{n\}$, and $\bar{x}$, where $x\{j\}$ is the random variable representing x on the jth trial of $\mathfrak{R}$ and

$$\bar{x} = \frac{1}{n} \sum_{j=1}^{n} x\{j\}. \tag{9-10}$$

It is the observed value of the random variable $\bar{x}$ that we use as our estimate of μ_x. Thus to estimate μ_x we perform a random experiment $\mathfrak{R}_n$ and use the observed value of the random variable $\bar{x}$ associated with $\mathfrak{R}_n$ as our estimate of μ_x. This same general procedure is followed regardless of what parameter γ we wish to estimate. A random experiment $\mathfrak{R}_n$ is performed, and the observed value of some random variable y is used as our estimate γ. The random variable y is called the *statistic* being used to estimate γ. The statistic we have used to estimate μ_x is $\bar{x}$. There are many other statistics which one could use to estimate μ_x, and a class of these will be considered in the problems, but $\bar{x}$ is the one normally used in practice. In Chapter 7 we proved that the expected value of $\bar{x}$ is μ_x so that x and $\bar{x}$ have the same expected value. A statistic y having the characteristic that its expected value is equal to the value of the parameter that one is trying to estimate, is called *unbiased*. The statistic $\bar{x}$ thus yields an unbiased estimate of μ_x. We also showed in Chapter 7 that $\sigma_{\bar{x}}^2$, the variance of $\bar{x}$, is less than σ_x^2, the variance of x, when $n > 1$, and in fact

$$\sigma_{\bar{x}}^2 = \sigma_x^2 / n. \tag{9-11}$$

Thus as n gets larger and larger the variance of $\bar{x}$ becomes less and less, thus implying that we expect on the average the observed value of $\bar{x}$ will be a good estimate of μ_x if n is chosen to be sufficiently large.

We should note carefully that $\bar{x}$ is a random variable. Hence if we made a number of independent trials of $\mathfrak{R}_n$ (each trial involving n independent trials of $\mathfrak{R}$), we would not in each case expect to observe the same value of $\bar{x}$, that is, obtain the same estimate of μ_x. However, we would expect to find the observed values of $\bar{x}$ more closely grouped about μ_x for large n than for small n. Note that we cannot claim that our estimate of μ_x on using $\mathfrak{R}_{n_1}$ will be better than that if we use $\mathfrak{R}_{n_2}$ when $n_1 > n_2$. Due to chance, it could quite possibly turn out that the estimate for $\mathfrak{R}_{n_2}$ is much better than for $\mathfrak{R}_{n_1}$. All we can claim is that on repetitions of $\mathfrak{R}_{n_1}$ and $\mathfrak{R}_{n_2}$ the estimates of μ_x will exhibit less variance in the former case than in the latter case. This observation brings up another important point. No matter how large n is we cannot guarantee that our estimate of μ_x will be correct to a specified level of accuracy (say three significant figures, for example). The best we can do is state the probability that the observed value of $\bar{x}$ will not deviate by more than a specified amount from μ_x.

It is often of interest to know how many repetitions of $\Re$ should be performed to estimate μ_x to some prespecified accuracy. As we have just noted, however, no matter how large n is we cannot be absolutely certain that the observed value of $\bar{x}$ will approximate μ_x to a given level of accuracy. Thus one generally proceeds by determining the smallest value of n for which the probability that $|\bar{x} - \mu_x| > \delta$ is less than some number α. Let us now study the problems involved in computing such an n. The important thing to observe is that we do not know μ_x. In general, however, the probability that $|\bar{x} - \mu_x| > \delta$ depends on the value of μ_x, and it would appear to be very difficult to determine n. We shall see below that usually this turns out not to be a problem, but let us first provide a very important example illustrating a case where the probability that $|\bar{x} - \mu_x| > \delta$ does depend on μ_x. Then we shall see how to avoid the problem.

Consider a process which can be assumed to be in statistical control and suppose that we wish to estimate p, the probability that any unit produced is defective. The number p is, of course, also the long run fraction defective. Furthermore, p is the expected value of the random variable x which has the value 1 if the unit produced is defective, and 0 if the unit produced is good. Let $\Re$ be the random experiment in which a unit is produced. Then to estimate p we perform n independent trials of $\Re$, this being the experiment $\Re_n$. Hence the observed value of $\bar{x}$ is r/n, where r is the number of defectives produced, since $x = 1$ if a defective is produced and 0 otherwise. Thus our estimate of p is r/n, as expected. Consider now the probability that $|(r/n) - p| > \delta$ for a fixed value of n. This probability definitely depends on p. We have in Figure 9-10 shown the graph of the probability that $|(r/n) - p| > \delta$ in the case where $n = 10$ and $\delta = 0.15$. Observe the very peculiar and discontinuous character of this curve. We ask the reader to explain the reasons why it looks this way in the problems. The important thing to note is that, regardless of what p is, the probability that $|(r/n) - p| > \delta$ is not greater than about 0.36. If one desired that the probability that $|(r/n) - p| > \delta$ be less than α, one could proceed by constructing a figure such as Figure 9-10 for each n and finding the smallest n for which the largest probability in the figure was less than α. This would guarantee that the probability that $|(r/n) - p| > \delta$ would be less than α, regardless of what p happened to be. The procedure just suggested, however, could require a tremendous computational effort. Fortunately, this can usually be avoided, and let us now see why this is true.

In (9-10) the random variables $x\{j\}/n$ are independent, since we make independent trials of $\Re$, and are identically distributed. We then know

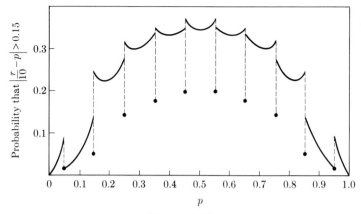

FIGURE 9-10

from the central limit theorem that as n gets larger and larger the distribution of $\bar{x}$ approaches a normal distribution with mean μ_x and standard deviation $\sigma_x/\sqrt{n}$. Let us assume that σ_x is known. If it is desired to obtain an accurate estimate of μ_x, it will be necessary in general to have n quite large, and in such cases it is reasonable to assume that to an adequate approximation $\bar{x}$ can be treated as being normally distributed. Now a characteristic of the normal distribution is that the probability that $|\bar{x} - \mu_x| > \delta$ does not depend on μ_x. This is the probability that $\bar{x} - \mu_x > \delta$ or $\bar{x} - \mu_x < -\delta$, and the probability is

$$\Phi\left(\frac{-\delta}{\sigma_x/\sqrt{n}}\right) + 1 - \Phi\left(\frac{\delta}{\sigma_x/\sqrt{n}}\right) = 2\left[1 - \Phi\left(\frac{\delta}{\sigma_x/\sqrt{n}}\right)\right]. \quad (9\text{-}12)$$

Suppose then that we want the probability that $|\bar{x} - \mu_x| > \delta$ to be equal to α. This means that we set the expression in (9-12) equal to α and hence obtain

$$\Phi\left(\frac{\delta}{\sigma_x/\sqrt{n}}\right) = 1 - \frac{\alpha}{2}, \quad (9\text{-}13)$$

or if λ is the value of t such that $\Phi(t) = 1 - (\alpha/2)$, then

$$\sqrt{n}\delta/\sigma_x = \lambda,$$

so that

$$n = (\lambda\sigma_x/\delta)^2. \quad (9\text{-}14)$$

The number computed from (9-14) may not be an integer, and thus n would be taken to be the smallest integer greater than or equal to $(\lambda\sigma_x/\delta)^2$, and using this n we know that the probability that our estimate of μ_x will deviate by more than δ from μ_x is roughly α. We say roughly α because even if (9-14) is an integer, a certain error may be made because the normal approximation is being used, and we are not certain that the probability is α.

The above procedure is based on the assumption that σ_x is known. It is almost never true that σ_x will be known exactly if μ_x is not known, but frequently σ_x will be known accurately enough that we can proceed as if it were known exactly. There are cases, however, where σ_x cannot be treated as known. One good example of this is the problem we were considering above involving the estimation of p, the probability of a defective. Here σ_x depends on p since $\sigma_x^2 = p(1 - p)$. We shall show in the examples below how this problem can be handled. In a later section we shall discuss the case where σ_x does not depend on μ_x, but σ_x is not known and must be estimated also.

In general then, if the normal approximation is used, we can determine how large n should be so that some specified number α approximately gives the probability that our estimate of μ_x will not deviate by more than some specified amount δ from μ_x. This can be done without a knowledge of the value of μ_x, and it is this property that makes the normal approximation so useful. Generally speaking, the fact that the normal density is only an approximation to the actual density function for x, thus implying that we do not know exactly the probability that $|\bar{x} - \mu_x| > \delta$, is not of great consequence. It is irrelevant whether it is 0.01 or 0.015. What we do care about is whether it is 0.01 or 0.2 or 0.9, i.e., the order of magnitude, but not the precise number is what is important. Let us now illustrate with a couple of examples how the theory just developed can be used to determine the number of trials of $\Re$ or the number of observations of x that will be needed in estimating μ_x. Before doing this, however, let us note that in decision theory problems, the determination of n is automatically made in the selection of the experiment to use, and we never face directly the problem of deciding how accurately we need to estimate some parameter. This is all taken account of in the costs, etc. which appear in the decision problem, and the proper precision is determined implicitly when the experiment is selected. In cases where one is considering an estimation problem outside of a decision theory context, some other method must be used to determine n, and the procedure we have just considered is a convenient one for doing so.

9-9 EXAMPLES

1. Consider the production process referred to in the previous section, and suppose that we wish to determine an n such that if we examine n

units and r are defective, the probability that r/n differs by more than 0.01 from p is not greater than 0.05. In this case r/n is the observed value of $\bar{x}$. Furthermore, $\sigma_x^2 = p(1 - p)$ and depends on the value of p. In Figure 9-11 we have plotted σ_x^2 as a function of p. Note that σ_x^2 passes

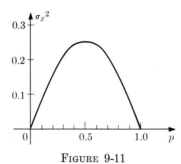

FIGURE 9-11

through a maximum at $p = 0.5$ and the maximum value of σ_x^2 is $\sigma_x^2 = 0.25$. To be on the safe side in determining n we can then use instead of σ_x the value $\sigma_0 = 0.50$. Suppose that we proceed in this way using the normal approximation for x. Now $1 - (\alpha/2) = 0.975$, and λ, the value of t such that $\Phi(t) = 0.975$, is $\lambda = 1.96$, so from (9-14)

$$n = \left[\frac{1.96(0.50)}{0.01}\right]^2 = 9600.$$

This is a rather large number and justifies the use of the normal approximation unless $p < 0.003$. If there was reason to believe that $p < 0.003$, one would probably wish to reformulate the original requirements because as they are stated one would not be requiring that such p values be measured with great accuracy.

We might observe that if something was known about p ahead of time one could use far fewer observations. Suppose, for example, that it was known that $p \leq 0.10$. Then the maximum value of σ_x occurs at $p = 0.10$ and has the value $\sigma_1 = \sqrt{0.09} = 0.30$, and if we use σ_1 instead of σ_0,

$$n = \left[\frac{1.96(0.30)}{0.01}\right]^2 = 3460,$$

which is about one third the number of observations required if nothing is known about p.

2. Consider once again the continuous filament rayon yarn used by the textile manufacturer in the example of Section 8-6. Recall that we were

there concerned with estimating the mean breaking strength of the yarn, and this was done by measuring the breaking strength on a number of pieces one inch in length, and then averaging the results. The standard deviation was assumed to be known and to have the value 3 lb. Suppose that we now determine the number of pieces whose breaking strength must be measured if the probability that the observed value of $\bar{x}$ deviates by more than 0.5 lb from μ_x is not greater than 0.02. On making the assumption that $\bar{x}$ is normally distributed, the value λ of t such that $\Phi(t) = 0.99$ is $\lambda = 2.327$, and from (9-14)

$$n = \left[\frac{2.327(3)}{0.5}\right]^2 = (13.95)^2 = 195.$$

Hence the breaking strength of 195 pieces should be measured.

3. From (9-14) we see that n is proportional to the variance of x, so that the larger the variance of x, the more observations will be needed for a fixed δ and α. This was something which we observed intuitively in Section 1-17 where we first introduced the notion of variance. Let us return to the random variables x and y, whose distributions are shown in Figures 1-9 and 1-10. Suppose that we were given σ_x and σ_y, but not μ_x and μ_y, and were asked how many observations of x would be needed if the probability that $|\bar{x} - \mu_x| > 0.2$ is to be less than 0.05 and how many observations of y would be needed if the probability that $|\bar{y} - \mu_y| > 0.2$ is to be less than 0.05. Now $\sigma_x = 2.76$ and $\sigma_y = 3.88$. The value λ of t such that $\Phi(t) = 0.975$ is $\lambda = 1.96$. Hence the number of observations of x which should be made is

$$n = \left[\frac{1.96(2.76)}{0.2}\right]^2 = 735.$$

In the actual experiment performed, which involved only 25 observations, we obtained $\xi = 0.72$, which differed by only 0.03 from $\mu_x = 0.75$. The probability of having $|\bar{x} - \mu_x| > 0.03$ when $n = 25$ is from (9-12)

$$2\left[1 - \Phi\left(\frac{0.03}{0.552}\right)\right] = 2[1 - \Phi(0.0545)] = 0.9474,$$

so that having $\bar{x}$ as close to μ_x as ξ represented an event which would occur only about one time in 20.

The number of observations of y which should be made is

$$n = \left[\frac{1.96(3.88)}{0.2}\right]^2 = 1450.$$

In the actual experiment performed, which involved only 25 observations, we obtained $\bar{\xi} = 1.6$, which differed by 0.85 from $\mu_y = 0.75$. The probability of having $|\bar{y} - \mu_y| > 0.85$ when $n = 25$ is from (9-12)

$$2\left[1 - \Phi\left(\frac{0.85}{0.776}\right)\right] = 2[1 - \Phi(1.09)] = 0.2758.$$

Thus although $\bar{\xi}$ seemed to be a very poor approximation to μ_y, it cannot be looked upon as a rare event, since about one time in four we would do this poorly or worse.

4. Suppose that we are asked to estimate μ_x for some random variable x. The number μ_x may, for example, be the mean breaking strength of the rayon yarn.   How shall we report our estimate of μ_x?   One way is to give ξ the observed value of $\bar{x}$, which is our estimate of μ_x.   However, this gives no hint as to how accurate our estimate is.   To be more precise, we could give ξ, and then the statement that the probability that $|\bar{\xi} - \mu_x| > \delta$ is less than or equal to α.   This is not, however, the way scientific results are typically presented.   Usually, they will be presented as $\bar{\xi} \pm \epsilon$, where $\bar{\xi}$ is the estimate of the physical parameter and ϵ indicates the magnitude of the experimental error involved, so that $\bar{\xi} \pm \epsilon$ is usually interpreted to mean that the true value of the physical parameter should be in the interval $\bar{\xi} - \epsilon$ to $\bar{\xi} + \epsilon$.

Classical statisticians developed a technique referred to as the method of *confidence intervals* for reporting estimates of parameters such as μ_x, which leads to a presentation of the results similar in form to that just considered.   Let us illustrate the procedure by considering the simplest case, which is that where x is normally distributed with a known σ_x.   Suppose n is chosen so that the probability of the event $|\bar{x} - \mu_x| > \delta$ is α. Hence the probability of the event $|\bar{x} - \mu_x| \le \delta$, that is, the event

$$-\delta \le \bar{x} - \mu_x \le \delta \tag{9-15}$$

is $1 - \alpha$.   This is equivalent to saying that the probability of the event

$$\mu_x - \delta \le \bar{x} \le \mu_x + \delta \tag{9-16}$$

is $1 - \alpha$.   This is true regardless of what value μ_x has in the case we are considering.

Note that in (9-15) and (9-16) we are referring to the probability that the observed value of the random variable lies in a specified interval. The interval does not depend on the outcome of the random experiment, that is, on the observed value of $\bar{x}$.   Suppose now that the value observed for $\bar{x}$ is $\bar{\xi}$.   Can we then conclude from (9-15) that the probability that μ_x lies in the interval

$$\bar{\xi} - \delta \le \mu_x \le \bar{\xi} + \delta$$

is $1 - \alpha$?   We must be careful here.   The interval is no longer fixed, but depends on the outcome of the experiment.   The interval either contains

μ_x or it does not. Thus the observed value $\bar{\xi}$ of $\bar{x}$ can be used to determine an interval I of length 2δ, whose end points are $\bar{\xi} - \delta$ and $\bar{\xi} + \delta$. In general, a different interval will be obtained each time $\mathfrak{R}_n$ is performed, since the end points depend on the value of $\bar{x}$. We can refer to I as a random interval, and if $\mathfrak{R}_n$ is performed a large number of times, we shall generate a sequence of these intervals. The long run fraction of the random intervals which contain μ_x will be $1 - \alpha$ since an interval will contain μ_x if, and only if, $|\bar{x} - \mu_x| \leq \delta$. Hence the probability that any particular random interval generated on performing $\mathfrak{R}_n$ contains μ_x is $1 - \alpha$. The random interval I generated on performing $\mathfrak{R}_n$ is referred to as a confidence interval. In making a report, a classical statistician would present his estimate for μ_x by writing $\bar{\xi} \pm \delta$, as is typical in scientific work, along with the statement that the probability is $1 - \alpha$ that the interval whose end points are $\bar{\xi} - \delta$ and $\bar{\xi} + \delta$ contains μ_x.

The reader should be careful to notice that the statement, which says the probability is $1 - \alpha$ that I contains μ_x, is not the same as the statement which says the probability that μ_x lies in I is $1 - \alpha$. To make the latter statement, we would need to think of μ_x as a random variable and I as being fixed. This is not what the method of confidence intervals does, since it treats μ_x as fixed and the interval as being random. Intuitively, however, what we really want to do is to be able to determine the probability that μ_x lies in any specified interval. To do so, however, we must use a Bayesian approach in which μ_x is treated as a random variable with some prior distribution. The experimentally observed value of $\bar{x}$ can then be used by means of Bayes' law to obtain a posterior distribution for μ_x. From this posterior distribution, one can compute the probability that μ_x lies in any given interval, and in particular, in the interval whose end points are $\bar{\xi} - \delta$ and $\bar{\xi} + \delta$. The probability so determined will not in general be $1 - \alpha$, but will depend on μ_x and on the prior distribution for μ_x.

9-10 ESTIMATION OF THE STANDARD DEVIATION

We have discussed in the previous sections the problem of estimating the expected value of some random variable. We would now like to say something about estimating σ_x^2 or σ_x. We have noted that to judge the accuracy of our estimate of μ_x we had to know something about σ_x. Before discussing the estimation of σ_x, we might note that normally in decision theory it is not as important to have as accurate an estimate of σ_x as of μ_x. The reason for this is that μ_x is frequently the principal determinant of the profit received on taking a given action, and the standard deviation while having some influence has a much smaller one than μ_x.

To estimate σ_x^2 suppose that n independent trials of $\mathfrak{R}$ are performed and that on the jth trial the value ξ_j of x is observed. We noted in Chapter 1 that if we compute the number

$$s_x^2 = \frac{1}{n} \sum_{j=1}^{n} (\xi_j - \mu_x)^2, \tag{9-17}$$

then as n gets larger and larger this number approaches σ_x^2, that is, σ_x^2 is the long run average square deviation of x from the expected value of x. Thus we should be able to use s_x^2 as our estimate of σ_x^2. There is one problem in using (9-17), however. In general, we do not know μ_x. The logical thing to do then is to use instead of μ_x our estimate $\bar{\xi} = \sum_{j=1}^{n} \xi_j/n$ of μ_x. If we do this our estimate, s_x^2, of σ_x^2 then becomes

$$s_x^2 = \frac{1}{n} \sum_{j=1}^{n} (\xi_j - \bar{\xi})^2. \tag{9-18}$$

Equation (9-18) is essentially the one normally used to estimate σ_x^2. Now s_x^2 is the observed value of a random variable z where

$$z = \frac{1}{n} \sum_{j=1}^{n} (x\{j\} - \bar{x})^2, \tag{9-19}$$

$x\{j\}$ and $\bar{x}$ being defined in Section 9-8. In other words z appears to be a suitable statistic to use in estimating σ_x^2. Let us then determine the expected value μ_z of z. To do this, we shall first add and subtract μ_x in (9-19) to yield

$$z = \frac{1}{n} \sum_{j=1}^{n} [(x\{j\} - \mu_x) - (\bar{x} - \mu_x)]^2$$

$$= \frac{1}{n} \sum_{j=1}^{n} [(x\{j\} - \mu_x)^2 - 2(x\{j\} - \mu_x)(\bar{x} - \mu_x) + (\bar{x} - \mu_x)^2]$$

$$= \frac{1}{n} \sum_{j=1}^{n} (x\{j\} - \mu_x)^2 - (\bar{x} - \mu_x)^2 \tag{9-20}$$

since

$$\frac{1}{n} \sum_{j=1}^{n} (x\{j\} - \mu_x) = \bar{x} - \mu_x.$$

Thus z is a linear combination of the random variables $(x\{j\} - \mu_x)^2$ and $(\bar{x} - \mu_x)^2$, and the expected value of z is then the same linear combination of the expected values of the random variables. However, the expected value of $(x\{j\} - \mu_x)^2$ is σ_x^2, and the expected value of $(\bar{x} - \mu_x)^2$ is σ_x^2/n. Consequently,

$$\mu_z = \frac{1}{n} \sum_{j=1}^{n} \sigma_x^2 - \frac{1}{n} \sigma_x^2 = \frac{n-1}{n} \sigma_x^2. \tag{9-21}$$

The expected value of z is not σ_x^2, and thus z is a biased estimator of σ_x^2. However, as n gets larger and larger $(n-1)/n$ approaches 1; and for large n, z is essentially unbiased. Although one prefers to use unbiased statistics, a slight amount of bias does not cause any serious problems. In the present case, we could obtain an unbiased statistic z^* merely by dividing by $n-1$ in (9-19) rather than n. The statistic z^* is the one usually used in estimating σ_x^2. For reasonably large n, however, there is essentially no difference in the estimate of σ_x^2 obtained using z and using z^*.

In Sections 9-8 and 9-9 we considered the problem of the number of observations needed to estimate μ_x. To determine n it was assumed that σ_x was known. How do we proceed if σ_x is not known? In this case one may perform an initial experiment using a relatively small value of n to estimate roughly σ_x. Using this rough estimate, one determines the n required to estimate μ_x as desired. One then performs $\mathcal{R}_n$ and estimates μ_x. Simultaneously, one may use the results of $\mathcal{R}_n$ to obtain a better estimate of σ_x. If this new estimate is larger than the original estimate, more observations may be called for in estimating μ_x.

9-11 ERRORS OF MEASUREMENT OR SELECTION

In all of our previous work we have assumed implicitly that when a random experiment was performed no errors or mistakes were made in determining what the outcome of this experiment was. For example, if a sample of n items was selected at random from a lot and the number of defectives determined, we assumed that the inspector actually determined the number of defectives and did not make any errors by classifying a defective unit as good or a good unit as defective. In the real world, of course, inspectors will occasionally make mistakes. As another example, suppose that we are attempting to estimate the expected value of the random variable x representing the diameter of ball bearings produced in a given plant. When a ball bearing is produced this ball bearing has a diameter ξ which is a value of x. However, when the diameter of the ball bearing is measured by an inspector, he may not obtain the value ξ as a result of his measurement, due to various measurement errors which may arise. Instead, the value he records as the diameter may be ξ_1, which is different from ξ.

The examples just given represent what may be called measurement errors because errors were introduced as a result of measuring the value of x determined on each trial of $\mathcal{R}$. There is another type of error which can arise frequently in some situations. This may be called a selection error. In our computations we frequently make the assumption that the sample being used has some special property such as having been selected at random from a lot. The results obtained depend critically on this assumption. Thus one must be careful to make the method of selecting the sample conform as closely as possible to the assumptions being made about the way the sample is selected. For example, one would not be selecting a random sample from a lot if all units were taken from the top layer in the lot. The supplier might suspect we were doing this and could pull the trick of placing essentially all good units on the top layer. Such a procedure would seriously *bias* the sample, and quite possibly lots would be accepted much more frequently than they should be. Very serious errors of selection have been made on occasions in opinion polls because the sample really did not represent a random sample from the lot of individuals concerned. The samples were biased in one way or another, and the results were similarly biased in one way or another and thus these results were very misleading. Such selection errors have caused a number of firms to make serious mistakes in marketing new products, for example. We shall not attempt to discuss in detail ways to avoid selection errors since the procedures can vary widely with the circumstances. A great deal of work has been done in this area, and it is often referred to under the general heading of design of experiments or sampling techniques.

Let us analyze in a little more detail, however, measurement errors. We can now think of the process of performing $\Re$ and measuring the value of x so generated as a two stage random experiment. The first stage consists in performing $\Re$ and generating a value ξ of x. At the second stage a random experiment is performed in which the value of x generated at the first stage is measured, and the result ξ_1 is obtained, which will in general be different from ξ. Normally, ξ_1 will be one of the allowable values of x (for otherwise it would presumably be clear that a mistake had been made). It is convenient to imagine that ξ_1 is the observed value of a random variable y, where y is the sum of the random variable x and the random variable ϵ, ϵ being the error introduced at the second stage, so that $y = x + \epsilon$. Suppose now that we are trying to estimate μ_x, and that n independent trials of $\Re$ are performed to do so. We would like to use the value of $\bar{x}$ so generated as our estimate of μ_x, but because of the errors introduced we shall use the observed value of $\bar{y}$ instead, where $\bar{y} = \sum_{j=1}^{n} y\{j\}/n$, $y\{j\}$ being the random variable representing y for the jth trial of $\Re$. Now if $\epsilon\{j\}$ is the random variable representing ϵ on the jth trial of $\Re$, then

$$\bar{y} = \bar{x} + \frac{1}{n}\sum_{j=1}^{n} \epsilon\{j\} = \frac{1}{n}\sum_{j=1}^{n} y\{j\}. \tag{9-22}$$

Let us denote the expected value of ϵ by η. Then each $\epsilon\{j\}$ has the expected value η. Since the expected value of $\bar{x}$ is μ_x, we see that $\mu_{\bar{y}}$, the expected value of $\bar{y}$, is

$$\mu_{\bar{y}} = \mu_x + \eta. \tag{9-23}$$

If $\eta \neq 0$, then the statistic $\bar{y}$ is biased and the bias is η. The bias is intro-duced by the measuring process. Note that the statistic $\bar{y} - \eta$ is unbiased. Thus if the expected value η of ϵ is known, one would use as the estimate of μ_x the value $\bar{\zeta} - \eta$, where $\bar{\zeta}$ is the value obtained for $\bar{y}$. Frequently, the measuring process does not introduce any bias so that $\eta = 0$, and in this case $\bar{y}$ is an unbiased estimator of μ_x.

Consider next the variance of $\bar{y}$, where $\bar{y}$ is given by (9-22). The set of $2n$ variables $x\{j\}$ and $\epsilon\{j\}$ are not necessarily independent random var-iables. If the n variables $\epsilon\{j\}$ are not independent, so that the measure-ment error on one trial of $\Re$ may be dependent on the measurement error on a previous trial, then the errors are said to be *correlated*. Very fre-quently, it is reasonable to assume that the errors are uncorrelated, so that the n random variables $\epsilon\{j\}$ are independent. This implies, for example, that the probability or probability density for making a certain error in measuring the diameter of the jth ball bearing will not depend on the errors made in measuring the diameters of the first $j - 1$. It appears quite reasonable that this should be true. Let us then assume that the errors are uncorrelated. Even though the random variables $\epsilon\{j\}$ are in-dependent and the random variables $x\{j\}$ are independent, it need not be true that the $2n$ random variables $x\{j\}$ and $\epsilon\{j\}$ are independent. The probability function or probability density for $\epsilon\{j\}$ may depend on the value of $x\{j\}$. In this case, the covariance of $\epsilon\{j\}$ and $x\{j\}$ need not be zero. Generally speaking, however, one would expect $\epsilon\{j\}$ to be inde-pendent of the $x\{j\}, i \neq j$. This then is equivalent to saying that we frequently expect the $y\{j\}$ to be independent random variables. When this is true, then $\sigma_{\bar{y}}^2 = n\sigma_y^2$, and since $y = x + \epsilon$,

$$\sigma_y^2 = \sigma_x^2 + \sigma_\epsilon^2 + 2\Delta,$$

where Δ is the covariance of x and ϵ. Hence

$$\sigma_{\bar{y}}^2 = n(\sigma_x^2 + \sigma_\epsilon^2 + 2\Delta) = \sigma_{\bar{x}}^2 + n(\sigma_\epsilon^2 + 2\Delta). \qquad (9\text{-}24)$$

When the $y\{j\}$ are independent, it follows from the central limit theorem that since the $y\{j\}$ are identically distributed, the distribution of $\bar{y}$ for large n will be essentially normal with mean $\mu_x + \eta$ and variance given by (9-24). This is a very useful result.

From what we have just shown, it follows at once that if $\eta = 0$ (so that the measurements are unbiased) and the $y\{j\}$ are independent random var-iables, then for large n, $\bar{y}$ is essentially normally distributed with mean μ_x just as $\bar{x}$ is. However, the variance of $\bar{y}$ is greater than the variance of $\bar{x}$ as we see from (9-24). In such a case, we can use $\bar{y}$ to estimate μ_x, but in general, more observations will be needed on account of the larger var-iance of $\bar{y}$ than would be the case when no measurement errors are made. If $\eta \neq 0$, but is known, $\bar{y} - \eta$ can be used as the statistic to estimate μ_x, and this statistic will be roughly normally distributed with mean μ_x and variance $\sigma_{\bar{y}}^2$. Thus we see that for a large number of important cases, measurement errors can be accounted for and the net result of them is that more observations may be required. Our discussion of how to take account of measurement errors has focused on the classical estimation problem. In decision theory, μ_x would be the state of nature, and as a result of performing an experiment, a value of $\bar{y}$ would be observed. What we then need to apply Bayes' law is the conditional density function or probability function for $\bar{y}$ given μ_x. However, we have just seen that for n large and for the case where the $y\{j\}$ are independent, $\bar{y}$ is essentially normally distributed with mean $\mu_x + \eta$ and variance (9-24). This then is precisely what we need to know. The determination of the distribution of $\bar{y}$, when n is small and the central limit theorem cannot be applied, can be quite complicated, and we shall not discuss this subject.

REFERENCES

The book by Schlaifer referred to in Chapter 4 and that of Moses and Chernoff referred to in Chapter 8 give some discussion of the relationship between decision theory and classical statistics. Essentially any statistics book will give at least a brief discussion of hypothesis testing and estimation. Some suitable references at a relatively elementary level are the following.

1. Burr, I. W., *Engineering Statistics and Quality Control.* McGraw-Hill, New York, 1953.
Concerned mainly with use of control charts and sampling plans in quality control work. No calculus is needed, although it is used a little.

2. Grant, E. L., *Statistical Quality Control*, 3rd ed. McGraw-Hill, New York, 1964.
A book quite similar in approach to Burr, although written at a slightly more elementary level.

3. Hodges, J. L., and E. L. Lehmann, *Basic Concepts of Probability and Statistics.* Holden-Day, San Francisco, 1964.
Quite elementary. No calculus required.

4. Hoel, P. G., *Introduction to Mathematical Statistics*, 3rd ed. Wiley, New York, 1962.
Elementary calculus required.

5. Neyman, J., *First Course in Probability and Statistics.* Holt, New York, 1950.
Elementary calculus required.

6. Wallis, W. A., and H. V. Roberts, *Statistics—A New Approach.* Free Press, Glencoe, Ill., 1956.
Elementary. No calculus required.

PROBLEMS

Sections 9-3 and 9-4

1. An engineer claims that a process which turns out ball bearings is in statistical control and that the diameter of any given ball bearing can be looked upon as the value of a random variable x which is normally distributed with mean 0.2510 and standard deviation 0.0020. Suppose that we believe that he is correct in stating that x is normally distributed with standard deviation 0.0020, but we are not sure about the mean. Imagine that we make the null hypothesis $\mu = 0.2510$, and to test this hypothesis, the diameters of ten ball bearings are measured. The mean diameter obtained is 0.2530. Would you reject the hypothesis at the five percent significance level? What statistic did you use? What is the critical number? For what range of α values would the hypothesis be rejected? Explain carefully the procedure used for testing the hypothesis and the reasoning behind it.

2. A brewer believes that he has developed a beer which can in taste be clearly distinguished from his competitor's brand. To test this he selects 25 individuals and allows them to sample his beer. He then gives each two unlabeled glasses, one containing his beer and one containing his competitor's beer, and asks them to select the glass which contains his beer. It turns out that 17 of them correctly identify his beer. At the five percent significance level should one agree that it is possible to distinguish his beer by its taste? What is the null hypothesis to be tested in this case? What is the statistic? For what range of α values would the null hypothesis be rejected? What is the critical number when $\alpha = 0.05$?

3. A producer of poultry feed claims that he has produced a new feed which will yield heavier broilers than his regular feed. To test this claim a farmer selects 100 baby chicks. He feeds 50 of them using the regular feed, and 50 using the new feed. When they are ready for sale, the average weight of those fed on regular feed is 10.2 lb, while for those fed on the new feed the average weight is 10.9 lb. Assume that from past experience the farmer has found that the weight of a chicken can be considered to be a random variable which is normally distributed with standard deviation 1.55 lb. He believes that this will remain true for the new feed. At the five percent significance level, should he agree that the new feed is better? Describe carefully the model being used here and the null hypothesis being tested. What is the critical number?

4. A chemist has developed for a tire company a new synthetic rubber which he feels is better than that being used currently. Extensive testing over the years on the synthetic rubber currently in use has shown that the mileage which can be put on a tire until wearout can be looked upon as a random variable x which is normally distributed with mean 15,000 mi and standard deviation 3000 mi. Fifty tires are tested using the new synthetic rubber, and the average mileage until wearout turns out to be 16,200 mi. At the one percent significance level, would it appear that the new synthetic rubber should be considered to be superior to that currently in use? What is the critical number?

5. Imagine that a random variable x has the normal distribution $n(x; \mu, 2)$, and it is desired to test the hypothesis that $\mu \leq 4$ by performing n independent trials of an experiment, where on each trial a value of x will be observed. Let $\bar{x}$ be the random variable used to test the hypothesis. Show that the hypothesis does not uniquely determine the distribution of $\bar{x}$. For any given value of $\mu \leq 4$, what is the distribution of $\bar{x}$. Compute the probability of rejecting the hypothesis as a function of μ, $\mu \leq 4$, when the critical value used for $\bar{x}$ is $\delta = 6$. Plot a graph of this probability as a function of μ, and show that the probability of rejection is largest when $\mu = 4$. Show that by specifying the maximum probability of rejection, call it α, one can then determine a unique critical value for $\bar{x}$, and that the value of δ so obtained is precisely the same as that which one would obtain for testing the null hypothesis $\mu = 4$ at the level of significance α. This is the way that the hypothesis $\mu \leq 4$ would normally be tested, that is, it would be tested as the hypothesis $\mu = 4$ at some specified significance level, using $\bar{x}$ as a statistic and assuming that only large values of $\bar{x}$ are unfavorable to the hypothesis.

Section 9-5

1. In Problem 3 for Sections 9-3 and 9-4, suppose that use of the new feed would increase the feeding cost per chicken by $0.30, and suppose that each extra pound of weight on a chicken is worth $0.35 to the farmer. Imagine that the farmer assumes that the prior distribution for the expected increase in weight per chicken on using the new feed is normal with mean 0.75 lb and standard deviation 0.33 lb. Re-solve Problem 3 using decision theory. What is the critical number which is obtained in this way?

2. In Problem 4 for Sections 9-3 and 9-4, suppose that using the new synthetic rubber would increase the cost of a tire by $0.75, but that the company could increase the price of the tire in proportion to the mean increased milage it gave the factor of proportionality being $1.00 per 1000 mi. The research director feels that the prior distribution for the expected increase in mileage is normal with mean 500 mi and standard deviation 500 mi. Re-solve Problem 4 using decision theory. What is the critical number which is obtained in this way?

Section 9-6

1. Consider Problem 1 of Sections 9-3 and 9-4. Suppose that the null hypothesis H_0 is $\mu = 0.2510$, and that we now consider an alternative hypothesis H_1 which is $\mu = 0.2560$. What must the sample size be if the probability of rejecting H_0, when H_0 is true, is to be 0.05 and the probability of accepting H_0, when H_1 is true, is 0.10 or less? What is the critical number in this case?

2. Consider Problem 3 of Sections 9-3 and 9-4. Suppose that the null hypothesis H_0 is that there is no improvement in the new feed, and that the farmer also considers the alternative hypothesis that the expected increase in weight per chicken is 0.5 lb, everything else remaining the same. How many chickens should be tested if the farmer wishes to have the probability of rejecting H_0 when it is true be 0.01 and accepting H_0 when H_1 is true be 0.05 or less? What is the critical number in this case?

3. Consider Problem 4 of Sections 9-3 and 9-4. Suppose that the null hypothesis H_0 is that there is no improvement in the new rubber, and an alternative hypothesis H_1 is considered, which says that the mean increase in mileage is 300 mi, everything else remaining unchanged. How many tires would need to be tested if it is desired to have the probability of rejecting H_0 when it is true be 0.001 and of accepting H_0 when H_1 is true be 0.001 or less? What is the critical number in this case?

4. Consider a coin and imagine that we make the null hypothesis H_0 that the probability p of a head satisfies $p \leq \frac{1}{2}$. Suppose that we take as the alternative hypothesis H_1, which says $p > \frac{1}{2}$. To test the hypothesis H_0, we toss the coin n times and use the random variable x, the number of heads obtained, as the statistic. Show that the distribution of x, given that H_0 is true, is not uniquely determined, and that neither is the distribution of x when H_1 is true. To determine the distribution of x, p must be specified. Suppose now that a value of n and a critical value δ for x are also selected. Given n and δ, let $q_1(p)$ be the probability of rejecting H_0 when H_0 is true and the probability of a head is p, $p \leq \frac{1}{2}$. Also let $q_2(p)$ be the probability of accepting H_0 when H_1 is true and the probability of a head is p, $p > \frac{1}{2}$. Consider the function

$$q(p) = \begin{cases} q_1(p), & p \leq \frac{1}{2} \\ q_2(p), & p > \frac{1}{2}. \end{cases}$$

This is the probability of making an error when the probability of a head is p. Show that $q_1(p)$ and $q_2(p)$ decrease as p gets farther and farther away from $\frac{1}{2}$. Also show that $q(p)$ can be discontinuous at $p = \frac{1}{2}$. Plot $q(p)$ for $n = 10$ and for $\delta = 4, 5, 6, 7$. Is it possible in this case to specify arbitrarily the maximum probability of a type 1 error and of a type 2 error? What is the difficulty here?

5. Let x be a random variable which has the distribution $n(x; \mu, 2)$. Suppose that the null hypothesis H_0 is made that $\mu \leq 4$, and the alternative hypothesis H_1 is taken to be $\mu > 4$. To test H_0, n independent trials of a random experiment are performed, where on each trial a value of x is observed. Let $\bar{x}$ be the statistic used to test H_0. Let δ be the critical value of $\bar{x}$ and $q(\mu)$ be the probability of making a wrong choice when the expected value of x is μ. The function $q(\mu)$ can be determined as in Problem 4. For $n = 100$, plot $q(\mu)$ in the cases where $\delta = 3.8$, 4, 4.2. Is it possible in this case to specify arbitrarily the maximum probability of a type 1 error and a type 2 error? What is the difficulty here?

6. It was shown in Problems 4 and 5 that difficulties can be encountered in testing a hypothesis such as $\mu \leq \mu_0$ against the alternative $\mu > \mu_0$. A typical way to resolve this difficulty is to reformulate the problem by selecting a $\mu_1 < \mu_0$ and a $\mu_2 > \mu_0$ and testing the hypothesis $\mu = \mu_1$ against $\mu = \mu_2$, the probabilities α and β being specified. This now reduces to a problem of the type studied in the text. For the situation outlined in Problem 4, suppose the H_0 is taken to be $p = 0.45$ and H_1 to be $p = 0.55$ with $\alpha = \beta = 0.1$. Determine the experiment to be performed and the critical value of x in this case.

7. Let x be a random variable with the distribution $n(x; \mu, \sigma)$, where σ is known. Discuss the difficulties encountered in testing the hypothesis H_0, which is $\mu = \mu_0$, against H_1, which is $\mu \neq \mu_0$. Can one specify arbitrarily the probabilities α and β in this case? What is the difficulty here, and how might it be avoided?

Section 9-7

1. Determine the operating characteristic curve for the sampling plan determined for the example in the text.

2. Re-solve the example of the text if it is specified that $\alpha = 0.05$ and $\beta = 0.10$, the AQL and $LTFD$ remaining unchanged.

3. For the example in the text, determine n and c if the $LTFD$ is changed to 0.02 instead of being 0.03. Everything else remains unchanged.

4. For the sampling plan obtained in the text, what is the probability of accepting a lot having a fraction defective $p = 0.01$? Suppose that five lots arrive each of which has $p = 0.01$. What is the probability that three or more of these lots will be accepted?

5. An electronics manufacturer was having difficulties with the production of a certain small computer due to transistor defects. A sampling plan with an AQL of 0.005 was being used. The chief engineer made the statement that since the AQL was 0.005, on the average, no more than 0.5 percent of the transistors in any lot accepted should be defective. Did he make a true statement? Discuss.

6. For the example studied in the text, suppose that rejected lots are inspected 100 percent, and all defective units are replaced by good ones. Then the lot is sent into production. Thus every lot received from the supplier ultimately goes into production. If a lot is accepted by the sampling plan, it goes directly to production (with the defectives in the sample being replaced by good units), and if it is rejected it is inspected 100 percent, and then goes into production. Suppose now that every lot received from the supplier had a lot fraction defective of p. Each lot going into production would then have a fraction defective of 0 (if the lot was rejected) or $p - (r/N)$ (if the lot was accepted) where r is the number of defectives in the sample, $r \le c$. Generally, r/N is negligible, so that the lot fraction defective going into production is then either p or 0. Imagine now that we ask, what is the long run average fraction of the units going into production which are defective when the fraction defective in each lot coming from the supplier is p? Show that this long run fraction defective is $pP_a(p)$, and show that this would be the fraction defective in a large bin where the units from many lots coming from the sampling plan have been placed. The number $pP_a(p)$ is called the average outgoing quality for the sampling plan and is abbreviated AOQ. For each p, there is determined an AOQ. Plot a curve giving the AOQ as a function of p for the sampling plan developed in the text. Note that the AOQ curve goes through a maximum. The maximum value of the AOQ is called the average outgoing quality limit and is abbreviated AOQL. What is the AOQL, and for what p value does it occur? The AOQL tells us what is the worst long run fraction defective one can have for units going into production, regardless of what the lot fraction defective of the incoming lots is.

7. A manufacturer purchases teflon washers in lots of 100,000 from a given supplier. He wants to develop a sampling plan for controlling incoming quality. He would like a sampling plan that accepts lots having a fraction defective of 0.075

about 95 percent of the time and that accepts lots having a fraction defective of 0.04 about 5 percent of the time. Determine such a sampling plan.

8. Obtain the operating characteristic curve for the sampling plan determined in Problem 7.

9. Determine an AOQ curve for the sampling plan obtained in Problem 7. See Problem 6 for the definition of an AOQ curve.

10. In using a single sampling plan to control the quality of some given item purchased from a supplier, it is helpful to maintain a control chart on which one plots the fraction defective in the sample (or the number of defectives in the sample) for each lot inspected. Explain the type of useful information which could be obtained by maintaining such a chart.

11. Let n be the sample size and c the acceptance number for the sampling plan obtained in Problem 7. Consider now a new sampling plan with the sample size being $2n$ and the acceptance number being $2c$. On the same graph, plot the operating characteristic curve for this new sampling plan and also the operating characteristic curve for the sampling plan obtained in Problem 7.

12. In the incoming inspection procedure discussed in the text, items were only classified as good or defective. Sometimes, however, it is more convenient to measure the value of some parameter such as the resistance or diameter of each unit. If the average value of the parameter lies in a certain interval, the lot is accepted; otherwise the lot is rejected. A simple case to analyze is that where high values of the parameter are preferred to lower values. Suppose, for example, that a textile manufacturer purchases a lot of continuous filament nylon yarn. It can be imagined that when the batch was made the mean breaking strength of the yarn was determined. The textile manufacturer feels that a mean breaking strength of 50 lb can be considered to be good yarn, while a breaking strength of 43 lb would be considered not to be acceptable. He would like to reject lots having a mean breaking strength of 50 lb about 10 percent of the time and accept lots having a breaking strength of 43 lb about 10 percent of the time. Determine the sampling plan which he should use, and obtain the operating characteristic curve for the sampling plan, if it is assumed that the standard deviation of the breaking strength always has the value 2 lb.

Sections 9-8 and 9-9

1. Explain in detail why Figure 9-10 looks like it does. Hint: The values which r/n can take on are independent of p. The set of these values for which $|(r/n) - p| > 0.15$ remains unchanged for a certain interval of p values, although the probabilities change as p is changed, and then the set of values increases or decreases by one as p passes through certain critical values. Actually compute the points for $p = 0.10, 0.18, 0.25$, and 0.30.

2. A chemist is interested in determining the sulfur content of a given organic chemical. The experiment performed to do so is really a random experiment, and the estimate of the sulfur content obtained can be looked upon as the value taken on by a random variable x. Studies on substances having a known sulfur content have shown that x can be considered to be normally distributed with a mean equal to the sulfur content (expressed as percent by weight) and a standard deviation of 0.5 (expressed as percent by weight). To improve the estimate of the sulfur content, the experiment is repeated on several different samples. How many times should the experiment be repeated if it is desired that the probability that the estimate deviates from the true sulfur content by more than 0.1 (percent by weight) is not greater than 0.05?

3. A company which produces stereo records is considering the purchase of a new high speed, continuous feed molding machine. There is some concern in management, however, about the fraction of records produced that will be defective. It is decided to make a test to determine this number. How many records should be produced if it is desired that the probability that the estimate of the fraction defective differs from the true value by more than 0.003 be less than or equal to 0.01? Answer this under the assumption that nothing is known about the fraction defective that will be produced, and then under the assumption that it is known that the fraction defective will not be greater than 0.05.

4. Suppose that to estimate μ_x we perform n independent trials of $\mathcal{R}$, on each trial observing a value of x. Let $x\{j\}$ be the random variable representing x on the jth trial. Consider the random variable

$$y = \sum_{j=1}^{n} \alpha_j x\{j\}, \quad \text{where} \quad \sum_{j=1}^{n} \alpha_j = 1 \quad \text{and} \quad \alpha_j \geq 0, \quad j = 1, \ldots, n.$$

Show that the statistic y is an unbiased estimator for μ_x for any set of α_j satisfying the conditions given above. What is σ_y^2? Note that $y = \bar{x}$ if $\alpha_j = 1/n$ for each j. Show by an example that when the α_j are not chosen so that $\alpha_j = 1/n$, then $\sigma_y^2 > \sigma_{\bar{x}}^2$. Do this for the case where $n = 3$ and $\alpha_1 = 0.5$, $\alpha_2 = 0.3$, and $\alpha_3 = 0.2$. This shows that in general we expect $\bar{x}$ to be a better estimator of μ_x than y when $y \neq \bar{x}$ since $\sigma_{\bar{x}}^2 < \sigma_y^2$. This is indeed correct. One can prove (see the following two problems) that $\sigma_y^2 > \sigma_{\bar{x}}^2$, except when $y = \bar{x}$. How can you explain these results intuitively?

5. Consider the situation described in Problem 4 for the case where $n = 2$. Use a graphical argument to show that the minimum of $\alpha_1^2 + \alpha_2^2$ for $\alpha_1 + \alpha_2 = 1$ is taken on at the unique point $\alpha_1 = \alpha_2 = \frac{1}{2}$. Interpret this result in terms of the discussion of Problem 4.

6.° Prove that the minimum of $\sum_{j=1}^{n} \alpha_j^2$ for those $\alpha_j \geq 0$ which satisfy $\sum_{j=1}^{n} \alpha_j = 1$ is taken on at the unique point $\alpha_j = 1/n$, $j = 1, \ldots, n$. Apply this result to the discussion of Problem 7.

7.° Suppose that a coin is tossed n times, and r heads are obtained. If p is the probability of a head, then the probability of obtaining the r heads and $n - r$ tails in the sequence in which they were obtained is $L = p^r(1 - p)^{n-r}$. The probability L is called the likelihood of the outcome. Show that the value of p which maximizes L, given r and n, is $p = r/n$. Thus our estimate r/n of p, which we would obtain using the statistic $\bar{x}$, has the characteristic that it maximizes the probability

° Problems marked with ° require the use of calculus for their solution.

of obtaining the outcome of $\mathcal{R}_n$ that was observed. Such an estimator is called a maximum likelihood estimator. Hint: Set the derivative with respect to p equal to 0.

8.° Suppose that x has a normal distribution with known standard deviation σ_x. Suppose that the mean μ_x is not known, but we perform n independent trials of $\mathcal{R}$ and observe the values ξ_1 of $x\{1\}, \ldots, \xi_n$ of $x\{n\}$. The $x\{j\}$ are independent random variables, and the joint density function for these n random variables is the product of the density functions $n(x\{j\}; \mu_x, \sigma_x)$. Denote by L the value of the joint density function when $x\{j\} = \xi_j, j = 1, \ldots, n$. Then

$$L = n(\xi_1; \mu_x, \sigma_x) n(\xi_2; \mu_x, \sigma_x) \cdots n(\xi_n; \mu_x, \sigma_x).$$

As in Problem 7, L is referred to as the likelihood of the given outcome of $\mathcal{R}_n$ (even though L is a probability density here). Show that the value of μ_x, which maximizes L, is $\mu_x = \bar{\xi}$, $\bar{\xi} = \sum_{j=1}^{n} \xi_j/n$. Thus our estimate $\bar{\xi}$ of μ_x, which we would obtain from the statistic $\bar{x}$, maximizes the likelihood L in this case also and is again referred to as a maximum likelihood estimator.

9. A lot contains N units, perhaps resistors or ball bearings. Associated with each unit j is a number x_j, which may be the resistance or diameter of the unit. Now a sample of n units is selected at random from the lot, and the value of the number associated with each unit is determined. Let $\bar{\xi}$ be the average of the numbers associated with the n units. Then $\bar{\xi}$ is a value of a random variable $\bar{x}$, since the average depends on which units happened to be selected. Show that

$$\mu_{\bar{x}} = \lambda \quad \text{and} \quad \sigma_{\bar{x}}^2 = \frac{s}{n}\left(\frac{N-n}{N-1}\right),$$

where

$$\lambda = \frac{1}{N}\sum_{j=1}^{N} x_j; \quad s^2 = \frac{1}{N}\sum_{j=1}^{N} (x_j - \lambda)^2.$$

Hint: Write $n\bar{x} = \sum_{j=1}^{N} x_j \delta\{j\}$, where the $\delta\{j\}$ are random variables which can only take on the values 0 and 1. The $\delta\{j\}$ are not independent random variables. Construct a model of the experiment and determine from it the probability function for $\delta\{j\}$ and the joint probability function for $\delta\{i\}$ and $\delta\{j\}$.

Section 9-10

1. What troubles are encountered if we try to determine the variance of z in (9-19)?

2.° Suppose that x is normally distributed with mean μ and standard deviation σ. Let n independent trials of $\mathcal{R}$ be performed, and let $x\{j\}$ be the random variable representing x on the jth trial. Consider the random variable

$$z = \frac{1}{n}\sum_{j=1}^{n} (x\{j\} - \mu)^2.$$

Determine the distribution of z and also determine its mean and variance.

3. Show that

$$s_x^2 = \frac{1}{n}\sum_{j=1}^{n} (\xi_j - \bar{\xi})^2 = \frac{1}{n}\sum_{j=1}^{n} \xi_j^2 - \bar{\xi}^2.$$

4. Suppose that we toss a penny n times and obtain r heads, so that our estimate of the probability of a head is r/n. Show that $s_x{}^2$ of (9-18) then yields

$$s_x{}^2 = \frac{r}{n}\left(1 - \frac{r}{n}\right).$$

5.° Suppose that x is normally distributed with mean μ_x and variance $\sigma_x{}^2$. Consider a case where μ_x is known, but σ_x is not. Assume that n independent trials of $\mathcal{R}$ are performed, and the values of x observed are $\xi_1, \ldots, \xi_n$. The value of the joint density function for $x\{1\}, \ldots, x\{n\}$ evaluated at $x\{j\} = \xi_j, j = 1, \ldots, n$, is

$$L = n(\xi_1; \mu_x, \sigma_x) n(\xi_2; \mu_x, \sigma_x) \cdots n(\xi_n; \mu_x, \sigma_x).$$

As we noted in Problem 8 of Sections 9-8 and 9-9, L is called the likelihood. Determine the value of $\sigma_x{}^2$ which maximizes L, and show that this value is $s_x{}^2$, where $s_x{}^2$ is given by (9-17), so that the statistic z whose value is (9-17) is a maximum likelihood estimator. Hint: Maximize $\log L$.

6.° Let x be normally distributed. Suppose that n independent trials of $\mathcal{R}$ are performed, yielding the values $\xi_1, \ldots, \xi_n$ of x which are to be used to estimate both μ_x and $\sigma_x{}^2$. Let the likelihood L be defined as in Problem 5. Find the values of μ_x and $\sigma_x{}^2$ which maximize L. Hint: Maximize $\log L$ by setting

$$\frac{\partial}{\partial \mu_x} \log L = \frac{\partial}{\partial \sigma_x} \log L = 0.$$

7. Consider a production process which turns out units such as resistors or ball bearings whose quality is determined by the value of a continuous random variable x, which might be the resistance of the resistors, for example. Let us examine what is involved in monitoring the process. Note that a change in the process could change the distribution $f(x)$ for x into a completely different distribution $g(x)$. It is difficult to monitor the process carefully enough to determine in any detail changes in the shape of the graph of $f(x)$. Generally, one settles for a much simpler approach which involves only the monitoring of the expected value and standard deviation of x. This is done through the use of control charts. We shall consider here only the control chart for the expected value of x. Let us suppose that it is believed that x has an expected value of μ_x and a standard deviation σ_x. Imagine now that a sample of n units is taken periodically and the value of x for each unit in the sample is determined, as well as the average $\bar{\xi}$ of these x values. Then $\bar{\xi}$ is a value of the random variable $\bar{x}$ which has expected value μ_x and standard deviation $\sigma_x/\sqrt{n}$. Furthermore, $\bar{x}$ will be roughly normally distributed even if n is not too large, say for $n \geq 4$. The procedure generally used to decide whether the process should be checked to see if something is wrong and μ_x has changed is as follows. If $\bar{\xi}$, the observed value of $\bar{x}$, is more than three standard deviations away from μ_x, action is taken; otherwise, no action is taken. This test can be conveniently carried out, while one simultaneously maintains a record of what has happened in the past by using a control chart, called an $\bar{x}$ chart (read x-bar chart), which looks like the one shown in Figure 5-4. The center line is now μ_x rather than np, and UCL $= \mu_x + 3(\sigma_x/\sqrt{n})$; LCL $= \mu_x - 3(\sigma_x/\sqrt{n})$. In practice, the sample size n is quite small, being about 5 or 6. If

x has an expected value of 1.25 and $\sigma_x = 0.10$, what value of n should be used if it is desired to catch a shift of 0.10 or more in the expected value of x with probability 0.80 in the first sample taken after the shift occurs? Assume that σ_x remains unchanged and that $\bar{x}$ can be treated as normally distributed. By catching the shift, we mean that $\bar{\xi}$ will lie outside the control limits.

8. Consider a process of the type described in Problem 7. Suppose that a unit is classified as good if $\gamma_1 \leq x \leq \gamma_2$ and defective otherwise. The numbers γ_1 and γ_2 are called the tolerance limits. One could proceed to control the process simply by classifying units in the sample as good or defective and not bothering to measure x at all. With this procedure, only one control chart of the type illustrated in Figure 5-4 would be needed. Suppose that this procedure was used. What would be the center line and control limits for the number of defectives if a sample of size n is used? What is the fraction defective p_1 produced if μ_x changes from 1.25 to 1.35, everything else remaining unchanged? Assume in making the computations that x is normally distributed and $\gamma_1 = 1.05$, $\gamma_2 = 1.50$. If one were using this procedure of only classifying units as good or defective, what would n have to be in order to catch a shift in the fraction defective from the value corresponding to $\mu_x = 1.25$ to p_1? Note that here n is larger than the n value obtained in Problem 7. This illustrates the general truth that by measuring x for each unit one obtains more information than by merely classifying the unit as good or defective, and therefore smaller sample sizes are needed to catch changes in the process.

Section 9-11

1. Draw a straight line on a piece of paper. Ask 50 different individuals to measure its length and record the answers they give. Construct a histogram for the lengths. Measure the length very carefully, and then construct a histogram for the measurement process. Does it appear that the error variable is normally distributed?

2. It is desired to determine the mean resistance of the resistors produced by a production process. These are to be sold as 1000 ohm resistors. Previous experience indicates that the random variable x representing the resistance of any given unit is normally distributed with a standard deviation of 25 ohms. The resistance is measured with an ohm meter. The measurement process can be looked upon as a random experiment whose outcome yields a reading which is the value of a random variable y. Assume that y is normally distributed with the mean being the actual resistance and the standard deviation being 10 ohms. It is believed that the measurement error is completely independent of the value of the resistance being measured. It is desired that the probability that the estimate of μ_x will differ from μ_x by more than 10 ohms be 0.01 or less. How many resistors should be included in the sample? How should μ_x be estimated? How large would the sample need to be if there were no measurement errors?

3. Suppose that no assumptions were made concerning the independence of the random variables $x\{j\}$ and $\epsilon\{j\}$ in (9-22). Write down the general expression for the variance of y.

CHAPTER 10

THE POISSON PROCESS

*Silently one by one, in the infinite
meadows of heaven blossomed the lovely
stars, the forget-me-nots of the angels.*

H. W. Longfellow, *Evangeline.*

10-1 STOCHASTIC PROCESSES

In this brief chapter we would like to introduce one of the simplest
examples of what is referred to as a *stochastic process.* A stochastic process
represents a generalization of the notion of a random experiment; it simultaneously generalizes the notion of a random variable to what is referred
to as a *random function.* We shall begin with an example to illustrate the
type of problem which we wish to consider.

A supermarket is interested in knowing something about the arrival
pattern of its customers. The number of customers entering the store
between 9 a.m. and 10 a.m. on a weekday can be looked upon as a random
variable x, which can take on the values $0, 1, 2, \ldots$. The number of
customers will not be the same every day, but will vary from one day to
another. Nonetheless, it will be found that the relative frequencies of
various numbers of customers appearing are stable. Thus one can conveniently imagine that a random experiment is performed each day which
determines the number of customers that will appear between 9 and 10 in
the morning, and we can think of the number of these customers as being
a random variable.

Now the store is not merely interested in learning something about the
number of customers arriving between 9 and 10 in the morning; it is also
interested in the number of customers arriving between 9 and 11, 9 and 12,
and in the entire day, and sometimes during other periods, such as 9 to
9:30 or 9 to 10:30. Associated with any one of these periods, we can

imagine that there is a random variable representing the number of customers that will arrive in the time period under consideration. The probability functions for the different random variables will, of course, be different since the lengths of the intervals vary. We can now go one step farther and imagine that associated with every time interval which begins at 9 in the morning and whose length t is not greater than the number of hours for which the store remains open, there is a random variable representing the number of customers that will arrive in the store in the interval of length t. In general, of course, there is no reason why the initial time must be 9 a.m. We could use any other time for the initial time.

The type of problem we have just described is somewhat different from the problems we have studied previously in that now we are not necessarily interested in a single random variable or two random variables, but instead in a whole collection of random variables, one for each value of t. Indeed, if we imagine that t can take on every value in some interval, then there is an infinite number of random variables of the type we have described. This association of a random variable with each real number t in some interval or with some unending sequence of t values $t_0, t_1, \ldots$, defines a function whose domain is a set of real numbers and whose range is a set of random variables. Such a function is called a *random function* and is sometimes denoted by $x(t)$. One must be careful not to become confused when using this terminology since $x(t)$, the image of t, is not a number, but is instead a random variable. We shall frequently be interested in dealing with the probability function for $x(t)$. For any value of t, the random variable $x(t)$, which represents the number of customers arriving in a time period of length t, can take on the values $0, 1, 2, \ldots$, and the probability that $x(t) = n$ will be denoted by $P_n(t)$. It might seem more in line with our previous notation to represent this probability by $p(n; t)$, but $P_n(t)$ is the notation normally used and we shall adopt it. The interesting question then arises as to whether we can develop mathematical models which are reasonably realistic representations of the real world and which make it possible to determine $P_n(t)$ for every n and t of interest. This can indeed be done, and we shall develop one such model in this chapter.

We noted in Chapter 1 when introducing the notion of a random variable that it is often convenient from an intuitive point of view to imagine that there is some chance mechanism which determines the value of the random variable when the corresponding random experiment is performed. Equally well, it is often convenient to imagine for the problem that we are currently studying that there is some chance process which determines the points in time at which customers arrive in the store, or stated in another way, the numbers of customers which arrive in various time intervals. Such a chance process is frequently referred to as a *stochastic process*.

From a mathematical point of view, a stochastic process is simply defined to be a random function $x(t)$. It is generally the case that when one uses the term stochastic process, one thinks of t in $x(t)$ as being time, as we did in the above example. However, not infrequently, one deals with random functions where t is not time, but may instead refer to length or volume or some other physical parameter. It is not typical to refer to $x(t)$ as a stochastic process when t is not time, although it would not violate the mathematical definition to do so. In general, the random variables appearing in a stochastic process need not be discrete as in our example; they can be continuous random variables. However, we shall only deal with cases where for each t, $x(t)$ is a discrete random variable.

The above example we used to introduce the notion of a stochastic process is just one of many which we could use. For example, instead of considering the arrivals of customers at a supermarket, we might have used the calls arriving at a telephone exchange, the failures of a certain type of vacuum tube in a piece of electronic equipment, the number of alpha particles emitted by a radioactive substance, or the number of deaths in a given city caused by cancer.

We shall now proceed to develop a mathematical model of one stochastic process which is referred to as the Poisson process. This is the only stochastic process we shall study. It is an extremely important one, however.

10-2 THE POISSON PROCESS

Let us consider some real world process in which at unpredictable times certain events occur. The interpretation of what we shall call an event can vary considerably depending on the physical situation we have in mind. An event may represent the arrival of a customer in a supermarket, an incoming call at a telephone exchange, the emission of an alpha particle by a radioactive substance, or the failure of a vacuum tube in a piece of electronic equipment. We shall be assuming that the times of occurrence of events cannot be predicted in advance, but are determined by chance. Intuitively we shall imagine that the occurrences of events are generated by a stochastic process. We would like to develop one possible model for such a situation from which we can determine $P_n(t)$, the probability that precisely n events occur in a time period of length t.

To construct such a model, we must make some assumptions about the nature of the process. Intuitively, we shall assume first of all that the nature of the stochastic process generating the events does not change with time. This assumption would imply, for example, that the average rate of arrival of customers at the supermarket did not change with the

time of day.   In reality, of course, there would be a change with the time
of day.   In practice, no stochastic processes are time invariant, and therefore our model will only approximately represent the nature of the real
world.   Nonetheless, it is a very convenient approximation to make, and
it often represents reasonably well the actual real world behavior over
time intervals which are not too long.   We shall make the additional
important assumption that the probability of n events occurring in a time
period of length t depends only on the length of the interval and is independent of where in time the interval begins.   This has a number of ramifica-
tions as we shall see later.   We shall also assume that two or more events
cannot occur simultaneously.   The time interval between the occurrence of
two successive events may be arbitrarily small, but they cannot occur
simultaneously.   This means, for example, we are assuming that two customers cannot arrive at the supermarket at precisely the same instant.
Let us now summarize the above in mathematical terms and simultaneously introduce one final assumption.

To proceed it is convenient to introduce a notation often used in mathematics.   We use the symbolism $o(h)$ to denote any function having the
characteristic that

$$\lim_{h \to 0} \frac{o(h)}{h} = 0. \qquad (10\text{-}1)$$

Typical functions $o(h)$ are h^2, $3h^3 - 2h^2$, $16h^4$, etc.   We shall now assume
that the stochastic process we are considering is characterized by the following two axioms:

1. The probability that precisely one event will occur between time t
and a later time $t + h$ is $\vartheta h + o_1(h)$, where $\vartheta > 0$ is a constant.   This is
completely independent of what has happened before time t.

Note that Axiom 1 implies essentially that the probability of having
precisely one event occur in a period of length h is proportional to h when
h is very small.   Furthermore, the constant of proportionality ϑ does not
depend on t or h.

2. The probability that more than one event occurs between time t and
a later time $t + h$ is $o_2(h)$.

Axiom 2 guarantees that two or more events cannot occur simultaneously, since the probability that two or more events occur in an interval
of length h, divided by the probability that one occurs, is $o_2(h)/(\vartheta h + o_1(h))$,
which approaches 0 as $h \to 0$.   However, this ratio is the long run ratio of
very short intervals having two or more events occurring in them, to those
having one event.   This ratio is 0, and thus the corresponding long run
frequency is 0.   This is as close as we can come in a probability model to
saying that two or more events cannot occur simultaneously.   In Axioms

1 and 2, we need not specify $o_1(h)$ and $o_2(h)$. As a matter of fact, they cannot be specified arbitrarily, but will be determined by the solution to the problem, as we shall see.

The two axioms just given completely characterize the stochastic process called the *Poisson process*. We shall now show how to determine the function $P_n(t)$, the probability that precisely n events occur in a period of length t. This is done using a technique which is somewhat different from those we have employed previously. Consider the time interval T_1 of length $t + h$ which begins at t_1 and ends at $t_1 + t + h$, and the time interval T_2 of length t which begins at time t_1 and ends at time $t_1 + t$. Also consider the time interval T_3 of length h which begins at time $t_1 + t$ and ends at time $t_1 + t + h$. Then $T_1 = T_2 \cup T_3$. The probability that precisely n events occur in T_1 is $P_n(t + h)$. We shall now relate this to what happens in T_2 and T_3. To be specific, we shall assume that each of the above time intervals includes the right-hand end point of the interval but not the left one. Then $T_2 \cap T_3 = \varnothing$. It is convenient (but not at all necessary), to do this, so that we need not be concerned about the possibility of an event occurring at time $t_1 + t$ being in both T_2 and T_3.

When $n \geq 1$, there are three mutually exclusive and collectively exhaustive ways in which n events can occur in the interval T_1. This can happen if n events occur in T_2 and none in T_3. The probability of this event, call it A, is

$$P_n(t)[1 - \vartheta h - o_1(h) - o_2(h)]. \tag{10-2}$$

It can also happen if $n - 1$ events occur in T_2, and one event occurs in T_3. The probability of this event, call it B, is

$$P_{n-1}(t)[\vartheta h + o_1(h)]. \tag{10-3}$$

Finally, if $n > 1$, n events can occur in the interval T_1 if r, $r < n - 1$, events occur in T_2 and $n - r$ occur in T_3. The probability of this event, call it C, is a function $o_3(h)$, since it involves the occurrence of two or more events in T_3. In obtaining (10-2) and (10-3), we made use of the fact that what happens in T_3 is totally independent of what happened in T_2. Thus we are dealing with independent events and the probabilities multiply.

Now the events A and B are exclusive, so that $p(A \cup B) = p(A) + p(B)$. But C and $A \cup B$ are exclusive, so

$$p(A \cup B \cup C) = p(A \cup B) + p(C) = p(A) + p(B) + p(C).$$

However, $p(A \cup B \cup C)$ is $P_n(t + h)$. Thus on using (10-2) and (10-3),

$$\begin{aligned} P_n(t + h) &= P_n(t)[1 - \vartheta h - o_1(h) - o_2(h)] + P_{n-1}(t)[\vartheta h + o_1(h)] + o_3(h) \\ &= P_n(t) - \vartheta h P_n(t) + \vartheta h P_{n-1}(t) + o_4(h), \end{aligned} \tag{10-4}$$

where $o_4(h)$ is

$$o_4(h) = o_3(h) - o_1(h)[P_n(t) - P_{n-1}(t)] - o_2(h)P_n(t),$$

and $o_4(h)$ satisfies (10-1). The term $o_3(h)$ does not appear when $n = 1$. On dividing (10-4) by $h > 0$, we can write

$$\frac{P_n(t + h) - P_n(t)}{h} = \vartheta P_{n-1}(t) - \vartheta P_n(t) + \frac{o_4(h)}{h}. \tag{10-5}$$

Now by (10-1), $\lim_{h \to 0+} o_4(h)/h = 0$. Also, since the limit of a constant is the constant, it follows that

$$\lim_{h \to 0+} [\vartheta P_{n-1}(t) - \vartheta P_n(t)] = \vartheta P_{n-1}(t) - \vartheta P_n(t). \tag{10-6}$$

Therefore the limit of the right-hand side of (10-5) exists as $h \to 0$ through positive values, and hence the limit of the left-hand side of (10-5) also exists.

Now

$$\lim_{h \to 0} \frac{P_n(t + h) - P_n(t)}{h} = \frac{d}{dt} P_n(t) = P_n'(t)$$

when the limit exists, by the definition of the derivative of a function. To be completely rigorous, we cannot immediately conclude that $P_n'(t)$ does exist because we have only shown that the limit as $h \to 0+$ exists. It is also necessary to show that the limit as $h \to 0-$ exists and is equal to (10-6). This can be shown by going through the above development taking T_1 to be the interval which extends from t_1 to $t_1 + t$, T_2 to be the interval which extends from t_1 to $t_1 + t - h$, and T_3 to be the interval which extends from $t_1 + t - h$ to $t_1 + t$. We ask the reader to provide the details in the problems. In this way one proves that $P_n'(t)$ exists for all $t > 0$ and in addition

$$P_n'(t) + \vartheta P_n(t) = \vartheta P_{n-1}(t), \quad n \geq 1. \tag{10-7}$$

Here we have a first order linear differential equation with constant coefficients which relates $P_n(t)$ to $P_{n-1}(t)$, so that if $P_{n-1}(t)$ is known, $P_n(t)$ can be found by solving the differential equation.

Our above analysis did not include the case where $n = 0$. There is only one way in which no events can occur in the interval T_1. It is to have no events occur in T_2 and also no events in T_3. The probability of this is

$$P_0(t)[1 - \vartheta h - o_1(h) - o_2(h)] = P_0(t)[1 - \vartheta h] + o_6(h). \tag{10-8}$$

Thus

$$P_0(t + h) = P_0(t) - \vartheta h P_0(t) + o_6(h), \tag{10-9}$$

or

$$\frac{P_0(t + h) - P_0(t)}{h} = \vartheta P_0(t) + \frac{o_6(h)}{h}, \tag{10-10}$$

and on taking the limit as $h \to 0$, we conclude that $P_0'(t)$ exists and

$$P_0'(t) + \vartheta P_0(t) = 0. \tag{10-11}$$

Here we have a linear differential equation involving only $P_0(t)$. It is a homogeneous equation with constant coefficients, and the set of all solutions has the form

$$P_0(t) = ce^{-\vartheta t}, \tag{10-12}$$

where c is any real number. It is not true that every one of these solutions will satisfy our axioms, however. Note that $c = P_0(0)$, where by $P_0(0)$ we mean $\lim_{h \to 0+} P_0(h)$. Now from Axioms 1 and 2 the probability that no event occurs from 0 to h is $1 - \vartheta h - o_1(h) - o_2(h)$, and as $h \to 0+$, this approaches 1. Thus we must have $c = P_0(0) = 1$ and

$$P_0(t) = e^{-\vartheta t}. \tag{10-13}$$

We have obtained here an interesting consequence of our axioms. It says that the probability that no events occur in a time period of length t is $e^{-\vartheta t}$.

Having determined $P_0(t)$, we can now determine the other $P_n(t)$ recursively from (10-7). Let us first show how to solve (10-7). There are a variety of ways this could be done. The simplest for our purposes is to first multiply (10-7) by $e^{\vartheta t}$ to yield

$$e^{\vartheta t}P_n'(t) + \vartheta e^{\vartheta t}P_n(t) = \vartheta e^{\vartheta t}P_{n-1}(t). \tag{10-14}$$

Now the right-hand side of (10-14) is nothing but the derivative of $e^{\vartheta t}P_n(t)$. Thus

$$\frac{d}{dt}[e^{\vartheta t}P_n(t)] = \vartheta e^{\vartheta t}P_{n-1}(t), \tag{10-15}$$

or if we integrate both sides from 0 to t, we have

$$e^{\vartheta t}P_n(t) - P_n(0) = \vartheta \int_0^t e^{\vartheta \tau}P_{n-1}(\tau)\, d\tau. \tag{10-16}$$

For $n \geq 1$, $P_n(0) = 0$, as we can immediately see from the axioms. When $n = 1$, the probability that an event occurs in the interval 0 to h is $\vartheta h + o_1(h)$, and this approaches 0 as $h \to 0+$. We of course reach the same conclusion for $n > 1$. Therefore

$$P_n(t) = \vartheta e^{-\vartheta t} \int_0^t e^{\vartheta \tau}P_{n-1}(\tau)\, d\tau, \quad n \geq 1. \tag{10-17}$$

Equation (10-17) can be used to compute $P_1(t)$ from $P_0(t)$, then $P_2(t)$ from $P_1(t)$, etc.

To proceed in this way, we note that

$$P_1(t) = \vartheta e^{-\vartheta t} \int_0^t e^{\vartheta \tau}e^{-\vartheta \tau}\, d\tau = \vartheta e^{-\vartheta t} \int_0^t d\tau = \vartheta t e^{-\vartheta t}. \tag{10-18}$$

Thus

$$P_2(t) = \vartheta e^{-\vartheta t} \int_0^t (\vartheta \tau)\, d\tau = \frac{(\vartheta t)^2}{2} e^{-\vartheta t}, \tag{10-19}$$

and

$$P_3(t) = \vartheta e^{-\vartheta t} \int_0^t \frac{(\vartheta \tau)^2}{2} \, d\tau = \frac{(\vartheta t)^3}{3!} e^{-\vartheta t}. \tag{10-20}$$

It would then appear that for all integers $n \geq 0$,

$$P_n(t) = \frac{(\vartheta t)^n}{n!} e^{-\vartheta t}. \tag{10-21}$$

This is indeed true, and the rigorous proof can easily be made by induction. We have already seen that (10-21) is true for $n = 0$ and $n = 1$. Suppose now that (10-21) holds for $n = k$. Then

$$P_{k+1}(t) = \vartheta e^{-\vartheta t} \int_0^t \frac{(\vartheta \tau)^k}{k!} \, d\tau = \frac{(\vartheta t)^{k+1}}{(k+1)!} e^{-\vartheta t}.$$

Consequently, if (10-21) holds for $n = k$, it also holds for $n = k + 1$, and since it holds for $n = 0$ and $n = 1$, it follows by the induction principle that it holds for all integers $n \geq 0$.

Equation (10-21) is a very interesting result because it says the probability that precisely n events will occur in any time period of length t is the Poisson probability $p(n; \vartheta t)$. Heretofore, we have thought of the Poisson probability function merely as being useful to approximate the binomial distribution. However, it has now appeared in a completely different context as characterizing a particular type of stochastic process. Because $P_n(t) = p(n; \vartheta t)$, the stochastic process characterized by axioms 1 and 2 is called a Poisson process. The Poisson process is a very important and useful one because it often represents with acceptable accuracy the behavior of the real world. The reason for this is that it is often fairly realistic to assume that the number of events which occur in an interval of length t does not depend on what happened prior to the beginning of the interval, that for short intervals the probability that an event will occur is proportional to the length of the interval, and that two or more events do not occur simultaneously (at least not very often).

We can now give a clear intuitive meaning to the constant which appeared in Axiom 1. The expected number of events which occur in a period of length t is ϑt and is proportional to the length of the interval. Thus ϑ is the expected number of events which will occur in one unit of time, and for this reason it is often referred to as the mean rate at which events occur. The physical dimensions of ϑ are number of events per unit of time. We shall see below that $1/\vartheta$ is the expected time between the occurrence of two successive events.

10-3 EXAMPLES

Let us now illustrate by some examples a few of the many applications of the Poisson process.

1. The Poisson distribution is used very frequently in inventory theory, since it is often realistic to assume that the number of orders arriving in any time interval is adequately described by the axioms for a Poisson process. Thus the probability that n orders arrive in a time period of length t is taken to be $p(n; \vartheta t)$, where ϑ is the average rate at which orders arrive (perhaps ten per day, for example). Generally, though, one is not interested in the number of orders received in a given time period but instead in the number of units demanded in the time period. If units are always or almost always demanded one at a time, that is, an order is always or almost always for precisely one unit, then the probability that n units are demanded in a time period of length t will be essentially $p(n; \vartheta t)$. On the other hand, if the order size is a random variable which shows quite a bit of fluctuation from one order to another, $p(n; \vartheta t)$ may be a very poor approximation to the probability that n units will be demanded in a time period of length t. If one knows the distribution of the random variable representing the order size, then it is possible in some cases to compute $P_n(t)$, the probability that n units will be demanded in time t. An example of such a computation is given in [2]. However, the resulting distributions so obtained are frequently sufficiently complicated that they are not used in practice. Often the Poisson distribution will be used even though the order may be frequently for two or three units rather than just a single one. In inventory theory, especially in dealing with models such as the one studied in Section 4-8 where more than a single order will be placed, it is necessary to know the probability of having n units demanded as a function of time because the costs involved depend on time. Examples of models of this type are to be found in [2] also.

Even in working with single stage inventory models it is sometimes very useful to know the probability that n units will be demanded in a time period of length t, as a function of t. Let us now provide a simple illustration of such a situation. The navy is in the process of building two identical special purpose nuclear submarines. It is desired to determine how many spares of an expensive heat exchanger used in the nuclear reactor should be produced at the time the submarines are being built. Each heat exchanger will cost $7000 when produced with the submarines and will cost $14,000 if manufactured later. Any heat exchangers left over when the submarines are scrapped will be a total loss. Partly on the basis of historical data the navy estimates the probability that n spares will be required in a period of t years for the two submarines will be the

Poisson probability $p(n; \vartheta t)$ where ϑ, the mean usage rate, is 0.2 per year. The navy is not sure how long the submarines will remain in the fleet, but it is estimated that the expected life will be ten years with the standard deviation being two years. Although it is difficult to determine with great accuracy, they feel that the probability density for the useful life of the submarines can be assumed to be a gamma distribution.

The above provides the data we need to determine the optimal number of spares to procure initially. The problem here is different from the type studied in Chapter 4 because the length of the period is not prespecified but is itself a random variable, and the probability that any given number of spares will be demanded will depend on the length of service for the submarines. The costs depend only on the number of units demanded, and thus the possible states of nature correspond to the various possible numbers of spares which can be demanded. Let x be the random variable representing the number of spares demanded. Consider now the determination of $p(x)$, the probability function for x. The value observed for x can be thought of as the result of a two stage experiment. At the first stage the service life t is determined, and then, given this value of t, the number of spares demanded is determined. The outcome of this two stage random experiment is then described by a pair of numbers $\langle \tau, n \rangle$, where τ is the observed value of the random variable t and n is the observed value of the random variable x. What we wish to compute is the probability function for x. According to (7-130), it is

$$p(n) = \int_0^\infty p(n; \vartheta t) g(t; \alpha, \lambda)\, dt, \qquad (10\text{-}22)$$

where $g(t; \alpha, \lambda)$ is the gamma function which is the density function for the service life. We have evaluated this integral in a different context in Chapter 8, and the result is given by (8-8), which for the notation being used here becomes

$$p(n) = \frac{\Gamma(\alpha + n + 1)}{n!\Gamma(\alpha + 1)} \left(\frac{\lambda}{\vartheta + \lambda}\right)^{\alpha+1} \left(\frac{\vartheta}{\vartheta + \lambda}\right)^n. \qquad (10\text{-}23)$$

We can now make an interesting observation. If α is an integer k, then

$$p(n) = \frac{(n + k)!}{n!k!}\, p^{k+1} q^n, \qquad (10\text{-}24)$$

where

$$p = \frac{\lambda}{\vartheta + \lambda} \quad \text{and} \quad q = 1 - p = \frac{\vartheta}{\vartheta + \lambda}. \qquad (10\text{-}25)$$

In this case $p(x)$ is the negative binomial distribution $b_n(x; k + 1, p)$ (see Problem 8 for Section 5-11). This suggests that (10-23) can be used to generalize the negative binomial distribution to the case where r is not an integer. This generalization is often useful. Thus we can say that when in a single stage inventory problem the demand is Poisson distributed in any interval and the length of the period is represented by a gamma distribution, then the marginal distribution of demand over the period has a negative binomial distribution.

In the event that α is not an integer, we can use (7-108) to show that (10-23) becomes

$$p(n) = \frac{1}{n!}(\alpha + n)(\alpha + n - 1)\cdots(\alpha + 1)p^{\alpha+1}q^n, \; n \geq 1;$$

$$p(0) = p^{\alpha+1}. \tag{10-26}$$

Let us now use (10-26) to solve the example we are studying. For the case under study, the gamma distribution has a mean of ten years and variance of four years squared. Thus from (7-109) and (7-110)

$$\lambda = \frac{\mu}{\sigma^2} = 2.5; \quad \alpha + 1 = \mu\lambda = 25. \tag{10-27}$$

Furthermore, the mean usage rate is $\vartheta = 0.2$ per year, so that

$$p = \frac{2.5}{2.7} = 0.9258; \quad q = \frac{0.2}{2.7} = 0.0742. \tag{10-28}$$

In the notation of Section 4-3, $C = 7000$ and $T = 14,000$. Furthermore, $S = 0$ since the units are not sold and $R = 0$ since they have no salvage value. Thus n^*, the optimal number of spares to order, is the smallest n for which

$$P(n) \geq \frac{(T - C)}{T} = \frac{7000}{14,000} = 0.5 \tag{10-29}$$

where $P(x)$ is the cumulative distribution for x. On using (10-27) and (10-28) in (10-26), we see that

$$P(0) = p(0) = 0.1455; \quad P(1) = p(0) + p(1) = 0.415;$$
$$P(2) = P(1) + p(2) = 0.675.$$

Thus $n^* = 2$, and two spare heat exchangers should be produced when the submarines are being constructed.

2.   We have in our discussions thus far always thought of the parameter t as being time. In a number of problems of practical interest, however, t has some other interpretation. In the weaving of cloth, for example, small defects occur from time to time due to some malfunction in the operation of some piece of equipment. It is essential to control the generation of defects in the fabric, just as it is to control the fraction defective for a process which turns out discrete units of some product. Generally, defects in the cloth will occur in bunches as the result of some out of control condition in the spinning or weaving equipment. However,

defects do occur occasionally even if all equipment is operating properly. To decide whether or not the process is operating in a satisfactory manner, it is convenient to introduce some idealized standard by which it can be judged. In other words, we need a definition of what is meant by the process being in statistical control. It is very convenient to define statistical control for the case under consideration as the situation where defects appear as if they were generated by a Poisson process, so that the probability of having precisely n defects in t square yards of cloth is $p(n; \vartheta t)$, where ϑ is the mean number of defects per square yard. When all the machinery is operating well, the spinning and weaving process will come quite close to behaving as if defects were generated by a Poisson process.

One can then use a control chart as an aid in controlling the process just as is done for processes where discrete units are produced. Periodically one inspects a sample of m square yards and determines the number of defects n in the sample. Based on the value of n one either takes no action, or if n is too large (or too small), one concludes that an investigation should be made to see if something is wrong. The same criterion is used as that in Example 1 of Section 5-8. If n is more than three standard deviations away from the mean, action is taken. Now the mean number of defects in the sample is ϑm, where ϑ is the average number of defects per square yard, and the standard deviation is $\sigma = \sqrt{\vartheta m}$. The center line for the control chart is then ϑm, the upper control limit is UCL $= \vartheta m + 3\sqrt{\vartheta m}$, and the lower control limit is LCL $= \vartheta m - 3\sqrt{\vartheta m}$. Usually it is preferable, instead of using the control chart just described, to use one in which one plots n/m, the average number of defects per square yard in the sample. This type of chart is preferable because the average number of defects per square yard is the variable which has immediate meaning to management. The center line for this chart would be ϑ and the UCL $= \vartheta + 3\sqrt{\vartheta/m}$ and LCL $= \vartheta - 3\sqrt{\vartheta/m}$, since if σ is the standard deviation of x, σ/m is the standard deviation of x/m. Control charts of the type just described are used extensively in the textile industry.

There are many other processes where the Poisson process can be used conveniently to define what is meant by statistical control, and where control charts of the type just described are useful. Some examples are the manufacture of plate glass, paper, wire, rope, and almond chocolate bars (to control the number of nuts per bar). The method is also useful for statistical control of errors in typesetting for newspapers or books and in many clerical type jobs.

3. A number of chemical elements possess the characteristic that they are unstable and decay into other chemical elements or more stable isotopes of the same element by emitting one of several type of particles, such as electrons or alpha particles from the nucleus. This is referred to as

radioactivity. The time at which any given nucleus will emit a particle cannot be predicted in advance, but must be imagined to be determined by chance. This time is independent of what other nuclei have done and is essentially independent of all external conditions. Once a nucleus has been transformed by emitting a particle, it may or may not at later times undergo additional transformation by emitting another particle (of the same or possibly a different kind). Let us here concentrate our attention on radioactive substances which undergo only one transformation by emitting a single particle, so that once a nucleus has emitted a particle, it is no longer radioactive.

Consider then a piece of radioactive material of this type, which contains millions of nuclei. Let us ask what is the probability that this piece of material will emit precisely n particles in a time period of length t? Experimental data suggest that for time periods which are not too long (we shall make this more precise below), the number of particles emitted behaves to a very good approximation as if the particles emitted were events generated by a Poisson process, so that the probability that n particles will be emitted in a time period of length t is $p(n; \vartheta t)$, where ϑ is the mean rate at which they are emitted.

The representation of the radioactive decay process as a Poisson process is only an approximate one as we can easily see from the following. Once a nucleus decays, it is no longer radioactive. Thus the total number of radioactive nuclei decreases with time, ultimately approaching 0, and hence ϑ, the mean rate at which particles are emitted, decreases with time, ultimately approaching 0. Let us now obtain a more realistic model which takes account of the fact that ϑ changes with time. Experimental evidence shows that the probability that a single nucleus does not decay in a time length t depends only on t and is in fact the Poisson probability $p(0; \beta t) = e^{-\beta t}$, where β is a number characteristic of the element under consideration. Then the probability that the nucleus does decay in a time interval of length t is $1 - e^{-\beta t}$. Suppose then that we begin with a mass containing m nuclei and determine the probability that precisely n have decayed and emitted a particle in a time period of length t. We can think of the random experiment which determines the number of nuclei that will decay in the time period of interest as consisting of m independent random experiments $\mathfrak{R}_j$, where the performance of $\mathfrak{R}_j$ determines whether the jth nucleus decays, the probability that it does not being $e^{-\beta t}$. Then $P_n(t)$ is the binomial probability of n successes in m trials, i.e.,

$$P_n(t) = \binom{m}{n} (1 - e^{-\beta t})^n (e^{-\beta t})^{m-n}. \tag{10-30}$$

This expression holds for all t, large or small.

Now if what we said at the beginning of our study of the radioactive decay process is correct, then (10-30) should reduce to the Poisson distribution $p(n; \vartheta t)$ for small t. Let us show that this is true. The mean number of nuclei which decay in a period of length t is the mean of (10-30), i.e., $m(1 - e^{-\beta t})$. When t is small,

$$1 - e^{-\beta t} = 1 - 1 + \beta t - (\beta t)^2/2 + \cdots \doteq \beta t, \qquad (10\text{-}31)$$

and the mean of (10-30) for small t is essentially $m\beta t$. Also when t is small the probability that a nucleus will decay is small. Furthermore, m is extremely large, so that even for small t, $m\beta t$ will be reasonably large. Thus for small t (10-30) should be well approximated by the Poisson probability $p(n; m\beta t)$, which is precisely what we wished to show. It also follows from this that $\vartheta = m\beta$.

Frequently in physics, the radioactive decay process is treated as being deterministic, with the rate of decay being proportional to the mass present. Thus if we represent the mass as a continuous variable and r is the undecayed mass present at time t, then $dr/dt = -\lambda t$. This differential equation has the solution $r = me^{-\lambda t}$, where m is the mass at $t = 0$. Let us now relate this to (10-30). The expected number of nuclei remaining undecayed at time t is from (10-30) $me^{-\beta t}$. It follows that treating the decay as being deterministic then yields precisely the expected mass remaining undecayed at time t. We also see that the constant of proportionality λ should be nothing but β. Let us now study what sort of fluctuations about this expected value can occur on the average. The expected fraction r/m of the mass remaining undecayed at time t is $e^{-\beta t}$. Consider the random variable y which represents the fraction undecayed at time t. Then the variance of y is of the form pq/n, which becomes for the case under consideration

$$\sigma_y{}^2 = (1/m)e^{-\beta t}(1 - e^{-\beta t}). \qquad (10\text{-}32)$$

Now

$$0 < e^{-\beta t}(1 - e^{-\beta t}) < 1,$$

and

$$\sigma_y{}^2 < 1/m.$$

However, $1/m$ is certainly not larger than 10^{-6} since there will be millions of nuclei in any piece of material. Thus we see that the fraction decayed in time t is essentially deterministic if t is long enough for any significant fraction to decay because the variance is negligible. This then provides the detailed justification for treating deterministically the fraction not decayed. The reader should be careful to note that although the variance for the fraction not decayed is very small, the variance for the number of nuclei which have decayed is $me^{-\beta t}(1 - e^{-\beta t})$ and this need not be small at all. Thus a probabilistic description is needed when one is concerned with problems such as counting the number of particles emitted. In the problems, we ask the reader to explain this apparent paradox.

Let us conclude this example by indicating how the number β introduced above could be measured experimentally. We have seen that $r/m = e^{-\beta t}$ is essentially a deterministic relation. Suppose that we then measure the time required for half the original mass to have decayed, i.e., the time required for r/m to become $\frac{1}{2}$. This time, call it $t_{1/2}$, is called the half life for the radioactive element. Then $\frac{1}{2} = e^{-\beta t_{1/2}}$ or

$$\beta = \frac{\log 2}{t_{1/2}}. \tag{10-33}$$

It may not always be convenient to note the time required for half the mass to decay. Clearly, any convenient fraction can be used instead of $\frac{1}{2}$.

10-4 THE POISSON PROCESS AS A RECURRENT EVENT PROCESS

For a Poisson process, the probability that no event occurs in a time period of length t is $e^{-\vartheta t}$, and hence the probability that one or more events occur in an interval of length t is $1 - e^{-\vartheta t}$. This is true regardless of how the initial point for the interval is chosen. Let us now imagine that we choose the initial point of the interval to be the time of occurrence of an event. Denote by τ the continuous random variable representing the time that will elapse before the next event will occur. We can now easily determine the density function $g(\tau)$ for τ. To do this, let us first ask what the probability $G(t)$ is that $\tau \le t$. We can have $\tau \le t$ if one or two or more events occur in the time interval of length t, and only under these circumstances will τ be $\le t$. But the probability that one or more events occurs in a time interval of length t is $1 - e^{-\vartheta t}$, so

$$G(t) = 1 - e^{-\vartheta t}. \tag{10-34}$$

We can immediately obtain $g(\tau)$ by differentiating (10-34). This yields

$$g(\tau) = \vartheta e^{-\vartheta \tau}, \tag{10-35}$$

and we have obtained the interesting result that for a Poisson process, the random variable τ representing the time between the occurrence of two successive events has an exponential distribution. From (7-75), the expected time between the occurrence of two successive events is $1/\vartheta$, or ϑ is the reciprocal of the expected time between the occurrence of two successive events. We might also note the important fact that not only is $g(\tau)$ the density function for the time between the occurrence of two successive events, it is also the density function for the random variable representing the time between our initial observance of the system and the occurrence of the first event. This is true regardless of what time is chosen for beginning the observation of the system.

We can now think of the occurrence of events in a Poisson process as being generated as follows. After each event occurs a random experiment $\Re$ is performed which determines the time τ of occurrence of the next event, the random variable τ having an exponential distribution. $\Re$ in no way depends on what has taken place prior to performing $\Re$. Thus the Poisson process can be looked upon as one in which an unending sequence of independent trials of $\Re$ are performed and on the jth trial a value τ_j of τ is generated. The number τ_j is then the time between the occurrence of the $j - 1$ and jth events, τ_1 being the time that the first event occurs after we start observing the system. If we then write

$$t_n = \sum_{j=1}^{n} \tau_j, \tag{10-36}$$

t_n becomes the time of occurrence of the nth event. A stochastic process having the characteristics we have just described is called a *recurrent event process*. A recurrent event process is one where events occur at distinct points in time, and it can be imagined that after an event occurs, a random experiment $\Re$ is performed to determine the time of occurrence of the next event. The experiment $\Re$ in no way depends on the history of the process prior to performing $\Re$. The Poisson process is thus an example of a recurrent event process. It is a recurrent event process with an exponential density function for the time interval between events. The Poisson process is by no means the only possible recurrent event process, since for every different density function $g(\tau)$ which one might use for the time interval between events, one obtains a different recurrent event process.

Let us denote by $\tau\{j\}$ the random variable representing the time between events $j - 1$ and j for a Poisson process, with $\tau\{1\}$ being the random variable representing the time until the first event occurs after we begin observing the system. Also let $t\{n\}$ be the random variable representing the time of occurrence of the nth event. Then

$$t\{n\} = \sum_{j=1}^{n} \tau\{j\}. \tag{10-37}$$

Now by the nature of the Poisson process the $\tau\{j\}$ are independent random variables, and each has the exponential distribution $\vartheta e^{-\vartheta\tau}$. Consequently, we know from Section 7-14 that $t\{n\}$ has the gamma distribution $g(t\{n\}; n - 1, \vartheta)$, so that the probability density that $t\{n\} = t_n$ is

$$g(t_n; n - 1, \vartheta) = \frac{\vartheta(\vartheta t_n)^{n-1}}{(n - 1)!} e^{-\vartheta t_n} = \vartheta p(n - 1; \vartheta t_n). \tag{10-38}$$

We can give an interesting interpretation to (10-38). Recall that the probability density at t_n gives the altitude of the histogram there, and hence the probability that the nth event occurs between t_n and $t_n + h$ for h small should be, according to (10-38), $(\vartheta h)p(n-1; \vartheta t_n)$. However, the nth event will occur in the interval $t_n < t \leq t_n + h$ if $n-1$ events occur between 0 and t_n, call this the event A, and precisely one event occurs between t_n and $t_n + h$, call this event B. The event n occurring between t_n and $t_n + h$ is then the event $A \cap B$. However, A and B are independent by the axioms for a Poisson process, so that $p(A \cap B) = p(A)p(B)$. However, $p(A) = p(n-1; \vartheta t_n)$, $p(B) = \vartheta h + o_1(h)$, and we obtain by this reasoning the same conclusion that is reached using (10-38).

From (7-109) and (7-110) we see on using (10-38) that the expected time until the occurrence of the nth event is n/ϑ and the variance of this time is n/ϑ^2. Since $1/\vartheta$ is the mean time between occurrences of events, n/ϑ, the expected time until the occurrence of the nth event, is n times the mean time between successive events, which is a result which we would expect intuitively.

REFERENCES

The books by Feller and by Fisz referred to previously discuss the Poisson process and a number of other stochastic processes. The following texts also discuss these processes.

1. Doob, J. L., *Stochastic Processes*. Wiley, New York, 1953.
   A good but very advanced treatment.

2. Hadley, G., and T. M. Whitin, *Analysis of Inventory Systems*. Prentice-Hall, Englewood Cliffs, N. J., 1963.

3. Parzen, E., *Stochastic Processes*. Holden-Day, San Francisco, 1962.
   An elementary introduction to the subject.

4. Pugachev, V. S., *Theory of Random Functions and Its Application to Control Problems*. Addison-Wesley, Reading, Mass., 1965.
   A translation of a Russian work. This is a large volume which is written at a reasonably elementary level and covers a wide variety of topics.

PROBLEMS

Sections 10-2 and 10-3

1. Given that $P_n(t) = p(n; \vartheta t)$, determine the functions $o_1(h)$, $o_2(h)$, $o_3(h)$, and $o_4(h)$ introduced in the derivation, and show that they do possess the properties hypothesized.

2. By use of the two axioms show in detail that the probability of $r < n-1$ events occurring in T_2 and $n-r$ occurring in T_3 is a function $o_3(h)$.

3. Differentiate $p(n; \vartheta t)$ and show that (10-7) is satisfied when $n \geq 1$.

4. Why was it necessary to define $P_0(0)$ as $\lim_{h\to 0+} P_0(h)$, that is, why does $P_0(0)$ not have a direct meaning?

5. Consider a Poisson process in which events occur at the mean rate of six per hour. What is the probability that we shall have to wait ten minutes or longer before the first event occurs after we begin observing the system?

6. For the situation discussed in Problem 5, how would the probability determined be changed if we were told at the time we began to observe the system that the last event had occurred five minutes earlier?

7. A candy store proprietor has observed that customers arrive in the store at an average rate of one every two minutes. What is the probability that no customers arrive in a five minute interval if the process can be treated as a Poisson process? What is the probability that eight customers will arrive in a ten minute interval?

8. A textile manufacturer turns out broadcloth shirting material with an average of 0.2 defects per square yard. A customer buys a shirt made from this fabric. Under the assumption that a Poisson process generates the defects and that the back of the shirt contains 0.6 square yards of fabric, what is the probability that the customer will find one defect on the back of his new shirt? What is the probability that two defects will be found?

9. The almond chocolate bars produced by a candy manufacturer average ten almonds per bar. Assuming that a Poisson process generates the almonds in the sheets of chocolate, what is the probability that a bar will have only five almonds in it? What is the probability that it will have 15?

10. Suppose that a production process turns out λ units per hour, with the long run fraction defective being p. Can one look at the process of generating defectives as a Poisson process, so that the probability of n defectives being produced in a period of length t is $p(n; \vartheta t)$ for some number ϑ? Are there conditions under which this is a valid approach? Are there conditions under which it is not a valid approach? Give a detailed discussion.

11. When the spinning and weaving process for producing a given fabric is under control, the average number of defects generated per square yard is 0.3. To control the process, once each three hours a sample of five square yards is inspected and the number of defects in the sample determined. What would be the center line and the control limits on a control chart where one plotted the number of defects in the sample? What would be the center line and control limits if one plotted the average number of defects per square yard?

12. For the situation described in Problem 11, what should the sample size be if it is desired to catch a shift in the average number of defects from 0.3 per square yard to 0.5 per square yard in the first sample taken after the shift occurs?

13. How can you explain the fact that in radioactive decay one can treat the fraction of the nuclei which have decayed in any time period as being essentially deterministic, whereas if one is concerned with counting the particles emitted one must use a probability model?

14. A particular radioactive element has a half life of five years. Consider a piece of material containing ten billion atoms of this element. What is the expected number of atoms which will decay in a period of ten minutes? What is the standard deviation of the random variable representing the number of nuclei which will decay in this period?

15. It is desired to determine how many spare vacuum tubes of a certain type should be stocked on an atomic submarine when it goes out on patrol. Assume that the demand for these spares due to failures in the equipment is Poisson distributed with the expected number demanded during a patrol being 3. Determine the number to stock if it is desired that the probability of not having a spare when it is needed be no greater than 0.01.

16. Spares for military aircraft are often produced when the planes are and can be obtained later only at great cost. The total number of spares required can be looked upon as a random variable. The expected number of spares required depends on the total number of flying hours. A manufacturer is currently producing 100 of a special purpose radar aircraft for the navy. It is desired to determine how many of a particular expensive spare part should be produced. Each spare costs $8000 when produced at the same time the aircraft is and $20,000 if it must be procured after production has ceased. The spare under consideration is one that is required infrequently, the mean usage rate being 0.1 per 10,000 flying hours. It can be assumed that a Poisson process generates the demands for these spares. It is difficult to predict in advance how many flying hours will be placed on the planes under consideration, but it is estimated that the expected number of flying hours for all 100 planes will be 500,000 with the standard deviation being 200,000. It is believed that sufficient accuracy will be obtained if one treats the total number of flying hours as a random variable having a gamma distribution. How many spares should be produced with the aircraft?

17. Consider a situation where two Poisson processes are generating events (the events generated by both processes will be imagined to be of the same kind). The mean rates of occurrence of events for the two processes will be denoted by ϑ_1 and ϑ_2, respectively. Consider now the problem of determining the probability $P_n(t)$ that the total number of events generated by the two processes in a time period of length t is n. Prove that $P_n(t) = p[n; (\vartheta_1 + \vartheta_2)t]$, so that the two Poisson processes acting together are equivalent to a single Poisson process in which the mean rate of occurrence of events is $\vartheta_1 + \vartheta_2$.

18. Carry out the details of the method suggested on p. 534 to show that the limit as $h \to 0-$ exists and is equal to (10-6).

Section 10-4

1. For a Poisson process, compute the conditional probability that no event occurs between $t_1 + h$ and $t_1 + h + \delta$, $\delta > 0$, given that the last event occurred at time t_1.

2. The occurrence of precisely n events of a Poisson process in a time interval of length t should be equivalent to the statement that $t\{n\} \leq t$ and $t\{n + 1\} > t$, if the convention is used that the left-hand end point of the interval is not included. Attempt to use this observation to obtain a new method for deriving $P_n(t)$ if we are given the distribution for $t\{n\}$ and $\tau\{n + 1\}$. Hint: Consider the joint distribution for $t\{n\}$ and $\tau\{n + 1\}$.

CHAPTER 11

SEQUENTIAL DECISION PROBLEMS

Those whom God hath joined together let no man put asunder.

Book of Common Prayer

11-1 THE BACKWARD SOLUTION

In Chapter 3 we showed how any sequential decision problem involving only a finite number of decisions could be solved.   This theory was applied in Chapter 8 to solving a special type of two stage problem.   We would now like to generalize the ideas introduced in Chapter 8 to develop a computational procedure for solving any sequential decision problem, which requires less computational effort than would be needed if one proceeded directly in the manner suggested in Chapter 3.   Even with this more efficient computational procedure, however, the numerical effort required to solve even a relatively simple sequential decision problem can be very large.   The new computational procedure is of interest, not only because it reduces the computational effort, but also because it gives additional insight into the nature of the problem.

We noted in Chapter 8 that a two stage decision problem could be solved by working backward progressively from the terminal branches of the decision tree to the node representing the initial decision.   This *backward solution method* as we shall call it will now be generalized to apply to an arbitrary sequential decision problem.   Consider then any sequential decision problem; part of the decision tree representing this problem is shown in Figure 11-1.   A strategy for this problem tells the decision maker what action to take each time a decision must be made.   Consider a particular strategy, call it S_2, which tells the decision maker that he should initially take action a_2.   Then we can write S_2 as $S_2 = \{a_2, \hat{S}_2\}$, where $\hat{S}_2$ is a partial strategy which tells him what to do in every case if he initially decides to take action a_2.   Let us now examine in a little more detail the structure of $\hat{S}_2$. When action a_2 is taken at the first step, then the decision maker will be at one of the nodes marked $1, \ldots, s$ in Figure 11-1 when he has to make the next decision (if any). Suppose, for example, that after the decision maker selects action a_2, nature selects f_k as the outcome of the first random experiment, and the decision maker is at the node numbered k in Figure 11-1 when the next decision is to be made. We shall assume that the branch labeled f_k is not a terminal branch, so that there is another decision to be made.

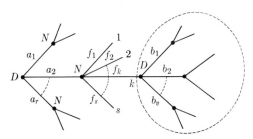

FIGURE 11-1

Consider now that part of the decision tree which is encircled in Figure 11-1. This contains all of the tree which can be reached from node k. We can next observe that the encircled part of Figure 11-1 is a tree for a decision problem, call it problem k. This tree represents the decision problem which the decision maker faces if he reaches node k. Denote by S_{2k} that part of $\hat{S}_2$ which tells the decision maker what to do at node k and at every node which can be reached from node k. Then S_{2k} is nothing but a strategy for the decision problem k. This is true regardless of which of the s numbered nodes we take k to be. The collection of s strategies S_{2k}, one for each k, completely characterize $\hat{S}_2$, so that we can write

$$\hat{S}_2 = \{S_{21}, \ldots, S_{2s}\}. \tag{11-1}$$

The reason for this is that if action a_2 is selected, one of the s numbered nodes in Figure 11-1 must be reached, and in (11-1) we have specified what to do at the node so reached and all others reached from it, so (11-1) provides a complete description of what $\hat{S}_2$ says to do after action a_2 is taken.

Let us now consider the problem of determining an optimal strategy for the given problem. Recall that the selection of a strategy S reduces a decision problem to a lottery. We wish to determine that lottery or lotteries which yield the largest expected utility. The corresponding strategy or strategies are optimal. Let us proceed as in Chapter 8 and subdivide all the strategies into r classes such that every strategy in a given class uses the same initial action. Let S_u be any strategy for which a_u is the initial action to be taken. Denote by S_u^* the optimal strategy or one of the optimal strategies for class u. In other words the lottery corresponding to S_u^* gives the largest expected utility for all strategies using a_u as the initial action. Hence one of the r strategies, S_u^*, will be an optimal one. If $\bar{U}_u$ is the expected utility for S_u^*, then an optimal strategy S^* is one which yields the largest of $\bar{U}_u$, $u = 1, \ldots, r$. If we can determine the S_u^* and $\bar{U}_u$, we can then easily solve the problem.

Consider now the determination, the S_u^*. To be specific, consider S_2^*. Let S_2 be any strategy which says to use action a_2 initially. Then we can write $S_2 = \{a_2, \hat{S}_2\}$, where $\hat{S}_2$ is given by (11-1). Specification of S_2 determines a multistage lottery. Similarly, each S_{2k} determines a lottery, and we can look at the lottery determined by S_2 to be a single stage lottery with the lotteries determined by the S_{2k} as prizes. Suppose now that for each k we knew $\bar{U}_{2k}(S_{2k})$, the expected utility for the lottery determined by S_{2k}, that is, the expected utility for problem k when S_{2k} is the strategy used. Denote by q_{2k} the probability that node k is reached in Figure 11-1 when action a_2 is selected initially. Then $\bar{U}(S_2)$, the expected utility for the lottery determined by S_2, that is, the expected utility for the entire problem if S_2 is the strategy used, is

$$\bar{U}(S_2) = \sum_{k=1}^{s} q_{2k} \bar{U}_{2k}(S_{2k}). \tag{11-2}$$

S_2^* is that strategy which maximizes $\bar{U}(S_2)$. Let us now concentrate our attention on the case where the decision maker always knows at which node of the decision tree he is when he is about to make a decision, that is, we shall assume he learned the outcome of each of the random experiments as he passed along on the decision tree in coming to the current decision. This is no real restriction. It is only a restriction on how the decision tree is drawn. We can always define the random experiments and draw the tree in such a way that every time a decision is to be made he knows at which node he is. We shall illustrate this in a little more detail later.

The value of $\bar{U}(S_2)$ depends on the strategies S_{2k} selected for each of the problems k, and $\bar{U}(S_2)$ will be maximized if and only if S_{2k} is selected so as to maximize the expected utility for problem k. Denote by S_{2k}^* an optimal strategy for problem k, that is, one that maximizes $\bar{U}_{2k}(S_{2k})$. Then $S_2^* = \{a_2, S_{21}^*, \ldots, S_{2s}^*\}$ is an optimal strategy given that a_2 is the initial action to be taken, and if

$$\bar{U}_2 = \bar{U}(S_2^*); \quad \bar{U}_{2k} = \bar{U}_{2k}(S_{2k}^*), \tag{11-3}$$

then from (11-2)

$$\bar{U}_2 = \sum_k q_{2k} \bar{U}_{2k}. \tag{11-4}$$

Each S_u^* can be determined in this way and yields a $\overline{U}_u$. Then an optimal strategy S^* for the entire problem is that S_u^* which yields the largest of the $\overline{U}_u$. Using the procedure just outlined, we have reduced the task of solving the original problem to one of solving a number of problems involving fewer decisions than the original problem. The solution of each of these new problems, say k, determines an optimal strategy S_{2k}^* and a corresponding maximum expected utility $\overline{U}_{2k}$ for that problem. Then $\overline{U}_2$ is the maximum expected utility given that a_2 is the initial action selected, but before the random experiment is performed that determines to which node k the decision maker will move from the initial node. If $\overline{U}^* = \max_u \overline{U}_u$, we can then associate each of the $\overline{U}$'s introduced above with a node of the decision tree, as shown in Figure 11-2.

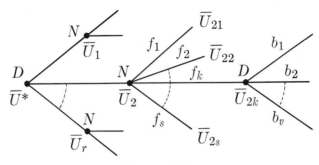

FIGURE 11-2

The question then arises as to how we solve the problems of the type k, that is, how we determine S_{2k}^* and $\overline{U}_{2k}$, for example. We merely repeat the above procedure all over again, treating problem k in the same way as we did the original problem. In this way we progressively work forward through the tree. Ultimately, for every path we reach a terminal branch and the procedure terminates. To actually solve a problem then, we proceed in the reverse direction, beginning with the terminal branches and progressively assigning a utility to each node, this utility being the maximum expected utility associated with that node. Simultaneously, we develop an optimal strategy. When the maximum expected utility for the initial node is determined, we are finished and we have simultaneously generated an optimal strategy.

We can now give two very simple rules for computing the expected utility to associate with any node in terms of previously determined expected utilities. Suppose that the node, call it α, is one where nature makes a decision, so that a random experiment is performed to determine what node is reached from α. Imagine that there are v nodes which can be reached from α and let j denote any one of them. Suppose that $\overline{U}_j$ is the maximum expected utility associated with node j, and $p_{\alpha j}$ is the probability that node j will be reached from α. Then $\overline{U}_\alpha$, the maximum expected utility to be associated with node α, is

$$\overline{U}_\alpha = \sum_{j=1}^{v} p_{\alpha j}\overline{U}_j. \tag{11-5}$$

This is illustrated in Figure 11-3.   Next suppose that the node, call it β,

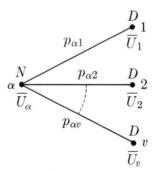

FIGURE 11-3

for which we wish to determine the maximum expected utility is one where a decision is made, that is, where the decision maker selects an action. Imagine that there are h different actions, call them $d_1, \ldots, d_h$, one of which will be selected.   There are thus h different nodes which can be reached from β; call them $1, \ldots, h$, and let $\overline{U}_i$ be the maximum expected

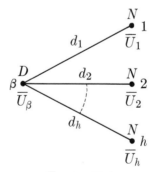

FIGURE 11-4

utility associated with the ith one.   The situation is illustrated in Figure 11-4.   Then $\overline{U}_\beta$, the expected utility to associate with node β, is simply the largest of the $\overline{U}_i$, i.e.,

$$\overline{U}_\beta = \max_i \overline{U}_i. \tag{11-6}$$

Simultaneously with determining $\overline{U}_\beta$ we determine the action to take if node β is reached. If $\overline{U}_\beta = \overline{U}_k$, then action d_k should be selected if node β is reached. By use of (11-5) and (11-6), one can solve in principle any sequential decision problem of the type we have been discussing by working backwards. In practice, of course, the numerical effort required can easily be too much even for a large scale computer. It is fortunate that one frequently does not need to construct explicitly the decision tree in order to use the procedure just described. We shall see in Section 11-3 how this can often be avoided.

Before going on to give some simple examples, we might note the difficulties that would be caused if the decision maker did not know at which node he was. Consider (11-2) and suppose, for example, that he did not know whether he was at node 1 or node 2. In such a situation, S_2 must tell him to take the same action if he arrives at node 1 that it tells him to take if he arrives at node 2, since the nodes are indistinguishable. Now if we used the procedure outlined above, S_{21}^* and S_{22}^* might not both say to take the same initial action for the respective problems. Thus we cannot proceed as above in this case, but must determine S_{21}^* and S_{22}^* jointly so as to maximize

$$q_{21}\overline{U}_{21}(S_{21}) + q_{22}\overline{U}_{22}(S_{22}), \tag{11-7}$$

where we require that the initial action be the same in S_{21} as S_{22}. This complicates tremendously the procedure outlined above. As we have already noted, however, it is nothing to be especially concerned about because the decision tree can always be constructed in such a way that the decision maker knows at which node he is.

The computational technique just introduced is a very important one for another reason. It suggests a procedure by which one may be able to simplify considerably the solution of a sequential decision problem. Recall that we indicated in Chapter 3 that usually we are interested in solving a sequential decision problem only for the purpose of deciding what the initial decision should be. Thus one only needs enough detail in the problem to make it possible to make a sound selection of the initial action. Now it is frequently the case that one can estimate with reasonable accuracy the maximum expected utility for some node without solving in detail the problem which follows from this node. In such a case one can reduce the computational effort by using the estimate and not bothering to compute the maximum expected utility directly. If one does this at as many nodes as possible, this can considerably reduce the computational efforts, and in fact, this procedure is often used to replace a sequential decision problem by a single stage decision problem.

11-2 EXAMPLES

Let us illustrate the above theory with three examples which, although not very realistic, illustrate the basic ideas.

1. To begin, we shall solve the sequential decision problem whose decision tree is shown in Figure 11-5. The problem is one having the characteristic

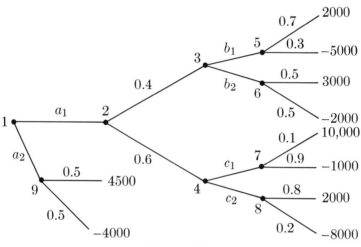

FIGURE 11-5

that if action a_2 is selected initially, no other decision must be made. The project is terminated after the performance of a random experiment. However, if action a_1 is selected, then after the performance of a random experiment it is necessary to make another decision and select either one of two actions (the actions to be selected depending on the outcome of the random experiment). After the second decision, the performance of another random experiment terminates the project. The final utilities are indicated at the ends of the terminal branches. The probabilities of the outcomes of the experiments are indicated on the appropriate branches. The nodes are numbered as indicated.

Denote by $\bar{U}_j$ the expected utility to be associated with node j. We shall now compute the $\bar{U}_j$ using the two rules given in the previous section and thus solve the problem. From (11-5),

$$\bar{U}_5 = 0.7(2000) + 0.3(-5000) = -100;$$
$$\bar{U}_6 = 0.5(3000) + 0.5(-2000) = 500;$$
$$\bar{U}_7 = 0.1(10{,}000) + 0.9(-1000) = 100;$$

$$\bar{U}_8 = 0.8(2000) + 0.2(-8000) = 0;$$
$$\bar{U}_9 = 0.5(4500) + 0.5(-4000) = 250.$$

From (11-6),

$$\bar{U}_3 = \max (\bar{U}_5, \bar{U}_6) = \bar{U}_6 = 500; \quad \bar{U}_4 = \max (\bar{U}_7, \bar{U}_8) = \bar{U}_7 = 100.$$

Thus if node 3 is reached b_2 is the action to take, and if node 4 is reached c_1 is the action to take.

Next from (11-5),

$$\bar{U}_2 = 0.4\bar{U}_3 + 0.6\bar{U}_4 = 0.4(500) + 0.6(100) = 260.$$

Finally, from (11-6)

$$\bar{U}_1 = \max (\bar{U}_2, \bar{U}_9) = \bar{U}_2 = 260. \tag{11-8}$$

Thus action a_1 should be selected initially, and if node 3 is reached then action b_2 should be selected, whereas if node 4 is reached then action c_1 should be selected. We can then write an optimal strategy for the problem as $S^* = \langle a_1, (b_2, c_1) \rangle$. This example illustrates how (11-5) and (11-6) make it possible for anyone to solve a sequential decision problem if he is given the decision tree. He need not know anything about decision theory to obtain the solution.

2. A small shop has received an order from the government for two large valve gates to be used in a new hydroelectric project. The production process involves two stages. First a casting is made, and then this casting is machined to yield the final gate. In both the casting and machining process, it is possible to generate defectives. Let us assume the probability that any given casting will turn out to be defective is 0.30, and the probability that any good casting going into the machine shop will end up defective is 0.20. Suppose that the shop will be paid $10,000 for the two castings. Each casting costs $1000 to make. The machining cost per casting amounts to $800. The scrap value of any defective castings (machined or not machined) is $250.

The nature of the decisions to be made is as follows. First it must be decided how many units will be cast initially. After these castings are made and the quality of each determined, more castings can be made if desired. However, once the second set of castings is made, there is no opportunity to make a third batch of castings. The castings obtained from the first two batches must be sent to machining. Furthermore, once the machining operations are underway, no time will be available to make more castings if they are needed. Thus all castings must be made before machining begins, but there exists the opportunity to make two separate batches of castings if it seems desirable to do so. In the event that this procedure does not ultimately yield two good machined parts, the contract deadline cannot be met. In this case, the shop must still supply the gates, but now it must do this by working overtime and using a different process which involves no casting but machining only. This alternative process will almost certainly not produce any defectives, but is very expensive. It is estimated that including the penalties, each gate which must be produced in this way costs $6000.

The problem under consideration can be looked upon as a two stage decision problem, where at the first stage the initial number of castings h_1 to be produced is selected, and then after this operation is completed and the number of good castings is determined, it is necessary to decide how many additional castings h_2 should be produced. Since two gates must be produced, there is no reason why h_1 would ever be taken to be less than 2. Thus h_1 can have the values 2, 3, 4, . . . , while h_2 can have the values 0, 1, 2, 3, ... The number of good castings obtained in the first batch is a random variable x, and by our above assumptions the probability that $x = r_1$ is the binomial probability $b(r_1; h_1, 0.7)$. Similarly, the number of good castings obtained in the second batch is a random variable y, and the probability that $y = r_2$ is $b(r_2; h_2, 0.7)$.

We shall assume that the cast pieces go through the machining operation one at a time so that if the first two are good, then no more castings are sent to machining. In other words, no machining is done on a casting unless it has to be done. If a machined casting turns out to be defective, this is not discovered until essentially the end of the machining operation, so that each casting which is machined, regardless of whether it turns out to be good or defective, incurs an $800 machining cost. With this procedure, the number of good gates produced will be either 2, 1, or 0. Suppose that r good castings are obtained from the two batches of castings. The probability that no good gates are produced is the probability that all r castings turn into defectives in the machining process. The probability of this event is $b(0; r, 0.8)$, since we have assumed above that the probability of turning out a good machined piece is 0.8. The probability that precisely one good gate will be produced is $b(1; r, 0.8)$. Now recall that operations are terminated once two good gates are machined. Thus the probability that two good gates are obtained is the probability that r or less trials will be needed to obtain 2 successes. This is $B_P(r; 2, 0.8)$, the cumulative Pascal probability. Since the number of good gates produced will be 0, 1, or 2, we must have

$$b(0; r, 0.8) + b(1; r, 0.8) + B_P(r; 2, 0.8) = 1, \qquad (11\text{-}9)$$

or

$$B_P(r; 2, 0.8) = 1 - B(1; r, 0.8). \qquad (11\text{-}10)$$

Here we have an interesting connection between the cumulative Pascal and binomial distributions. Equation (11-10) says that the probability that r or less trials will be needed to obtain two successes is equal to the probability of obtaining two or more successes in r trials.

We are now ready to give a precise formulation of the problem as a two stage decision problem. At the first stage a value of h_1 is selected, $h_1 = 2, 3, \ldots$ being the number of gates to cast. There then appear to be an infinite number of possible actions for the first stage. Of course, in actuality there is a definite upper limit to the number of castings which could be made. Let us suppose that it is 10, so that there are nine possible actions for the first stage. Once h_1 is selected, a random experiment is performed which determines r_1, the number of good castings obtained. The probability of r_1 is $b(r_1; h_1, 0.7)$. At the second stage h_2 is selected, $h_2 = 0, 1, \ldots, 10$ (we shall again assume that no more than 10 castings can be made). After h_2 is selected another random experiment is performed which determines the final outcome. Let us consider this experiment in a little more detail. It can be conveniently imagined to be a two stage random experiment. At the first stage the number r_2 of the h_2 castings which turn out to be good is determined. The probability of r_2 is $b(r_2; h_2, 0.7)$. The total number of good castings if r_1 good ones were obtained at the previous stage is $r_1 + r_2$. Now the final outcome will depend on how many of the $r_1 + r_2$ castings are actually machined and on how many good gates are obtained. If no good gates are produced, all $r_1 + r_2$ will be machined. The probability of this is $b(0; r_1 + r_2, 0.8)$. Denote by $p(0, r_2 | h_2, r_1)$ the conditional probability that when r_1 good castings are obtained at the first stage and h_2 are cast at the second stage then r_2 good castings will be obtained at the second stage and no good machined gates are obtained. Thus

$$p(0, r_2 | h_2, r_1) = b(0; r_1 + r_2, 0.8) b(r_2; h_2, 0.7). \qquad (11\text{-}11)$$

When only one good gate is obtained, all $r_1 + r_2$ good castings will be machined and the probability of getting one good gate on machining $r_1 + r_2$ is $b(1; r_1 + r_2, 0.8)$. If $p(1, r_2 | h_2, r_1)$ is the conditional probability that when r_1 good castings are obtained at the first stage and h_2 are cast at the second stage, then r_2 good castings will be obtained at the second stage and one good machined gate is obtained. Thus

$$p(1, r_2 | h_2, r_1) = b(1; r_1 + r_2, 0.8) b(r_2; h_2, 0.7). \qquad (11\text{-}12)$$

When two good gates are obtained then 2 or 3 or $\ldots$ or $r_1 + r_2$ castings may need to be machined to obtain the two good gates. If v must be machined, then the number of defectives produced in machining is $u = v - 2$. Thus the probability that two good gates will be produced and u defective ones is the Pascal probability

$$b_P(u + 2; 2, 0.8) = 0.8 b(1; u + 1, 0.8). \qquad (11\text{-}13)$$

Of course, (11-13) is also the negative binomial probability $b_n(u; 2, 0.8)$.

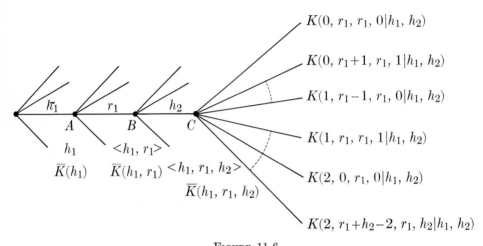

FIGURE 11-6

If $p(2,u,r_2|h_2,r_1)$ denotes the conditional probability that when r_1 good castings are obtained at the first stage and h_2 are cast at the second stage then r_2 good castings are obtained from the h_2, two good gates are obtained and u defectives are machined. Hence

$$p(2,u,r_2|h_2,r_1) = 0.8b(1; u + 1,0.8)b(r_2; h_2,0.7),$$
$$0 \le u \le r_1 + r_2 - 2. \quad (11\text{-}14)$$

Consider now the utilities. It will be assumed that monetary values accurately represent the firm's utility. Since it receives \$10,000 from the government independently of what happens, the minimization of expected costs is equivalent to maximizing expected profits. Thus we shall proceed by minimizing expected costs. The costs include the cost of castings, plus the cost of machining, plus the cost of special processing if two good gates are not obtained. To be deducted from these costs is the scrap value of any defective castings. The cost of casting $h_1 + h_2$ units is $1000(h_1 + h_2)$. The machining cost if less than two good gates are obtained is $800(r_1 + r_2)$ and is $800(u + 2)$ if two good gates are obtained. The cost of special processing is \$6000 if one good gate is produced and one must be made by special processing and is \$12,000 if no good gates are obtained and two must be made by special processing. The proceeds from the sale of scrap is then $250(h_1 + h_2 - i)$, where i is the number of good gates produced, since all units cast which are not good are sold as scrap. Denote by $K(i,u,r_1,r_2|h_1,h_2)$ the cost when h_1 and h_2 are the number of units cast at the first and second stages, r_1 and r_2 are the respective number of good castings obtained, i is the number of good gates machined, and u the number of defectives produced in machining. Then

$$K(0,r_1 + r_2,r_1,r_2|h_1,h_2) = 12{,}000 + 750(h_1 + h_2) + 800(r_1 + r_2); \quad (11\text{-}15)$$

$$K(1,r_1 + r_2 - 1,r_1,r_2|h_1,h_2)$$
$$= 6250 + 750(h_1 + h_2) + 800(r_1 + r_2); \quad (11\text{-}16)$$

$$K(2,u,r_1,r_2|h_1,h_2) = 500 + 750(h_1 + h_2) + 800(u + 2). \quad (11\text{-}17)$$

At last we are ready to solve the problem. The nature of the decision tree is shown in Figure 11-6. The entire tree is too complicated to illustrate and we have only shown part of it. There will be a node of type C for every possible triple of numbers $\langle h_1,r_1,h_2 \rangle$. Denote by $\bar{K}(h_1,r_1,h_2)$ the expected cost to be associated with a node of type C. Then $\bar{K}(h_1,r_1,h_2)$ is the expected cost when h_1 are cast at the first stage and r_1 good castings are obtained and h_2 are cast at the second stage. It follows that

$$\bar{K}(h_1,r_1,h_2) = \sum_{r_2=0}^{h_2} K(0,r_1 + r_2,r_1,r_2|h_1,h_2)p(0,r_2|h_2,r_1)$$

$$+ \sum_{r_2=0}^{h_2} K(1,r_1 + r_2 - 1,r_1,r_2|h_1,h_2)p(1,r_2|h_2,r_1)$$

$$+ \sum_{r_2=\varphi}^{h_2} \sum_{u=0}^{r_1+r_2-2} K(2,u,r_1,r_2|h_1,h_2)p(2,u,r_2|h_2,r_1), \quad (11\text{-}18)$$

where φ is the larger of 0 and $2 - r_1$.

There is a node of type B for each pair of numbers $\langle h_1,r_1 \rangle$ and associated with each such node is an expected cost $\bar{K}(h_1,r_1)$, which is the minimum expected cost if h_1 are cast at the first stage and r_1 turn out to be good. Then

$$\bar{K}(h_1,r_1) = \min_{h_2} \bar{K}(h_1,r_1,h_2). \quad (11\text{-}19)$$

The key to solving the problem efficiently is to note that it is unnecessary to evaluate $\bar{K}(h_1,r_1,h_2)$ for all h_2 to determine $\bar{K}(h_1,r_1)$. If we begin, perhaps at $h_2 = 0$, and increase h_2 one unit at a time, we can stop as soon as $\bar{K}(h_1,r_1,h_2)$ goes through a minimum, and $\bar{K}(h_1,r_1)$ is this minimum value.

Finally, there is a node of type A for every value of h_1 and associated with each such node is an expected cost $\bar{K}(h_1)$, which is the minimum expected cost if h_1 units are cast initially. The optimal number to cast initially is that value of h_1 which yields the smallest value of $\bar{K}(h_1)$ and

$$\bar{K}(h_1) = \sum_{r_1=0}^{h_1} \bar{K}(h_1,r_1)b(r_1; h_1,0.7). \quad (11\text{-}20)$$

Let us now illustrate how the computations are made. It is not feasible to give all the details because, even for a problem as simple as this, about twenty pages of computation are needed. As an example of the determination of $\bar{K}(h_1,r_1,h_2)$, consider the case where $h_1 = 2$, $r_1 = 2$, and $h_2 = 1$, that is, two units are cast initially and both turn out to be good, and at the second stage one unit is cast. Now the unit cast at the second stage may turn out to be either good or defective, i.e., $r_2 = 1$ or 0. When $r_2 = 0$, one finds on using (11-11) through (11-17)

$$K(0,2,2,0|2,1) = 15,850; \quad p(0,0|1,2) = 0.012$$
$$K(1,2,2,0|2,1) = 10,100; \quad p(1,0|1,2) = 0.096$$
$$K(2,0,2,0|2,1) = 4350; \quad p(2,0,0|1,2) = 0.192.$$

Similarly, one can obtain the costs and probabilities for $r_2 = 1$. Then from (11-18) we find that

$$\bar{K}(2,2,1) = 5030. \tag{11-21}$$

Going through the whole procedure again for $h_1 = 2$ and $r_1 = 2$, using $h_2 = 0$ and $h_2 = 2$, we find that

$$\bar{K}(2,2,0) = 5894; \quad \bar{K}(2,2,2) = 5954. \tag{11-22}$$

Note that $\bar{K}(2,2,1)$ is smaller than the corresponding values for $h_2 = 0$ and $h_2 = 2$. Thus if we note that for $h_2 > 2$ the expected cost will be greater than for $h_2 = 2$, we see from (11-19) that

$$\bar{K}(2,2) = 5030, \tag{11-23}$$

and hence if $h_1 = 2$ and $r_1 = 2$, one should select $h_2 = 1$. Going through the same procedure once again for $h_1 = 2$ but with $r_1 = 1$ and $r_1 = 0$, we find that

$$\bar{K}(2,1) = 6862; \quad \bar{K}(2,0) = 7002. \tag{11-24}$$

Also if $h_1 = 2$ and $r_1 = 1$, then one should select $h_2 = 3$; and if $r_1 = 0$, one should select $h_2 = 4$. Note, for example, that $\bar{K}(2,1)$ is the minimum expected cost given that two units are cast initially and one of these two units turns out to be good, the other being defective. Thus from (11-20)

$$\bar{K}(2) = 7002\, b(0; 2,0.7) + 6862\, b(1; 2,0.7) + 5030\, b(2; 2,0.7)$$
$$= 7002(0.09) + 6862(0.42) + 5030(0.49) = 5967. \tag{11-25}$$

$\bar{K}(2)$ is the expected cost of producing the two gates if two gates are cast initially. A similar calculation shows that $\bar{K}(3) = 5200$ and $\bar{K}(h_1) > \bar{K}(3)$, $h_1 > 3$. Thus it is optimal to schedule three castings initially, and the minimum expected cost is \$5200, so that the maximum expected profit is $10,000 - 5200 = \$4800$. In determining $\bar{K}(3)$, one computes $\bar{K}(3, r_1)$ for each $r_1 = 0, 1, 2, 3$, and in finding $\bar{K}(3, r_1)$, one determines $\hat{h}_2(r_1)$, which is the optimal number to cast in the second batch if r_1 good castings are obtained in the first batch. It turns out that

$$\hat{h}_2(0) = 4, \quad \hat{h}_2(1) = 3, \quad \hat{h}_2(2) = 1, \quad \hat{h}_2(3) = 0. \tag{11-26}$$

Thus we have solved the example and have determined an optimal strategy for the decision maker to use.

3. In the previous section we indicated that to use the method developed there, it was necessary for the decision maker to know at which node of the decision tree he was when each decision was made. We indicated that the decision tree could always be constructed in such a way that this was true. We shall now illustrate, using an extremely simple example, how a decision tree which is constructed in the normal way and does not have this property can be converted to one which does.

A missile manufacturer has just received a lot of 500 very expensive liquid type batteries used in the blast-off phase of the rocket. These batteries are activated by a plunger and have an operational life of only a few minutes. Testing of a battery of this type requires that it be activated by the plunger and this then destroys the battery and it cannot be used again, i.e., testing is destructive. The following type of sampling plan is used to check on the quality of the lot. First two batteries are selected at random and are tested. On the basis of the outcome of this test, the lot is either accepted or rejected, or unlike the previous cases we have studied, a third action is allowed for. The third action involves selecting two more batteries at random from the lot and testing them before a decision is made. After the second set of two batteries is tested, then the lot will be either accepted or rejected. The sampling plan we have just outlined is a special case of what is referred to as a *double sampling plan*. With a double sampling plan two samples may be taken. If after checking the first sample the lot appears good, it will be accepted, and if it appears bad, it will be rejected. If the first sample does not clearly suggest whether the quality is good or poor, another sample is taken before making a decision.

To keep things as simple as possible, let us suppose that it is believed that the fraction defective in the lot will be either 0.002 or 0.05, so that these are the only two possible states of nature, and imagine that the prior probability assigned to the smaller lot fraction defective is 0.95. As a result of taking the first sample, either 0, 1, or 2 defective batteries will be found. Denote by $p(r_1|e_1)$, $p(r_1|e_2)$ the conditional probabilities of obtaining r_1 defectives given that the state of nature is e_1 and e_2, respectively, e_1 referring to a lot fraction defective of 0.002. If a second sample is taken, denote by $p(r_2|r_1,e_1)$, $p(r_2|r_1,e_2)$ the conditional probabilities of obtaining r_2 defectives in the second sample if r_1 defectives were obtained in the first sample when the state of nature is e_1 and e_2, respectively.

The natural way to draw the decision tree for this problem, which represents the proper time sequencing, is that shown in Figure 11-7. The initial experiment then determines the state of nature. We have not drawn the complete tree, but have given the complete structure only for the case where one defective battery is found in the initial sample. One obtains precisely the same structure for each of the other two possibilities. When the tree is drawn in this way, however, the decision maker does not

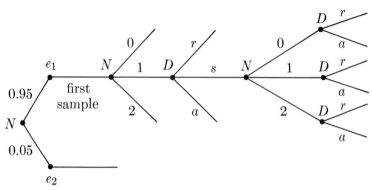

FIGURE 11-7

ever know at precisely which node he is. In particular, when he makes the initial decision he does not know whether the state of nature is e_1 or e_2, and therefore he does not know at which of the two nodes that correspond to obtaining r_1 defectives in the first sample he is. He faces a similar situation when he makes the second decision (if it is needed). The thing that causes the difficulty is that the outcome of the experiment which determines the state of nature is not known, and this experiment appears first in the tree. To eliminate the problem, the random experiment which determines the state of nature is moved to the end of the tree as was done in Chapter 8. This yields the decision tree shown in Figure 11-8 for the case where the initial experiment yields r_1 defectives.

In the tree of Figure 11-8 the decision maker always knows at which node he is, and hence the methods of the previous section can be applied to solving the problem. The important thing to observe, however, is that when changing the position of random experiments in the decision tree, the probabilities associated with the various branches will change in general, and one must be very careful to determine the proper probabilities. The probability of obtaining r_2 defectives on the second sample given that r_1 were obtained on the first is

$$p(r_2|r_1) = p(r_2|r_1,e_1)(0.95) + p(r_2|r_1,e_2)(0.05),$$

and the probability that the state of nature is e_j given that only one sample is taken is $p(e_j|r_1)$ and is $p(e_j|r_1,r_2)$ when two samples are taken. These latter probabilities are determined by Bayes' law. The reader should check that the probability of taking only one sample and finding r_1 defectives when e_j is the state of nature and is the same in Figures 11-7 and 11-8. This must be true, of course. The same is also true in the case where

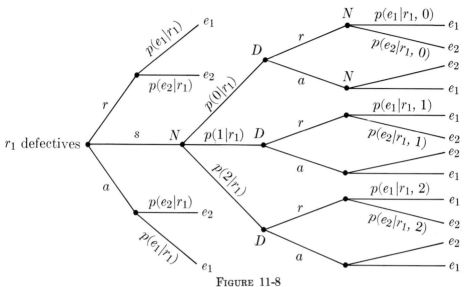

FIGURE 11-8

two samples are taken. We ask the reader to carry out the details of solving this example in the problems, where information about the various costs is provided.

11-3   MULTISTAGE INVENTORY PROBLEMS

We shall conclude by generalizing the single stage inventory problem studied in Chapter 4 to one we shall refer to as a multistage problem. Consider a situation in which one desires to control the inventory of some single item over n periods of time. The periods do not have to be of equal length, although normally in practice they would be. The nature of the system is such that orders to replenish the inventory can be conveniently placed only at the beginning of a period. In the model we shall develop then, it will be assumed that it is not possible to place orders for additional stock except at the beginning of a period. It is unnecessary, however, to place an order at the beginning of a period unless it is desirable to do so. We shall imagine that the demand for the item in period j can be treated as a random variable $x\{j\}$. The random variable $y\{j\}$ representing the total demand from the beginning of period 1 to the end of period j is then related to the $x\{u\}$, $u = 1, \ldots, j$ by

$$y\{j\} = \sum_{u=1}^{j} x\{u\}. \tag{11-27}$$

In practice, the $x\{j\}$ are usually not independent random variables. However, it is complicated if one does not treat the variables as being independent when developing a mathematical model. Thus we shall assume that in our model the random variables representing the demands in different periods are independent. The model so obtained is often useful even though the assumption of independence is only an approximation to the real world.

Let us next consider what happens if in some period the demand for the item exceeds the available stock. There exists a variety of things which could take place in such a case. Usually, attention is restricted to two cases; either each demand for a unit which cannot be met from stock is a lost sale, or all units demanded when the system is out of stock are backordered and the demands are met when more stock arrives. These are referred to as the lost sales case and the backorders case, respectively. In general, quite different models are needed to treat the lost sales and backorders cases, and the lost sales case is much more difficult to handle than the backorders case. In our development, we shall study the backorders case, but only in an especially simple framework. The important simplifying assumption we shall introduce is the same one used in Section 4-8. This is the assumption that the procurement lead time is zero, which means that we shall assume that no time elapses between the time when an order is placed and when the units are available in the warehouse. This is made only to simplify the discussion. We shall imagine that when an order arrives in the warehouse, any outstanding backorders are filled before the units in the order can be used to meet demands occurring in the period.

Suppose that the number of units ordered at the beginning of period j is $Q_j \geq 0$. Let us now introduce a new random variable $I\{j\}$ which we shall refer to as the net inventory at the end of period j. If the value of $I\{j\}$ is positive or zero, $I\{j\}$ is the on-hand inventory, and if $I\{j\}$ is negative, the negative of the value of $I\{j\}$ is the number of backorders outstanding. By definition

$$I\{j\} = I_0 + \sum_{u=1}^{j} Q_u - \sum_{u=1}^{j} x\{u\} = I_0 + \sum_{u=1}^{j} Q_u - y\{j\}, \quad (11\text{-}28)$$

where I_0 is the net inventory at the beginning of period 1 before any order is placed. Thus the value of $I\{j\}$ is the sum of the initial net inventory and replenishment stocks ordered through period j, less the demands in the first j periods. Since all demands are met ultimately, we see that $I\{j\}$ does have the interpretation given above.

Consider now the various costs incurred in stocking the item. We shall imagine that there are costs associated with purchasing stock, with carrying inventory, and with being unable to meet demands, i.e., with incurring

backorders.   Denote by $C_j(Q_j)$ the cost of procuring Q_j units at the beginning of period j.   We shall not attempt to develop a very realistic model
of carrying and backorder costs.   We shall simply suppose that the cost
of carrying inventory for period j is proportional to the on-hand inventory
at the end of period j.   Now the on-hand inventory at the end of period j
is the value of $I\{j\}$ if this is positive.   Thus if $I\{j\} = I_j > 0$, we shall
suppose that the inventory carrying cost for the period is $k_j I_j$.   Similarly,
we shall suppose that the cost of backorders for period j is proportional to
the number of backorders on the books at the end of period j.   Thus if
$I\{j\} = I_j < 0$, the cost of backorders for period j will be assumed to be
$-h_j I_j$.   Note that as we have defined the costs it is not possible to incur
both a carrying cost and a backorder cost in the same period.   If $I\{j\} = I_j$, and Q_j units are procured in period j, then the costs incurred in period
j can be written

$$R_j(Q_j, I_j) = C_j(Q_j) + \delta_j I_j, \qquad (11\text{-}29)$$

where $\delta_j = k_j$ if $I_j \geq 0$ and $\delta_j = -h_j$ if $I_j < 0$.
    The cost of operating the system in period j is by (11-29) a function of
Q_j and the value of $I\{j\}$.   From (11-28), $I\{j\}$ is a function of $Q_1, \ldots, Q_j$
and $x\{1\}, \ldots, x\{j\}$.   Thus if for each j the value of Q_j is specified and, in
addition, it is specified that $x\{j\} = x_j$, then the values of the $I\{j\}$ are

$$I_j = I_0 + \sum_{u=1}^{j} Q_u - \sum_{u=1}^{j} x_u.$$

Furthermore, the cost of stocking the item for the n periods is also determined and is

$$K(Q_1, \ldots, Q_n, x_1, \ldots, x_n) = \sum_{j=1}^{n} \alpha^j [C_j(Q_j) + \delta_j I_j]. \qquad (11\text{-}30)$$

The α^j are assumed to be discounting factors, so that the cost is the discounted cost, discounted to the beginning of the first period.   If discounting is not needed, it is only necessary to set $\alpha = 1$.   We have now obtained
an expression for the discounted cost for every combination of actions
which the decision maker can take and for every possible outcome of each
of the n random experiments involved.
    In the above development we did not indicate what happens to any units
left over at the end of the last period, or what is done about any backorders
which are outstanding at the end of the last period.   The reason for this
is that usually one will imagine that the item under consideration is to be
stocked indefinitely.   All one is really trying to do is to decide how much to
order at the beginning of the first period.   To do this, however, later
periods must be considered.   Thus a planning horizon of n periods is used.
The value of n is imagined to be chosen sufficiently large so that what happens at the end of period n has no influence on the initial decision.   If the

item was no longer stocked after the end of period n, then one could assume, for example, that units left over at the end are sold for their salvage value and any backorders remaining are never filled.

Consider now the nature of the decision tree for the problem. We shall assume that at the time the decision maker is ready to decide how much to order at the beginning of period k, he knows how much was demanded in each of the first $k - 1$ periods as well as what he ordered in the first $k - 1$ periods. Thus the information vector for the decision maker at the beginning of period k has the form $\langle I_0, Q_1, x_1, \ldots, Q_{k-1}, x_{k-1} \rangle$. The schematic structure of the tree is shown in Figure 11-9. There is a terminal branch

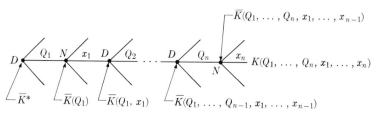

FIGURE 11-9

for every possible combination of values $Q_1, \ldots, Q_n, x_1, \ldots, x_n$. Thus there can be a huge number of terminal branches, and it would often be totally impossible to construct the decision tree in detail. We do not need to construct the decision tree in detail in order to solve the problem, however. Let us then see how to apply the method developed in Section 11-1 to the problem at hand. Denote by $p_j(x_j)$ the probability that in period j, $x\{j\} = x_j$. Recall that we are assuming that the $x\{j\}$ are independent random variables. The first step is to compute $\bar{K}(Q_1, \ldots, Q_n, x_1, \ldots, x_{n-1})$ by taking the expected value of $K(Q_1, \ldots, Q_n, x_1, \ldots, x_n)$ with respect to $x\{n\}$. Now note that since the inventory at the end of period n is the inventory at the beginning of period n plus Q_n less the demand in period n, we have

$$I_n = I_{n-1} + Q_n - x_n, \qquad (11\text{-}31)$$

and

$$K(Q_1, \ldots, Q_n, x_1, \ldots, x_n) = \sum_{j=1}^{n-1} \alpha^j [C_j(Q_j) + \delta_j I_j]$$
$$+ \alpha^n [C_n(Q_n) + \delta_j(I_{n-1} + Q_n - x_n)]. \quad (11\text{-}32)$$

Furthermore, $I_1, \ldots, I_{n-1}$ do not involve x_n. Hence

$$\bar{K}(Q_1, \ldots, Q_n, x_1, \ldots, x_{n-1}) = \sum_{x_n=0}^{\infty} p_n(x_n) K(Q_1, \ldots, Q_n, x_1, \ldots, x_n)$$

$$= \sum_{j=1}^{n-1} \alpha^j [C_j(Q_j) + \delta_j I_j] + \alpha^n \sum_{x_n=0}^{\infty} p_n(x_n) [C_n(Q_n) + \delta_j(I_{n-1} + Q_n - x_n)].$$
$$(11\text{-}33)$$

In practice one might quite possibly assume that $p_j(x_j)$ was a Poisson density function. This is why we used ∞ as the upper limit in the summations in (11-33). In general, the mean of the Poisson distribution would change from one period to the next, of course.

Next we minimize over Q_n, i.e.,

$$\bar{K}(Q_1, \ldots, Q_{n-1}, x_1, \ldots, x_{n-1})$$
$$= \min_{Q_n} \bar{K}(Q_1, \ldots, Q_n, x_1, \ldots, x_{n-1}). \quad (11\text{-}34)$$

The interesting thing is that Q_n appears only in the last term in (11-33). Therefore, (11-33) will be minimized with respect to Q_n if

$$\sum_{x_n=0}^{\infty} p_n(x_n)[C_n(Q_n) + \delta_n(I_{n-1} + Q_n - x_n)] \quad (11\text{-}35)$$

is. Now the minimum of (11-35) will in general depend on the value of I_{n-1}. Suppose that we determine the minimum for each value of I_{n-1} and also determine the corresponding Q_n which yields the minimum. For each I_{n-1} there is a number, which we shall denote by $\Lambda_n(I_{n-1})$, that is the minimum of (11-35) with respect to Q_n. We shall denote by $\hat{Q}_n(I_n)$ the value of Q_n, which yields the minimum of (11-35). Then $\Lambda_n(I_{n-1})$ and $\hat{Q}_n(I_{n-1})$ can be looked upon as functions of I_{n-1}, and we can write

$$\Lambda_n(I_{n-1}) = \min_{Q_n} \sum_{x_n=0}^{\infty} p_n(x_n)[C_n(Q_n) + \delta_n(I_{n-1} + Q_n - x_n)]. \quad (11\text{-}36)$$

Thus

$$\bar{K}(Q_1, \ldots, Q_{n-1}, x_1, \ldots, x_{n-1})$$
$$= \sum_{j=1}^{n-1} \alpha^j[C_j(Q_j) + \delta_j I_j] + \alpha^n \Lambda_n(I_{n-1}). \quad (11\text{-}37)$$

Note that $\hat{Q}_n(I_{n-1})$ is the optimal quantity to order at the beginning of period n if the net inventory at the beginning of period n before the order is placed is I_{n-1}. It is interesting to observe that the optimal quantity depends only on the net inventory at the time the order is placed. In other words, the only way that the decision maker's knowledge of I_0, $Q_1, \ldots, Q_{n-1}$ and $x_1, \ldots, x_{n-1}$ enters into his decision as to what value to select for Q_n is in the form

$$I_{n-1} = I_0 + \sum_{j=1}^{n-1} Q_j - \sum_{j=1}^{n-1} x_j.$$

This is clear intuitively. The only thing from the past that should influence his decision on how much to order is the net inventory at the time the order is placed.

Let us now continue the above process. On writing

$$I_{n-1} = I_{n-2} + Q_{n-1} - x_{n-1} \quad (11\text{-}38)$$

and noting that $I_1, \ldots, I_{n-2}$ do not depend on x_{n-1}, we see that

$$\bar{K}(Q_1, \ldots, Q_{n-1}, x_1, \ldots, x_{n-2})$$

$$= \sum_{j=1}^{n-2} \alpha^j [C_j(Q_j) + \delta_j I_j] + \alpha^{n-1} \sum_{x_{n-1}=0}^{\infty} p_{n-1}(x_{n-1})[C_{n-1}(Q_{n-1})$$

$$+ \delta_{n-1}(I_{n-2} + Q_{n-1} - x_{n-1}) + \alpha \Lambda_n(I_{n-2} + Q_{n-1} - x_{n-1})]. \quad (11\text{-}39)$$

Next we minimize over Q_{n-1}, i.e.,

$$\bar{K}(Q_1, \ldots, Q_{n-2}, x_1, \ldots, x_{n-2})$$

$$= \min_{Q_{n-1}} \bar{K}(Q_1, \ldots, Q_{n-1}, x_1, \ldots, x_{n-2}). \quad (11\text{-}40)$$

Observe now that Q_{n-1} appears in $\bar{K}(Q_1, \ldots, Q_{n-1}, x_1, \ldots, x_{n-2})$ only in the second term of (11-39), so that the Q_{n-1} which minimizes this term will be the value we seek. Let us write

$$\Lambda_{n-1}(I_{n-2}) = \min_{Q_{n-1}} \sum_{x_{n-1}=0}^{\infty} p_{n-1}(x_{n-1})[C_{n-1}(Q_{n-1}) + \delta_{n-1}(I_{n-2} + Q_{n-1} - x_{n-1})$$

$$+ \alpha \Lambda_n(I_{n-2} + Q_{n-1} - x_{n-1})], \quad (11\text{-}41)$$

and denote by $\hat{Q}_{n-1}(I_{n-2})$ the value of Q_{n-1} which yields the minimum in (11-41). The minimum in (11-41) will depend on I_{n-2} and we have indicated this by writing $\Lambda_{n-1}(I_{n-2})$, and similarly the value of Q_{n-1} which yields the minimum will in general depend on I_{n-2}. Note that $\hat{Q}_{n-1}(I_{n-2})$ is the optimal quantity to order at the beginning of period $n-2$ when the net inventory at the beginning of the period is I_{n-2}. The optimal quantity to order depends only on I_{n-2}.

The procedure we have developed can be continued until the problem is solved. Let us define recursively the set of functions $\Lambda_k(I_{k-1})$, $k = 1, \ldots, n$ as follows.

$$\Lambda_k(I_{k-1}) = \min_{Q_k} \sum_{x_k=0}^{\infty} p_k(x_k)[C_k(Q_k) + \delta_k(I_{k-1} + Q_k - x_k)$$

$$+ \alpha \Lambda_{k+1}(I_{k-1} + Q_k - x_k)], k = 1, \ldots, n-1, \quad (11\text{-}42)$$

where $\Lambda_n(I_{n-1})$ is given by (11-36). Denote by $\hat{Q}_k(I_{k-1})$ the value of Q_k which yields the minimum in (11-42). Then, following through the procedure for evaluating the $\bar{K}$'s, we see that the minimum expected cost is

$$\bar{K}^* = \Lambda_1(I_0), \quad (11\text{-}43)$$

and $Q_1^* = \hat{Q}_1(I_0)$ is the optimal quantity to order at the beginning of the first period. The function $\hat{Q}_k(I_{k-1})$ is nothing but an optimal decision rule for the kth stage. It tells how much to order given the initial net inventory at the beginning of period k. An optimal strategy for the n-stage inventory problem is then

$$S^* = \langle Q_1^*, \hat{Q}_2(I_1), \ldots, \hat{Q}_n(I_{n-1}) \rangle. \quad (11\text{-}44)$$

We have now developed an interesting procedure for solving the n-stage inventory problem. This is done by computing the functions $\Lambda_k(I_{k-1})$ and simultaneously determining $\hat{Q}_k(I_{k-1})$. Let us summarize the procedure and simultaneously simplify the notation a little. We shall write

$$F_k(I_{k-1} + Q_k) = \sum_{x_k=0}^{\infty} p_k(x_k)[\delta_k(I_{k-1} + Q_k - x_k)], \qquad (11\text{-}45)$$

so that $F_k(Q_k + I_{k-1})$ is the expected cost of carrying inventory and of backorders in period k when the net inventory after receipt of any order placed is $I_{k-1} + Q_k$. Then (11-36) and (11-42) become

$$\Lambda_n(I_{n-1}) = \min_{Q_n}[C_n(Q_n) + F_n(I_{n-1} + Q_n)]; \qquad (11\text{-}46)$$

$$\Lambda_k(I_{k-1}) = \min_{Q_k} [C_k(Q_k) + F_k(I_{k-1} + Q_k)$$

$$+ \alpha \sum_{x_k=0}^{\infty} p_k(x_k)\Lambda_{k+1}(I_{k-1} + Q_k - x_k)],$$

$$k = 1, \ldots, n-1. \quad (11\text{-}47)$$

We begin by determining $\Lambda_n(I_{n-1})$ for each value I_{n-1} which the net inventory could have at the beginning of period $n-1$. Simultaneously $\hat{Q}_n(I_{n-1})$ is determined. The function $\Lambda_n(I_{n-1})$ is then used in the computation of $\Lambda_{n-1}(I_{n-2})$ which is in turn used to determine $\Lambda_{n-2}(I_{n-3})$ for each value I_{n-3} which the net inventory could have at the beginning of period $n-3$. This is continued until $\Lambda_1(I_0)$ is determined; $\Lambda_1(I_0)$ is evaluated for just a single number I_0. Simultaneously, Q_1^* is determined. The functions $\Lambda_k(I_{k-1})$ have a simple intuitive interpretation; $\Lambda_k(I_{k-1})$ is the minimum expected discounted cost of stocking the item for periods k through n when the net inventory at the beginning of period k is I_{k-1}. The procedure we have developed for solving the problem by computing recursively the Λ_k functions is usually referred to as the method of *dynamic programming*. We shall not attempt to give an example, since generally a computer must be used to carry out the numerical computations. Neither shall we attempt to study any additional properties of the model. The reader is referred to [1] for a detailed discussion of dynamic programming and to [1] and [2] for more discussion of multistage inventory models.

REFERENCES

There do not seem to be any references which treat in detail the procedures for solving the general sequential decision problem, although special types of problems receive attention in a number of works such as the following.

1. Hadley, G., *Nonlinear and Dynamic Programming*. Addison-Wesley, Reading, Mass., 1964.
2. Hadley, G., and T. M. Whitin, *Analysis of Inventory Systems*. Prentice-Hall, Englewood Cliffs, N. J., 1963.

PROBLEMS

Sections 11-1 and 11-2

1. Consider some decision problem and the associated set of lotteries determined by all the different strategies for this problem. Describe in detail the manner in which the backward solution technique proceeds to determine an optimal lottery.

2. What would be the solution to the problem of Figure 11-5 if the number -5000 was replaced by -3000?

3. What would the probability of receiving the prize 4500 in Figure 11-5 have to be if the decision maker is indifferent between taking action a_1 or a_2 initially?

4. Solve Problem 1 of Section 3-4 using the method introduced in Section 11-1.

5. Solve Problem 2 of Section 3-4 using the method introduced in Section 11-1.

6. Go through the details of evaluating K $(2,2,0)$ and K $(2,2,2)$ for Example 2 of Section 11-2.

7. Go through the details of evaluating K $(2,1)$ for Example 2 of Section 11-2.

8. Go through the details of evaluating $K(3)$ for Example 2 of Section 11-2.

9. Solve the third example of Section 11-2 if each defective battery results in a loss of a $100,000 rocket and each battery tested costs $300. Assume that only 496 batteries are needed, and if the second sample is not taken the batteries can be returned for a refund of their cost.

Section 11-3

1. Formulate the multistage inventory problem for the case where there is a one-period lag in reporting demands, so that when the decision maker must decide how much to order at the beginning of period k, he does not know what the demand was in period $k - 1$.

2. Formulate the multistage inventory problem for the case where there is a two-period lag in reporting demands.

3. What difficulties are introduced in the formulation of this section if the procurement lead time is not zero?

4. Attempt to develop a model similar to that of the text which applies to the lost sales case.

5. Modify the formulation given in the text to the case where any units remaining at the end of the last period are sold and the salvage value per unit is R.

6. Solve the following two stage inventory problem using the dynamic programming method. The probability function for the number of units demanded is the same for both periods and is $p(0) = 0.5$, $p(1) = 0.3$, $p(2) = 0.2$. Assume that delivery is instantaneous. Assume also that any units demanded when the system is out of stock are lost. The cost of each unit is $2500 and the selling price is $3500. Any units left over at the end of the second period can be sold for $1800. The cost of carrying one unit for one period is $200.

TABLES

VALUES OF THE BINOMIAL PROBABILITY FUNCTION $b(x; n, p)$

n	x	$p = .05$	.1	.2	.3	.4	n	x	$p = .05$	.1	.2	.3	.4
2	0	.9025	.8100	.6400	.4900	.3600	8	0	.6634	.4305	.1678	.0576	.0168
	1	.0950	.1800	.3200	.4200	.4800		1	.2793	.3826	.3355	.1977	.0896
	2	.0025	.0100	.0400	.0900	.1600		2	.0515	.1488	.2936	.2965	.2090
3	0	.8574	.7290	.5120	.3430	.2160		3	.0054	.0331	.1468	.2541	.2787
	1	.1354	.2430	.3840	.4410	.4320		4	.0004	.0046	.0459	.1361	.2322
	2	.0071	.0270	.0960	.1890	.2880		5		.0004	.0092	.0467	.1239
	3	.0001	.0010	.0080	.0270	.0640		6			.0011	.0100	.0413
4	0	.8145	.6561	.4096	.2401	.1296		7			.0001	.0012	.0079
	1	.1715	.2916	.4096	.4116	.3456		8				.0001	.0007
	2	.0135	.0486	.1536	.2646	.3456	9	0	.6302	.3874	.1342	.0404	.0101
	3	.0005	.0036	.0256	.0756	.1536		1	.2985	.3874	.3020	.1556	.0605
	4		.0001	.0016	.0081	.0256		2	.0629	.1722	.3020	.2668	.1612
5	0	.7738	.5905	.3277	.1681	.0778		3	.0077	.0446	.1762	.2668	.2508
	1	.2036	.3280	.4096	.3602	.2592		4	.0006	.0074	.0661	.1715	.2508
	2	.0214	.0729	.2048	.3087	.3456		5		.0008	.0165	.0735	.1672
	3	.0011	.0081	.0512	.1323	.2304		6		.0001	.0028	.0210	.0743
	4		.0005	.0064	.0284	.0768		7			.0003	.0039	.0212
	5			.0003	.0024	.0102		8				.0004	.0035
6	0	.7351	.5314	.2621	.1176	.0467		9					.0003
	1	.2321	.3543	.3932	.3025	.1866	10	0	.5987	.3487	.1074	.0282	.0060
	2	.0305	.0984	.2458	.3241	.3110		1	.3151	.3874	.2684	.1211	.0403
	3	.0021	.0146	.0819	.1852	.2765		2	.0746	.1937	.3020	.2335	.1209
	4	.0001	.0012	.0154	.0595	.1382		3	.0105	.0574	.2013	.2668	.2150
	5		.0001	.0015	.0102	.0369		4	.0010	.0112	.0881	.2001	.2508
	6			.0001	.0007	.0041		5	.0001	.0015	.0264	.1029	.2007
7	0	.6983	.4783	.2097	.0824	.0280		6		.0001	.0055	.0368	.1115
	1	.2573	.3720	.3670	.2471	.1306		7			.0008	.0090	.0425
	2	.0406	.1240	.2753	.3176	.2613		8			.0001	.0014	.0106
	3	.0036	.0230	.1147	.2269	.2903		9				.0001	.0016
	4	.0002	.0026	.0287	.0972	.1935		10					.0001
	5		.0002	.0043	.0250	.0774							
	6			.0004	.0036	.0172							
	7				.0002	.0016							

TABLE B

Values of $b(x; n, p)$ for $p = 0.5$

n	x	p = .5	n	x	p = .5	n	x	p = .5	n	x	p = .5	n	x	p = .5
2	0	.2500	13	0	.0001	18	0	.0000	23	2	.0000	27	3	.0000
	1	.5000		1	.0016		1	.0001		3	.0002		4	.0001
3	0	.1250		2	.0095		2	.0006		4	.0011		5	.0006
	1	.3750		3	.0349		3	.0031		5	.0040		6	.0022
4	0	.0625		4	.0873		4	.0117		6	.0120		7	.0066
	1	.2500		5	.1571		5	.0327		7	.0292		8	.0165
	2	.3750		6	.2095		6	.0708		8	.0584		9	.0349
5	0	.0312	14	0	.0001		7	.1214		9	.0974		10	.0629
	1	.1562		1	.0009		8	.1669		10	.1364		11	.0971
	2	.3125		2	.0056		9	.1855		11	.1612		12	.1295
6	0	.0156		3	.0222	19	1	.0000	24	2	.0000		13	.1494
	1	.0938		4	.0611		2	.0003		3	.0001	28	3	.0000
	2	.2344		5	.1222		3	.0018		4	.0006		4	.0001
	3	.3125		6	.1833		4	.0074		5	.0025		5	.0004
7	0	.0078		7	.2095		5	.0222		6	.0080		6	.0014
	1	.0547	15	0	.0000		6	.0518		7	.0206		7	.0044
	2	.1641		1	.0005		7	.0961		8	.0438		8	.0116
	3	.2734		2	.0032		8	.1442		9	.0779		9	.0257
8	0	.0039		3	.0139		9	.1762		10	.1169		10	.0489
	1	.0312		4	.0417	20	1	.0000		11	.1488		11	.0800
	2	.1094		5	.0916		2	.0002		12	.1612		12	.1133
	3	.2188		6	.1527		3	.0011	25	2	.0000		13	.1395
	4	.2734		7	.1964		4	.0046		3	.0001		14	.1194
9	0	.0020	16	0	.0000		5	.0148		4	.0004	29	4	.0000
	1	.0176		1	.0002		6	.0370		5	.0016		5	.0002
	2	.0703		2	.0018		7	.0739		6	.0053		6	.0009
	3	.1641		3	.0085		8	.1201		7	.0143		7	.0029
	4	.2461		4	.0278		9	.1602		8	.0322		8	.0080
10	0	.0010		5	.0667		10	.1762		9	.0609		9	.0187
	1	.0098		6	.1222	21	1	.0000		10	.0974		10	.0373
	2	.0439		7	.1746		2	.0001		11	.1328		11	.0644
	3	.1172		8	.1964		3	.0006		12	.1550		12	.0967
	4	.2051	17	0	.0000		4	.0029	26	3	.0000		13	.1264
	5	.2461		1	.0001		5	.0097		4	.0002		14	.1445
11	0	.0005		2	.0010		6	.0259		5	.0010	30	4	.0000
	1	.0054		3	.0052		7	.0554		6	.0034		5	.0001
	2	.0269		4	.0182		8	.0970		7	.0098		6	.0006
	3	.0806		5	.0472		9	.1402		8	.0233		7	.0019
	4	.1611		6	.0944		10	.1682		9	.0466		8	.0055
	5	.2256		7	.1484	22	1	.0000		10	.0792		9	.0133
12	0	.0002		8	.1855		2	.0001		11	.1151		10	.0280
	1	.0029					3	.0004		12	.1439		11	.0509
	2	.0161					4	.0017		13	.1550		12	.0806
	3	.0537					5	.0063					13	.1115
	4	.1208					6	.0178					14	.1354
	5	.1934					7	.0407					15	.1445
	6	.2256					8	.0762						
							9	.1186						
							10	.1542						
							11	.1682						

TABLE C

VALUES OF THE POISSON PROBABILITY FUNCTION $p(x; \beta)$

x	.1	.2	.3	.4	β .5	.6	.7	.8	.9	1.0
0	.9048	.8187	.7408	.6703	.6065	.5488	.4966	.4493	.4066	.3679
1	.0905	.1637	.2222	.2681	.3033	.3293	.3476	.3595	.3659	.3679
2	.0045	.0164	.0333	.0536	.0758	.0988	.1217	.1438	.1647	.1839
3	.0002	.0011	.0033	.0072	.0126	.0198	.0284	.0383	.0494	.0613
4		.0001	.0003	.0007	.0016	.0030	.0050	.0077	.0111	.0153
5				.0001	.0002	.0004	.0007	.0012	.0020	.0031
6							.0001	.0002	.0003	.0005
7										.0001

x	1	2	3	4	β 5	6	7	8	9	10
0	.3679	.1353	.0498	.0183	.0067	.0025	.0009	.0003	.0001	.0000
1	.3679	.2707	.1494	.0733	.0337	.0149	.0064	.0027	.0011	.0005
2	.1839	.2707	.2240	.1465	.0842	.0446	.0223	.0107	.0050	.0023
3	.0613	.1804	.2240	.1954	.1404	.0892	.0521	.0286	.0150	.0076
4	.0153	.0902	.1680	.1954	.1755	.1339	.0912	.0572	.0337	.0189
5	.0031	.0361	.1008	.1563	.1755	.1606	.1277	.0916	.0607	.0378
6	.0005	.0120	.0504	.1042	.1462	.1606	.1490	.1221	.0911	.0631
7	.0001	.0034	.0216	.0595	.1044	.1377	.1490	.1396	.1171	.0901
8		.0009	.0081	.0298	.0653	.1033	.1304	.1396	.1318	.1126
9		.0002	.0027	.0132	.0363	.0688	.1014	.1241	.1318	.1251
10			.0008	.0053	.0181	.0413	.0710	.0993	.1186	.1251
11			.0002	.0019	.0082	.0225	.0452	.0722	.0970	.1137
12			.0001	.0006	.0034	.0113	.0264	.0481	.0728	.0948
13				.0002	.0013	.0052	.0142	.0296	.0504	.0729
14				.0001	.0005	.0022	.0071	.0169	.0324	.0521
15					.0002	.0009	.0033	.0090	.0194	.0347
16						.0003	.0014	.0045	.0109	.0217
17						.0001	.0006	.0021	.0058	.0128
18							.0002	.0009	.0029	.0071
19							.0001	.0004	.0014	.0037
20								.0002	.0006	.0019
21								.0001	.0003	.0009
22									.0001	.0004
23										.0002
24										.0001

TABLE D

STANDARDIZED NORMAL DENSITY FUNCTION $\varphi(t) = \dfrac{1}{\sqrt{2\pi}}\, e^{-t^2/2}$

t	$\varphi(t)$	t	$\varphi(t)$
0	.3989	1.1	.2179
0.05	.3984	1.2	.1942
0.10	.3970	1.3	.1714
0.15	.3945	1.4	.1497
0.20	.3910	1.5	.1295
0.25	.3867	1.6	.1109
0.30	.3814	1.7	.09405
0.35	.3752	1.8	.07895
0.40	.3683	1.9	.06562
0.45	.3605	2.0	.05399
0.50	.3521	2.1	.04398
0.55	.3429	2.2	.03547
0.60	.3332	2.3	.02833
0.65	.3230	2.4	.02239
0.70	.3123	2.5	.01753
0.75	.3011	2.6	.01358
0.80	.2897	2.7	.01042
0.85	.2780	2.8	.00792
0.90	.2661	2.9	.00595
0.95	.2541	3.0	.00443
1.0	.2420	3.1	.00327

Table E

Cumulative standardized normal distribution $\Phi(t)$

$$\Phi(t) = \int_{-\infty}^{t} \varphi(\zeta)\, d\zeta$$

t	.00	.01	.02	.03	.04	.05	.06	.07	.08	.09
.0	.5000	.5040	.5080	.5120	.5160	.5199	.5239	.5279	.5319	.5359
.1	.5398	.5438	.5478	.5517	.5557	.5596	.5636	.5675	.5714	.5753
.2	.5793	.5832	.5871	.5910	.5948	.5987	.6026	.6064	.6103	.6141
.3	.6179	.6217	.6255	.6293	.6331	.6368	.6406	.6443	.6480	.6517
.4	.6554	.6591	.6628	.6664	.6700	.6736	.6772	.6808	.6844	.6879
.5	.6915	.6950	.6985	.7019	.7054	.7088	.7123	.7157	.7190	.7224
.6	.7257	.7291	.7324	.7357	.7389	.7422	.7454	.7486	.7517	.7549
.7	.7580	.7611	.7642	.7673	.7704	.7734	.7764	.7794	.7823	.7852
.8	.7881	.7910	.7939	.7967	.7995	.8023	.8051	.8078	.8106	.8133
.9	.8159	.8186	.8212	.8238	.8264	.8289	.8315	.8340	.8365	.8389
1.0	.8413	.8438	.8461	.8485	.8508	.8531	.8554	.8577	.8599	.8621
1.1	.8643	.8665	.8686	.8708	.8729	.8749	.8770	.8790	.8810	.8830
1.2	.8849	.8869	.8888	.8907	.8925	.8944	.8962	.8980	.8997	.9015
1.3	.9032	.9049	.9066	.9082	.9099	.9115	.9131	.9147	.9162	.9177
1.4	.9192	.9207	.9222	.9236	.9251	.9265	.9279	.9292	.9306	.9319
1.5	.9332	.9345	.9357	.9370	.9382	.9394	.9406	.9418	.9429	.9441
1.6	.9452	.9463	.9474	.9484	.9495	.9505	.9515	.9525	.9535	.9545
1.7	.9554	.9564	.9573	.9582	.9591	.9599	.9608	.9616	.9625	.9633
1.8	.9641	.9649	.9656	.9664	.9671	.9678	.9686	.9693	.9699	.9706
1.9	.9713	.9719	.9726	.9732	.9738	.9744	.9750	.9756	.9761	.9767
2.0	.9772	.9778	.9783	.9788	.9793	.9798	.9803	.9808	.9812	.9817
2.1	.9821	.9826	.9830	.9834	.9838	.9842	.9846	.9850	.9854	.9857
2.2	.9861	.9864	.9868	.9871	.9875	.9878	.9881	.9884	.9887	.9890
2.3	.9893	.9896	.9898	.9901	.9904	.9906	.9909	.9911	.9913	.9916
2.4	.9918	.9920	.9922	.9925	.9927	.9929	.9931	.9932	.9934	.9936
2.5	.9938	.9940	.9941	.9943	.9945	.9946	.9948	.9949	.9951	.9952
2.6	.9953	.9955	.9956	.9957	.9959	.9960	.9961	.9962	.9963	.9964
2.7	.9965	.9966	.9967	.9968	.9969	.9970	.9971	.9972	.9973	.9974
2.8	.9974	.9975	.9976	.9977	.9977	.9978	.9979	.9979	.9980	.9981
2.9	.9981	.9982	.9982	.9983	.9984	.9984	.9985	.9985	.9986	.9986
3.0	.9987	.9987	.9987	.9988	.9988	.9989	.9989	.9989	.9990	.9990
3.1	.9990	.9991	.9991	.9991	.9992	.9992	.9992	.9992	.9993	.9993
3.2	.9993	.9993	.9994	.9994	.9994	.9994	.9994	.9995	.9995	.9995
3.3	.9995	.9995	.9995	.9996	.9996	.9996	.9996	.9996	.9996	.9997
3.4	.9997	.9997	.9997	.9997	.9997	.9997	.9997	.9997	.9997	.9998

The entries from 3.49 to 3.61 all equal .9998.
The entries from 3.62 to 3.89 all equal .9999.
All entries from 3.90 and up equal 1.0000.

INDEX